ISS Exam Question Bank 2009-2023

Indian Statistical Service (ISS)

Exam Question Bank, Guideline and Syllabus

15 Years Question Papers Included 2009-2023

Pradeep Kumar Panda

Bharti Publications

New Delhi-110002 (India)

Title: Indian Statistical Service (ISS) Exam Question Bank, Guideline and Syllabus
Author: Pradeep Kumar Panda

First Published, 2025
ISBN: 978-93-48059-21-5

Published by:
Bharti Publications
4819/24, 2nd Floor, Mathur Lane
Ansari Road, Darya Ganj, New Delhi-110002
Phone: 011-46172797, 011-23247537, Mobile : 9899897381
E-mail: bhartipublications@gmail.com
Website: www.bhartipublications.com

Dedicated to
All ISS Aspirants

Preface

This book serves as Guideline for The Indian Statistical Service (ISS) Exam. The ISS is an organized Group 'A' Central Service and was constituted in the year 1961. ISS is a technical service with high degree of proficiency in Statistical methods and applications. With the main mandate of producing quality Official Statistics with better methods and techniques, provide solutions to the data and information needs and interpretation and analysis of statistics, a majority portion of the probationary training programme is to be devoted to acquiring of technical knowledge in the field of official statistics, economics, financial statistics, survey methodology etc. The posts are recruited through UPSC examination. The minimum eligibility criterion is Bachelor's degree with Statistics or Mathematical Statistics or Applied Statistics as one of the subject.

The UPSC conducts a combined competitive examination for recruitment to Grade IV officers of the services of Indian Economic and Indian Statistic. ISS exam consist of six papers namely General English, General Studies, Statistics – I (Objective), Statistics – II (Objective), Statistics – III (Descriptive) and Statistics – IV (Descriptive).

This book explains about ISS, about ISS Exam, exam pattern and structure, exam syllabus and previous year question papers of all six subjects from the year 2009 to 2023.

All the very best to all the Indian Statistical Service Aspirants!

Best of Luck!

Jai Hind!

Pradeep Kumar Panda

Acknowledgement

It feels nice to have got this opportunity to give vent the unbridled feelings of gratitude imprisoned in the core of my heart.

Many people have contributed to this book's development. I gratefully acknowledge all the insightful comments.

It is my privilege to express profound sense of gratitude to all our teachers for their valuable guidance, keen and sustained interest, intuitive ideas and persistent endeavors. Their inspiring assistance, laconic reciprocation and affectionate care enabled me to venture in this arena.

My sincere regards and indebtedness to all my family members who have been my constant source of help and inspiration, standing by us at every moment of life, from zenith to nadir. Diction is not enough to express our unbound gratitude, profound adoration and hearty devotion our beloved parents for their supreme sacrifice and eternal benediction in the evolution of these tiny personalities.

I profusely thank Bharti Publication for bringing out this book in desirable shape.

At the nib but not neap tide, I bow our head before the omnipresent Almighty whose unseen inspiration have enabled us to complete this tiny endeavor successfully. I still seek His blessings to proceed further.

Pradeep Kumar Panda

Contents

GENERAL STUDIES SECTION

STATISTICS-I

STATISTICS-II

STATISTICS-III

STATISTICS-IV

About ISS

The Indian Statistical Service (ISS) is an organized Group 'A' Central Service.

ISS is a technical service with high degree of proficiency in Statistical methods and applications. With the main mandate of producing quality Official Statistics with better methods and techniques, provide solutions to the data and information needs and interpretation and analysis of statistics, a majority portion of the probationary training programme is to be devoted to acquiring of technical knowledge in the field of official statistics, economics, financial statistics, survey methodology etc. The posts are recruited through UPSC examination. The minimum eligibility criterion is Bachelor's degree with Statistics or Mathematical Statistics or Applied Statistics as one of the subject.

History

A committee under the chairmanship of Shri V.T.Krishnamachari, the then Deputy Chairman of erstwhile Planning Commission was constituted for examining the matter of establishing statistical cadres after the cabinet decision of 26 July 1952. The Committee submitted its report in September 1953 and recommended formation of 'Statistical and Economic Advisory Service'. However, Professor Prasanta Chandra Mahalanobis, the then Honorary Statistical Adviser to the Cabinet did not favor the idea of a combined Statistical and Economic Advisory Service and suggested an alternative scheme for creation of a Central Statistical Pool. After deliberating on various contradictory views, the Cabinet on 12 February 1958 decided that two separate services namely Statistical Service and Economic Service should be formed. This decision paved the way for formation of ISS and finally the service was constituted in 1961 as a cadre of qualified professional with core discipline of Statistics.

The Indian Statistical Service along with Indian Economic Service (IES) was constituted as a Group-A Central Service on 1 November 1961 by a Gazette notification. Direct recruitment in the Service was initiated in 1967 through an examination organized by Union Public Service Commission (UPSC) and the first batch joined in October 1968. The Indian Statistical System is a decentralised system and the officers of Indian Statistical Service have pivotal role in compiling Official Statistics at central level for use of government and nongovernment entities.

Cadre strength

The Ministry of Statistics and Programme Implementation (MoSPI) is the Cadre Controlling Authority (CCA) for the ISS officers. Officers of ISS cadre having a strength of 814 sanctioned posts are serving in various Ministries and offices across the country at different levels .The CCA is responsible for policy decision related to service matters and the management of the service on the basis of the service rules notified time to time.

At the entry grade of ISS i.e. Junior Time Scale, 50% of the posts are recruited through UPSC examination. The minimum eligibility criterion is Bachelor's degree with Statistics or Mathematical Statistics or Applied Statistics as one of the subject. Like any other government service, ISS officers are put to probation for a period of two years on joining the service . Remaining 50% by promotion of officers from Subordinate Statistical Service (SSS). The National Statistical System Training Academy (NSSTA), Greater Noida (UP) is the training academy for the ISS officers. The direct recruits undergo a two-years comprehensive probationary training comprising the foundation course, training on survey methodology, micro & macro economics and econometrics at the Indian Statistical Institutes, training on various modules at several national institutes of repute across the country, attachment with different Ministries, National Sample Survey Office (NSSO) and State Directorate of Economics and Statistics (DES) etc.

The Cadre strength of ISS is periodically reviewed by the ISS Board chaired by the Cabinet Secretary and the final Cadre strength is approved by the Cabinet. The latest Cadre Review was approved by the Cabinet on 29 July 2015 and the ISS rules 2016 were notified on 7 June 2016. At present, the cadre strength of the service is 814 and distributed in various grades as under:

Sl. No.	Grade / Designation	Pay Structure	Sanctioned Strength
1	HAG Plus (Director General)	Level -16	5
2	HAG (Additional Director General)	Level -15	18
3	SAG (Deputy Director General)	Level -14	136
4	JAG/NFSG (Joint Director/Director)	Level-12 & 13	176
5	STS (Deputy Director)	Level -11	179
6	JTS (Assistant Director)	Level-10	300

Role of ISS Officers

Generally, the ISS officers serves at various Ministries/Departments at various part of our Country. The cadre posts of the ISS are spread across 40 different Ministries of the Central Government. Besides manning Cadre posts, the ISS officers go on deputation to serve in various domestic and international organizations such as Central Staffing Scheme, UN bodies, foreign governments, state governments, PSUs etc.

As per latest cadre review, ISS are serving to the following Ministries/Departments :

(i) Ministry of Agriculture& Farmer Welfare:

(ii) Ministry of AYUSH

(iii) Ministry of chemical & Fertilizer

(iv) Ministry of Civil Aviation

(v) Ministry of Coal: Coal control

(vi) Ministry of Commerce & Industries: Directorate General of Foreign Trade, Directorate General of Commercial Intelligence and Statistics (DGCIS), Directorate General of Supply and Disposal, Department of Commerce- Office of Economic Adviser, Department of Industrial Policy and Promotion, Directorate of Anti-Dumping. (vii) Ministry of Communications and Information Technology

(viii) Ministry of Corporate Affairs (ix) Ministry of Culture- Anthropological Survey of India

(x) Ministry of Defence: Army Statistical Organisation, Management Information Systems Organisations (MISO), Director General (DG) Infosys, Directorate General of Resettlement, Naval Headquarters, Additional Director General (ADG) Systems, Military Training Directorate, Air Headquarters Computer Centre, Directorate of Flight Safety

(xi) Ministry of Development of North Eastern Region

(xii) Ministry of Drinking Water and Sanitation

(xiii) Ministry of Environment, Forest and Climate Change: Forest Survey of India (FSI), Dehradun

(xiv) Ministry of Finance: Department of Economic Affairs, Department of Financial Service, Department of Expenditure- Pay Research Unit, Department of Revenue, Tax Research Unit, Financial Intelligence Unit, Directorate of Data Management Customs and Central Excise, Directorate of Income (Tax-Research-Statistics), Publication and Public Relations (RSP and PR)

(xv) Ministry of Food Processing Industries

(xvi) Ministry of Health and Family Welfare: Department of Health and Family Welfare, Directorate General of Health Services (DGHS)- All India Institute of Hygiene and Public Health, National Centre for Disease Control, National Antimalaria Programme (NAMP), National Tuberculosis Institute, Central Bureau of Health and Intelligence(CBHI)

(xvii) Ministry of Heavy Industries and Public Enterprises

(xviii) Ministry of Home Affairs: Registrar General of India (RGI), Intelligence Bureau (IB), National Crime Records Bureau (NCRB)

(xix) Ministry of Housing and Urban Poverty Alleviation

(xx) Ministry of Human Resources Development: Department of School Education and Literacy, Department of Secondary and Higher Education

(xxi) Ministry of Labour and Employment: Ministry Proper, Directorate General of Employment and Training (DGET), Directorate General of Mines Safety, Labour Bureau

(xxii) Ministry of Micro Small and Medium Enterprises (MSME)

(xxiii) Ministry of Mines: Indian Bureau of Mines (IBM)

(xxiv) Ministry of Minority Affairs

(xxv) Ministry of New and Renewable Energy

(xxvi) NITI Aayog

(xxvii) Ministry of Petroleum and Natural Gas

(xxviii) Ministry of Power

(xxix) Ministry of Road Transport and Highways

(xxx) Ministry of Rural Development: Department of Rural Development, Department of Land Resources

(xxxi) Ministry of Science and Technology : Department of Bio-technology

(xxxii) Ministry of Shipping

(xxxiii) Ministry of Social Justice and Empowerment: Department of Social Justice, Department of Disability Affairs

(xxxiv) Ministry of Steel

(xxxv) Ministry of Textiles

(xxxvi) Ministry of Tourism

(xxxvii) Ministry of Tribal Affairs

(xxxviii) Ministry of Water Resources, River Development and Ganga Rejuvenation: Ministry Proper, Central Water Commission (CWC), Central Water and Power Research Station (CWPRS), Central Ground Water Board (CGWB)

(xxxix) Ministry of Women and Child Development

(xxxx) Ministry of Statistics and Programme Implementation. have full-fledged statistical divisions, while most others have only a nucleus cell.

Each Ministry/Department are expected to maintain relevant databases and also undertake monitoring and evaluation of all the concerned projects and programmes. The ISS officers are involved in compilation of different kind of statistics and formulation/monitoring/evaluation of different schemes in these Ministries/Departments and are under the administrative control of the concerned Ministries.

About ISS Exam

The UPSC conducts a combined competitive examination for recruitment to Grade IV officers of the services of Indian Economic and Indian Statistic.

Eligibility Criteria

Education: The candidates must have obtained a Bachelor's Degree with Statistics/Mathematical Statistics/Applied Statistics as one of the subject or else the candidates should hold a Master's degree in Statistics/Mathematical Statistics/Applied Statistics from a recognized university or a foreign university approved by the Central Government of India from time to time.

Age: You must have attained the age of 21 years and must not have attained the age of 30 years on 1st August of the year of exam.

Exam Pattern

Part I is written examination carrying a maximum of 1000 marks. The exam is of conventional type. Part II is viva-voce of such candidates as may be called by the Commission, carrying a maximum of 200 marks.

S. No.	Subject	Marks	Time
1	General English	100	3 hours
2	General Studies	100	3 hours
3	Statistics – I (Objective)	200	3 hours
4	Statistics – II (Objective)	200	3 hours
5	Statistics – III (Descriptive)	200	3 hours
6	Statistics – IV (Descriptive)	200	3 hours

ISS Exam Syllabus

ISS General English and General Studies Syllabus: The standard of papers in General English and General Studies will be such as may be expected of a graduate of an Indian University. The standard of papers in the other subjects will be that of the Master's degree examination of an Indian University in the relevant disciplines. The candidates will be expected to illustrate theory by facts, and to analyse problems with the help of theory. They will be expected to be particularly conversant with Indian problems in the field of Economic or Statistics.

General English

Candidates will be required to write an essay in English. Other questions will be designed to test their understanding of English and workmanlike use of words. Passages will usually be set for summary or precis.

General Studies

General Knowledge including knowledge of current events and of such matters of every day observation and experience in their scientific aspects as may be expected of an educated person who has not made a special study of any scientific subject. The paper will also include questions on Indian Polity including the political system and the Constitution of India, History of India and Geography of a nature which the candidate should be able to answer without special study.

STATISTICS – I (OBJECTIVE TYPE)

(i) Probability:

Classical and axiomatic definitions of Probability and consequences. Law of total probability, Conditional probability, Bayes' theorem and applications. Discrete and continuous random variables. Distribution functions and their properties. Standard discrete and continuous probability distributions - Bernoulli, Uniform, Binomial, Poisson, Geometric, Rectangular, Exponential, Normal, Cauchy, Hyper geometric, Multinomial, Laplace, Negative binomial, Beta, Gamma, Lognormal. Random vectors, Joint and marginal distributions, conditional distributions, Distributions of functions of random variables. Modes of convergences of sequences of random variables - in distribution, in probability, with probability one and in mean square. Mathematical expectation and conditional expectation. Characteristic function, moment and probability generating functions, Inversion, uniqueness and continuity theorems. Borel 0-1 law, Kolmogorov's 0-1 law. Tchebycheff's and Kolmogorov's inequalities. Laws of large numbers and central limit theorems for independent variables.

(ii) Statistical Methods:

Collection, compilation and presentation of data, charts, diagrams and histogram. Frequency distribution. Measures of location, dispersion, skewness and kurtosis. Bivariate and multivariate data.

Association and contingency. Curve fitting and orthogonal polynomials. Bivariate normal distribution. Regression-linear, polynomial. Distribution of the correlation coefficient, Partial and multiple correlation, Intraclass correlation, Correlation ratio. Standard errors and large sample test. Sampling distributions of sample mean, sample variance, t, chi-square and F; tests of significance based on them, Small sample tests. Non-parametric tests-Goodness of fit, sign, median, run, Wilcoxon, Mann-Whitney, Wald-Wolfowitz and Kolmogorov-Smirnov. Order statistics-minimum, maximum, range and median. Concept of Asymptotic relative efficiency.

(iii) Numerical Analysis:

Finite differences of different orders: , E and D D operators, factorial representation of a polynomial, separation of symbols, sub-division of intervals, differences of zero. Concept of interpolation and extrapolation: Newton Gregory's forward and backward interpolation formulae for equal intervals, divided differences and their properties, Newton's formula for divided difference, Lagrange's formula for unequal intervals, central difference formula due to Gauss, Sterling and Bessel, concept of error terms in interpolation formula. Inverse interpolation: Different methods of inverse interpolation. Numerical differentiation: Trapezoidal, Simpson's one-third and three-eight rule and Waddles rule. Summation of Series: Whose general term (i) is the first difference of a function (ii) is in geometric progression. Numerical solutions of differential equations: Euler's Method, Milne's Method, Picard's Method and Runge-Kutta Method.

(iv) Computer application and Data Processing:

Basics of Computer: Operations of a computer, Different units of a computer system like central processing unit, memory unit, arithmetic and logical unit, input unit, output unit etc., Hardware including different types of input, output and peripheral devices, Software, system and application software, number systems, Operating systems, packages and utilities, Low and High level languages, Compiler, Assembler, Memory – RAM, ROM, unit of computer memory (bits, bytes etc.), Network – LAN, WAN, internet, intranet, basics of computer security, virus, antivirus, firewall, spyware, malware etc.

Basics of Programming: Algorithm, Flowchart, Data, Information, Database, overview of different programming languages, frontend and backend of a project, variables, control structures, arrays and their usages, functions, modules, loops, conditional statements, exceptions, debugging and related concepts.

STATISTICS – II (OBJECTIVE TYPE)

(i) Linear Models:

Theory of linear estimation, Gauss-Markov linear models, estimable functions, error and estimation space, normal equations and least square estimators, estimation of error variance, estimation with correlated observations, properties of least square estimators, generalized inverse of a matrix and solution of normal equations, variances and covariances of least square estimators. One way and two-way classifications, fixed, random and mixed effects models. Analysis of variance (two-way classification only), multiple comparison tests due to Tukey, Scheffe and Student-Newmann-Keul-Duncan.

(ii) Statistical Inference and Hypothesis Testing:

Characteristics of good estimator. Estimation methods of maximum likelihood, minimum chisquare, moments and least squares. Optimal properties of maximum likelihood estimators. Minimum variance unbiased estimators. Minimum variance bound estimators. Cramer-Rao inequality. Bhattacharya bounds. Sufficient estimator. factorization theorem. Complete statistics. Rao-Blackwell theorem. Confidence interval estimation. Optimum confidence bounds. Resampling, Bootstrap and Jacknife.

Hypothesis testing: Simple and composite hypotheses. Two kinds of error. Critical region. Different types of critical regions and similar regions. Power function. Most powerful and uniformly most powerful tests. Neyman-Pearson fundamental lemma. Unbiased test. Randomized test. Likelihood ratio test. Wald's SPRT, OC and ASN functions. Elements of decision theory.

(iii) Official Statistics:

National and International official statistical system

Official Statistics: (a) Need, Uses, Users, Reliability, Relevance, Limitations, Transparency, its visibility (b) Compilation, Collection, Processing, Analysis and Dissemination, Agencies Involved, Methods National Statistical Organization: Vision and Mission, NSSO and CSO; roles and responsibilities; Important activities, Publications etc.

National Statistical Commission: Need, Constitution, its role, functions etc; Legal Acts/ Provisions/ Support for Official Statistics; Important Acts Index Numbers: Different Types, Need, Data Collection Mechanism, Periodicity, Agencies Involved, Uses

Sector Wise Statistics: Agriculture, Health, Education, Women and Child etc. Important Surveys & Census, Indicators, Agencies and Usages etc.

National Accounts: Definition, Basic Concepts; issues; the Strategy, Collection of Data and Release.

Population Census: Need, Data Collected, Periodicity, Methods of data collection, dissemination, Agencies involved.

Misc: Socio Economic Indicators, Gender Awareness/Statistics, Important Surveys and Censuses.

STATISTICS – III (DESCRIPTIVE TYPE)

(i) Sampling Techniques:

Concept of population and sample, need for sampling, complete enumeration versus sampling, basic concepts in sampling, sampling and Non-sampling error, Methodologies in sample surveys (questionnaires, sampling design and methods followed in field investigation) by NSSO. Subjective or purposive sampling, probability sampling or random sampling, simple random sampling with and without replacement, estimation of population mean, population proportions and their standard errors. Stratified random sampling, proportional and optimum allocation, comparison with simple random sampling for fixed sample size. Covariance and Variance Function. Ratio, product and regression methods of estimation, estimation of population mean, evaluation of Bias and Variance to the first order of approximation, comparison with simple random sampling. Systematic sampling (when population size (N) is an integer multiple of sampling size (n)). Estimation of population mean and standard error of this estimate, comparison with simple random sampling. Sampling with probability proportional to size (with and without replacement method), Des Raj and Das estimators for n=2, Horvitz-Thomson's estimator

Equal size cluster sampling: estimators of population mean and total and their standard errors, comparison of cluster sampling with SRS in terms of intra-class correlation coefficient. Concept of multistage sampling and its application, two-stage sampling with equal number of second stage units, estimation of population mean and total.Double sampling in ratio and regression methods of estimation. Concept of Interpenetrating sub-sampling.

(ii) Econometrics:

Nature of econometrics, the general linear model (GLM) and its extensions, ordinary least squares (OLS) estimation and prediction, generalized least squares (GLS) estimation and prediction, heteroscedastic disturbances, pure and mixed estimation. Auto correlation, its consequences and tests. Theil BLUS procedure, estimation and prediction, multi-collinearity problem, its implications and tools for handling the problem, ridge regression. Linear regression and stochastic regression, instrumental variable estimation, errors in variables, autoregressive linear regression, lagged variables, distributed lag models, estimation of lags by OLS method, Koyck's geometric lag model. Simultaneous linear equations model and its generalization, identification problem, restrictions on structural parameters, rank and order conditions. Estimation in simultaneous equations model, recursive systems, 2 SLS estimators, limited information estimators, k-class estimators, 3 SLS estimator, full information maximum likelihood method, prediction and simultaneous confidence intervals.

(iii) Applied Statistics:

Index Numbers: Price relatives and quantity or volume relatives, Link and chain relatives composition of index numbers; Laspeyre's, Paasches', Marshal Edgeworth and Fisher index numbers; chain base index number, tests for index number, Construction of index numbers of wholesale and consumer prices, Income distribution-Pareto and Engel curves, Concentration curve, Methods of estimating national income, Inter-sectoral flows, Inter-industry table, Role of CSO. Demand Analysis

Time Series Analysis: Economic time series, different components, illustration, additive and multiplicative models, determination of trend, seasonal and cyclical fluctuations. Time-series as discrete parameter stochastic process, auto covariance and autocorrelation functions and their properties. Exploratory time Series analysis, tests for trend and seasonality, exponential and moving average smoothing. Holt and Winters smoothing, forecasting based on smoothing.

Detailed study of the stationary processes: (1) moving average (MA), (2) auto regressive (AR), (3) ARMA and (4) AR integrated MA (ARIMA) models. Box-Jenkins models, choice of AR and MA periods. Discussion (without proof) of estimation of mean, auto covariance and autocorrelation functions under large sample theory, estimation of ARIMA model parameters. Spectral analysis of weakly stationary process, periodogram and correlogram analyses, computations based on Fourier transform.

STATISTICS – IV (DESCRIPTIVE TYPE)

(Equal number of questions i.e. 50% weightage from all the subsections below and candidates have to choose any two subsections and answer)

(i) Operations Research and Reliability:

Definition and Scope of Operations Research: phases in Operation Research, models and their solutions, decision-making under uncertainty and risk, use of different criteria, sensitivity analysis. Transportation and assignment problems. Bellman's principle of optimality, general formulation, computational methods and application of dynamic programming to LPP. Decision-making in the face of competition, two-person games, pure and mixed strategies, existence of solution and uniqueness of value in zero-sum games, finding solutions in 2x2, 2xm and mxn games. Analytical structure of inventory problems, EOQ formula of Harris, its sensitivity analysis and extensions allowing quantity discounts and shortages. Multi-item inventory subject to constraints. Models with random demand, the static risk model. P and Q- systems with constant and random lead times.

Queuing models – specification and effectiveness measures. Steady-state solutions of M/M/1 and M/M/c models with associated distributions of queue-length and waiting time. M/G/1 queue and Pollazcek-Khinchine result. Sequencing and scheduling problems. 2-machine n-job and 3-machine n-job problems with identical machine sequence for all jobs Branch and Bound method for solving travelling salesman problem. Replacement problems – Block and age replacement policies.

PERT and CPM – basic concepts. Probability of project completion. Reliability concepts and measures, components and systems, coherent systems, reliability of coherent systems.

Life-distributions, reliability function, hazard rate, common univariate life distributions – exponential, weibull, gamma, etc. Bivariate exponential distributions. Estimation of parameters and tests in these models.

Notions of aging – IFR, IFRA, NBU, DMRL and NBUE classes and their duals. Loss of memory property of the exponential distribution.

Reliability estimation based on failure times in variously censored life-tests and in tests with replacement of failed items. Stress-strength reliability and its estimation.

(ii) Demography and Vital Statistics:

Sources of demographic data, census, registration, ad-hoc surveys, Hospital records, Demographic profiles of the Indian Census. Complete life table and its main features, Uses of life table. Makehams and Gompertz curves. National life tables. UN model life tables. Abridged life tables. Stable and stationary populations.

Measurement of Fertility: Crude birth rate, General fertility rate, Age specific birth rate, Total fertility rate, Gross reproduction rate, Net reproduction rate.

Measurement of Mortality: Crude death rate, Standardized death rates, Age-specific death rates, Infant Mortality rate, Death rate by cause.

Internal migration and its measurement, migration models, concept of international migration. Net migration. International and postcensal estimates. Projection method including logistic curve fitting. Decennial population census in India.

(iii) Survival Analysis and Clinical Trial:

Concept of time, order and random censoring, likelihood in the distributions – exponential, gamma, Weibull, lognormal, Pareto, Linear failure rate, inference for these distribution. Life tables, failure rate, mean residual life and their elementary classes and their properties. Estimation of survival function – actuarial estimator, Kaplan – Meier estimator, estimation under the assumption of IFR/DFR, tests of exponentiality against non-parametric classes, total time on test. Two sample problem – Gehan test, log rank test.

Semi-parametric regression for failure rate – Cox's proportional hazards model with one and several covariates, rank test for the regression coefficient. Competing risk model, parametric and non-parametric inference for this model.

Introduction to clinical trials: the need and ethics of clinical trials, bias and random error in clinical studies, conduct of clinical trials, overview of Phase I – IV trials, multicenter trials.

Data management: data definitions, case report forms, database design, data collection systems for good clinical practice.

Design of clinical trials: parallel vs. cross-over designs, cross-sectional vs. longitudinal designs,

review of factorial designs, objectives and endpoints of clinical trials, design of Phase I trials, design of single-stage and multi-stage Phase II trials, design and monitoring of phase III trials with sequential stopping,

Reporting and analysis: analysis of categorical outcomes from Phase I – III trials, analysis of survival data from clinical trials.

(iv) Quality Control:

Statistical process and product control: Quality of a product, need for quality control, basic concept of process control, process capability and product control, general theory of control charts, causes of variation in quality, control limits, sub grouping summary of out of control criteria, charts for attributes p chart, np chart, c-chart, V chart, charts for variables: R, (X, R), (X, σ) charts.

Basic concepts of process monitoring and control; process capability and process optimization. General theory and review of control charts for attribute and variable data; O.C. and A.R.L. of control charts; control by gauging; moving average and exponentially weighted moving average charts; Cu-Sum charts using V-masks and decision intervals; Economic design of X-bar chart. Acceptance sampling plans for attributes inspection; single and double sampling plans and their properties; plans for inspection by variables for one-sided and two sided specification.

(v) Multivariate Analysis:

Multivariate normal distribution and its properties. Random sampling from multivariate normal distribution. Maximum likelihood estimators of parameters, distribution of sample mean vector.

Wishart matrix – its distribution and properties, distribution of sample generalized variance, null and non-null distribution of multiple correlation coefficients.

Hotelling's T and its sampling distribution, application in test on mean vector for one and more multivariate normal population and also on equality of components of a mean vector in multivariate normal population.

Classification problem: Standards of good classification, procedure of classification based on

multivariate normal distributions. Principal components, dimension reduction, canonical variates and canonical correlation — definition, use, estimation and computation.

(vi) Design and Analysis of Experiments:

Analysis of variance for one way and two way classifications, Need for design of experiments, basic principle of experimental design (randomization, replication and local control), complete analysis and layout of completely randomized design, randomized block design and Latin square design, Missing plot technique. Split Plot Design and Strip Plot Design.

Factorial experiments and confounding in 2 and 3 experiments. Analysis of covariance. Analysis of non-orthogonal data. Analysis of missing data.

(vii) Computing with C and R :

Basics of C: Components of C language, structure of a C program, Data type, basic data types, Enumerated data types, Derived data types, variable declaration, Local, Global, Parametric variables, Assignment of Variables, Numeric, Character, Real and String constants, Arithmetic, Relation and Logical operators, Assignment operators, Increment and decrement operators, conditional operators, Bitwise operators, Type modifiers and expressions, writing and interpreting expressions, using expressions in statements. Basic input/output.

Control statements: conditional statements, if - else, nesting of if - else, else if ladder, switch statements, loops in c, for, while, do - while loops, break, continue, exit ( ), goto and label declarations, One dimensional two dimensional and multidimensional arrays.

Storage classes: Automatic variables, External variables, Static variables, Scope and lifetime of declarations.

Functions: classification of functions, functions definition and declaration, assessing a function, return statement, parameter passing in functions. Pointers (concept only).

Structure: Definition and declaration; structure (initialization) comparison of structure variable;

Array of structures : array within structures, structures within structures, passing structures to functions; Unions accessing a union member, union of structure, initialization of a union variable, uses of union. Introduction to linked list, linear linked list, insertion of a node in list, removal of a node from list.

Files in C: Defining and opening a file, input – output operation on a file, creating a file, reading a file.

Statistics Methods and techniques in R

GENERAL ENGLISH SECTION

GENERAL ENGLISH
2023

Time Allowed : Three Hours | *Maximum Marks: 100*

QUESTIONS PAPER SPECIFIC INSTRUCTIONS

Please read each of the following instructions carefully before attempting questions.

*Attempt all the questions. Marks allotted for a particular question/part are indicated against it. Word limit of the answers, if specified, should be adhered to. You must not disclose your identity in any of your answers. Answers must be written in **ENGLISH** only.*

---

1. Write an essay on any one of the following topics in about 800 words: **30**

(a) Nature Nuturee when Nutred

(b) Prospects of Women Entrepreneurship in India

(c) Mental Healthcare for all

(d) Culture and Society feed each other

(e) Animal Rights vis-a-vis Human Rights

2. Write a precis of the following passage in your own words in about one-third of the original length: **30**

The Earth is a home for a rich and diverse array of living organisms, whose genetic diversity and relationship with each other, constitute the planet's biodiversity. It includes species as well as varieties found within the same species, as also the enormous ecosystems and habitats: forests, grasslands, oceans and its depths, peats and peat bogs. Worldwide, an area of tropical forest equal to a football field, is disappearing every second. Forests are being cleared for agriculture, cattle ranching and for timber. They get submerged when dams are constructed. When forests are felled we deal a blow to biodiversity, the richness of life. Five great waves of extinctionn have decimated our planet's species in the remote past. The sixth wave, which we are witnessing, is largely man made. One-fourth of the Earth's total biological diversitry, amounting to about 1.6 million species, risk of existence and if we ignore the biodiversity crisis, we would lose these species in the next 25 years. If we respond with knowledge and technology, we might hold the loss to 10 percent, but even this amounts to millions of species.

It is a well-known fact the ecosystem is undergoing changes due to pollution, invasive species, over-exploitation by humans, climate change and many other reasons. Most of the people are beginning to recognize that biodiversity is not only for availing the benefits, but is also to be conserved in all its forms. The importance of species diversity conservation is usually justified by the direct use of the species by man, as food sources, fibre, fuel, new chemicals and raw materials. When a species is lost, it is lost for ever. Our ethics tell us that we should not deprive our future generations from the economic and aesthetic benefits that can be derived from biodiversity. It is our moral duty to look after our planet and pass it on to our future generations in good health. The decisions taken by us now, as an individual and as a society will determine the diversity of genes, species or ecosystems that remain in future. Top priority should be given to check destruction or degradation of habitats, because it is most responsible for the loss of biodiversity. More knowledge is required to conserve biodiversity in view of reduced space under increased pressure of human activities. Unless immediate actions are taken to protect the biodiversity, we will lose forever the opportunity of reaping its full potential benefit in the present and in future.

Conservation of biodiversity is concerned with the protection of genes and species and their number in population, ecosystems or habitats. It is important to conserve numerous varieties of plants and animals. Each variety within a species contains unique genes. The diversity of genes within a species increases its adaptability to pollution, diseases, stresses and other environmental changes. When varieties of plants and animals are destroyed the genetic diversity within the species is diminished. Biodiversity conservation refers to the efforts to maintain or enhance biodiversity involving protection, upliftment and scientific management at its optimum level in order to derive sustainable benefits for the present as well as for the future.

Biodiversity conservation study is aimed at knowing how human activities affect the diversity of plants and animals and developing ways to protect it. Thus conservation of biodiversity, the Earth's biological heritage, is one of today's most pressing environmental issues. The challenge lies before individuals, organisations and government agencies for nations and the world as a whole to protect and enhance biological diversity, while continuing to meet people's need for natural resources. If these goals are not met, the future generations will live in a biologically impoverished world.

There are two approaches of biodiversity conservation namely *in situ* (on site) conservation, which tries to protect the species where they are, i.e., in their natural habitats and *ex situ* (off site) conservation, which attempts to protect and preserve a species in a place away from its natural habitat. (673 words)

3. Write a paragraph in about 200 words on any one of the following expressions statements : 10

(a) Nothing sustains a person like self-belief.

(b) Life is what you make it.

(c) A painting is a poem without words.

(d) Man is born free.

(e) Home is where the heart is.

4. Use the following words, each in a single sentence. Bring out the meaning clearly without changing the form of the word. No credit will be given for a vague or ambiguous sentence.

2×5=10

(a) Altercation

(b) Blatantly

(c) Cacophony

(d) Delirious

(e) Invigorate

5. Use the following idioms and phrasal verbs in sentences, so as to bring out their meaning clearly :

2×5=10

(a) a pinch of salt

(b) down the alley

(c) at an arm's length

(d) under the cloud

(e) in the eye of the storm

6. Correct the following sentences without changing their meaning. Do not make unnecessary changes in the original sentence :

1×10=10

(a) It is a matter of gravest importance.

(b) He was hankering for success.

(c) Neither she comes nor she writes.

(d) Too many a roadblock can be very frustrative for drivers.

(e) The contents of the box was an enigma for everyone.

(f) We were happy to see acres and acres of expensive lush green fields.

(g) Even though this pen cost me dearly, it is value for money.

(h) Everyone must bide by the rules of the game.

(i) Your lack in clarity of thought can be detrimental to your welfare.

(j) He coaxed me to agree with his proposal.

GENERAL ENGLISH
2022

Time Allowed : Three Hours

Maximum Marks: 100

QUESTIONS PAPER SPECIFIC INSTRUCTIONS

Please read each of the following instructions carefully before attempting questions.

Attempt all the questions. Marks allotted for a particular question/part are indicated against it. Word limit of the answers, if specified, should be adhered to. You must not disclose your identity in any of your answers. Answers must be written in ***ENGLISH*** *only.*

1. Write an essay on any one of the following topics in about 800 words: **30**

(a) Right to Privacy: Intrinsic to Life and Liberty.

(b) Make in India : Big Boost to Industry and Employment.

(c) Significance of Renewable Energy Sources in the context of Global climate change.

(d) Can Artificial Intelligence Replace Human Agency?

(e) Women's participation in Sports is still a challenge in India.

2. Write a precis of the following passage in your own words in about one-third of the original length : **30**

Joy and sadness are experienced by people in all cultures around the world, but how can we tell when other people are happy or despondent ? It turns out that the expression of many emotions may be universal. Smiling is apparently a universal sign of friendliness and approval. Baring the teeth in a hostile way, as noted by Charles Darwin in the nineteenth century, may be a universal sign of anger. As the originator of the theory of evolution, Darwin believed that the universal recognition of facial expressions would have survival value. For example, facial expressions could signal the approach of enemies (or friends) in the absence of language.

Most investigators concur that certain facial expressions suggest the same emotions in all people. Moreover, people in diverse cultures recognize the emotions manifested by the facial expressions. In classic research Paul Ekman took photographs of people exhibiting the emotions of anger, disgust, fear, happiness and sadness. He then asked people around the world to indicate what emotions were being depicted in them. Those queried ranged from European college students to members of the Fore, a tribe that dwells in the New Guinea highlands. All groups, including the Fore, who had almost no contact with Western culture, agreed on the portrayed emotions. The

Fore also displayed familiar facial expressions when asked how they would respond if they were the characters in stories that called for basic emotional responses. Ekman and his colleagues more recently obtained similar results in a study of ten cultures in which participants were permitted to report that multiple emotions were shown by facial expressions. The participants generally agreed on which two emotions were being shown and which emotion was more intense.

Psychological researchers generally recognize that facial expressions reflect emotional states. In fact, various emotional states give rise to certain patterns of electrical activity in the facial muscles and in the brain. The facial-feedback hypothesis argues, however, that the causal relationship between emotions and facial expressions can also work in the opposite direction. According to this hypothesis, signals from the facial muscles are sent back to emotion centres of the brain, and so a person's facial expression can influence that person's emotional state. Consider Darwin's words : "The free expression by outward signs of an emotion intensifies it. On the other hand, the repression, as far as possible, of all outward signs softens our emotions." Can smiling give rise to feelings of goodwill, for example, and frowning to anger?

Psychological research has given rise to some interesting findings concerning the facial-feedback hypothesis, causing participants in experiments to smile, for example, leads them to report more positive feelings and to rate cartoons as being more humorous. When they are caused to frown, they rate cartoons as being more aggressive.

What are the possible links between facial expressions and emotion ? One link is arousal, which is the level of activity or preparedness for activity in an organism. Intense contraction of facial muscles, such as those used in signifying fear, heightens arousal. Self-perception of heightened arousal then leads to heightened emotional activity. Other links may involve changes in brain temperature and the release of neurotransmitters (substances that transmit nerve impulses). The contraction of facial muscles both influences the internal emotional state and reflects it. Ekman has found that the so-called Duchenne smile, which is characterized by "crow's-feet" wrinkles around the eyes and a subtle drop in the eye cover fold so that the skin above the eye moves down slightly toward the eyeball, can lead to pleasant feelings.

Ekman's observation may be relevant to the British expression "Keep a stiff upper lip" as a recommendation for handling stress. It might be that a "stiff" lip suppresses emotional response - as long as the lip is not quivering with fear or tension. But when the emotion that leads to stiffening the lip is more intense, and involves strong muscle tension, facial feedback may heighten emotional response. (639 words)

3. Write a paragraph in about 200 words on any one of the following: **10**

(a) Justice delayed is justice denied.

(b) All's well that ends well.

(c) A thing of beauty is a joy forever.

(d) Rituals and scientific thinking.

(e) Is internet a menace to children ?

4. Use the following words, each in a single sentenc. Bring out the meaning clearly without changing the form of the word. No credit will be given for a vague or ambiguous sentence: **2×5=10**

(a) specious

(b) uncouth

(c) prevaricate

(d) chagrin

(e) connmsseur

5. **Use the following idioms and phrasal verbs in sentences so as to bring out their meaning clearly:** **2×5=10**

(a) swan song
(b) in sync with
(c) to smell a rat
(d) go to the dogs
(e) to break the ice

6. **Correct the following sentences without changing their meaning. Do not make unnecessary changes in the original sentences:** **1×10 = 10**

(a) The shepherd was tending his sheeps.
(b) I do not understand why he is so angry at me.
(c) What is the time in your watch ?
(d) Look at the correct meaning of the word in the dictionary.
(e) I avoid to go there.
(f) He or his friends has done this.
(g) Mr. Sharma was accused for murder.
(h) He says that he owns a car beside a scooter.
(1) He is a coward fellow.
(j) The children thought of making merry but the rain spoiled there dream.

GENERAL ENGLISH
2021

Time Allowed : Three Hours

Maximum Marks: 100

Question Paper Specific Instructions

Please read each of the following instructions carefully before attempting questions.

*There are FOUR questions and **all** are to be attempted. Candidates should attempt questions/parts as per the instructions given in the questions. The number of marks carrid by a question/part is indicated against it. Candidates are required to write clear, legible and concise answers and to adhere to word limits, wherever indicated. Failure to adhere to word limits may be penalized. Any page or portion of the page left blank in the Question-cun-Answer Booklet must be clearly struck off. Answers must be written in ENGLISH only.*

---

1. **Answer all the following (in not or more than 200 words each):** 5×5=25

   (a) Describe the economic conditions of Later Vedic Period. How was it different from Rig Vedic life

   (b) Discuss the similarities and differences between the basic tenets of Buddhism and Jainism.

   (c) Trace the evolution of Temple architecture in South India.

   (d) How did the Bhakti Movement contribute to the growth of regional languages?

   (e) Highlight the role of Peoples movement towards the integration of Princely States into the India Union.

2. **Answer *all* the following (in not more than 200 words each):** 5×5=25

   (a) "Climate change is likely to adversely affect certain countries dependent on agriculture." Examine this statement citing relevant examples.

   (b) Many countreis prefer coal rather than solar or wind energy as a source of fuel. Why?

   (c) "Air pollution and water shortages are among the problems faced by urban centres across the globe." Examine this statement.

   (d) What factors inluence the location of industries in India today?

   (e) "Degradation of forest resources and wildlife is a fallout of agriculture and urbanization." Assess this statement giving examples from India.

3. Answer *all* the following (in not more than 200 words each): **5×5=25**

(a) Critically examine Indian Agriculture Acts of 2020.

(b) "Privatization of Public Sector Banks is fraught with huge risk". Elucidate.

(c) Do you believe that Aatmanirbhar Bharat Abhiyaan, 2020 will be able to combat the COVID-19 crisis of the Indian economy? Justify your answer.

(d) Analyse the recommendations of the Narasimham Committee Report I and II in controlling Non-Perorming Assets (NPAs) of the banking sector in India.

(e) Discuss the roles and responsibilites of the Anganwadi workers and helpers under Integrated Child Development Services Scheme (ICDS).

4. Answer *all* the following (in not more than 200 words each): **5×5=25**

(a) "The Indian Constitution is a living document." Discuss.

(b) Critically examine the financial emergency powers of the President and their effects.

(c) "The Rajya Sabha has certain special powers vis-a-vis the Lok Sabha that adds to its prestige." Comment.

(d) Compare the writ jurisdictions of the Supreme Court and the High Court.

(e) "The Indian Goverment's response to the COVID-19 pandemic has shifted the federal balance in its favour." Illustrate with suitable examples.

GENERAL ENGLISH
2020

Time Allowed : Three Hours | *Maximum Marks: 100*

Question Paper Specific Instructions
Please read each of the following instructions carefully before attempting questions.

*There are **SIX** questions and all are to be attempted. The number of marks carrid by a question/part is indicated against it. Answers must be written in **ENGLISH** only. Candidates are required to write clear, legible and concise answers and to adhere to word limits, wherever indicated. Failure to adhere to word limits may be penalized. Any page or portion of the page left blank in the Question-cun-Answer Booklet must be clearly struck off.*

1. **Write an essay on any one of the following topics in about 800 words:** 30

   (a) Effects of Global Warming

   (b) Role of an Effective Opposition in Democracy

   (c) Life is Action, not Contemplation

   (d) Education as a Means to Women's Empowerment

   (e) Effect of Social Media on Youth

2. **Make a precis of the following passage in about one-third of the original length, using your own words:** 30

   What part should reading play in our lives? It should certainly not be a substitute for action, not for independent thinking, nor for conversation; but it may be a help and stimulant to action, thought and talk; and it is capable of providing almost infinite pleasure. Thereon our bookshelves or on summons from a library are wit, wisdom, adventure, romance from all ages and all over the world. Is there any wonder that our eyes sometimes stray wistfully to the bookshelves and away from a dull visitor, or that we shirk a tiresome duty for an exciting book?

   Books or people? Reading or conversation or, nowadays, listening in to the radio? Which is the better way to gain knowledge or to spend your leisure? Some fortuante people seem always to find time for both and to enjoy both almost equally. My great friend, Arthur Wauchope, a fine soldier, a most able administrator and a very gifted personality, was a constant reader, yer was always ready to lay aside a book for talk and was a most interesting and interested talker.

The advantages of reading over talk are of course that we can select the book that suits our mood, can go at our own pace, skip. or turn back, whereas we cannot turn over two pages of a tedious companion or close him, or her, with a bang. But reading lacks the human touch, the salt of life, and is, therefore, a dangerous substifute for thought or action. Bacon in one of his essays says that reading maketh a full man; conference (that is talking) a ready man; and writing an exact man. One would like to be full of knowledge, ready in speech, and exact by training. But full of what? What sort of reading has impressed itself on my memory and what books have found a permanent place on my bookshelves?

To begin with my profession, soldiering. I do not believe that soldiering, a practical business, in which human nature is the main element, can be learnt from text-books, and more than can boxing or cricket or golf. But for those who have grasped the principles of war and have understood that the human factor is the most important element in it, there is military reading that is fascinating and valuable.

'Read and re-read the campaigns of the great commanders,' saidNapoleon. I would venture to put it differently and would say that the lives and characters of the great commanders are what students of war should examine, since their campaigns are only incidents in them; and that the behaviour of leaders and of their men in the field is the subject for study. Take Napoleon's first campaign of 1796. The text-book will tell you that he won by manoeuvre on interior lines or by the principle of concentration of force or some similar conjuration. One learn nothing, I hold, by such dogma.

In my general reading, history, biography and travel occupy, I think, first place; and since I have spent a considerable proportion of my life in the East there are a good number of volumes on India and the Middle East. There is plenty of poetry on my shelves and a good deal of it in my head. I have put my notions of poetry in a book already and will not repeat them here, except to express my firm belief that poetry in some shape or another is one of the most precious of our heritages, and that much of what tries to pass for poetry nowadays is not poetry at all, and not even camouflaged as such. Poetry should dance in the mind, and blow one a kiss; or gallop to adventure with a cheer; or whisper gently of sad things past; not shuffle or slouch past with dark incomprehensible mutterings. Perhaps I am getting old, anyway I prefer the old poets.

Lastly comes what is sometimes called 'escapist' literature, the books we read with no other aim than to rest or to amuse the mind, to forget the day's chores and the morrow's anxieties. This is perhaps the most pleasant form of reading for most. (701 words)

3. Write a paragraph in about 200 words on any one of the following expressions/statements: **10**

(a) Punctuality is a precious virtue.

(b) It is better to do a thing badly than not to do it at all.

(c) Courage is the necessity of life.

(d) Love of money is the root of all evils.

(e) Is censorship of Internet necessary?

4. Use the following words in sentences so as to bring out their meaning clearly. Do not change the form of the word. No credit will be given for a vague or ambiguous sentence. 2×5=10

(a) Gregarious

(b) Hostility

(c) Affluence

(d) Boisterous

(e) Affinity

5. Use the following idioms and phrasal verbs in sentences so as to bring out their meaning clearly: 2×5=10

(a) A vested interest

(b) At cross purposes

(c) At a loss for words

(d) Look down on/upon

(e) Put across

6 Correct the following sentences without changing their meaning. Do not make unnecessary changes in the original sentence: 1×10=10

(a) I did not like him disturbing me at that late hour.

(b) Death is preferable than dishonour.

(c) He is enough wise to understand the situation.

(d) He is seldom or ever to be seen at his shop.

(e) The teacher has not yet entered into the classroom.

(f) I am prepared to say it at his face.

(g) He insisted to leave immediately.

(h) He always says the truth.

(i) Wealth is only means, the end is happiness.

(j) I doubt that he will come.

GENERAL ENGLISH
2019

Time Allowed : Three Hours | *Maximum Marks: 100*

Question Paper Specific Instructions
Please read each of the following instructions carefully before attempting questions.

*There are **SIX** questions and all are to be attempted. The number of marks carrid by a question/part is indicated against it. Answers must be written in **ENGLISH** only. Candidates are required to write clear, legible and concise answers and to adhere to word limits, wherever indicated. Failure to adhere to word limits may be penalized. Any page or portion of the page left blank in the Question-cun-Answer Booklet must be clearly struck off.*

1. **Write and eassay on any *one* of the following topics in about 800 words:** **30**
   (a) Can the Reservation Policy ensure social justice?
   (b) Responsibility of news media in India
   (c) Free speech as a democratic right
   (d) Hazards of pollution and possible solutions
   (e) Representation of women in Indian cinema

2. **Make a precis of the following passage in about one-third of the original length, using your own words:** **30**

   Indians are known for jealously preserving their cultural idenity. They continue to cling to their norms of endogamy, marital stability and family solidarity, kin orientation, religion and mother tongue. They are always nostalgic about Indian food and their women tend to stick to their lovely *saris*.

   As for the mechanisms of their cultural preservation, mention must be made of temples and gurdwaras, practice of *keertan* and *akhand path*, audio cassettes devotional songs, video cassettes of *Ramayan* and *Mahabharat*, festivals and functions, and ethnic associations and organisations. What is more, even picnics provide occasions to reinforce old cultural practices. For instance, I was trulyastonished to see *antakshari* (a verbal game in which the last letter of the verse another participant has to be used as the starting letter of the verse by another participant) played in Sanskrit hymns in a picnic of Indians in Salt Lake City in USA.

Overseas Indians adhere to their traditional cultureso ostensibly that at times it appears that they are are more Indian in their cultural orientations and practices than resident Indians in India. Take, for instance, the Sikhs who are quick to take to modern ways in India but they tend to be rather orthodox abroad. Even those Indians who couldn't care less for their culture in India become quite observant of it in foreign lands.

Why do Indians get so faithful to their culture in foregin lands while at home they seem to favour Western culture? Several explanations come to mind. One, that they find in their culturea defence mechanism against a sense of insecurity in alien settings. Two, that they might be banking on their culture as a compensatory mechanism for the loss of status in foreign lands. Three, maybe there is something in the Indian culture - perhaps its adhesive quality - that accounts for it. Four, may be it is sense of pride of belonging to one of the oldest cultures of the world that makes them so reverent to it. Fifth, it may well be so because the immigrants get stuck to their conception of Indian culture of the time when had left India and remain blissfully unaware of the changes it has undergone since then.

As important as it is, the question of cultural identity of overseas Indians needs careful scrutiny. It involves several issues. The first is the issue of how Indians abroad perceive their self-identity. Do they view themselves as Indians or as Punjabis, Gujaratis, etc.? In other word, do they identify themselves in terms of pan-Indian identity or in terms of a parochial ethnic category. According to Fisher (1980) Indians have diffficulty in organising as Indians. More often than not they tend to identify themselves in terms of narrow ethnic categories. By and large determines their self-identity. It seems that while dealing with the non-Indians they tend to take on pan-Indian. But when it comes to interacting among second issue is how others look upon Indians. Are they viewed as Indians or as Asians? That depends on several things including their relative numerical strength in the host country. Wherever Indians form a substantial group, they are viewed as Indians having a distinctive identity. In the countries where their number is small and the ethnic groups of other nationalities are also present they tend to be bracketed with the other Asians.

Even at the risk of sounding outrageous, it may be remarked that perhaps too much is made in the existing literature of the instinct of cultural preservation and identity of Indians in foreign settings. For one thing, perhaps every ethnic group tends to stick to its culture in strange surroundings about as fastidiously as do the Indians. Are Chinese immigrants any different from Indians? It requires a comparative study of various immigrant communities, including Indians, to maintain that the Indians stand amoung others. For another, there is no dearth of contradictory evidence to show that any number of Indians have abandoned their culture in favour of the cultures of their adopted lands. Third, there is a generational context to it. While the first generation immigrants tend to stick to Indian culture with vigour, the second and subsequent generations give evidence of distancing from it. (731 words)

3. **Write a paragrabh in about 200 words on any *one* of the following expressions/statements: 10**

(a) It is better to conquer yourself than to win a thousand battles.

(b) Politics makes strange bedfellows.

(c) Strike the iron while it is hot.

(d) To be yourself in a world that is constantly trying to make you something else is the greatest accomplishment.

(e) If you want to test a man's character, give him power.

4. **Use the following words in sentences so as to bring out their meaning clearly. Do not change the form of the word. No credit will be given for a vague or ambiguous sentence.** 2×5=10

   (a) Acrimony

   (b) Credulous

   (c) Itinerant

   (d) Precarios

   (e) Bereavement

5. **Use the following idioms and phrasal verbs in sentences so as to bring out their meaning clearly:** 2×5=10

   (a) Fall through

   (b) Throw a spanner

   (c) Go overboard

   (d) Come a cropper

   (e) Drive home

6. **Correct the following sentences without changing their meaning. Do not make unnecessary changes in the original sentence:** 1×10=10

   (a) His daughter-in-law is a M.A. in English.

   (b) Rina has been deprived from her share in her father's property.

   (c) All the books in the old library has perished.

   (d) The aggrieved man said that he will not forgive the wrong-doer.

   (e) Despeite of the doctor's advice, he smoked.

   (f) The principal could not attend the meeting in account of illness.

   (g) In the court-room the advocate referred an old case.

   (h) The old man was so weak to climb the stairs.

   (i) My father has stopped living in the official quarter.

   (j) They cannot issue the ticket unless you do not pay the fare.

GENERAL ENGLISH
2018

Time Allowed : Three Hours

Maximum Marks: 100

Questions Paper Specific Instructions

Please read each of the following instructions carefully before attempting questions :

There are SIX questions and all are to be attempted.

The number of marks carried by a question / part is indicated against it.

Answers must be written in ENGLISH only.

Candidates are required to write clear, legible and concise answers and to adhere to word limits wherever indicated. Failure to adhere to word limits may be penalized.

Any page or portion of the page left blank in the Question-cum-Answer Booklet must be clearly structk off.

1. Write an essay on any one of the following topics in about 800 words : **30**

(a) Accountability, not mere stability, essential for good governance

(b) Pros and Cons of online education and examinations

(c) Rural Sector's potential to contribute to the Indian economy

(d) Social Media attains credibility with objectivity and humanity

(e) Effective Centralised Enforcement Agency necessary to prevent harassment and violence against women

2. Make a precis of the following passage in about one-third of the original length, using your own words : **30**

Education has not been of the kind that can help you towards happiness. It has not been of the kind that can make you capable of freedom. The aim of education in a democracy must be the same for all the people. Education must aim at making them all capable of freedom, for they are all to be free. Whatever education will achieve, this aim must be given to every person in proportion to his capacity to receive it. If education is necessary for one, it must be necessary for all. Only in this way can we hope to prevent the exploitation of one group by another. Only in this way can we develop a true community. The citizens must be able to understand one another. They must have a common culture. They must have the intellectual training needed to comprehend it and to communicate with those who share it.

Education for freedom consists in transmitting to the rising generation the civilization they have inherited, together with the techniques by which it may be understood. No man or woman is equipped to be a ruler without this education. As liberal education helps us to establish a free community, so does it to preserve it. As Thomas F. Woodlock has said in the Wall Street Journal, "Democracy rests ultimately upon 'public opinion' as its base. Public opinion follows upon free speech, free interchange of ideas, of judgements, of opinions; it is generated by these things. Men interchange these things by words Sound logic it was that put grammar, logic, and rhetoric as preliminary to geometry, arithmetic, music, and astronomy in the scheme of the seven liberal arts in an age which was notable for the clearness of its thinking and the exactitude of its expression. Both these things are absolutely necessary for the functioning of democracy as the best form of government. If we are going to 'educate for democracy', we had better find the right way to teach them." And the ability to read and write is the best defence against anti-democratic propaganda. Under the name of 'indoctrination of democracy' a host of lies is being propagated. When a person equipped with the liberal arts has critically studied the basic theoretical questions, he is proof against the seductions of the New Order. The reason why we may justly fear such propaganda today is that we are uneducated.

In addition to all the above merits, liberal education has yet another: it is the best vocational training. Vocational training of the usual sort trains hands. The ideal education for freedom is a liberal education in the liberal arts and the cultural heritage of the country. Since it is the ideal, we must aim at it for every citizen. Unless the citizen can master the liberal arts and the fundamental principles of a free society he cannot function as a member of a free community. He cannot help to keep the community as a free community.

If we cannot give liberal education to every citizen in proportion to his capacity to receive it we might as well give up our hopes achieving a democratic community. We cannot insist on free men and at the same time say that we cannot educate our population for freedom. We cannot insist on a community and at the same time say that it is impossible to strengthen the basis of communication among our people. Individual happiness, good citizenship, and the improvement of society all depend on our success in helping the people to achieve liberal education. These objectives do not depend on our success in training people to earn a living or in adjusting them to their environment. What the world needs, what the country must have, is free minds. This does not mean minds loaded with archaic information or equipped with obsolescent techniques. It means minds committed to the general good by good moral and intellectual habits. It means minds informed by principles derived from human experience through the ages, minds that will operate well no matter what waves of change beat upon them.

If we are to admit everybody to citizenship we must try to give everybody this kind of education. In so far as men are men they must have this education. Since in our society all men are politically equal, since all men are either rulers or the ruled, they must all be educated to be rulers and the ruled. If we cannot give them all this education, we may as well drop the pretence of democracy. We may as well admit that, though it was a good idea, it would not work.

(770 words)

3. **Write a paragraph in about 200 words on any one of the following expressions statements :**

(a) Every cloud has a silver lining.

(b) Handsome is as handsome does.

(c) Good fences make good neighbours.

(d) That's the way the cookie crumbles.

(e) If gold rusts, what shall the iron do.

4. **Use the following words in sentences so as to bring out their meaning clearly. Do not change the form of the word. No credit will be given for a vague or® ambiguous sentence. 2x5=10**

(a) recondite

(b) largesse

(c) macabre

(d) zealot

(e) disingenuous

5. **Use the following idioms and phrasal verbs in sentences so as to bring out their meaning clearly ;** **2x5 = 10**

(a) infringe upon

(b) hear on the grapevine

(c) fend for

(d) caught in the crossfire

(e) go off at a tangent

6. **Correct the following sentences without changing their meaning. Do not make unnecessary changes in the original sentence :** **1x10=10**

(a) My friend reached the airport on time to have a coffee before boarding.

(b) He was found guilty of stealing his employer.

(c) Sonu got a present from his father but he hasn't opened it.

(d) I am obliged to serve him, isn't it ?

(e) I would watch a football match than a cricket series.

(f) They were annoyed at not to be able to see the puppet show properly.

(g) The economics of the plan is worrying the investors.

(h) He got up at 5 O'clock not to be late for the interview.

(i) If they offered me the position, I shall decline it.

(j) I go to the work in afternoon.

GENERAL ENGLISH
2017

Time Allowed : Three Hours | *Maximum Marks: 100*

Questions Paper Specific Instructions

Please read each of the following instructions carefully before attempting questions :

There are SIX questions and all are to be attempted.

The number of marks carried by a question / part is indicated against it.

Answers must be written in ENGLISH only.

Candidates are required to write clear, legible and concise answers and to adhere to word limits wherever indicated. Failure to adhere to word limits may be penalized.

Any page or portion of the page left blank in the Question-cum-Answer Booklet must be clearly structk off.

---

1. **Write an essay on any one of the following topics in not less than 800 words:** **30**
   (a) Books vs e-Books
   (b) Sports bodies should be governed by Sportspersons
   (c) Rights of Persons with Disabilities in India
   (d) Uses and Abuses of Sting operations in India
   (e) Family and Globalization

2. **Make a precis of the following passage in about one-third of the original length, using your own words :** **30**

   (Note : The precis must be written only on the special sheets provided for this purpose writing one. word in each block.)

   Two principal forms of the constitution arc known to history — one is called unitary and the other is federal. The two essential characteristics of a unitary constitution are : (1) the supremacy of the central polity, and (2) the absence of subsidiary sovereign polities. On the contrary, a federal constitution is marked: (1) by the existence of a central polity and subsidiary polities side by side, and (2) by each being sovereign in the field assigned to it. In other words, federation means the establishment of a dual polity. The draft constitution is a federal constitution inasmuch as it establishes what may be a dual polity. This dual polity under the proposed constitution will consist of the Union at the centre and the States at the periphery, each endowed with sovereign powers to be exercised in the field assigned to them respectively by the constitution. This dual polity resembles the American Constitution. The American polity is also a dual polity, one of it is known as the Federal government and the other government of the States which correspond respectively to the Union government and the State governments of the draft constitution. Under the American Constitution the Federal government is not a mere league of the States nor are the States administrative units or agencies of the Federal government. In the same way, the Indian Constitution proposed in the draft constitution is not a league of States nor are the States administrative units or agencies of the Union government. Here, however, the similarities between the Indian and American Constitutions come to an end. The differences that distinguish them are more fundamental and glaring than the similarities between the two.

The points of difference between the American federation and the Indian federation are mainly two. In the USA, this dual polity is followed by a dual citizenship. In the USA there is a citizenship of the USA. But there is also a citizenship of the State. No doubt the rigours of this double citizenship are much assuaged by the Fourteenth Amendment to the Constitution of the United States which prohibits the States from taking away the rights, privileges and immunities of the citizen of the United States. At the same time, as pointed out by William Anderson, in certain political matters, including the right to vote and to hold public office, the States may and do discriminate in favour of their own citizens. This favouritism goes even further in many cases. Thus to obtain employment in the service of a State or Local government one is in most places required to be a local resident or citizen. Similarly, in the licensing of persons for the practice of such public professions as law and medicine, residence or citizenship in the State is frequently required and in business where regulation must necessarily be strict, as in the sale of liquor, and of stocks and bonds, similar requirements have been upheld.

Each State has also certain rights in its own domain that it holds for the special advantage of its own citizens. Thus wild game and fish in a sense belong to the State. It is customary for the States to charge higher hunting and fishing license fees to non-residents than to its own citizens. The States also charge non-residents higher tuition in the State colleges and universities, and permit only residents to be admitted to their hospitals and asylums except in emergencies.

In short, there are a number of rights that a State can grant to its own citizens or residents that it may and does legally deny to non-residents, or grant to nonresidents only on more difficult terms than those imposed on residents. These advantages, given to the citizen in his own State, constitute the special rights of State citizenship. Taken all together, they amount to a considerable difference in rights between citizens and non-citizens of the State. The transient and the temporary sojourner is everywhere under some special handicaps.

The proposed Indian Constitution is a dual polity with a single citizenship. There is only one citizenship for the whole of India. It is Indian citizenship. There is no State citizenship. Every Indian has the same rights of citizenship, no matter in what State he resides.

The dual polity of the proposed Indian Constitution differs from the dual polity of the USA in another respect. In the USA, the Constitutions of the Federal and the State governments are loosely connected. In describing the relationship between the Federal and the State governments, Bryce has said, "The central or national governments may be compared to a large building and a set of smaller buildings standing on the same ground, yet distinct from each other." (781 words)

3. **Write a paragraph in about 200 words on any one of the following expressions/statements:** **10**

(a) 'Make hay while the sun shines.'

(b) One swallow does not make a summer.

(c) Discretion is the better part of valour.

(d) As you sow, so shall you reap.

(e) 'If winter comes, can spring be far behind.'

4. **Use the following words in sentences so as to bring out their meaning clearly. Do not change the form of the word. No credit will be given for a vague or ambiguous sentence.** **2x5=10**

(a) Prefatory

(b) Ostentatious

(c) Nemesis

(d) Expatriate

(e) Lascivious

5. **Use the following idioms and phrasal verbs in sentences so as to bring out their meaning clearly.** **2x5=10**

(a) Make away with

(b) Play fast and loose

(c) Set off the hook

(d) Eating humble pie

(e) Square pegs in round holes

6. **Correct the following sentences without changing their meaning. Do not make unnecessary changes in the original sentence :** **1x10=70**

(a) Shocked of finding an unknown person, the army officer briskly caught hold of him.

(b) High population growing rate is one of the major reasons of poverty in India.

(c) He decided to reveal the corruption in his department to the media.

(d) T would have waited for you at the station if 1 knew that you would come.

(e) Although my car is expensive, I had a lot of trouble with it.

(f) He would have lent me some money if he was knowing that I had lost everything.

(g) No sooner the news reached him than he fainted.

(h) According to the Census Bureau, India will have a more problem.

(i) Mr. Misra said that he is doing fine now.

(j) Non-teaching staffs of the college are agitating for their demands.

(k) The President of France has left India yesterday.

(l) Rahul stays with his parents in the Railway quarter.

(m) He went on committing crime after crime and in spite of my best efforts I could not prevent him from doing so.

(n) To transport goods by the sea is cheaper than land.

(o) It is a penal offence bribing a public servant.

GENERAL ENGLISH
2016

Maximum Marks: 100

---

before attempting questions :

ttempted.

ndicated against it.

nly.

nd to adhere to word limits
y be penalized.

) provided. These précis
ok.

n the answer book.

clearly struck off.

---

0 words : 30

on.

r the responsibility

th, using your
30

his purpose,
the answer

hy
errorism an
d from AIDS than
ity can develop in many
is important to fight ter-
human insecurity and its

ucation can have a power-
ind. It is useful to consider
glects in education can con-

and innumeracy are forms
unt or communicate is a tre-
ainty of deprivation and the

ol education is a direct reduc-
rence that basic education can
even by the poorest of families.
asic education to their children,
which they—the parents—had

reams of parents. The economic
hem, particularly when there are
ly removed.

d and parents often worried about
re other barriers as well. Very poor
ven the children, and this can com-
ctice, though generated out of hard-
s by male the economic benefits of
e in understanding the contribution
on can be very important in helping
ic connection, while always present,
which qual y control and production

and and invoke their legal rights can be
other kinds of deprivation. Indeed, this
om of the ladder, whose rights are often

Why is it so imoortant to close the educational gaps, and to remove the enormous disparities in educational access, inclusion and achievement? One reason, among others, is the importance of this lor mpking the world more secure as well as more fair H. G. Wells was not exaggerat'ng wnen he said, in his *OvHine* of *History* . "human history becomes more and more a race between education and catastrophe". If we continue to leave vast sections of the 0 people of the world outside the orbit of education, we make the world not only less just, but also less secure.

The precariousness of the world is now greater than it already was in H. G. Wells's time in the early twentieth century. Indeed, since the ternble events of September 11, 2001—and what followed after that—the world has been very aware of problems of p[illegible]sical insecurity. But human insecurity comes in many different ways—not just through [illegible] d violence. Indeed, even on the very day of September 11, 2001, more people die [illegible] from physical violence ncluding the atrocity in New York. Human insecur [illegible] different ways, and physical violence is only one of them. While it [illegible] rorism and genocide, we must also recognize the plural nature of [illegible] diverse manifestations.

As it happens, widening the coverage and effectiveness of basic ed [illegible] fully preventive role in reducing human nsecurity of nearly every k [illegible] briefly the different ways in which removing discrepancies and ne [illegible] tribute to reducing human insecuty across the world.

The most basic issue relates to the elementary fact that illiteracy [illegible] of insecurity in themselves. Not to be able to read or wril 2 or co [illegible] mendous deprivation. The extreme case of insecurity is the cer [illegible] absence of any chance of avoiding that fate.

The first and the most immediate contribution of successful sch [illegible] tion of this basic deprivation—th 3 extreme insecurity. The diff [illegible] make to human life is easy to see. It is also readily appreciated [illegible] The parents of even the most depressed fan des long to give b [illegible] to make them grow up without the terrible handicaps from [illegible] themselves suffered.

Of course, there are many obstacles in giving shape to the [illegible] circumstances of the families often make it very hard for t [illegible] fees to be paid. This obstacle of unaffordability must be firm [illegible]

There are other obstacles too like schools being thinly staffe [illegible] the safety of children, especially girl children. Then there a [illegible] fam es often rely on labour contributions from everyone, [illegible] pete v ith the demands of schooling. This unfortunate pra [illegible] ship, must also be removed, through regulation aswell [illegible] schooling clearer to all. This brings us to the second issu [illegible] of schooling in removing human security Basic educati [illegible] people to get jobs and gainful employment. This econo [illegible] is particularly critical in a rapidly globalizing world in [illegible] according to strict specification can be crucial.

Also, when people are illiterate, their ability to underst [illegible] very limited, and educational neglect can also lead to [illegible] tends to be a persistent problem for people at the bott [illegible]

GENERAL ENGLISH
2016

Time Allowed : Three Hours | *Maximum Marks: 100*

INSTRUCTIONS

Please read each of the following instructions carefully before attempting questions :

There are SIX questions and all are to be attempted.

The number of marks carried by a question / part is indicated against it.

Answers must be written in ENGLISH only.

Candidates are required to write clear, legible and concise answers and to adhere to word limits wherever indicated. Failure to adhere to word limits may be penalized.

Précis question must be attempted only on the special précis sheet(s) provided. These précis sheets must be attached securely to the answer book.

All parts and sub-parts of a question are to be attempted together in the answer book.

Any page or portion of the page left blank in the answer book must be clearly struck off.

1. **Write an essay on any one of the following topics in not less than 800 words :** 30

   (a) India suffers from paucity of role models.

   (b) The progress of a nation depends on the way its universities funcv. on.

   (c) "The more comprehensive and diversified the social order, the greater the responsibility and the freedom of the indhidua) "

   (d) Should betting in sports be legalized?

   (e) The benefits of organic foods are greatly overrated.

2. **Make a precis of the following passage in about one-third of the original length, using your own words :** 30

   (*Note* : The precis must be written only on the special sheets provided for this purpose, writing one word in each block. The sheets should be fastened securely inside the answer book.)

Why is it so imoortant to close the educational gaps, and to remove the enormous disparities in educational access, inclusion and achievement? One reason, among others, is the importance of this lor mpking the world more secure as well as more fair H. G. Wells was not exaggerat'ng wnen he said, in his *OvHine* of *History* . "human history becomes more and more a race between education and catastrophe". If we continue to leave vast sections of the 0 people of the world outside the orbit of education, we make the world not only less just, but also less secure.

The precariousness of the world is now greater than it already was in H. G. Wells's time in the early twentieth century. Indeed, since the ternble events of September 11, 2001—and what followed after that—the world has been very aware of problems of physical insecurity. But human insecurity comes in many different ways—not just through terrorism and violence. Indeed, even on the very day of September 11, 2001, more people died from AIDS than from physical violence ncluding the atrocity in New York. Human insecurity can develop in many different ways, and physical violence is only one of them. While it is important to fight terrorism and genocide, we must also recognize the plural nature of human insecurity and its diverse manifestations.

As it happens, widening the coverage and effectiveness of basic education can have a powerfully preventive role in reducing human nsecurity of nearly every kind. It is useful to consider briefly the different ways in which removing discrepancies and neglects in education can contribute to reducing human insecuty across the world.

The most basic issue relates to the elementary fact that illiteracy and innumeracy are forms of insecurity in themselves. Not to be able to read or wril 2 or count or communicate is a tremendous deprivation. The extreme case of insecurity is the certainty of deprivation and the absence of any chance of avoiding that fate.

The first and the most immediate contribution of successful school education is a direct reduction of this basic deprivation—th 3 extreme insecurity. The difference that basic education can make to human life is easy to see. It is also readily appreciated even by the poorest of families. The parents of even the most depressed fan des long to give basic education to their children, to make them grow up without the terrible handicaps from which they—the parents—had themselves suffered.

Of course, there are many obstacles in giving shape to the dreams of parents. The economic circumstances of the families often make it very hard for them, particularly when there are fees to be paid. This obstacle of unaffordability must be firmly removed.

There are other obstacles too like schools being thinly staffed and parents often worried about the safety of children, especially girl children. Then there are other barriers as well. Very poor fam es often rely on labour contributions from everyone, even the children, and this can compete v ith the demands of schooling. This unfortunate practice, though generated out of hardship, must also be removed, through regulation aswell as by male the economic benefits of schooling clearer to all. This brings us to the second issue in understanding the contribution of schooling in removing human security Basic education can be very important in helping people to get jobs and gainful employment. This economic connection, while always present, is particularly critical in a rapidly globalizing world in which qua] y control and production according to strict specification can be crucial.

Also, when people are illiterate, their ability to understand and invoke their legal rights can be very limited, and educational neglect can also lead to other kinds of deprivation. Indeed, this tends to be a persistent problem for people at the bottom of the ladder, whose rights are often effectively alienated because of their inability to read and see what they are entitled to demand and how. The educational gap clearly has a class connection. It also has a gender connection since it can be very important for women's security. Women are often deprived of their due, thanks to illiteracy. There are often legal rights that are not used because the aggrieved cannot read. This distances them from the ways and means of fighting against gender discrimination.

Empirical work in recent years has brought out very clearly how the relative respect and regard for women's well-being is strongly influenced by women's literacy and educated participat in decisions wi :hin and outside the family. Even the survival disadvantage of women compared with men seems to go down sharply—and may even get eliminated— with progress in women's empowerment, for which literacy is a basic ingredient. (780 words)

3. **Write a paragraph in about 200 words on any one of the following expressions/statements: 10**

   (a) The hand that rocks the cradle rules the world.

   (b) Those who live in glasshouses shouldn't throw stones.

   (c) Two wrongs don't make a ri^ht

   (d) No man is an island.

   (e) Actions speak louder than words.

4. **Use the following words in sentences so as to bring out their meaning clearly. Do not change the form of the word. No credit will be given for a vague or am Diguous sentence : 2x5=10**

   (a) venerate

   (b) aberration

   (c) callous

   (d) circumspect

   (e) enunciate

5. **Use the following phrasal verbs in sentences so as to bring out their meaning clearly. 1x5=5**

   (a) abide by

   (b) iron out

   (c) wear down

   (d) rule out

   (e) scape through

6. **Correct the following sentences without changing their meaning. Do not make unnecessary changes n the on final sentence : 1x15=15**

   (a) The latest copy of the book is more preferable to any that has been published so far.

   (b) Scarcely had the doctor left after examining him chan the pauent died.

   (c) I don't think I have met the girl whom you say has topped in the examination.

   (d) Raids were carried in all over the city to unearth illegal ammunition.

   (e) The teacher did not taKe the test todav as all tne students -were not present

   (f) There is hardly no reason to suspect his story.

(g) One of mv friends are going abroad this summer

(h) Unless the entire nation does not coperates, we cannot hope to maintian law and order.

(i) Every one in the room were amazed at the ease with which he was evading the law and order.

(j) It is unfortunate that she could not avail of the opportunity to better her prospects.

(k) The doctor has prescribed two spoonful of the medicine to be taken three times everyday.

(l) The teacher was saying that one must do his duty honesty.

(m) Had you played well you would in the match.

(n) He hehaves as if he was the chief of the organization.

(o) The teacher asked me if I was not ashamed of what I did.

GENERAL ENGLISH
2015

Time Allowed : Three Hours | *Maximum Marks: 100*

INSTRUCTIONS

Please read each of the following instructions carefully before attempting questions :

There are SEVEN questions and all are to be attempted.

The number of marks carried by a question / part is indicated against it.

Answers must be written in ENGLISH only.

Candidates are required to write clear, legible and concise answers and to adhere to word limits wherever indicated. Failure to adhere to word limits may be penalized.

Précis question must be attempted only on the special précis sheet(s) provided. These précis sheets must be attached securely to the answer book.

All parts and sub-parts of a question are to be attempted together in the answer book.

You must not disclose your identity in any of your answers.

---

1. **Write an essay on any one of the following topics in not less than 800 words.** **30**

   (a) Leadership is not a position but a responsibility.

   (b) Does the rise of materialism lead to erosion of values?

   (c) Understanding is the best form of hospitality.

   (d) Individual freedom versus Social responsibility.

   (e) The scientific temper of the modern world.

2. **Make a precis of the following passage in about one-third of the original length, using your own words.**

   (*Note* : The precis must be written only on the special sheets provided for this purpose, writing one word in each block. The sheet should be fastened securely inside the answer book.) **20**

There are two ways in which science affects human affairs. The first is familiar to everyone: Directly, and to an even greater extent indirectly, science produces aids that have completely transformed human existence. The second way is educational in character —it works on the mind. Although it may appear less obvious to cursory examination, it is no less incisive than the first.

The most conspicuous practical effect of science is that it makes possible the contriving of things that enrich life, though they complicate it at the same time— inventions such as the steam engine, the railway, electric power and light, the telegraph, radio, automobile, airplane, dynamite, etc. To these must be added the life-preserving achievements of biology and medicine, especially the production of pain relievers and preservative methods of storing food. The greatest practical benefit which all these inventions confer on man I see in the fact that they liberate him from the excessive muscular drudgery that was once indispensable for the preservation of bare existence. Insofar as we may at all claim that slavery has been abolished today, we owe its abolition to the practical consequences of science.

On the other hand, technology—or applied science — has confronted mainkind with depends on a satisfactory solution of these problems. It is a matter of creating the kind of social institutions and traditions without which the new tools must inevitably bring disaster of the worst kind.

Technology has shortened distances and created new and extraordinary effective means of destruction which, in the hands of nations claiming unrestricted freedom of action, become threats to the security and very survival of mainkind. The situation requires a single judicial and executive power for the entire planet, and the creation of such a central authority is desparately opposed by national traditions. Here too we are in the midst of a struggle whose issue will decide the fate of all us.

Means of communication, finally — reproduction possesses for the printed word, and the radio — when combined with modern weapons, have made it possible to place body and soul under bondage to a central athority — and there is a third source of danger to mainkind. Modern tyrannies and their destructive effects show plainly how far we are from exploiting these achievements organizally for the benefit of mainkind. Here too circumstances require an international solution, with the psychological foundation for such a solution not yet laid.

Let us now turn to the intellectual effects that proceed from science. In prescientific times was not possible by means of thought alone to attain results that all mainkind could have accepted as certain and necessary. Still less was there a conviction that all that hapeens. Still less was there a conviction that all that happens in nature is subject to inexorable laws. The gragmentary character of natural law, as seen by the primitive oberver, was such as to foster a belief in ghosts and spirits. Hence even toady primitive man lives in constant fear that supernatural and aribitary forces will intervene in his destiny.

It stands to the everlasting credit of science that by acting on the human mind it has overcome man's insecurity before himself and before nature. In creating elementary mathematics the Greeks for the first time wrought a system of thought whose conclusions no one could escape. The scientists of the Renaissance then devised the combination of systematic experiment with mathematical method. This union made possible such precision in the formulation of natural laws and such certainty inchecking them by experience that as a result there was no longer room for basic differences of opinion in natural science. Since that time each generation has built up the heritage of knowledge and understanding, without the slightest danger of a crisis that might jeopardize the whole structure.

The general public may be able to follow the details of scientific research to only a modest degree; but it can register at least one great and important gain: confidence that human thought is dependable and natural law universal. (670 words)

3. Write a paragraph in about 200 words on any one of the following expressions/statements. **16**

(a) All that glitters is not gold.

(b) Time and tide wait for none.

(c) A bird in hand is worth two in the bush.

(d) Brevity is the soul of wit.

(e) To err is human; to forgive is divine.

4. Use the following words in sentences so as to bring out their meaning clearly. Do not change the form of the word. No credit will be given for a vague or ambiguous sentence. **5 × 2 =10**

(a) Loquacious

(b) Topsy-turvy

(c) Mentor

(d) Enigmatic

(e) Nefarious

5. Use the following homonyms in sentences so as to bring out the difference in meaning clearly without changing the form. **5x2=10**

(a) Compliment
Complement

(b) Canvas
Canvass

(c) Device
Devise

(d) Ghostly
Ghastly

(e) Cite
Site

6. Make the directed changes in the following sentences without changing their meaning. **5×2=10**

(a) I know him.
(Change into passive voice)

(b) The stranger said, "Could you tell me where the post office is ?"
(Change into indirect speech)

(c) I did not spend as much money as you. (Change into comparative degree)

(d) You are allowed into the club only if you are a member.
(Rewrite the sentence using 'unless')

(e) Join the two simple sentences to make one complex sentence.
We enjoyed our holiday. It rained a lot.

7. **Correct the following sentences without changing their meaning. Do not make unnecessary changes in the original sentence.** **10x1**

(a) Despite of repeated reminders, the company has not responded.

(b) All the students will attend the function, wouldn't they ?

(c) This is one of the best books that has been recently purchased for the library.

(d) Flying on the northern part of India we could see the peak of the Everest.

(e) Your friend is waiting for you since morning.

(f) People expect a lot from an university scholar.

(g) The sun is rising in the East everyday.

(h) When we arrived at the station, the train already left.

(i) Neither the officer nor his PS were in the office.

(j) The minister along with his wife are leaving for London.

GENERAL ENGLISH
2014

Time Allowed : Three Hours | Maximum Marks: 100

INSTRUCTIONS

Please read each of the following instructions carefully before attempting questions :

There are SIX questions and all are to be attempted.

The number of marks carried by a question / part is indicated against it.

Answers must be written in ENGLISH only.

Candidates are required to write clear, legible and concise answrs and to adhere to word limits wherever indicated. Failure to adhere to word limits may be penalized.

Précis question must be attempted only on the special précis sheet(s) provided. These précis sheets must be attached securely to the answer book.

All parts and sub-parts of a question are to be attempted together in the answer book.

You must not disclose your identity in any of your answers.

---

1. Write an essay on any one of the following topics in not less than 800 words: 30

(a) Use of Social Media in Politics

(b) Impact of FDI in Retail on Agriculture

(c) Eco-tourism and challenges it faces

(d) Diversification of Crops and Chemical Pollution

(e) Genetic Engineering - Prospects and Hazards

2. Make a precis of each of the following two passages in about one-third of the original length, using your own words:

(*Note* : The pricis must be written only on the special sheets provided for the purpose, writing one word in each block. The sheet should be fastened securely inside the answer book.) 20+10=30

(a) Let us first consider what state of things is described by the word "civilization". Its true test lies in the fact that people living in it make bodily welfare the object of life. We will take some examples. Formerly, only a few men wrote valuable books. Now, anybody writes and prints anything he likes and poisons people's minds. Formerly, men travelled in wagons. Now, they fly through the air in trains at the rate of four hundred and more miles per day. This is considered the height of civilization. It has been stated that, as men progress, they shall be able to travel in airships and reach any part of the world in a few hours. Men will notneed the use of their hands and feet. They will press a button,, and they will have their clothing by their side. They will press another button, and they will have their newspaper. A third, and a motorcar will be in waiting for them. They will have a variety of delicately dished up food. Everything will be done by machinery. Formerly, when people wanted to fight with one another, they measured between them their bodily strength; now it is possible to take away thousands of lives by one man working behind a gun from a hill. This is civilization. Formerly, men worked in the open air only as much as they liked. Now thousands of workmen meet together and for the sake of maintenance work in factories or mines. Their condition is worse than that of beasts. They are obliged to work, at the risk of their lives, at most dangerous occupations, for the sake of millionaires, Formerly, men were made slaves under physical compulsion. Now they are enslaved by temptation of money and of the luxuries that money can buy. There are now diseases of which people never dreamt before, and an army of doctors is engaged in finding out their cures, and so hospitals have increased. This is a test of civilization. Formerly, special messengers were required and much expense was incurred in order to send letters; today, anyone can abuse his fellow by means of a letter for one penny. True, at the same cost, one can send one's thanks also. Formerly, people had two or three mealsconsisting of homemade bread and vegetables; ® now, they require something to eat every two hours so that they have hardly leisure for anything else. What more need I say' ? All this you can ascertain from several authoritative books. These are all true tests of civilization. And if anyone speaks to the contrary, know that he is ignorant. This civilization takes note neither of morality nor of religion. Its votaries calmly state that their business is not to teach religion. Some even consider it to be a superstitious growth. Others put on the cloak of religion, and prate about morality. But, after twenty years' experience; I have come to the conclusion that immorality is often taught in the name of morality. Even a child can understand that in all I have described above there can be no inducement to morality. Civilization seeks to increase bodily comforts, and it fails miserably even in doing so.

This civilization is such that one has only to be patient and it will be selfdestroyed. According to the teaching of Mohammed this would be considered a Satanic Civilization. Hinduism calls it a Black Age. I cannot give you an adequate conception of it. It is eating into the vitals of the English nation. It must be shunned. Parliaments are really emblems of slavery. If you will sufficiently think over this, you will entertain the same opinion and cekse to blame the English. They rather deserve our sympathy. They are a shrewd nation and I therefore believe that they will cast off the evil. They are enterprising and industrious, and their mode of thought is not inherently immoral Neither are they bad at heart. I therefore respect them. Civilization is not an incurable disease, but it should never be forgotten that the English are at present afflicted by it.

(b) The real implication of equal distribution is that each man shall have the wherewithal to supply all his natural needs and no more. For example, if one man has a weak digestion and requires only a quarter of a pound of flour for his bread and another needs a pound, both should be in a position to satisfy their wants. To bring this ideal into being the entire social order has got to be reconstructed. A society based on non-violence cannot nurture any other ideal. We may not perhaps be able to realize the goal, but we must bear it in mind and work unceasingly to go near it. To the same extent as we progress towards our goal we shall find contentment and happiness, and to that extent too shall we have contributed, towards the bringing into being of a non-violent society,

It is perfectly possible for an individual to adopt this way of life without having to wait for others to do so. And if an individual can observe a certain rule of conduct, it follows that a group of individuals can do likewise. It is necessary for me to emphasize the fact that no one needwait for anyone else in order to adopt a right course. Men generally hesitate to make a beginning if they feel that the objective cannot be had in its entirety. Such an attitude of minds is in reality a bar to progress.

Now let us consider how equal distribution can be brought about through non-violence. The first step towards it is for him who has made this ideal part of his being to bring about the necessary changes in his personal life* He would reduce his wants to a minimum, bearing in mind the poverty of India.

3. **Write a paragraph in about 200 words on any one of the following phrases/expressions; 10**

   (a) Two wrongs don't make a right.

   (b) The pen is mightier than the sword.

   (c) When in Rome, do as the Romans do.

   (d) No man is an island.

   (e) Fortune favours the bold.

4. **Use the following words in sentences so as to bring out their meaning clearly. Do not change the form of the word. No credit will be given for a vague or ambiguoussentence. 2x5=10**

   (a) Quagmire
   (b) Remuneration
   (c) Penchant
   (d) Verbiage
   (e) Niche

5. **Make the directed changes in the following sentences without changing their meaning: 2x5=10**

   (a) He said, "I have passed the examination." (Change into indirect speech)

   (b) I have a piece of bread please?

   (Use the modal auxiliary May or Might)

   (c) Our generation is modern. (Use the superlative)

   (d) John Lennon died while he lived in New York. (Progressive or Continuous forms)

   (e) Germany invaded Poland in 1939, thus initiating the Second World War.

   (Change into passive voice)

6. Correct the following sentences without changing their meaning. Do not make unnecessary changes in the original sentence. **1x10=10**

(a) I would rather die than begging alms.

(b) Neither of the five players was selected.

(c) The fisherman held several fish from the sea.

(d) I asked him that how many brothers had he.

(e) He cannot dare to come here.

(f) This is the man which killed his father.

(g) No sooner had she arrived when the telegram came,

(h) John is a tall boy, isn't it ?

(i) They have disposed off their farm house.

(j) My hand writing is superior than any of yours.

GENERAL ENGLISH
2013

Time Allowed : Three Hours | *Maximum Marks: 100*

INSTRUCTIONS

Candidates should attempt ALL questions unless otherwise directed.

The number of marks carried by each question is indicated at the end fo the question.

Answer must be written only in ENGLISH.

Candidates are requested to write clear, legible and concise answers and to adhere to word limits wherever indicated. Failure to adhere to word limits will be penalized.

Précis question must be attempted only on the special précis sheet(s) provided. These précis sheets must be attached securely to the answer book by the candidate.

Whenever a question is being attempted, all its parts/sub-parts must be completed before moving on to the next question.

1. Write an essay on any one of the following in not less than 800 words : **30**

(a) The Effect of Advertisements on Mass Consumerism

(b) Disaster Management: The need of the hour

(c) Are Indian Soaps on TV socially relevant?

(d) The vulnerability of our frontiers

(e) Economy versus the environment debate

2. Make a precis of each of the following too passages in about one-third of the original length, using your own words.

(*Note* : The precis must be written, only on the special sheets provided for the purpose, writing one word in each block. The sheets should be fastened securely inside the answer book)
20+10=30

(a) In the United States they have opened their first rehabilitation centre for Internet Addicts. De-addiction camps in China were in the news recently for the death of a teenager because of the brutal methods used to cure "Internet Addiction" (IA). Our country must seriously think about such centres that help de-addict compulsive Internet-users, both young and old.

IA for now is a catch-all term that not only stands for addiction to specific activities such as gambling or gaming but also refers to longer hours devoted to the computer network at the expense of other activities. Though the Internet is only a medium of communication and information transmission and retrieval (like the printed book or television), "addiction" is being used in this case with concern because of a fundamental dialectic : 'quantity becomes quality.'

A whole new world is just a click away with the Internet. It is a medium just like books and television, but the amount of interaction it makes possible with others, sometimes replacing the need for real-world interaction, makes it vastly different. Educators, neuroscientists, and those others having public health concerns in all developing and developed countries have woken up to this reality, According to expert neuropsychiatry opinion, IA is somewhere between Obsessive Compulsive Disorder and addiction due to substance abuse. Substance abuse-led addiction focuses on gratification which this form of attachment provides, though there is no chemical ingestion. At the same time, the behavioural modifications are similar to those with Obsessive Compulsive Disorder. It is almost like the 'rush' gamblers get out of a purely gratification-oriented . repetitive action.

(b) The greatest fact in the story of man on Earth is not his material achievements, the empires he has built and broken, but the growth of his soul from age to 'age in its search for truth and goodness. Those who take part in this adventure of the soul secure an enduring place in the history of human' culture. Time has discredited heroes as easily as it has forgotten everyone else; but the saints remain. The greatness of Gandhi is more in his holy living than in his heroic struggles, in his insistence on . the creative power of the soul and its life-giving quality at a time when the destructive forces seem to be in the ascendant, Gandhi is known tothe world as the one man more than any othei^ who is mainly responsible for the mighty upheaval of the Indian nation which has shaken and loosened its chains* Politicians are not generally reputed to take religion seriously, for the values to which they are committed, such as the political control of one people by another, the economic exploitation of the poorer and. weaker human beings, are so clearly inconsistent with the values of religion that the latter could not be taken too seriously or interpreted too accurately. But for Gandhi, all life is of one piece. 'To see the universal and all-pervading Spirit of Truth face to face one, must be able to love the meanest of creation as oneself. And a man who aspires after that cannot afford to keep out of any field of life."

3. Write a paragraph in about 200 words on any one of the following phrases/expressions : 10

(a) Waste not, want not

(b) Health is wealth

(c) The pen is mightier than the sword

(d) We will reap tomorrow what'we sow today

4. Use the following words in sentences so as to bring out their meaning clearly. Do not change the form of the word. No credit will be given for a vague or ambiguous sentence. 2x5=10

(a) Inflammatory

(b) Zenith

(c) Utopia

(d) Exodus

(e) Dissenter

5. **Make the directed changes in the following sentences without changing their meaning.** **2x5=10**

(a) My father said, "Wait till I have finished all that I have to say," (Change into indirect speech)

(b) I think that she has been caught in the traffic. (Use the modal auxiliary 'must')

(c) This is one of his more readable books. (Use the superlative degree)

(d) If it rains, the college will close. (Use the past tense)

(e) Road accidents injure many people everyday, (Change into passive voice)

6. **Correct the following sentences without changing their meaning. Do not make unnecessary changes in the original sentence.** **1x10=10**

(a) Nobody likes to be cheated, isn't it ?

(b) Choose only such friends whom you can trust.

(c) He is a MA in Geology.

(d) They had left yesterday.

(e) We are looking forward to see you soon.

(f) One of the file is lost.

(g) If he came early, you could have met him.

(h) It was so cold that the water freezed.

(i) Are there some more papers left to be signed ?

(j) We will be going to the church for Sunday Mass.

GENERAL ENGLISH
2012

Time Allowed : Three Hours | *Maximum Marks: 100*

INSTRUCTIONS

The Candidates should attempt **ALL** *questions, unless otherwise directed.*

The number of marks carried by each question is indicated at the end of the question.

Answers must be written in **ENGLISH***.*

Candidates are requested to write clear, legible, and concise answers and to adhere to word limits wherever indicated. Irrelevance, diffuseness, and disorganization will be penalized.

Précis question must be attempted only on the special précis sheet(s) provided. These précis sheets must be attached securely to the answer book by the candidate.

Whenever a question is being attempted, all its parts/sub-parts must be completed before moving on to the next question.

---

1. **Write an essay on any one of the following topics in about 1000 words:** **30**
   (a) Significance of education in women's empowerment.
   (b) Medical/Health Tourism: Making India a favourite destination.
   (c) Social Responsibilities of Corporate Groups
   (d) Picnic in Space : A future possibility or mere utopia?
2. **Make a precis of each of the following two passages in about one-third of the original length, using your own words. State the number of words used and suggest a suitable title to each. (*Note : The precis must be written only on the special sheets provided for the purpose, writing one word in each block. The sheets should be fastened securely inside the answer-book*).** **20+10=30**
   (a) Article 13(2) of the UN Declaration of Human Rights states that "everyone has the right to leave any country". There is, however, no consequential right to enter another country. This right gets vested in the nation-state, which adopts rules and regulations to regulate entry of persons. The governments use the instrumentality of visa to achieve this objective.

Visa has, therefore, become an important tool in achieving national objectives by all the governments. It is the same when the British Prime Minister wants to attract the best and the brightest from the world, including India, or optsfor stringent visa conditions for the stay of international students from non-EU countries under domestic pressure, even though it weakens the links with the Commonwealth countries. It is the same when Malaysia adopts an "off and on" policy on granting visas to Indians on arrival, or India adopts a similar visa facility for a select group of countries. In diplomatic parlance, it is categorised as visa diplomacy.

Signing of the India - Pakistan Visa Agreement in September, replacing the 1974 Visa Agreement, falls in the armoury of visa diplomacy. The agreement was signed by the Foreign Ministers of the two countries and not by the Home Secretaries, even though all the contours had been finalised. This was to convey a diplomatic signal on the desire to improve bilateral relations. It is a forward movement as it liberalises the existing visa regime, as it existed under the 1974 Visa Agreement. Primarily, its focus was on overall liberalisation on the visa conditions for travel between the two countries.

The main thrust is two-pronged. Firstly, to facilitate easy travel by all and, secondly, to facilitate travel by the business community and catering to their needs in keeping with the increase in bilateral trade. Three major changes were made in the visitor visa category, which include increasing the duration of validity of visa from three months to six months and allowing visits to five places, instead of three, as in the past.

Another change was to provide flexibility on the points of arrival and departure and mode of travel, as hitherto the visitors had to enter and leave from the same point. Special provisions have been made for senior citizens above 65 years of age; they can be issued visa valid for two years with multiple entries and the same would be applicable to spouses belonging to the other nationality. In addition, senior citizens would also be accorded the facility of visa on arrival at the Attari-Wagah border, limited to 45 days.

A significant feature of the new visa policy is the creation of a separate category of business visa. Two categories of businessmen's visa are created, linked to the standing of the business in terms of income and turnover. Businessmen having an annual turnover of Pakistani rupees 30 million or income of Pakistani rupees 5 million would be granted one-year multiple entry visa valid for 10 places. In other cases, those with an income of Pakistani rupees half a million or turnover of Pakistani rupees three million would be given one-year visa, with four entries to five places. This meets the longpending demand for multiple-entry visas for a longer duration.

Another new visa category was also introduced such as group tourist visa for 30 days for groups between 10 - 50 persons, organised by approved tour operators. These facilities would also be available to students of educational institutions. Both governments agreed to exchange details on tourist destinations and recognised tour operators. Another interesting feature was the fixing of the time limit for the processing of visa applications: 30 days for diplomatic visas, 45 days for non-diplomatic visas and 35 days for business visas.

Visa liberalisation has been hailed as a major step as it is expected to bring about greater connectivity at the people-to-people level and help in further building commercial linkages, as the bilateral trade is expected to increase from the current level of $ 2-5 billion to $ 10 billion in a couple of years. It looks big optically, seen in the India-Pakistan context, although it is a small step and many more such steps are needed.

(b) Average life expectancy in India jumped up by 4-6 years in the decade up to 2008, according to the latest data released by the Registrar General of India. Since this was also the period when economic reforms had the maximum impact, it gives the lie to an idea that's caught the fancy in public discourse — that reforms benefited only a tiny elite, leaving the rest of India's population untouched (or even worse off than before, going by some versions). The steady improvements in life expectancy at birth of the average Indian to 66'1 years by 2008 highlights steady improvement in overall living conditions and the general success of reforms.

What makes these gains more impressive are their inclusive character, with women and the rural population making more substantial gains. While women's life expectancy improved faster to 67-7 years, that of men rose more slowly to 64-6 years. This is especially significant given that life expectancy of women had lagged that of men till the early 1980s. While the overall gains indicate access to more nutritious food and health care and better hygiene, the larger improvements in the life expectancy of women indicate a faster dip in the mortality rates of the girl child. Similarly, greater life expectancy gains in the rural sector show that the benefits of higher growth were not restricted to urban areas, as many choose to believe.

It is of course necessary that the government design policies which make the benefits of reform percolate faster and deeper. The focus has to be on easing the ways of doing business and pushing up investments to enable growth to pick up. Only a substantial enlargement of the manufacturing sector ba^e, by ushering in more flexible labour regulations and improving the supply of a skilled and trained workforce, land and quality infrastructure, can provide employment to the millions who join the workforce each year. The solution, therefore, is more reforms, not less. But the big question remains- will the direction and pace of the reforms have broad public acceptance ?

3. Write a single paragraph in about 200 words on any one of the following phrases/expressions.

(a) Properity makes friends, adversity tries them

(b) Small is beautiful

(c) Child is the father of Man

(d) When you smile the world smiles with you; when you weep, you weep alone

4. Use the following words in sentences so as to bring out their meaning clearly. Do not change the form of the word. No credit will be given for a vague or ambiguous sentences:2x 5 = 10

(a) Conscientious

(b) Deleterious

(c) Nebulous

(d) Perservance

(e) Wistful

5. Make the directed changes in the following sentences without changing their meaning: 2 x 4 = 10

(a) Roma (write) letters when she (hear) a noise outside. (Rewrite the sentence using the correct form of the verbs in bracketes)

(b) It is necessary for you to sumbmit the application today. (Rewrite the sentence using an appropriate modal auxiliary)

(c) India has won the cricket match. It is a great news. (Combine the two senteces starting with 'that')

(d) He said to me, "When are you leaving for Mumbai ? I want to give you a small packet for my son." (Change the narration)

(e) Someone has already paid the plumber his daily wages. (Change the voice)

6. Correct the following sentences without changing their meaning. Please do not make unnecessary changes in the original sentences : 1x10=10

(a) I never remember to have met you anywhere.

(b) He went to the Railway Station with a view to receive the guests.

(c) No sooner had he started writing the letter when he discovered that he forgot his spectacles at home.

(d) Neither the manager nor the secretary are present in the office.

(e) He asked Ram why your father had lost his temper.

(f) The fireman could not succeed to rescue the child although he could put out the fire.

(g) The doctor told his patient that he will start the treatment only if he pays his fee.

(h) Ram is the tallest of all the other boys in the class.

(i) You don't want to marry her, isn't it ?

(j) Man and woman are waiting for you outside.

GENERAL ENGLISH
2011

Time Allowed : Three Hours | *Maximum Marks: 100*

INSTRUCTIONS

Candidates should attempt ALL questions unless otherwise directed.

The number of marks carried by each question is indicated at the end of the quetion.

Answers must be written only in ENGLISH.

Candidates are requested to write clear, legible and concise answers and the adhere to word limits wherever indicated.–Failure to adhere to word limits will be penalized.

Précis question must be attempted only on the special précis sheet(s). provided on this question paper. These précis sheets must be carefully detached from the question paper and attached securely to the answer book by the candidate.

1. **Write an essay on any one of the following in not less than 800 words:** **30**

   (a) The common man is a victim of the culture of consmerism.

   (b) Increasing the size of the pie or distributing the pie better — what should be the focus of Indian policy planners?

   (c) Looking for alternative energy sources.

   (d) Increasing privatisation in higher education — a boon or a bane?

2. **Make a precis of the following passage, keeping the word count between 210 and 250 words. Marks will be deducted if the length of the precis is beyond the prescribed word count. It is not necessary to suggest any title. Write in your own words as far as practicable.**

   (The precis must be written only on the special sheet(s) provided for the purpose (one word in each block) and the sheet(s) should be fastened securely inside the answer book) **20**

   To avoid the various foolish operations to which mankind are prone, no superhuman genius is required. A few simple rules will keep you, not from *all* error, but. from silly error,

   If the matter is one that can be settled by observation, make the observation yourself, Aristotle could Have avoided the mistake, of thinking that women have fewer teeth than men, by the simple device of asking Mrs. Aristotle to keep her mouth open while he counted. He did not do so because he thought he knew. Thinking that you know when in fact you don't is a fatal mistake, to which we are all prone. I believe myself that hedgehogs eat black beetles, because I have been told that they do; but if I were writing a book on the habits of hedgehogs, I should not commit myself until I had seen one enjoying this unappetizing diet. Aristotle, however, was less cautious. Ancient and medieval authors knew all about unicorns and salamanders; not one of them thought it necessary to avoid dogmatic statements about them because he had never seen one of them.

Many matters, however, are less easily brought to the test of experience. If, like most of mankind, you have passionate convictions on many such matters, there are ways in which you can make yourself aware of your own bias. If an opinion contrary to your own makes you angry, that is a sign that you are subconsciously aware of having no good reason for thinking as you do. If some one maintains that two *and* two are five, or that Iceland is on the Equator, you feel pity rather than anger, unless you know so little of arithmetic or geography that his1 opinion shakes your own contrary conviction. The most savage controversies are those about matters as to which there is no good evidence either way Persecution is used in theology, not in arithmetic, because in arithmetic there is knowledge, but in theology there is only opinion. So whenever you find yourself getting arigry about a difference of opinion, be on your guard; you will probably find, on examination, that your belief is going beyond what the evidence warrants.

A good way of ridding yourself of certain kinds of dogmatism is to become aware of opinions held in social circles different from your own. When I was young, I lived much outside my own country — in France, Germany, Italy, and the United States. I found this very profitable in diminishing the intensity of insular prejudice. If you cannot travel, seek out people with whom you disagree, and read a newspaper belonging to a party that is not yours. If the people and the newspaper seem mad, perverse, and wicked, remind yourself that you seem; so to them. In this opinion both parties may be right, but they cannot both be wrong. This reflection should generate a certain caution.

Becoming aware of foreign customs, however, does not always have a beneficial effect. In the seventeenth century, when the Manchus ^conquered China, it''was' the rcustom among the Chinese for the women to have small feet,- and among the Manchus for the men to wear pigtails. Instead of each dropping their own foolish custom, they each, adopted the foolish custom of the other, and the Chinese continued to wear pigtails until they shook off the dominion of the Manchus in the revolution of 1911.

For those who have enough psychological imagination, it is a good plan to imagine an argument with a person having a different bias. This has one advantage, and only one, as compared with actual conversation with opponents; this one advantage is that the method is not subject to the same limitationsof time and space. Mahatma Gandhi deplored railways and steamboats and machinery; he would have liked to undo the whole of the industrial revolution. You may never have an opportunity of actually meeting any one who holds this opinion, because in Western countries most people take the J advantage of modern technique for granted. But if you want to make sure that you are right in agreeing with the prevailing opinion, you will find it a good plan to test arguments that occur to you by considering what Gandhi might have said in refutation of them, I have sometimes been led actually to change my mind as a result of this kind of imaginary dialogue, and, short of this, I have frequently found myself growing less dogmatic and cocksure through realizing the possible reasonableness of a hypothetical opponent.

3. Write a paragraph each on any *two* of the following (Each paragraph is to be in about 200 words) : **2x10=20**

(a) 'The essential thing is not to have conquered but to have fought well.'

(b) 'Doing easily what others find difficult is talent, doing what is impossible for talent is genius/

(c) 'Examples are better than precepts/

(d) 'Physician, heal thyself/

(e) 'Professional integrity is as important as personal integrity/

4. Use each of the following in a separate sentence of your own to bring out the meaning clearly. Do not change the form of the words. No marks will be given for vague or ambiguous sentences. **2x5=10**

(a) Corpus

(b) Insidious

(c) Lateral

(d) Servile

(e) Rubric

5. Rewrite the following sentences as directed without changing their meaning : **2x5=10**

(a) The test match was played in an amicable manner,

(Change the voice of the verb)

(b) There was an accident. Ten people died in it. We saw the dead bodies.

(Combine the sentences to form *one* complex sentence)

(c) He was a thief. He stole the valuable ornaments. (Combine the sentences to form *one* simple sentence)

(d) He was so rude that he did not even ask us to sit down.

(Rewrite using "too")

(e) He told her, "Do not telephone me again."

(Change from direct speech to indirect speech)

6. Correct the following sentences without changing their meaning. Please do not make unnecessary changes in the original sentences. In case you think there is no error, write down the sentence as it is. **1x10**

(a) You have made a blunder mistake.

(b) The newspaper came today morning.

(c) Neither Ram or Shyam was willing to do this work.

(d) I am having a big house.

(e) My school is superior than his school.

(f) I and you must do this work.

(g) He found himself in dire strait.

(h) Each one of us have to go out of the room.

(i) I am seeing you after a long time.

(j) Women do not always like their mother-in-laws.

GENERAL ENGLISH
2010

Time Allowed : Three Hours | *Maximum Marks: 100*

INSTRUCTIONS

The Candidates should attempt ***ALL*** *questions, unless otherwise directed.*

The number of marks carried by each question is indicated at the end of the question.

Answers must be written in ***ENGLISH.***

Candidates are requested to write clear, legible, and concise answers and to adhere to word limits wherever indicated. Irrelevance, diffuseness, and disorganization will be penalized.

Précis question must be attempted only on the special précis sheet provided, which should thereafter be fastened securely inside the answer book.

1. **Write an essay on any one of the following topics in about 1000-1200 words:** **40**

   (a) Causes and remedies for the Maoist insurgency in the North-Eastern states.

   (b) India's major problem is not unemployment, rather 'unemployable educated*.

   (c) Consequences of Global Warming — Myth and Reality.

   (d) Where injustice prevails, it is crime to be a silent spectator.

2. **Write a precis of the following passage in about one-third of the original length using your own words as far as possible. Please state the number of words used in your precis and suggest a suitable title. (Note : the precis must be written only on the special sheet provided for this purpose — one word in each block — and the sheet should be fastened securely inside the answer book.);** **20**

"No matter how eloquently a dog may bark, he cannot tell you that his parents were j>oor but honest," said Bertrand Russell once. What the famous philosopher asserted in effect [1] is that language is the exclusive property of the human species. The idea of talking animals is as old and as widespread among human societies as language itself cultures have legends in which some animal plays a speaking role. All over West Africa, children listen to folk tales in which a "spider-man" is the hero. "Coyote" is a favourite figure in many Native American tales, and many an animal takes the stage in Aesop's famous fables. The fictional Doctor Doolittle's forte was communicating with all manner oT animals, from giant snails to tiny sparrows.

If language is viewed only as a system of communication, then many species communicate. Humans also use systems other than language to relate to each other and to send and receive "messages," like so-called "body language." The question is whether the communication systems used by other species are at all like human linguistic knowledge, which is acquired by children with no externa] instruction, and which is used creatively rather than in response to internal or external stimuli.

Most humans who acquire language use speech sounds to express meanings* but such sounds are not a necessary aspect of language, as evidenced by the sign languages. The use of speech sounds is therefore not a basic part of what we have been calling language. The chirping of birds, the squeaking of dolphins, and the dancing of bees may potentially represent systems similar to human languages. If animal communication systems are not like human language, it will not be due to a lack of speech.

Conversely, when animals vocally imitate human utterances, it does not mean they possess language. Language is a system that relates? sounds or gestures to meanings. Talking birds such as parrots and mynah birds are capable of faithfully reproducing words and phrases of human language that they have heard, but their utterances carry no meaning. They are speaking neither English nor their own language when they sound like us.

Talking birds do, not dissect the sounds of their imitations into discrete units. *Polly* and *Molly* do not rhyme for a parrot. They are as different as *hello* and *goodbye*, One property of all human languages is the discreteness of the speech or gestural units, which are ordered and reordered* combined and split apart. Generally, a parrot says what it is taught, or what it hears, and no more. If Polly learns "Polly wants a cracker" and "Polly wants a chocolate" and also learns to imitate the single words "cake" and "bun," she will not spontaneously produce, as children do, "Polly wants a cake" or "Polly wants a bun," or "Polly wants a cake and a bun." If she learns *cat* and *cats*, and *dog* and *dogs*, and then learns the word *parrot*, she will be unable to form the plural *parrots* as children do by the age of three; nor can a parrot form an unlimited set of utterances from a finite set of units* nor understand utterances never heard before. Therefore, the ability to produce sounds similar to those used in human language, even if meanings are related to these sounds, cannot be equated with the ability to acquire the complex grammar of a human language-

3. Write a single paragraph of about 200 words on any *one* of the following : 10

(a) Struggle with your mind is the greatest struggle.

(b) Sweet are the uses of adversity.

(c) Time heals even the deepest wound.

(d) Fortune favours only the brave.

4. Use each of the following words to make sentences that brings out the meaning of each clearly. Do not change the form of the words. No marks will be given for vague or ambiguous sentences : 2x5=10

(a) Meltdown

(b) Imbroglio

(c) Cerebral

(d) Convergence

(e) Obligation

GENERAL ENGLISH
2009

Time Allowed : Three Hours | *Maximum Marks: 100*

INSTRUCTIONS

The Candidates should attempt **ALL** *questions, unless otherwise directed. The number of marks carried by each question is indicated at the end of the question. Answers must be written in* **ENGLISH.** *Candidates are requested to write clear, legible, and concise answers and to adhere to word limits wherever indicated. Irrelevance, dijfuseness, and disorganization will be penalized. Failure to adhere to word limits will also be penalized. Candidates are also requested not to reproduce crammed material but to present their own ideas in their own words. Precis should be written only in the special précis sheet provided, which should thereafter be fastened securely inside the answer book*

---

1. **Write an essay on any one of the following topics in about 1000—1200 words :** **40**

   (a) The relevance of traditional values in a globalised world.

   (b) The consumer culture in India — a waste of resources or an engine of growth?

   (c) India's space programme — problems and prospects.

   (d) The global recession — an obstacle to development or an opportunity for change?

2. **Write a precis of the following passage in about 190 words, using your own words as far as possible. Please state the number of words used in your precis and suggest a suitable title. (Note : the precis must be written only on the special sheet provided for this purpose — one word in each block — and the sheet should be fastened securely inside the answer book.):** **20**

   Knowledge, says the proverb, is power. Education ultimately leads to knowledge and hence to power. But this power is the power of the mind, and is perhaps not attainable by everybody. There are several stages before one can reach the final state : *patha* (learning) and *shiksha* (education) should ideally lead to *vidya* (knowledge), *bodhi* (wisdom), and lastly *gnana* (enlightenment). In his concept of education Tagore sought to attain these goals by combining formal study with the nurturing of creativity and the inculcation of self-discipline and social consciousness.

The very layout of the educational complex at Santiniketan in Tagore's time bore testimony to this holistic vision. The research library was located at the very centre of the complex with two sprawling playgrounds on either side — the idea was that the little boys would observe their seniors at work and strive to emulate them, while the researchers, instead of losing their way in abstract book-leaming, would remain close to life in the midst of frolicking children. Classes for the juniors were held in the open air under trees to break the monotony of continuous lectures, and most of the science classes were based on direct observation of nature. Formal examinations were abolished for the younger children to make study a pleasure rather than a chore.

Self-discipline was instilled even in the youngest child through a clear demarcation of responsibilities. The students were expected to be alert to matters of health and hygiene and keep the complex clean, with duties distributed among them on a rotational basis. Moreover, the entire responsibility for self-governance was delegated to the students themselves. It was they who were expected to devise means to deal with day-to-day problems — be it the mischievous conduct of a fellow student or the enforcement of rules within the student fraternity. Teachers took classes and supervised the work, but intervened directly only when absolutely necessary. Thus students gained both leadership skills and the ability to work as a team, and became oriented towards innovation and initiative, thereby enhancing their competence to deal with the many challenges of day-to-day life. Student activity in these schools went beyond quantifiable learning goals to embrace the nurturing of creative energy, and the development of moral values through social service and community improvement programmes. Hand written and illustrated magazines containing creative work by students date from the earliest days of the ashrama, Study and social work went hand in hand to make the students not only academically aware but also socially and culturally sensitive. Except for the very young ones, students regularly went out to serve in the neighbouring villages, especially in times of distress such as floods and drought Camps were held in the rural areas on school holidays, with students instructing the villagers in the rudiments of hygiene.

Tagore was equally sensitive to the importance of vocational education, and to the fact that it is unjustifiably devalued in formal academic programmes. To alleviate this lack he set up another school at Sriniketan, three kilometers from Santiniketan, to teach skills such as carpentry, weaving, animal husbandry and other pursuits suitable for the local inhabitants of the region. Soon adult education classes were also introduced by popular demand from members of the adjoining rural communities. Through his various educational schemes Tagore wished to produce self-reliant individuals and responsible members of society rather than merely learned scholars.

3. Write a single paragraph in about 200 words on any one of the following : **10**

(a) A little learning is a dangerous thing.

(b) Self-interest is but the survival of the animal in us.

(c) No man is a hero to his valet.

(d) Wealth is the product of man's capacity to innovate.

4. Use each of the following words to make sentences that brings out the meaning of each clearly. Do not change the form of the words. No marks will be given for vague or ambiguous sentences : **2x5=10**

(a) Alleviate

(b) Obfuscation

(c) Succinct

(d) Grapevine

(e) Dissimulation.

5. **Rewrite each of the following sentences as directed without changing the meaning of each :** $2 \times 5 = 10$

(a) He is so weak that he cannot even sit up.

(Rewrite using 'too')

(b) If you speak the truth, you will be rewarded.

(Rewrite as a compound sentence)

(c) Someone switched on the light and opened the door.

(Change into the passive voice)

(d) The work must be completed. There must be absolutely no delay.

(Combine the sentences to form one simple sentence)

(e) The teacher was very ill. The students heard the news. They went to see him at the hospital.

(Combine the sentences to form one complex sentence)

6. **Correct the following sentences without changing their meaning. Please do not make unnecessary changes in the original sentence in each case. In case you think there is no error, then write down the sentence as it is :** $1 \times 10 = 10$

(a) He told that he was tired.

(b) Running down the road, I saw him enter the shop.

(c) Where you think he is going and with who ?

(d) She said she would come, won't she ?

(e) You have eaten ?

(f) I'm not sure who is that person.

(g) There is very less sugar in that jar.

(h) I am really excited to visit my grandparents next month.

(i) Can you please give me advice on the best options for investment ?

(j) There is absolutely none I can trust.

GENERAL STUDIES SECTION

GENERAL STUDIES
2023

Time Allowed : Three Hours

QUESTIONS PAPER SPECIFIC INSTRUCTIONS

Please read each of the following instructions carefully before attempting questions.

*There are **FOUR** questions and all are to be attempted. Candidates should attempt questions/parts as per the instructions given in the questions. The number of marks carried by a question/part is indicated against it. Candidates are required to write clear, legible and concise answers and to adhere to word limits, wherever indicated. Failure to adhere to word limits may be penalized. The answers must be written within the space provided in the Question-cum-Answer Booklet. Any page or portion of the page left blank in the Question-cum-Answer Booklet must be clearly struck off. Answers must be written in **ENGLISH** only.*

---

1. Answer all of the following (in not more than 200 words each) : **5×5=25**

(a) What features of architecture indicate that Mohenjo-daro was a planned urban centre?

(b) Why is the Maurya Rule important in the history of India?

(c) Evaluate the contributions of Kabir and Guru Nanak Dev to the promotion of unity among the people.

(d) Who provided leadership to the Revolt of 1857? Discuss the role of any three of them.

(e) Why did Mahatma Gandhi consider Salt Tax more oppressive than other taxes? What was the outcome of his Dandi March?

2. Answer all of the following (in not more than 200 words each) : **5×5=25**

(a) "Heat waves are expected to become longer and more intense and frequent over the Indian subcontinent." Examine the statement.

(b) Why are millets said to be climate friendly? Explain it in the context of International Year of Millets (2023) declared by the United Nations.

(c) What are the consequences of rapidly ageing population in India?

(d) "Human activity seems to be primarily responsible for Joshimath's crisis." Comment.

(e) Why do we have fewer cyclones in the Arabian Sea than in the Bay of Bengal?

3. **Answer all of the following (in not more than 200 words each) : 5×5=25**

(a) Infrastructure development is considered a key element for accelerating growth rate of the Indian economy. Do you agree? Discuss.

(b) "Free trade agreements with important economies in the world are good for India." Discuss.

(c) Examine the major obstacles towards replacing non-renewable energy by renewable ones in India.

(d) A rising income and wealth inequality in India may not be good for India's long-term goals. Do you agree? Critically discuss.

(e) What are the major obstacles for the development of human capital in India despite everyone is in agreement that human capital is a major driver of growth in future? Elaborate.

4. **Answer all of the following (in not more than 200 words each) : 5x5=25**

(a) What are the basic structures of theIndian Constitution? Can they be amended? Explain.

(b) Critically examine the concept of judicial activism in the working of the Indian constitutional system.

(c) The Indian Constitution is enriched by the Constitutions of other countries. Elaborate.

(d) What is cooperative federalism? Is Indian federal system an example of cooperative federalism? Critically analyse.

(e) "India's foreign policy has moved from non-alignment to multi-alignment." Discuss.

GENERAL STUDIES
2022

Time Allowed : Three Hours

QUESTIONS PAPER SPECIFIC INSTRUCTIONS

Please read each of the following instructions carefully before attempting questions.

There are ***FOUR*** *questions and all are to be attempted. Candidates should attempt questions/parts as per the instructions given in the questions. The number of marks carried by a question/part is indicated against it. Candidates are required to write clear, legible and concise answers and to adhere to word limits, wherever indicated. Failure to adhere to word limits may be penalized. The answers must be written within the space provided in the Question-cum-Answer Booklet. Any page or portion of the page left blank in the Question-cum-Answer Booklet must be clearly struck off. Answers must be written in* ***ENGLISH*** *only.*

1. Answer all the following (in not more than 200 words each) : 5x5=25

1.(a) Discuss the significant advances made in the field of science of astronomy, mathematics and medicine during the Gupta period.

1.(b) Assess the cultural and artistic achievements of the Vijayanagar empire.

1.(c) Discuss the contribution of Sufis to Indian society and culture.

1.(d) Evaluate the role of Indian National Army (INA) in the freedom struggle of India.

1.(e) "Non-cooperation Movement and the Civil Disobedience Movement mark a strategic shift in the freedom struggle". Discuss.

2. Answer all of the following (in not more than 200 words each): 5×5=25

2.(a) Why are the farmers of India still haunted by recurrence of drought and flood despite river valley planning ?

2.(b) How does conservation of biodiversity, especially in the humid tropics, assure sustenance of livelihood of the people below the poverty line ?

2.(c) Enumerate the factors responsible for high frequency and magnitude of landslide in the mountain ecosystem.

2.(d) Assess the prospect of food processing industry with suitable examples from India.

2.(e) What are the pros and cons of infrastructural development in the coastal zone ?

3. Answer all the following (in not more than 200 words each): 5×5=25

3.(a) What is Non-filers Monitoring System? Explain how it can increase tax compliance.

3.(b) Explain the difference between subsidies, cash-in-lieu of subsidies and freebies. Discuss their rationality in eradicating poverty.

3.(c) Distinguish between Repo Rate and Reverse Repo Rate. Explain their relevance in the present context of inflation.

3.(d) What is Replacement Fertility Rate (RFR)? Does a decline in RFR impact demographic dividend ?

3.(e) Explain the concept of venture capital. Discuss the reasons for venture capitalists favouring software start-ups compared to MSME start-ups.

4. Answer all of the following (in not more than 200 words each): 5×5=25

4.(a) "The Preamble is the key to the whole constitution". Comment.

4.(b) Analyse the powers of the Governor and the causes for their frequent friction with states.

4.(c) Illustrate the challenges and concerns of Parliamentary democracy.

4.(d) Discuss the advantages and disadvantages of Collegium System in India.

4.(e) Critically examine the recent power shift in Pakistan.

GENERAL STUDIES
2021

Time Allowed : Three Hours | *Maximum Marks: 100*

Question Paper Specific Instructions

Please read each of the following instructions carefully before attempting questions.

*There are FOUR questions and **all** are to be attempted. Candidates should attempt questions/parts as per the instructions given in the questions. The number of marks carrid by a question/part is indicated against it. Candidates are required to write clear, legible and concise answers and to adhere to word limits, wherever indicated. Failure to adhere to word limits may be penalized. Any page or portion of the page left blank in the Question-cun-Answer Booklet must be clearly struck off. Answers must be written in ENGLISH only.*

---

1. **Answer all the following (in not or more than 200 words each):** 5×5=25

   (a) Describe the economic conditions of Later Vedic Period. How was it different from Rig Vedic life

   (b) Discuss the similarities and differences between the basic tenets of Buddhism and Jainism.

   (c) Trace the evolution of Temple architecture in South India.

   (d) How did the Bhakti Movement contribute to the growth of regional languages?

   (e) Highlight the role of Peoples movement towards the integration of Princely States into the India Union.

2. **Answer *all* the following (in not more than 200 words each):** 5×5=25

   (a) "Climate change is likely to adversely affect certain countries dependent on agriculture." Examine this statement citing relevant examples.

   (b) Many countreis prefer coal rather than solar or wind energy as a source of fuel. Why?

   (c) "Air pollution and water shortages are among the problems faced by urban centres across the globe." Examine this statement.

   (d) What factors inluence the location of industries in India today?

(e) "Degradation of forest resources and wildlife is a fallout of agriculture and urbanization." Assess this statement giving examples from India.

3. Answer *all* the following (in not more than 200 words each): 5×5=25

(a) Critically examine Indian Agriculture Acts of 2020.

(b) "Privatization of Public Sector Banks is fraught with huge risk". Elucidate.

(c) Do you believe that Aatmanirbhar Bharat Abhiyaan, 2020 will be able to combat the COVID-19 crisis of the Indian economy? Justify your answer.

(d) Analyse the recommendations of the Narasimham Committee Report I and II in controlling Non-Perorming Assets (NPAs) of the banking sector in India.

(e) Discuss the roles and responsibilites of the Anganwadi workers and helpers under Integrated Child Development Services Scheme (ICDS).

4. Answer *all* the following (in not more than 200 words each): 5×5=25

(a) "The Indian Constitution is a living document." Discuss.

(b) Critically examine the financial emergency powers of the President and their effects.

(c) "The Rajya Sabha has certain special powers vis-a-vis the Lok Sabha that adds to its prestige." Comment.

(d) Compare the writ jurisdictions of the Supreme Court and the High Court.

(e) "The Indian Goverment's response to the COVID-19 pandemic has shifted the federal balance in its favour." Illustrate with suitable examples.

GENERAL STUDIES
2020

Time Allowed : Three Hours | *Maximum Marks: 100*

Question Paper Specific Instructions
Please read each of the following instructions carefully before attempting questions.

*There are FOUR questions and **all** are to be attempted. Candidates should attempt questions/parts as per the instructions given in the questions. The number of marks carrid by a question/part is indicated against it. Candidates are required to write clear, legible and concise answers and to adhere to word limits, wherever indicated. Failure to adhere to word limits may be penalized. Any page or portion of the page left blank in the Question-cun-Answer Booklet must be clearly struck off. Answers must be written in ENGLISH only.*

1. **Answer all the following (in not or more than 200 words each):** 5×5=25

(a) Elucidate the main aspects of the policy of Dhamma as propounded by Ashoka. To what extent are they relevant to present-day India?

(b) Underlining the chief characteristics of the Mansabdari system, discuss the way it organized the Mughal administration.

(c) Critically examine those developments in the second half of the nineteenth century which led to the emergence of modern Indian nationalism.

(d) It can be said that the Non-Cooperation Movement proved to be a stage from which India's freedom struggle entered in a new trajectory. Give reasons for your argument.

(e) When and where was the Quit India Resolution passed? Analyze the causes and nature of this movement.

2. **Answer *all* the following (in not more than 200 words each):** 5×5=25

(a) A greening and browning of the Himalya and the Arctic is occurring. What dirvers are causing such a phenomenon and is there any way to minimize this trend?

(b) Is India overpopulated? Provide arguments to substantiate your answer.

(c) Forests play a vital role in providing a wide range of ecosystem services and benefits to humans. Summarize these in brief and assess the state of India's forests in the past decade.

(d) Most Indian cities are beset with a number of problems. Offer suggestions to tackle these in a multipronged manner.

(e) The recent wildfires that swept across eastern Australia are unmatched in terms of severity and intensity. Explain why the 2019-2020 Australian bushfire was so severe and its fallout on various species of flora and fauna.

3. Answer *all* the following (in not more than 200 words each): **5×5=25**

(a) What are the risks posed to the flexible inflation targeting in India under the Monetary Policy Committee? Should India as developing country tolerate a certain degree of inflation to ensure growth? Discuss.

(b) Is the ongoing trade war between China and the United States an opportunity for India to replace China as a major exporter of manufactured goods? Discuss.

(c) How do you think Covid-19 pandemic and rural distress can be seen as prominent reasons behind the current slowdown in the Indian economy? Give reasons in support of the argument.

(d) Analyze the reasons of declining female labour force participation rate in India and suggest appropriate measures to tackle the situation.

(e) Do you think that the banking industy has come full circle since the Nationalization of Banks in India? Critically assess the success of Indian public sector banks in this context.

4. Answer *all* the following (in not more than 200 words each): **5×5=25**

(a) "73rd and 74th Constitutional Amendment Acts completed twenty-five years of their existence, however, a lot is yet to be achieved." Discuss the statement in the light of devolution of powers enshrined in the Constitution.

(b) "Political values of Indian society are derived from the Preamble of the Indian Constitution." Comment on the statement in the context of political socialization of 'socialist' nad 'secular' values in the Preamble.

(c) Critically examine the role of the Court as the guardian of the Indian Constitution.

(d) Comment on the Legislative controls over administration.

(e) Goal-2 of the Sustainable Development Goals Agenda 2030 aspires to "end hunger, achieve food security and improved nutrition and promote sustainable agriculture". In order to achieve this, the National Livelihood Mission can be an interventinist strategy. Discuss.

GENERAL STUDIES
2019

Time Allowed : Three Hours | *Maximum Marks: 100*

Question Paper Specific Instructions

Please read each of the following instructions carefully before attempting questions.

*There are FOUR questions and **all** are to be attempted. Candidates should attempt questions/parts as per the instructions given in the questions. The number of marks carrid by a question/part is indicated against it. Candidates are required to write clear, legible and concise answers and to adhere to word limits, wherever indicated. Failure to adhere to word limits may be penalized. Any page or portion of the page left blank in the Question-cun-Answer Booklet must be clearly struck off. Answers must be written in ENGLISH only.*

1. **Answer all of the following (in not more than 200 words each):** 5×5=25

   (a) Write a critical note on the findings of science and technology in ancient India. Could it get appropriate recognition in modern period?

   (b) The art and architecture of Mughal period was a mix of Muslim and Hindu art traditions and elements. Discuss with suitable examples.

   (c) The emergence of new social classes in India was the direct consequence of the establishment of the British rule in India. Discuss.

   (d) "The Cabinet Mission Plan of 1946 created more issues than solutions in the transfer of power." Analyse the statement in the context of independence of India

   (e) Critically explain that Gandhiji's ideasand philosophy are relevant and practicable in the 21st century.

2. **Answer all of the following (in not more than 200 words each):** 5×5=25

   (a) Give reasons for desertification in Rajasthan and highest rainfall on the windward side of Meghalaya Plateau in India.

   (b) Comment on ambient air qualityin Megacities of India especially during the winter months.

   (c) Why is literacy considered as the best contraceptive in view of differential rates of population growth in various growth in various States of India?

(d) "Poor people have not been excluded from the process of urbanisation in India." Elucidate.

(e) Suggest suitable measures for controlling hunger and malnutrition to assure food security in India.

3. **Answer all of the following (in not more than 200 words each):** **5×5=25**

(a) "The nationwide Goods and Services Tax (GST) reaps the benefit of common market India offers." Examine, in the light of the statement, how GST is beneficial for the Indian economy.

(b) In what ways are the terms of reference of the Fifteenth Finacne Commission different from that of all the previous Union Finance Commissions?

(c) Is India ready for universal basic income (UBI)? Discuss, in the context of Indian ecoomy, the pros and cons of UBI.

(d) "Degree of fiscal decentralisation varies from one State to another." Examine, in the light of this statement, devolution to Panchayats across States after the 73rd Constitutional Amendment Act.

(e) Why is credit deposit (CD) ratio of scheduled commercial banks low in low income States in India?

4. **Answer all of the following (in not more than 200 words each):** **5×5=25**

(a) Critically examine the role of pressure groups in Indian politics.

(b) Discuss some of the major controversies surrounding the proposed Citizenship (Amendment) Bill, 2016. Why did the Bill evoke sharp criticisms in Assam?

(c) In the light of a looming threat of a nuclear conflict, discuss the long-term implications of the recent military flare-ups on the bilateral relations between India and Pakistan.

(d) Critically analyse the present electoral system in Indai and suggest possible reforms to bring about fairnes, accountability and transparency.

(e) Highlight the major differeces between judicial review and judicial activism. Do you agree that the tilt towards judicial activism has become far more pronounced in the recent past?

GENERAL STUDIES
2018

Time Allowed : Three Hours | *Maximum Marks: 100*

INSTRUCTIONS

Please read each of the following instructions carefully before attempting the questions.

There are FOUR questions and all are to be attempted.

Candidates should attempt questions/parts as per the instructions given in the questions.

The number of marks carried by a question/part is indicated against it.

Candidates are required to write clear, legible and concised answers and to adhere to word limits wherever indicated. Failure to adhere to word limits may be penalized. The answers must be written within the space provided in the Question-cum-Answer-Booklet.

Answer must be written in ENGLISH only.

Any page or portion of the page left blank in the Question-cum-Answer Booklet must be clearly struck off.

Ql. Answer all of the following (in not more than 200 words each) : 5x5=25

(a) Do you think Kautilya's 'Arthashastra' provides guidelines to modern Indian polity or governance ? Discuss.

(b) Do you consider that the rise of British power in India, primarily owes to the decline of Mughal power or British naval and trade supremacy ? Give reasons.

(c) During 1940s Gandhiji said, "We do not seek independence out of British ruin." Explain the circumstances and outcome of the Gandhian policy in this context.

(d) Nehru preferred "non-linguistic states in the interests of a strong centre," which could not be enforced. Elucidate.

(e) Was 'Rama Setu', a 'man made' or 'nature made' monument ? Explain with reference to the recent researches and findings of the various commissions.

Q2. Answer all of the following (in not more than 200 words each) : 5x5=25

(a) Assess the climatic impact of the existence of the Himalayas in the north along with oceans and seas in three other directions of India.

(b) What is the significance of biodiversity conservation in the forests and water bodies of India ?

(c) Comment on the relative performance of the Indian states in terms of population growth and human development.

(d) "High pace of urbanisation in India, though transforming landscape, is a necessary process of development." Give your arguments.

(e) Account for the recent emphasis on rainwater harvesting and small check dams on rivulets in India in preference to big dams on the main rivers.

Q3. Answer all of the following (in not more than 200 words each) : 5x5=25

(a) "India is a fast transforming knowledge economy." Comment.

(b) Give an account on the growth of Information Technology and Biotechnology sectors and their impact on GDP and employment in India.

(c) Explain the term 'Demonetisation'. Assess the effects of demonetisation on the economy and on black money.

(d) Farmers' suicides in India are the result of agrarian crisis. Give reasons for it and suggest remedial measures.

(e) Critically examine the 'Universal Healthcare Scheme' as pronounced in the Union Budget, 2018.

Q4. Answer all of the following (in not more than 200 words each) : 5x5=25

(a) What is the significance of inner party democracy in political parties ? How could it be ensured in our political system ?

(b) What are the salient features of a welfare state ? Is India a welfare state? Give reasons for your answer.

(c) Do you agree with the view that the elections to the Lok Sabha and the State Legislative Assemblies be held simultaneously ? Give reasons for your answer.

(d) Khap Panchayats have been in the news for functioning as conscience keepers of society, often delivering pronouncements on the legality of marriage. Discuss the stand taken by the Supreme Court in this regard.

(e) What are the economic constraints which hinder the success of the South Asian Association for Regional Cooperation (SAARC) ?

GENERAL STUDIES
2017

Time Allowed : Three Hours | *Maximum Marks: 100*

INSTRUCTIONS

Please read each of the following instructions carefully before attempting the questions.
There are FOUR questions and all are to be attempted.
Candidates should attempt questions/parts as per the instructions given in the questions.
The number of marks carried by a question/part is indicated against it.
Candidates are required to write clear, legible and concised answers and to adhere to word limits wherever indicated. Failure to adhere to word limits may be penalized. The answers must be written within the space provided in the answer-book.
Answer must be written in ENGLISH only.

---

1. Answer all the following (in not more than 200 words each): **5x5=25**

1. (a) Assess the impact of Iron Technology on the history of ancient India.

1. (b) Present a sketch of major Sufi orders in India. What was their goal ?

I. (c) Examine the ideas and ideology of Jyotiba Phule. Can he be termed a radical?

1. (d) Write an essay on the main revolutionary groups operating in India till early 1930s.

1. (c) Given the odds and the opposition from princely states, their integration was a huge achievement. Whom do you consider the architect of Indian integration after independence ? Discuss.

2. Answer all the following (in not more than 200 words cach) : **5*5=25**

2. (a) Why do the river systems of Peninsular India How to the cast to Bay of Bengal ?

2. (b) Why do iron and steel industries tend to locate closer to the areas of mining of ores and other raw materials ?

2. (c) How does the population distribution of India relate to the broad physical divisions of the country ?

2. (d) How can global climate change affect food security of India ?

2. (e) Which areas of India and why, are the most susceptible to earthquakes ?

3. Answer all of the following (in not more than 200 words each): 5x5=25

3. (a) Does recent budget (2017) aim to Transform, Energise and Clean (TEC) Indian Economy to ensure empowering common man in India? Discuss.

3. (b) What is Green Energy? Explain the policies envisaged by the Government of India to promote Green Energy sources.

3. (c) In India, do you agree growth of service sector is sustainable and will it ensure the equity in terms of creating employment ?

3. (d) Examine the main economic implications of Goods and Services Tax (GST) in India.

3. (e) Examine how Demographic Dividend is affected by the lack or investment in the human capital.

4. Answer all of the following (in not more than 200 words each): 5*5=25

4. (a) "The rights must be reconciled with the duties." Examine, in the light of this statement, how fundamental duties in one citizen imply fundamental rights in other citizens.

4. (b) In view of the prolonged relationship between black money and politics in India, there is now a growing feeling that an effort must be made to cleanse the system of political funding in our country. Do you agree with this feeling? Give reasons for your answer.

4. (c) Discuss the role of the Attorney-General of India.

4. (d) Examine the impact of globalization on the developing countries.?

4. (e) How does the Supreme Court Collegium's recent decision end the impasse on judicial appointment procedure ?

GENERAL STUDIES
2016

Time Allowed : Three Hours | *Maximum Marks: 100*

INSTRUCTIONS

Please read each of the following instructions carefully before attempting the questions.

There are FOUR questions and all are to be attempted.

Candidates should attempt questions/parts as per the instructions given in the questions.

The number of marks carried by a question/part is indicated against it.

All parts and sub-parts of a questions are to be attempted together in the answer-book.

Answer must be written in ENGLISH only.

Candidates are required to write clear, legible and concise answers and to adhere to word limits wherever indicated. Failure to adheree to word limits may be penalized.

Any page or portion of the page left blank in the answer book must be clearly struck off.

---

1. **Answer all of the following (in not more than 200 words each):**

   (a) Both Subhas Chandra Bose and Manatma Gandhi launched struggles against the British during the 2nd World War. How were their ideas and strategies different?

   (b) Discuss the role of intellectuals in giving shape to the nationalism in India during the freedom struggle.

   (c) The division of India into province? and evolving a system of provincial administration by Akbar was an effective system of governance. Comment.

   (d) Why were a number of European trading companies attracted to India during the 16th - 17th centuries ?

   (e) What does Yoga represent in Indian philosophical tradition ? Is it the same as that practised by the masses in the present day ?

2. **Answer all of the following (in not more than 200 words each):** 5x5=25

   (a) What is Polar Shifting ? Discuss its geographic significance with regard to catastrophic consequences on humanity.

   (b) What are Western disturbances and Westerlies and how are they different from monsoons ? In which part of India are they confined ?

   (c) Discuss the impact of Information Technology in the Industrial Revolution of India.

   (d) Discuss the changing scenario of pulses cultivation as well as their production.

   (e) What are the differences between Himalayan and Peninsular rivers ? Discuss.

3. **Answer all of the following (in not more than 200 words each):** 5×5=25

   (a) Explain the reasons for political turmoil among middle level castes in recent times seeking OBC reservations in India.

   (b) What do you understand by tax-havens ? Explain how they promote corruption in India.

   (c) Discuss the importance of Rashtriya Krishi Vikas Yojana in achieving holistic development of agriculture in India.

   (d) What do you understand by Protein Inflation ? Explain the causes for Protein Inflation in India.

   (e) Discuss the major causes for low human development in India.

4. **Answer all of the following (in not more than than200 words each):** 5x5W5

   (a) Discuss the impact of the Indo-Pak War in 1971.

   (b) Discuss the imperatives for South Asian Association for Regional Cooperation (SAARC).

   (c) 'The notion that there can he only one concept of what constitutes a nation, and that every other view is anti national, is intellectually empty at best and authoritarian at worst." Examine, in the light of this statement, the current debate with regard to the concept of nationalism.

   (d) Discuss the role of the Comptroller and Auditor General of India.

   (e) Analyse the impact of the Constitution (42nd Amendment) Act on environmental protection and improvement.

GENERAL STUDIES
2015

Time Allowed : Three Hours | *Maximum Marks: 100*

INSTRUCTIONS

Please read each of the following instructions carefully before attempting questions.
There are FOUR questions and all are to be attempted.
Candidates should attempt questions/parts as per the instructions given in the questions.
The number of marks carried by a question/part is indicated against it.
Candidates are required to write clear, legible and concise answers and to adhere to word limits wherever indicated. Failure to adheree to word limits may be penalized.
All parts and sub-parts of a questions are to be attempted together in the answer-book.
Answer must be written in ENGLISH only.

---

1. **Answer all of the following (in not more than 200 words each) :** 5x5=25

   (a) Do you agree with the view that the reversal of Akbar's Rajput policy by Aurangzeb was responsible for the disintegration- of the Mughal empire? Discuss.

   (b) List out the contributions of Raja Ram Mohun Roy in social reforms in India. Discuss four major issues plaguing the country where we further need social reforms.

   (c) Discuss the impact of industrial revolution in India.

   (d) Discuss the role played by Indian Army (soldiers) in World War I and II.

   (e) Discuss the background leading to the rise of LTTE.

2. **Answer all of the following (in not mere than 200 words each) :** 5×5-25

   (a) Even though hydroelectric power potential is high in North-East India, it is not fully tapped. Why?

   (b) What is the importance of Aksai Chin?

   (c) What axe the main recommendations of the Kasthuri Rangan Report on Western Ghats?

   (d) Explain as to how organic farming helps conservation of environment.

   (e) What is the pacific ring of fire? Discuss its geographical significance.

3. Answer all of the following (in not more than 200 words each) : **5x5=25**

(a) Discuss the various reasons for the fall in oil prices in international market.

(b) Critically analyze the need of high-speed (Bullet) trains in India.

(c) Government has launched the Soil Health Card scheme recently. Discuss the reasons for which the scheme has been envisaged. What are the challenges expected in success of the scheme?

(d) Is glass ceiling a deterrent to women empowerment in India? Discuss.

(e) Critically compare nuclear energy with the nonconventional energy sourcing.

4. Answer all of the following (in not more than 200 words each) : **5x5=25**

(a) The 42nd Amendment to the Constitution of India added the words 'secular' and 'socialist' to the Preamble of the Constitution in 1976. What prompted this Amendment? What relevance do they have today? Discuss.

(b) What do you understand by Judicial Activism? Why is it considered as a deterrent to executive authority?

(c) Evaluate critically the role of University Grants Commission in the development and financing of higher education in India.

(d) Discuss the basis laid down by Election Commission of India for recognizing a political party as National and State party.

(e) What are the differences in the roles of Attorney General of India and Solicitor General of India?

GENERAL STUDIES
2014

Time Allowed : Three Hours

Maximum Marks: 100

INSTRUCTIONS

Please read each of the following instructions carefully before attempting questions.

There are FOUR questions and all are to be attempted.

Candidates should attempt questions/parts as per the instructions given in the questions.

The number of marks carried by a question/part is indicated against it.

Candidates are required to write clear, legible and concise answers and to adhere to word limits may be penalized.

All parts and sub-parts of a questions are to be attempted together in the answer-book.

Answer must be written in ENGLISH only.

---

1. Answer *all* of the following (in not more than 200 words each) : **5×5=25**

(a) Discuss the reasons for the decline of the Indus Valley Civilization in the beginning of the 2nd Millennium BC. 5

(b) Discuss the contributions of Chandragupta Maurya in creating the first Indian empire.

(c) Why is Bhakti Movement considered an important secularizing force in a medieval India? 5

(d) Should the era of the Great Mughals be considered as successful in creating a harmonious and strong empire in India? Discuss, 5

(e) How was the controversial McMahon Line responsible for the Indo-China War of 1962? 5

2. Answer *all* of the following (in not more than 200 words each) : **5×5=25**

(a) If Himalayas were not there, what could have been the geographical/climatic conditions in northern part of India? 5

(b) How do El Nino and La Nina affect the climate in different parts of the world? 5

(c) Petroleum refineries in India axe not necessarily located in the areas of production of crude oil. Discuss. 5

(d) Discuss the ecological significance of mangroves on tropical estuaries. 5

(e) Does climate change make India more vulnerable to natural disaster? 5

3. **Answer *all* of the following (in not more than 200 words each) :** **5×5=25**

(a) Discuss critically the collegiums system for the appointment of the Higher Judiciary. 5

(b) Discuss the significance of the Fundamental Duty added with the 86th Amendment to the Indian Constitution. 5

(c) Should MPLAD be abolished? Critically examine. 5

(d) What is the significance of 'Zero Hour' □% in the proceedings in the Indian Parliament? 5

(e) Discuss how the Election Commission of India ensures smooth conduct of elections. 5

4. **Answer *all* of the following (in not more than 200 words each) :** **5x5=25**

(a) How can genetic engineering help in India's struggle for food security? 5

(b) Despite of a poor public health care system in the countiy, India could achieve the distinction of a polio-free countiy. Discuss. 5

(c) What do you understand by sting journalism? What are its ethical and legal dilemmas? 5

(d) Elucidate the significance and legal sanctity of DNA test / matching in determining the heredity.

(e) What has/have been the objective(s) of Mark Zuckerberg in buying WhatsApp?

GENERAL STUDIES
2013

Time Allowed : Three Hours

Maximum Marks: 100

INSTRUCTIONS

The the FIVE questions are to be attempted.
Candidates should attempt questions/parts as per the instructions given in each question.
The number of marks carried by a question/part is indicated against it.
All parts and sub-parts of a question are to be attempted together in the answer-book.
Attempt of a part/question shall be counted in chronological order. Unless struck off, attempt of a part/question shall be counted even if attempted partly. any page or portion of the page left blank in the answer-book must be clearly struck off.
Answers must be written only in ENGLISH.

1. Answer any four of the following in about 250 words each : 7×4 =28

(a) The Vedic Aryan culture became the foundation of Indian culture. Discuss. 7

(b) In which parts of India is the cyclone a major environmental hazard and why? 7

(c) Article 356 of the Constitution of India is the most un-federal provision. Analyse. 7

(d) Regional disparity in India is one of the major reasons for the growing militancy activities in the countiy. Discuss critically. 7

(e) Though Russia is Syria's important ally, it has agreed with USA for action against Syria recently. Discuss the case, tracing back the historical background and bringing out the key issues. 7

2. Answer any four of the following in about 200 words each : 6×4=24

(a) Discuss the reasons which led to the war between India and China in 1962. 6

(b) Swami Vivekananda was a visionary who contributed towards the freedom movement through social reforms. Comment. 6

(c) India is rich in iron-ore reserves but these are confined to certain areas. Elaborate. 6

(d) Is there a need to replace the Parliamentaiy form of Government in India with the Presidential form of Government like in USA? Critically analyse. 6

(e) Discuss the impact of the proposal of the Government to bifurcate the State of Andhra Pradesh. 6

3. Answer any four of the following in about 150 words each ; 5×4 = 20

(a) Of all the extant Ashokan pillars, the one at Sarnath is unique in itself. Elaborate. 5

(b) What are the differences between the Himalayan and Peninsular rivers? Discuss, 5

(c) Discuss the powers of the President in promulgation of ordinance during recess of the Parliament. 5

(d) Emergence of National Advisory Council {NAC) has diluted the importance of PMO and the coordinating role of Cabinet Secretariat. Analyse? 5

(e) Discuss the Indian stand in refusing to sign the CTBT. 5

4. Answer any four of the following in about100 words each : 4×4=16

(a) What is meteor shower? 4

(b) What is Human Genome Project? Discuss its advantages and disadvantages. 4

(c) What do you understand by vector- borne diseases? Discuss any three of such diseases. 4

(d) What is MTCR? How is it posing a hurdle for India in developing longrange cruise missiles? 4

(e) What do you understand by cryonics? 4

5. Write short notes on the following, bringing out as to why these/they were in news, in not more than 30 words each : 1×12=12

(a) Kudankulam

(b) Kishanganga Project

(c) Chabahar Port

(d) Higgs Boson

(e) Voyager 1

(f) Mars One

(g) Usain Bolt

(h) Obabiya Aishah Ajibola

(i) Narendra Dabholkar

(j) Bashar al-Assad

(k) Malala Yousafzai

(I) Norman Woodland

GENERAL STUDIES
2012

Time Allowed : Three Hours | *Maximum Marks: 100*

INSTRUCTIONS

Candidates should attempt ALL questions, unless otherwise directed.
The number of marks carried by each question is indicated for the question.
answers must be written only in ENGLISH.
All parts/sub-parts of a question being attempted must be completed before moving on to the next question.

All parts/sub-parts of a question being attempted must be completed before moving on to the next question.

1. **Answer any four of the following in about 250 words each :** **10x4=40**

   (a) Write a note on the history of census operations in pre-independent India.

   (b) Compare and contrast the 'capability approach' (of Amartya Sen) with the 'capabilities approach' (of Martha Nussbaum) towards well-being and development.

   (c) Critically comment on the extent, scope, and implications of Non-Communicable Diseases (NCDs) in India.

   (d) Comment on the salient features of the Global Hunger Index (GHI) report of 2012 with special reference to India.

   (e) Examine the sources and scope for the use of renewable energy in India.

2. **Answer any six of the following in about 100 words each :** **5x6=30**

   (a) Evaluate the role of bio-diversity parks in the conservation of wildlife.

   (b) Comment on the features of the proposed National Investment Board (NIB) in the country.

   (c) What are the features of the new visa regime between India and Pakistan signed recently?

   (d) Bring out the significance of the Right to Constitutional Remedies as guaranteed in the Constitution.

(e) What are the functions mandated to be performed by the Union Public Service Commission (UPSC) ?

(f) Comment on the recent milestones and the proposed initiatives of the Indian Space Research Organisation (ISRO),

(g) What were the salient features of the Government of India Act of 1935 ?

3. Answer any six of the following in less than 50 words each : **3x6=18**

(a) In the context of motions moved in Parliament, what is a 'cut motion' and what are its types ?

(b) What do you understand by the term 'counter-urbanisation' in the Indian context?

(c) Bring out the concept and salient highlights of Forensic Auditing (FA).

(d) What are Support Vector Machines (SVMs) and what are their important applications?

(e) What is the significance of qubits in computing ? Mention any recent significant advances in this area.

(f) Comment on the work for which Alvin Roth and Lloyd Shapley have won the 2012 Nobel Prize in Economics.

(g) Comment on the applications of the linkages of Global Positioning System (GPS) technology with Geographical Information Systems (GISs).

4. Why have the following been in the news recently ?

Answer in not more than a sentence or two each : 1x12=12

(a) William 'Bill' Moggridge

(b) Raghuram Rajan

(c) Lance Armstrong

(d) Bo Xilai

(e) Michelle Catherina

(f) Hugo Chavez

(g) Michael Phelps

(h) Agriello Dias and Santosh Padhi

(i) Girish Rulkarni

(j) Jeet Thayil

(k) Kapila Vatsyayan

(1) Irom Sharmila Charm

GENERAL STUDIES
2011

Time Allowed : Three Hours | Maximum Marks: 100

INSTRUCTIONS

Candidates should attempt ALL questions, unless otherwise directed.
The number of marks carrieed by each question is indicated for the question.
Answers must be written only in ENGLISH.

---

1. **Answer any TWO of the following in about 100 words each :-** **2×5=10**

   (a) Discuss the rich corpus of India's soft power.

   (b) Discuss the Fundamental Duties of Indian citizens as enshrined in the Constitution of India.

   (c) Comment on the Advisory jurisdiction of the Supreme Court of India.

2. **Write about, any TWO of the following in about 100 words each :-** **2×5=10**

   (a) Prehistoric cultures of India.

   (b) Sangam Literature.

   (c) Kautilya's views on taxation as enunciated in the 'Arthashastra'?

3. **Answer any TWO of the following in about 100 words each:-** **2x5=10**

   (a) What is the purpose of creating the National Optical Fibre Network, as recommended by the Telecom Commission ?

   (b) What is Carbon footprint ? Describe a few simple ways of reducing it.

   (c) How do biofertilizers help in maintaining the soil health ?

4. **Answer any TWO of the following in about 100 words each :-** **2x5=10**

   (a) Describe how the physiography of India affects its foreign trade.

   (b) Write about Swabhimaan Programme.

   (c) Explain the impact of JNNURM on environmental improvement of metropolitan cities.

5. **Locate and comment on the following events in about 40 words each in the context of India's freedom struggle :-** **5x2=10**

   (a) Full Swaraj -Resolution of Indian National Congress.

   (b) The 'Communal Award'.

   (c) The Gandhi-Irwin Pact.

   (d) Mountbatten Plan.

   (e) The Moplah Rebellion.

6. **Write about the famous festivals/fairs held at the following places, in about 40 words each:-** **5x2=10**

   (a) Sonepur

   (b) Hemis Gompa.

   (c) Pushkar

   (d) Khajuraho

   (e) Thiruvaiyaru,

7. **Write about the following in about 40 words each :-** **5x2=10**

   (a) Biodiesel .

   (b) Large Hadron Collider

   (c) Ultrasonography

   (d) Satellite transponder

   (e) GM crops.

8. **Write about the following National Institutes in about 40 words each :-** **5x2=10**

   (a) Institute of Economic Growth (IEG).-

   (b) National Institute of Science Communication and Information Resources (NISCAIR).

   (c) National Institute of Health and Family Welfare (NIHFW).

   (d) V.V. Giri National Labour Institute.

   (e) National Institute of Oceanography.

9. **Write about the following in about 40 words each :-** **5x2=10**

   (a) 'R' programming language.

   (b) Global. Peace Index.

   (c) Security features available in our currency notes.

   (d) The reason for which Sargent and Sims have been awarded the 2011 Nobel Prize in Economic Sciences.

   (e) Reasons for Moody's downgrading of the financial strength rating of the State Bank of India (SBI) recently.

10. Why have the following been in the news recently ? Answer in not more than one or two sentences each :- **10x1=10**

(a) C. Rangarajan

(b) Sebastian Vettel

(c) Calyampudi Radhakrishna Rao (C.R. Rao)

(d) M.J. Varadkar and S. Ponvannan

(e) Dr. M.K" Mani

(f) Chandrasekhar Kambar

(g) Saina Nehwal

(h) Baby Nargis

(i) Abdel-Rahim al-Keeb

(j) Lobsarig Sangay.

GENERAL STUDIES
2010

Time Allowed : Three Hours | *Maximum Marks: 100*

INSTRUCTIONS

Candidates should attempt ALL questions, unless otherwise directed.

The number of marks carrieed by each question is indicated for the question.

Answers must be written only in English.

***Important note** : The question paper contains an outline map of India. This is to be detached carefully from the question paper and attached firmly to the answer book while attempting Question No. 4. Do not write your roll number or name on the map.*

---

1. Answer any FIVE of the following, in about 75 words each : 5x5=25

(a) Discuss the role of Carbon Credit as a means of awareness in pollution control.

(b) Distinguish between hydrological characteristics of North Indian and South Indian rivers.

(c) Assess the importance of power in the industrial development of India.

(d) Explain how the President of India is an integral part of Parliament.

(e) Discuss the concept of Dyarchy introduced by the Government of India Act of 1919.

(f) Write a critical note on 'food security' issues debated in the Indian Parliament.

2. Write briefly on any FIVE of the following (in about 30 words each): 2x5=10

(a) What is invisible web ?

(b) What is genomics ?

(c) What are the uses of graphene ?

(d) What are the uses of phytoremediation ?

(e) Explain the role of UNIDO.

(f) Discuss Geographic Information System.

3. **Write on any FIVE of the following (in about 30 words each) :** **2×5=10**

(a) Allauddin Khalji's market reforms.

(b) Kandukuri Veeresalingam Pantulu

(c) INA

(d) Kailasanath temple at Ellora.

(e) Poona Pact of 1932.

(f) Charter Act of 1813.

4. **Show any FIVE of the following places on the outline map of India that is attached to your question paper. (The map must then be detached carefully from the question paper and attached to your answer book firmly) On your answer book, write about the significance of the five places marked by you, in about 20 words each:-** **(1+1)x5=10**

(a) Dehradun

(b) Digboi

(c) Pachmarhi

(d) Nagaij Unasagar

(e) Paradip

(f) Vadodara.

5. **Explain any FIVE of the following terms, in about 30 words each :-** **2×5=10**

(a) Effect of El Nino on Indian Climate.

(b) Open Source.

(c) Natural Rubber Producing Areas of India.

(d) Formation of Oxbow Lakes.

(e) Radioactive Pollution,

(f) Scientometrics.

6. **Write notes on any EIGHT of the following, in about 35 words each :-** **2½×8=20**

(a) Privileges enjoyed by the members of Indian Parliament individually.

(b) Constitutional limitations on the powers of Rajya Sabha.

(c) Effects of the dissolution of Lok Sabha.

(d) Article 360.

(e) Social Audit.

(f) Censure Motion.

(g) Writ of Prohibition,

(h) Paid News.

(i) 'Honour Killings'.

(j) Hypertext.

7. Write about the following in not more than a sentence or two each:- **1x10=10**

(a) Lagoon
(b) Xerophytes
(c) Digital Signature
(d) Coral reefs
(e) 'The Finkler Question'
(f) 'Before Memory Fades'
(g) Inter Tropical Front
(h) Suspensive Veto Power
(i) Erosion
(j) Equinox,

8. Why were the following in the news recently ? (Answer to each should be in a sentence or two only) :?- **1×5=5**

(a) ONV Kurup
(b) Dileep Padgaonkar
(c) Krishna Poonia
(d) Liu Xiaobo
(e) D. Udai Kumar.?

DO NOT WRITE YOUR ROLL NO. ON THIS SHEET

(*Note to Candidate* : This sheet is to be detached from the question paper and fastened to the answer book carefully and securely)

A–HLR–K–HT

INDIA – POLITICAL

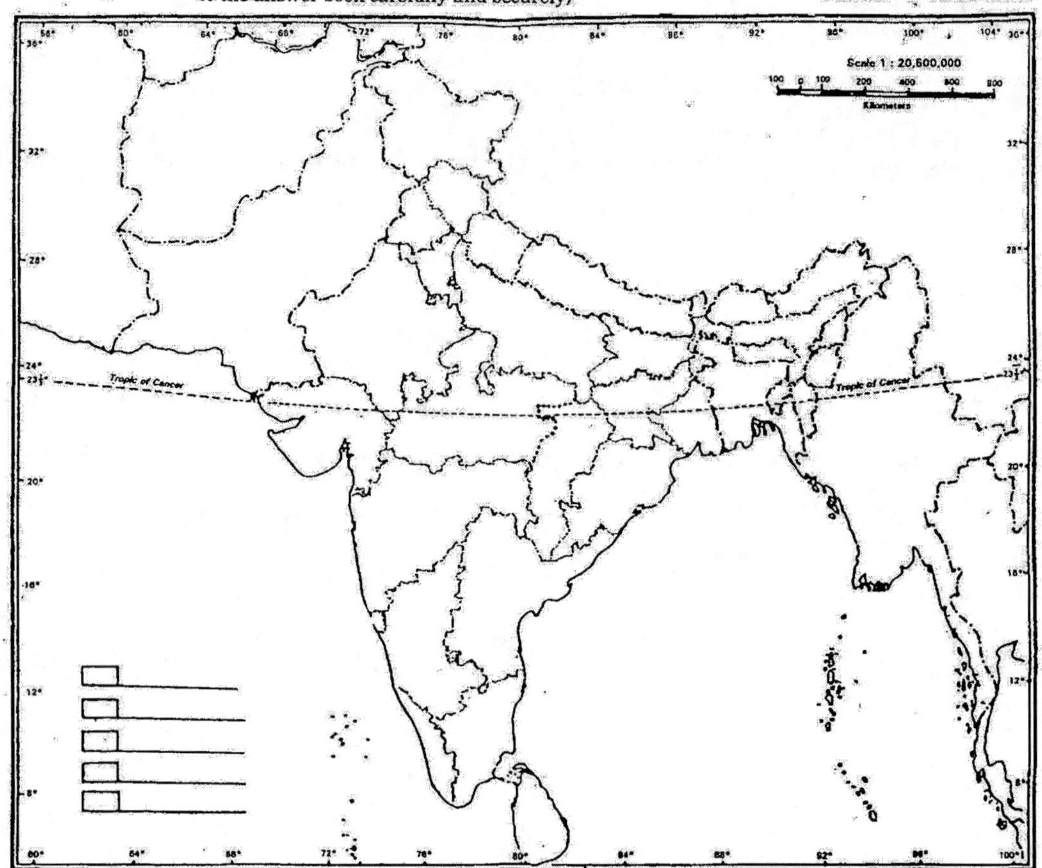

GENERAL STUDIES
2009

Time Allowed : Three Hours | *Maximum Marks: 100*

INSTRUCTIONS

Candidates should attempt ALL questions, unless otherwise directed.

The number of marks carrieed by each question is indicated for the question.

Answers must be written only in ENGLISH.

***Important note :** The question paper contains an outline map of India. This is to be detached carefully from the question paper and attached firmly to the answer book while attempting Question No. 4. Do not write your roll number or name on the map.*

---

1. Answer any five of the following, in about 75 words each : **5x5-25**

(a) What is a Breeder Reactor? Comment briefly on its main features and its significance for India's nuclear energy programme.

(b) Outline the socio-economic aspects of the Indian Constitution, mentioning the relevant Articles.

(c) Explain the factors that cause a Tsunami?

(d) What are transgenic crops? Give a few examples and comment briefly on their benefits and perceived risks, if any.

(e) What is the government's policy towards Indian diaspora? Comment on whether it is beneficial to the country, and if so, how.

(f) Give an account of participatory watershed management in the country.

2. Write briefly on any five of the following (in about 30 words each) : **2x5=10**

(a) What is BEE rating and what is it used for ?

(b) What is biological oxygen demand ? What does a high value of BOD indicate?

(c) What are nutraceuticals ? Give a few examples.

(d) Where would you find a catalytic converter ? What does it do ?

(e) What is a charge-coupled device ? What are its main advantages over photographic film?

(f) What are biodegradable plastics ? What are their important applications ?

3. Write on any five of the following (in about 30 words each): **2x5=20**

(a) Pir Muridi

(b) Swami Dayanand's Contributions Towards the Upliftment of Women

(c) Nayankar System

(d) The Wavell Plan

(e) Valentine Chirol

(f) Uagha' Jatin Mukherjee

4. Show any five of the following places on the outline map of India that is attached to your question paper. (The map must their be detached carefully from the question paper and attached to your answer book firmly.) On your answer book, write about the significance of the five places marked by you, in about 20 words each : **(1+1)×5=10**

(a) Gurushikhar

(b) Mawsynram

(c) Simlipal

(d) Didwana Lake

(e) Indira Point

(f) Annaimudi

(g) Dantewata

5. Explain any five of the following terms, in about 30 words each : **2x5=10**

(a) Exo sphere

(b) Isobath

(c) Antemeridian

(d) Glacier Budget

(e) Supernova

(f) Anti Collision Device (ACD)

6. Answer any eight of the following, in about 35 words each : **2½x8=20**

(a) Explain the role of the IAEA.

(b) Highlight the Articles of the Constitution that provide safeguards to minorities.

(c) What is the 'Look East Policy' of the Government of India ?

(d) What is the present system of appointment of Judges of High Courts ?

(e) What are the different modes through which the TJPSC recommends candidates for Government service ?

(f) What is a 'letter rogatory* ?

(g) In the context of computer software, distinguish between a 'virus' a 'worm', and a 'Trojan Horse'.

(h) What is 'fuzzy logic' and what are its important applications ?

(i) What are 'free radicals' in the body and what are their effects ?

(j) What are the highlights of the recent Indo-China agreement on climate change issues ?

7. Mention what the following are in not more than a sentence or two each : 1x10=10

(a) KALPANA-I

(b) Theodolite

(c) Isthmus

(d) Geosyncline

(e) 4 Willy-willy'

(f) 'Pietra dura' work

(g) International Date Line

(h) Nag ATGM

(i) Islets of Langerhans

(j) Sea of Tranquility

8. Why are the following in the news recently ? (Answer to each should be in a sentence or two only) : 1x5=5

(a) Sitara Devi

(b) Sharad Goekar

(c) Ignatius Tirkey

(d) Nandan Nilekani

(e) Juan Martin del Potro

STATISTICS-I

STATISTICS-I
2023

Time Allowed : Three Hours	*Maximum Marks: 200*

INSTRUCTIONS

1. IMMEDIATELY AFTER THE COMMENCEMENT OF THE EXAMINATION, YOU SHOULD CHECK THAT THIS TEST BOOKLET DOES NOT HAVE ANY UNPRINTED OR TORN OR MISSING PAGES OR ITEMS, ETC. IF SO, GET IT REPLACED BY A COMPLETE TEST BOOKLET.
2. Please note that it is the candidate's responsibility to encode and fill in the Roll Number and Test Booklet Series Code A, B, C or D carefully and without any omission or discrepancy at the appropriate places in the OMR Answer Sheet. Any omission/discrepancy will render the Answer Sheet liable for rejection.
3. You have to enter your Roll Number on the Test Booklet in the Box provided alongside. DO NOT write anything else on the Test Booklet.
4. This Test Booklet contains 80 items (questions). Each item comprises four responses (answers). You will select the response which you want to mark on the Answer Sheet. In case you feel that there is more than one correct response, mark the response which you consider the best. In any case, choose ONLY ONE response for each item.
5. You have to mark all your responses ONLY on the separate Answer Sheet provided. See directions in the Answer Sheet.
6. All items carry equal marks.
7. Before you proceed to mark in the Answer Sheet the response to various items in the Test Booklet, you have to fill in some particulars in the Answer Sheet as per instructions sent to you with your Admission Certificate.
8. After you have completed filling in all your responses on the Answer Sheet and the examination has concluded, you should hand over to the Invigilator ***only the Answer Sheet***. You are permitted to take away with you the Test Booklet.
9. Sheets for rough work are appended in the Test Booklet at the end.
10. Penalty for wrong answers :

THERE WILL BE PENALTY FOR WRONG ANSWERS MARKED BY A CANDIDATE IN THE OBJECTIVE TYPE QUESTION PAPERS.

(i) There are four alternatives for the answer to every question. For each question for which a wrong answer has been given by the candidate, one-third of the marks assigned to that question will be deducted as penalty. ·

(ii) If a candidate gives more than one answer, it will be treated as a wrong answer even if one of the given answers happens to be correct and there will be same penalty as above to that question.

(iii) If a question is left blank, i.e., no answer is given by the candidate, there will be no penalty for that question.

DO NOT OPEN THIS TEST BOOKLET UNTIL YOU ARE TOLD TO DO SO

1. The members of a firm rent cars from three rental agencies: 60% from Agency-1, 30% from Agency-2 and 10% from Agency-3. If 9% of cars from Agency-1 need an oil change, 20% of cars from Agency-2 need an oil change and 6% of cars from Agency-3 need an oil change, then what is the probability that a rental car delivered to the firm will need an oil change ?

   (a) 0·006 (b) 0·054

   (c) 0·06 (d) 0·12

2. If $X \sim N(0, 1)$ and $Y|X = x \sim U(x - 1, x, x + 1)$, then what is the value of $E(E^2|X))$?

   (a) 1 (b) 2

   (c) 3 (d) 4

3. If $X \sim \exp(\theta)$, then consider the following statements:

   1. Variance > Mean if $0 < \theta < 1$
   2. Minimum order statistics is chi-square distribution
   3. Lack of memory property exists only if $\theta > 1$

   Which of the statements given above is/are correct?

   (a) 1 only (b) 3 only

   (c) 1 and 2 (d) 1 and 3

4. A random variable X has probability mass function given by

   $$P(X = x) = \frac{1}{5^{10}}\binom{10}{x} 2^x 3^{10-x};\ x = 0, 1, 2, \ldots, 10$$

   The mean and variance of X are respectively:

   (a) 2, 4 (b) 2.4, 4

   (c) 4, 2.4 (d) 4, 2

5. If $X \sim$ log-normal (μ, σ^2) and $Y = \mu X^{\mu}$; $\sigma > 0$, $-\infty < \mu < \infty$, then what is the value of $\text{Var}\left(\left(\log\frac{Y}{\sigma} - \mu^2\right)^2\right)$?

   (a) $105\ \mu^4\sigma^4$ (b) $15\ \mu^4\sigma^4$

   (c) $3\ \mu^4\sigma^4$ (d) $2\ \mu^4\sigma^4$

6. The pdf of a random variable X is given be $f(x) = \begin{cases} 0.2 & 0 \le x \le 5 \\ 0, & \text{otherwise} \end{cases}$

   Consider the following probabiliteis:

   1. $P(2 \le X \le 3) = 0.2$
   2. $P(X > 3) = 0.3$
   3. $P(|x| \ge 2) = 0.6$
   4. $P(X < 4) = 0.8$

   How many of the probabilities given above are correct?

(a) Only one (b) Only two

(c) Only three (d) All four

7. If φ(.) is pdf of N(0, 1) distribution and A represents a circle of unit area with centre at origin, then what is the value of $\iint_A \varphi(x)\,\varphi(y)\,dx\,dy$

(a) $\frac{1}{2}+e^{-\pi}$ (b) $1-e^{-\frac{1}{2\pi}}$

(c) $1-e^{-2\pi}$ (d) $1-e^{-\frac{1}{\sqrt{\pi}}}$

Consider the following for the next threee (03) items that follow:

Let joint pdf of two random variables X and Y be $f(x, y) = \frac{1}{\sqrt{2\pi y}} e^{-\frac{1}{2y}(x-12y)^2}$; $-\infty < x < \infty, 0 < y < 1$

8. What is the value of E(X)?

(a) 1 (b) 2

(c) 4 (d) 6

9. What is the value of Var(X)?

(a) 1 (b) 2

(c) 12 (d) 12.5

10. What is the value of Cov (X, Y)?

(a) 1 (b) 2

(c) 2.5 (d) 3

11. If random variable X follows Binomial distribution with n = 10 and $p = \frac{1}{4}$, then what is the value of third cumulant of Y = 10 – X?

(a) $-\frac{15}{16}$ (b) $\frac{15}{16}$

(c) $\frac{5}{8}$ (d) $\frac{5}{16}$

12. If X, Y and Z are iid exponential (1) variates, then the distribution of (X + Y + Z)/3 is:

(a) Exponential (1/3) (b) Exponential (3)

(c) Gamma (n = 3, λ = 1/3) (d) Gamma (n = 3, λ = 3)

13. If random variable X assumes non negative integral values and $P(s) = E(s^X)$, then what is the value of $\sum_{n=0}^{\infty} s^{2n}\ P(X \le n)$?

(a) $\frac{P(\sqrt{s})}{1-s^2}$ (b) $\frac{P(s)}{1-s^2}$

(c) $\frac{P(s^2)}{1-s^2}$ (d) $\frac{P(\sqrt{s})}{1-s}$

14. If a random variable assumes non negative integral values and $E(X) = \mu$, $Var(X) = \sigma^2$, then what is the value of $2\sum_{x=0}^{\infty} xP(X > x)$?

(a) $\sigma^2 + \mu^2$ (b) $\sigma^2 + \mu^2 - \mu$

(c) $(\sigma^2 - \mu)/2$ (d) $(\sigma^2 + \mu^2 - \mu)/2$

Consider the following for the next three (03) items that follow:

The joint pmf of two random variables X and Y is given below:

X \ Y	−2	−1	0	1	2
−1	θ	2θ	3θ	θ	θ
0	2θ	3θ	θ	0	0
1	θ	θ	θ	θ	2θ

where $0 < \theta < 1$.

15. What is the moment generating function of $X | Y = 2$?

(a) $\dfrac{e^{-t} + 2e^{t}}{3}$ (b) $\dfrac{1 + e^{-t} + e^{t}}{3}$

(c) $\dfrac{2e^{-t} + e^{t}}{3}$ (d) $(1 - 2t)^{-1}$

16. What is the value of $Var(X | Y = 2)$?

(a) 1/3 (b) 2/3

(c) 8/9 (d) 2/9

17. What is the value of $E(XY | Y = 2)$?

(a) 1 (b) 1/3

(c) 2/3 (d) 8/9

Consider the followinng for the next three (03) items that follow:

Let the joint pdf of X and Y be

$$f(x, y) = \begin{cases} \dfrac{\lambda x^{12}}{(1 + xy)^{20}}; & x > 0, y > 1 \\ 0; & \text{otherwise} \end{cases}$$

18. What is the value of λ?

(a) $\dfrac{1}{B(12, 7)}$ (b) $\dfrac{19}{B(12, 7)}$

(c) $\dfrac{7}{B(12, 7)}$ (d) $\dfrac{8}{B(12, 7)}$

where $B(m, n) = \int_0^1 X^{m-1} (1 - x)^{n-1} dx$

19. What is the marginal distributio of X?
    (a) Beta Type-II distribution with parameters (12, 7)
    (b) Beta Type-II distribution with parameters (3, 7)
    (c) Beta Type-I distribution with parameters (12, 7)
    (d) Beta Type-I distribution with parameters (13, 7)

20. Marginal distribution of Y has pdf:
    (a) $\frac{7}{y^8}$; y > 1 and 0 otherwise
    (b) $\frac{11}{y^{12}}$; y > 1 and 0 otherwise
    (c) $\frac{18}{y^{19}}$; y > 1 and 0 otherwise
    (d) $\frac{12}{y^{13}}$; y > 1 and 0 otherwise

21. Which of the following are examples of data condensing?
    1. Data array
    2. Frequency distribution
    3. Histogram
    4. Ogives

    Select the correct answer using the code given below:
    (a) 1, 2 and 4 only
    (b) 1 and 3 only
    (c) 2, 3 and 4 only
    (d) 1, 2, 3 and 4

22. For the variable X, following observations are taken:
    X = 2, 5, 0, 6, 3, 8, 1, 3, 0, 2
    What is Var(2X + 2)?
    (a) 24.8
    (b) 26.8
    (c) 28.8
    (d) 29.6

23. What is the 3rd central moment of Binomial distribution with parameters n = 10 and p = 1/2?
    (a) 25
    (b) 5
    (c) 2.5
    (d) 0

24. Consider the contingency table presenting the number of skilled and unskilled labour against their gender. What is the value of χ^2 for testing the associatio between gender and the nature of work?

	Skilled	Unskilled
Male	30	30
Female	20	20

    (a) 50
    (b) 16.66
    (c) 12.07
    (d) 0

25. If Var(X) = 4, Cov(X, Y) = 32 and correlation coefficient r(X, Y) = 0.8 for some bivariate data, then what is V(Y) equal to?

(a) 400 (b) 200

(c) $200\sqrt{2}$ (d) $400\sqrt{2}$

Consider the following for the next five (05) items that follow:

The pdf of Bi-variate normal distribution is given by

$f(x, y) = \lambda e^{-(2x^2+3xy+4y^2-7x-11y)}; -\infty < x < \infty, -\infty < y < \infty,$

where λ is constant.

26. What is the value of E(X) + E(Y) + 3?

(a) 0 (b) 1

(c) 4 (d) 5

27. What is the value of 23(Var(X) + Var(Y))?

(a) 4 (b) 8

(c) 12 (d) 17

28. If r is correlation coefficient between X and Y, then what is the value of $\sqrt{2}r$?

(a) $-\frac{3}{4}$ (b) $-\frac{1}{4}$

(c) $-\frac{1}{\sqrt{2}}$ (d) $-\frac{1}{2}$

29. What is the distribution of $Y | X = x$ equal to?

(a) $N\left(\frac{11-3x}{8}, \frac{1}{8}\right)$ (b) $N\left(1, \frac{1}{8}\right)$

(c) $N\left(\frac{1+x}{2}, \frac{1}{8}\right)$ (d) $N\left(\frac{4-3x}{8}, \frac{7}{8}\right)$

30. If $E(X) = \mu_1$ and $E(Y) = \mu_2$, then what is the value of $2\pi f(\mu_1, \mu_2)$?

(a) $\sqrt{23}$ (b) $\sqrt{6}$

(c) $4\sqrt{2}$ (d) $16\sqrt{2}$

31. If $(X, Y) \sim BVN(0, 0, 1, 1; \rho)$, then what is the value of $\frac{E((Y-\rho X)^4 | X)}{(1-\rho^2)^2}$?

(a) 1 (b) 3

(c) 9 (d) 81

32. For h families containing equal number k of members in each family, the range of intra-class correlation coefficient ρ is:

(a) 0 to 1 (b) -1 to 1

(c) $-1/(k-1)$ to 0 (d) $-1/(k-1)$ to 1

33. If the correlation coefficient between heights of fathers and sons from a random sample of 900 is calculated as 0.67, what is the standard error?

(a) 0.018 (b) 0.04

(c) 0.18 (d) 1.8

34. The mean height obtained from a random sample of size 100 is 64 inches. The standard deviation of the height distributionis known to be 3 inches. What is the 95% confidence interval for mean height of the population? (Assume $Z_{0.025} = 2$)

(a) (63.4, 64.6) (b) (63.1, 64.1)

(c) (62.8, 65.8) (d) (62, 66)

35. In an art school, 380 children out of 800 were found to be singers. If E is the sandard error of proprtion of singers, then what is $1280000E^2$ equal to?

(a) 39.9 (b) 399

(c) 3990 (d) 4399

36. If a sample of size n is taken from $N(\mu, \sigma^2)$ and let $\bar{x}$ and s^2 be sample mean and sample variance respectivley, then distributio of $\frac{(n-1)\,s^2}{\sigma^2}$ is:

(a) Chi-square with (n – 1) degrees of freedom

(b) Chi-square with n degrees of freedom

(c) Student-t with (n – 1) degrees of freedom

(d) Student-t with n degrees of freedom

37. For a bivariate data, using the principles of least-squares, the following models were constructed:

E1: $Y = 3X + 5$ with $\Sigma(Y_i - 5)^2 = 15.48$

E2: $Y = X^2 + 8X + 2$ with $\Sigma(Y_i + X_i^2 - 2)^2 = 13.36$

What is the estimated value of Y for X = 6?

(a) 4.5 (b) 14

(c) 18.5 (d) 23

38. Let $x_1, x_2, x_3, \ldots, x_n$ be a random sample from a Normal population with mean μ_0 and variance σ^2. If $\bar{X}$ is the sample mean, then the distribution of $\frac{\bar{X} - \mu_0}{\left(\frac{\sigma}{\sqrt{n}}\right)}$ is:

(a) N(0, 1) (b) t with n degrees of freedom

(c) t with (n – 1) degrees of freedom (d) χ^2 with (n – 1) degrees of freedom

Consider the following for the next two (02) items that follow:

$(X, Y) \sim BVN(0, 0, 1, 1; \rho)$

39. What si the vlaue of $Cov(Y - \rho X, X)$?

(a) 0 (b) 0.5

(c) 0.75 (d) 1

40. What is the moment generating function of $X^2 + Y^2 - 2\rho XY$?

(a) $(1-2t)^{-1}$ (b) $(1-2\rho t)^{-1}$

(c) $(1-2t+2\rho^2 t)^{-1}$ (d) $(1-2t+2\rho t)^{-1}$

41. What is the minimum number of arguments required to find the third divided difference of the function $f(x) = x^3 - 2x + 1$?

(a) 2 (b) 3

(c) 4 (d) 5

42. What is $\Delta^2_{y,z}\, x^3$ equal to?

(a) $\frac{1}{x}+\frac{1}{y}+\frac{1}{z}$ (b) $x+y+z$

(c) $x^2+y^2+z^2$ (d) $\frac{1}{x^2}+\frac{1}{y^2}+\frac{1}{z^2}$

43. Let U(x) be a polynomial of degree 3. Given that U(0) + U(4) = 72 and U(1) + U(3) = 42. What is the value of U(2) assuming that differencing interval h = 1?

(a) 1 (b) 2

(c) 4 (d) 16

44. If differencing interval is of length h, then what is $(x^2 + hx + 1)$, $\tan(\Delta \tan^{-1} x)$ equal to?

(a) 1 (b) h

(c) h + 1 (d) $h^2 + 1$

45. If $x^{(r)} = x(x-1)(x-2)\ldots(x-(r-1))$, then what is the coefficient of x^4 in $2x^{(5)} - 5x^{(4)} + 3x^{(3)} + 2x^{(2)} + 1$?

(a) 2 (b) – 1

(c) – 10 (d) – 25

46. In case of equi-spaced tabular data, the error for linear interpolation is bounded by one eighth of the:

(a) first difference (b) second difference

(c) third difference (d) fourth difference

47. The integral $\int_0^1 x^3\,dx$ is evaluated by the Trapezoidal rule with step length h. Then the error is:

(a) $h^2/12$ (b) $h^2/6$

(c) $h^2/4$ (d) $h^2/3$

48. What is the value of b if $\int_0^h f(x)\,dx = ahf(0) + bhf\left(\frac{h}{3}\right) + chf(h)$ exists for a polynomial of degree as high as possible?

(a) 1 (b) 3/4

(c) 1/2 (d) 0

49. What is the value of the expression $\Delta^6(1-x)(1-3x^2)(1-4x^3))$, when interval of differencing is 1?

(a) 8640 (b) 2160

(c) – 2160 (d) – 8640

50. If $\delta = \sqrt{E} - \frac{1}{\sqrt{E}}$ and $\mu = \frac{1}{2}\left(\sqrt{E} + \frac{1}{\sqrt{E}}\right)$, then what is $2\left(\sqrt{1+\delta^2\mu^2}\right)y_x$ equal to?

(a) $y_{x+2} - 2y_{x+1} + y_x$ (b) $y_{x+1} - y_{x-1}$

(c) $y_{x+1}\ 6\ y_{x-1}$ (d) $y_{x+2} - y_x$

Consider the following for the next two (02) items that follow:

It is given that $u_3 = 4.8$, $u_4 = 8.4$, $u_5 = 14.5$, $u_6 = 23.6$, $u_7 = 36.2$, $u_8 = 52.8$, $u_9 = 73.9$.

51. What is the value of u_2 according to Newton-Greogy forward difference interpolation formula?

(a) 3.1 (b) 3.2

(c) 3.3 (d) 3.4

52. What is the approximate value fo $u_{8.5}$ according to Newton-Gregory backward difference interpolation formula?

(a) 62.75 (b) 64.75

(c) 66.75 (d) 68.75

53. Suppose $t_0 = 0 < t_1 < t_2 < t_n = 1$. If f is a continuous function and $f(t_i)$ are given for $0 \le i \le n$, which quadrature formula is applicable to compute $\int_0^1 f(x)\,dx$?

(a) Trapezoidal rule (b) Simpson's one-third rule

(c) Simpson's three-eighth rule (d) No quadrature formula

54. Let f: [0, 1] → ℝ be a continuous function. If $f\left(\frac{t}{10}\right)$ are given for t = 0, 1, 2, 3, 4, 5 and $f\left(\frac{t}{20}\right)$ are given for t = 11, 12, 13, ..., 20, which quadrature formula will one use to utilize the given data for the computation of $\int_0^1 f(x)\,dx$?

(a) Trapezoidal rule only

(b) Simpson's one-third rule only

(c) Simpson's three-eight rule

(d) Trapezoidal rule or combiation of Trapezoidal rule and Simpson's one-third rule

55. Consider the following for equi-spaced arguments with h as the interval of diferencing:

1. $x^{(-r)} = \dfrac{2}{(x+rh)^{(r)}}$

2. $\Delta^m x^{(-r)} = r(r+1)(r+2)\ldots(r+m)\,h^m\,x^{(-r-m)}$ for $m \le r$

Which of the statements given above is/are correct?

(a) 1 only (b) 2 only

(c) Both 1 and 2 (d) Neither 1 nor 2

56. Consider the following:

1. $\Delta(u_x v_x) = u_x \Delta v_x + v_{x+1} \Delta u_x$
2. $\Delta(u_x v_x) = v_x \Delta u_x + u_{x+1} \Delta v_x$

Which of the above equalities is/are valid?

(a) 1 only (b) 2 only

(c) Both 1 and 2 (d) Neither 1 nor 1

57. Euler's method is applied to the initial value problem $\frac{dy}{dx} = \lambda y;\ y(0) = 1,\ \lambda < 0$. Then, the method is stable (absolutely) for step size h that satisfies:

(a) $-2 < \lambda h < 2$ (b) $0 < \lambda h < 2$

(c) $-1 < \lambda h < 1$ (d) $-2 < \lambda h < 0$

58. The classical Runge-Kutta fourth order method is applied to $\frac{dy}{dx} = -y;\ y(0) = 1$. The result obtained after applyinng one step of length h is:

(a) $1 - h + \frac{h^2}{2}$ (b) $1 - h + \frac{h^2}{2} + \frac{h^3}{6} + \frac{h^4}{24}$

(c) $1 - h + \frac{h^2}{2} - \frac{h^3}{6} + \frac{h^4}{24}$ (d) $1 - h - \frac{h^2}{2} - \frac{h^3}{6} - \frac{h^4}{24}$

For the next two (02) items that follow:

Consider the series 12, 40, 90, 168, 280, 432, ... Let f(x) be the polynomial of least degree related to this series.

59. What is the degree of f(x)?

(a) 2 (b) 3

(c) 4 (d) 5

60. What is the constant term in f(x)?

(a) 0 (b) 1

(c) 8 (d) 12

61. Consider the following in respect of two kinds of microprocessors CISC (Complex Instruction Set Computer) and RISC (Reduced Instruction Set Computer):

1. The instructions of CISC are of variable length.
2. RISC supports parallel processing.
3. AMO is based on RISC.

Which of the statements given above are correct?

(a) 1 and 2 only (b) 2 and 3 only

(c) 1 and 3 only (d) 1, 2 and 3

62. Which of the following are audio file formats?

    1. MPEG
    2. WAV
    3. TIFF
    4. WMA

    Select the correct answer using the code given below:

    (a) 1, 2 and 3 (b) 1, 2 and 3

    (c) 1, 3 and 4 (d) 2, 3 and 4

63. The technique of dividing the physical memory space into multiple blocks is known as:

    (a) Paging (b) Segmentation

    (c) Fragmentation (d) Swapping

64. In TCP/IP reference model, consider the following prtocols belonging to various layers:

    1. SMPT
    2. FTP
    3. DHCP
    4. IP
    5. TCP

    Which of the above are the Application Layer Protocols?

    (a) 1, 2 and 3 (b) 1, 3 and 4

    (c) 1, 3 and 5 (d) 3, 4 and 5

65. Consider the following statements regarding cache memory in the computer system:

    1. The size of cache memory is always kept higher than the size of RAM.
    2. Cache memory is faster to access than RAM but slower to access than CPU registers.
    3. The effectiveness of cache memory is measured by hit rate.

    Which of the statements given above are correct?

    (a) 1 and 3 only (b) 2 and 3 only

    (c) 1 and 2 only (d) 1, 2 and 3

66. Which one of the following Operating Systems responds to an event within a predetermined time?

    (a) Time Sharing Operating System (b) Embedded Operating System

    (c) Real-time Operating System (d) Batch Operating System

67. Consider the following statements:

    1. In number system if $(110)_X = (1100)_2$, then the value of X is 3.
    2. The gray coded equivalent of the binary number $(01010010)_2$ is (011111011).

    Which of the statements given above is/are correct?

    (a) 1 only (b) 2 only

    (c) Both 1 and 2 (d) Neither 1 nor 2

68. Division of a computer program in terms of functions and modules is one of the vital features of:
    (a) Assembly language (b) Machine language
    (c) Structural language (d) Low level language

69. Which of the following Operating Systems is an open source?
    (a) Windows 10 (b) iOS 16
    (c) Linux (d) MS-DOS

70. Consider the following statemens:
    1. TCP/IP is the communication protocol used in Internet.
    2. A Network Interface Card (NIC) is used to connect a computer to Internet.
    3. IP address is also known as hardware address that is assigned uniquely to every computer connected to the Internet.

    Which of the statements given above are correct?
    (a) 1 and 2 only (b) 2 and 3 only
    (c) 1 and 3 only (d) 1, 2 and 3

71. Consider the following statements in respect of SQL:
    1. SQL can execute queries against a database.'
    2. SQL can update records in a database.
    3. SQL query automatically eliminates duplicates.

    Which of the statements given above are correct?
    (a) 1 and 2 only (b) 2 and 3 only
    (c) 1 and 3 only (d) 1, 2 and 3

72. Which of the following statements is/are correct?
    1. Encryption process convers cipher text into plain text.
    2. Digital signature employs two keys-private key and public key.
    3. Secret Key Cryptography uses a single key for both, encryption and decryption.

    Select the correct answer using the code given below:
    (a) 2 only (b) 2 and 3 only
    (c) 3 only (d) 1, 2 and 3

73. A device that converts digital signal into analog and vice-versa is known as:
    (a) Network switch (b) Modern
    (c) Network hub (d) Network router

74. Which one of the following is the core component of UNIX?
    (a) Shell (b) Kernel
    (c) Process (d) Directories

75. Which of the following devices are used for recognizing the characters in the supermarkets?

(a) OCR device only
(b) OMR device only
(c) MICR device
(d) Both OCR and OMR devices

76. RISC processors are always preferred to CISC processors because of:

1. Compact size
2. Small instruction set
3. Executing multiple clock cycles

Which of the above are correct?

(a) 1 and 2 only
(b) 2 and 3 only
(c) 1 and 3 only
(d) 1, 2 and 3

77. Which of the following algorithms are stable?

1. Bubble sort
2. Quick sort
3. Merge sort
4. Insertion sort

Select the correct answer using the code given below:

(a) 1, 2 and 3
(b) 1, 2 and 4
(c) 1, 3 and 4
(d) 2, 3 and 4

78. Consider the following statements:

1. Steps for developing software program remain same irrespective of the Operating System.
2. If the program is using exp() function, then the object code of this function should be brought from the 'math' library of the system and linked to the main program.

Which of the statments given above is/are correct?

(a) 1 only
(b) 2 only
(c) Both 1 and 2
(d) Neither 1 nor 2

79. What is the equivalent hexadecimal number of the octal number 6251?

(a) 9CA
(b) AC9
(c) DB9
(d) CA9

80. Which of the following are Firewall Related Terminology?

1. Gateway
2. Proxy server
3. Screening routers

Select the correct answer using the code given below:

(a) 1 and 2 only
(b) 2 and 3 only
(c) 1 and 3 only
(d) 1, 2 and 3

STATISTICS
Paper- I 2022

Time Allowed : Three Hours | *Maximum Marks: 200*

INSTRUCTIONS

1. IMMEDIATELY AFTER THE COMMENCEMENT OF THE EXAMINATION, YOU SHOULD CHECK THAT THIS TEST BOOKLET DOES NOT HAVE ANY UNPRINTED OR TORN OR MISSING PAGES OR ITEMS, ETC. IF SO, GET IT REPLACED BY A COMPLETE TEST BOOKLET.
2. Please note that it is the candidate's responsibility to encode and fill in the Roll Number and Test Booklet Series Code A, B, C or D carefully and without any omission or discrepancy at the appropriate places in the OMR Answer Sheet. Any omission/discrepancy will render the Answer Sheet liable for rejection.
3. You have to enter your Roll Number on the Test Booklet in the Box provided alongside. DO NOT write anything else on the Test Booklet.
4. This Test Booklet contains 80 items (questions). Each item comprises four responses (answers). You will select the response which you want to mark on the Answer Sheet. In case you feel that there is more than one correct response, mark the response which you consider the best. In any case, choose ONLY ONE response for each item.
5. You have to mark all your responses ONLY on the separate Answer Sheet provided. See directions in the Answer Sheet.
6. All items carry equal marks.
7. Before you proceed to mark in the Answer Sheet the response to various items in the Test Booklet, you have to fill in some particulars in the Answer Sheet as per instructions sent to you with your Admission Certificate.
8. After you have completed filling in all your responses on the Answer Sheet and the examination has concluded, you should hand over to the Invigilator ***only the Answer Sheet***. You are permitted to take away with you the Test Booklet.
9. Sheets for rough work are appended in the Test Booklet at the end.
10. Penalty for wrong answers :

THERE WILL BE PENALTY FOR WRONG ANSWERS MARKED BY A CANDIDATE IN THE OBJECTIVE TYPE QUESTION PAPERS.

(i) There are four alternatives for the answer to every question. For each question for which a wrong answer has been given by the candidate, one-third of the marks assigned to that question will be deducted as penalty. ·

(ii) If a candidate gives more than one answer, it will be treated as a wrong answer even if one of the given answers happens to be correct and there will be same penalty as above to that question.

(iii) If a question is left blank, i.e., no answer is given by the candidate, there will be no penalty for that question.

DO NOT OPEN THIS TEST BOOKLET UNTIL YOU ARE TOLD TO DO SO

1. Suppose X_1, X_2, X_3 and X_4 are independent where X_1, X_2, X_3 has a Bernoulli $\left(\frac{1}{3}\right)$ distribution and X_4 follows $B\left(3, \frac{2}{3}\right)$. Then the distribution of $X_1 + X_2 + X_3 + 3 - X_4$ is:

(a) $B\left(5, \frac{1}{3}\right)$ (b) $B\left(6, \frac{1}{3}\right)$

(c) $B\left(6, \frac{2}{3}\right)$ (d) not a Binomial

2. A large number of candidates from three States A, B, C appear at a selection test. Suppose 10 candidates are selectionindependently out which X, Y, Z are respectively from A, B and C. If a candidate from State A had twice as much chance as one from B or from C to be selected, then cov(Y, Z) equals:

(a) $-\frac{5}{4}$ (b) $-\frac{5}{8}$

(c) 0 (d) $\frac{15}{8}$

3. Suppose $\{X_n : n \geq 1\}$ is a sequence of independent random variables, and for each $n \geq 1$, X takes the values $\frac{-3n}{2}, -n, \frac{n}{2}$, and n with probability $\frac{1}{4}$ each. Then the sequence $Y_n = \frac{1}{n^{\alpha}}\sum_{i=1}^{n}\frac{X_i}{i}$ converges in probability to 0 if and only if:

(a) $\alpha > 1$ (b) $\alpha = 1$

(c) $\alpha \geq 1$ (d) $\alpha > \frac{3}{2}$

4. A certain city receives three newspapers A, B and C. Newspaper A has 50% of the readers in that city, newspaper B has 30% of the readers and newspaper C has the remaining 20% of the readers. Assuming that no one in that city reads more than one paper, the probability that among 6 randomly chosen readers in that city, 3 will read newspaper A, 2 will read newspaper Band 1 (one) will read newspaper C, is:

(a) $\frac{1}{4}$ (b) $\frac{1}{8}$

(c) $\frac{27}{100}$ (d) $\frac{27}{200}$

5. If X is a Poisson random variable with $P(X = 1) = P(X = 2)$, then what is. V(X) equal to?

(a) 0 (b) 1

(c) 2 (d) 3

6. If X has binomial distribution with n = 3 and $P = \frac{1}{3}$ then what is the value of $E((X-1)^3)$?

(a) $\frac{1}{9}$ (b) $\frac{2}{9}$

(c) $\frac{4}{9}$ (d) $\frac{5}{9}$

7. The random variables X andY have the joint probability mass function given by :

$$p(x, y) = \begin{cases} \frac{x+y}{21} \text{ for } x = 1, 2, 3; & y = 1, 2 \\ 0 & \text{otherwise} \end{cases}$$

What is $P(X - Y \le 0{\cdot}5)$ equal to?

(a) $\frac{2}{3}$ (b) $\frac{4}{7}$

(c) $\frac{3}{7}$ (d) $\frac{17}{21}$

8. A group of 2n boys and 2n girls is divided at random into two equal batches. What is the probability that each batch will be equally divided into boys and girls ?

(a) $\frac{C(2n, n)}{C(4n, n)}$ (b) $\frac{\{C(2n, n)\}^2}{C(4n, n)}$

(c) $\frac{\{C(2n, n)\}^2}{\{C(4n, n)\}^2}$ (d) $\frac{C(2n, n)}{\{C(4n, n)\}^2}$

Consider the following for the next two (02) items that follow:

Let the joint density function of X and Y be

$$f(x, y) = \begin{cases} \frac{y}{(1+x)^4} \exp, & x \ge 0, y \ge 0 \\ 0, & \text{otherwise} \end{cases}$$

9. What is the value of E[Y I X= 10] ?

(a) 22 (b) 25

(c) 30 (d) 32

10. What is the equation of regression ofY on X?

(a) $Y = 2X + 2$ (b) $Y = 3X + 5$

(c) $y = (X/2) + 5$ (d) $Y = 3X + (5/2)$

11. Consider the following bivariate data :

X	1	2	3	4	5
Y	4	1	0	1	4

What is the correlation coefficient ?

(a) 0 (b) $-\frac{1}{2}$

(c) −1 (d) 1

12. Let $X_1, X_2, \ldots X_5$ be a random sample of size 5 from a population having standard normal distnbutwn. Let $\bar{X} = \frac{\sum_{i=1}^{5} X_i}{5}$ and $T = \sum_{i=1}^{5}(x_i - \bar{X})^2$. What is $E(T^2 + \bar{X})^2$ equal to?

(a) 4·0 (b) 4·2

(c) 24·2 (d) 25·2

13. If (X, Y) ~ BVN(10, 20, 100, 100, 0·5), then what is the value of $E(e^{X+Y})$?

(a) e^{150} (b) e^{180}

(c) e^{100} (d) e^{220}

14. It is given that n = 4, $\Sigma x^2 = 164$, $\Sigma y^2 = 572$, $\Sigma x = 24$, $\Sigma y = 44$ and $\Sigma xy = 300$. What is the estimated value of X when Y = 10?

(a) 2·59 (b) 3·59

(c) 4·59 (d) 5·59

15. Let (X_1, X_2) follow bivariate normal with $E(X_1) = E(X_2) = 0$, $V(X_1) = V(X_2) = 1$ and $Corr(X_1, X_2) = \rho$. What is the value of $E(X_1^2, X_2^2)$?

(a) $\rho^2 + \frac{1}{2}$ (b) $\frac{\rho^2}{2} + \frac{2}{3}$

(c) $3\rho^2 + 4$ (d) $2\rho^2 + 1$

16. For a trivariate distribution, it is given that $r_{12} = r_{13} = r_{23} = r$ where r_{ij} is the correlation coefficient between X_i and X_j for all $i \neq j$. If $R_{1.23}^2$ is the multiple correlation coefficient, then the expression for $(1 - R_{1.23}^2)$is:

(a) $(1 - r)(1 - 2r)(1 + r)^{-1}$ (b) $(1 - r)(1 + 2r)(1 + r)^{-1}$

(c) $(1 - r)(1 - 2r)(1 - r)^{-1}$ (d) $(1 - r)(1 + 2r)(1 - r)^{-1}$

17. If X is normally distributed with mean μ and variance 1 and Y^2 is independently distributed as central χ^2 with f degrees of freedom, then what is the value of $\int_{-\infty}^{\infty}\int_{0}^{\infty} y^{f-2} e^{\frac{-x^2+y^2)}{2}+\mu x} dy^2\, dx$?

(a) $\Gamma\left(\frac{f}{2}\right) 2^{\frac{\mu+1}{2}}$ (b) $\Gamma\left(\frac{f}{2}\right) 2^{\frac{f+1}{2}} \sqrt{\pi}\, e^{\frac{\mu^2}{2}}$

(c) $\sqrt{\pi}\, e^{\frac{\mu^2}{2}}$ (d) $\Gamma\left(\frac{f}{2}\right) 2^{\frac{f+1}{2}} \sqrt{\pi}\, e^{-\frac{\mu^2}{2}}$

18. Let (X, Y) – BVN(0, 0, 1, 1, r).

Consider the following statements :

1. (X + Y) and (X − Y) are independently distributed.
2. (X + Y) follows normal distribution with mean 0 and variance 2 (1 + ρ).
3. (X − Y) follows normal distribution with mean 0 and variance 2 (1 − ρ).

Which of the statements given above is/are correct?

(a) 1 only (b) 1 and 2 only

(c) 2 and 3 only (d) 1, 2 and 3

19. If r is a sample correlation coefficient in a random sample of size n from a bivariate normal population with $\rho = 0$, then the distribution of r^2 is:

(a) $\beta(1, n-2)$ (b) $\beta(112, (n-2)/2)$

(c) $\beta(2, n-3)$ (d) $\beta(113, (n-3)/3)$

20. If $R_{1.23} = 0$, then which of the following statements is/are correct?

1. X_1 is uncorrelated with X_2 and X_3.
2. X_2 is uncorrelated with X_3.
3. $(1 - r_{12}^2)(1 - r_{13.2}^2) = 1$.

Select the correct answer using the code given below:

(a) 1 only (b) 1 and 2

(c) 1 and 3 (d) 2 and 3

21. Suppose f is a three time differentiable function on [0, 2). The integral $\int_0^2 f(x)\,dx$ computed using trapezoidal rule partitioning [0, 2] into 10 equal sub-intervals. Then the error is given by:

(a) $-\frac{2}{25} f'(t)$ for some $t \in [0. 2]$ (b) $-\frac{1}{150} f''(t)$ for some $t \in [0. 2]$

(c) $-\frac{1}{300} f''(t)$ for some $t \in [0. 2]$ (d) $-\frac{1}{150} f'''(t)$ for some $t \in [0. 2]$

22. Euler method is ·used to solve the initial value problem $\frac{dy}{dt} = \sin y,\ y(0) = 1,\ t \in (0, 7)$. Then the local truncation error is always bounded by:

(a) $\frac{h}{2}$ (b) $\frac{h^2}{2}$

(c) $\frac{h^2}{4}$ (d) $\frac{3h}{2}$

23. What is $\left(\frac{\Delta^2}{E}\right) e^X \times \frac{Ee^X}{\Delta^2 e^X}$ equal to?

(with interval of differencing equal to h)

(a) 0 (b) e^{-x}

(c) e^{2x} (d) e^x

24. Consider the following data:

x	0	1.0	1.5	2.0
f(x)	1.1	2.4	5.7	8.1

Let $I = \int_0^2 f(x)\,dx$. Application of combination of Trapezoidal rule on [0, 1] and Simpson's one-third rule on [1, 2] gives the value of I as:

(a) 7·30 (b) 5·55

(c) 3·65 (d) 3·33

25. What is $\frac{1}{E-8}(x^2 2^x)$ equal to?

(take interval of differencing to be unity)

(a) $-\frac{2^x}{54}(9x^2 - 6x - 1)$ (b) $\frac{2^x}{54}(9x^2 - 6x - 1)$

(c) $-\frac{2^x}{54}(9x^2 + 6x + 5)$ (d) $\frac{2^x}{54}(9x^2 + 6x + 5)$

26. Bessel's interpolation formula is most appropriate when p = (x – x0)/h :

(a) lies between – 0·25 and + 0·25 (b) lies between 0·25 and 0·75

(c) lies between 0·75 and 1 (d) is greater than 1

27. Applying Lagrange's formula inversely, the value of x from the data $y_1 = 4$, $y_3 = 12$, $y_4 = 19$ and $y_x = 7$ is approximately:

(a) 1·86 (b) 1·98

(c) 2·16 (d) 2·36

28. Central finite difference approximation for second order derivative of f(x) at x_i with equally spaced points of step length h is:

(a) $\frac{f_{i-1} + f_i + f_{i+1}}{h^2}$ (b) $\frac{f_{i+1} - f_{i-1}}{2h^2}$

(c) $\frac{f_{i-1} - 2f + f_{i+1}}{h^2}$ (d) $\frac{f_i - 2f_{i-1} + f_{i-2}}{h^2}$

29. If $f(x) = \frac{1}{x}$, then the value of $f(x_1, x_2, \ldots\ldots, x_n)$ is equal to:

(a) $(-1)^n \frac{1}{x_1 x_2 \ldots\ldots x_n}$ (b) $(-1)^{n-1} \frac{1}{x_1 x_2 \ldots\ldots x_n}$

(c) $\frac{n}{x_1 x_2 \ldots\ldots x_n}$ (d) $\frac{1}{x_1 x_2 \ldots\ldots x_n}$

30. What is $E(\Delta^n e^{ax+b})$ equal to?

(Step length h = 1)

(a) $e^{ax+b}(e^a - 1)^{n+1}$ (b) $e^{ax+b} e^a(e^a - 1)^n$

(c) $e^{ax+b}(e^a - 1)^n$ (d) $e^{ax+b} e^a(e^a - 1)^{n+1}$

31. Which one of the following registers keeps 35. The 2's complement representation of the track of the next instruction to be executed ?
    (a) Program counter
    (b) Instruction register
    (c) Accumulator RAM
    (d) Memory Address Register
32. The highest digit possible in any number system is:
    (a) equal to base of the number system
    (b) equal to one less tpan the base of the number system
    (c) equal · to one more than the radix of number system
    (d) equal to two less than the base of the number system
33. Consider the following conditions :
    1. Mutual exclusion
    2. Hold and wait
    3. No pre-emption

    Under which of the above conditions deadlock situation may arise?
    (a) 1 and 2 only
    (b) 1 and 3 only
    (c) 2 and 3 only
    (d) 1, 2 and 3
34. Which one of the · following refers to associative memory?
    (a) The address of the data is generated by the CPU
    (b) The address of the data is supplied by the users
    (c) The data are accessed sequentially
    (d) There is no need for an address because the data is used as an address
35. The 2's complement representation of the number - 59 in an 8-bit word size computer system is:
    (a) 11000100
    (b) 11000101
    (c) 00111011
    (d) 11011010
36. Which of the following are raster image formats?
    1. JPEG
    2. GIF
    3. PNG
    4. SVG

    Select the correct answer using the code given below:
    (a) 1, 2 and 3
    (b) 1, 2 and 4
    (c) 1, 3 and 4
    (d) 2, 3 and 4
37. Data Encryption Standard (DES) is:
    (a) Asymmetric-key cryptographic algorithm
    (b) Symmetric-key cryptographic algorithm
    (c) High speed data transmission algorithm
    (d) Low speed data transmission algorithm

38. Which one of the following is a dedicated phone line that connects a computer to internet?
    (a) Dial-up access
    (b) Digital subscriber line
    (c) Integrated Services Digital Network
    (d) Leased line

39. In octal number system, the hexadecimal number (32FC. 75) is equivalent to:
    (a) $(31375.452)_8$ (b) $(73256.732)_8$
    (c) $(31374.352)_8$ (d) $(26753.175)_8$

40. Consider the following statements about Batch processing operating systems :
    1. All jobs are processed as per their priority.
    2. The debugging of a program at execution time is not possible in this system.
    3. After the execution of one job, next job is fetched automatically.

    Which of the above statements are correct ?
    (a) 1 and 2 only (b) 2 and 3 only
    (c) 1 and 3 only (d) 1, 2 and 3

41. A sequence of independent and identically distributed (i.i.d.) random variables $\{X_k\}$ obeys the strong law of large numbers if:
    (a) $Var(X_k) < \infty$
    (b) $Var(X_k) = \infty$
    (c) $E(X_k) < \infty$
    (d) Information is insufficient to conclude

42. An urn contains 3 white and 4 black balls. A ball is drawn at random. Its colour is noted and returned to the urn along with two additional balls of the same colour. If a ball is drawn ·again from the urn, then what is the probability that the ball drawn is white ?
    (a) $2\overline{X}$ (b) $\frac{4}{7}$
    (c) $\frac{1}{3}$ (d) $\frac{5}{9}$

43. Let X be a continuous variable with density $f(x) = \frac{1}{2}e^{-|x|}; -\infty < x < \infty$. What is $P(-1 < X < 2)$ equal to?
    (a) $\frac{1}{2}(2 - e^{-1} - e^{-2})$ (b) $\frac{1}{2}(2 + e^{-1} - e^{-2})$
    (c) $\frac{1}{2}(2 - e^{-1} + e^{-2})$ (d) $\frac{1}{2}(2 + e^{-1} + e^{-2})$

44. A box contains two coins, one of which is "fair" and the other is "two. headed". One .coin is chosen at random and tossed twice. If two heads appear, then what is the probability that the chosen coin was "two headed" ?

(a) $\frac{1}{2}$ (b) $\frac{1}{3}$

(c) $\frac{1}{4}$ (d) $\frac{4}{5}$

45. What is the limiting distribution function of the sequence of distribution functions

$$F_n(x) = \begin{cases} 0, & \text{for} \quad x < -n \\ \frac{x+n}{2n}, & \text{for} \quad -n \le x \le n? \\ 1, & \text{for} \quad x > n \end{cases}$$

(a) Distribution function of a random variable degenerating at 0

(b) Distribution function of a random variable degenerating at 1

(c) Distribution function of a U(0, 1) random variable

(d) The limiting distribution function does not exist

46. The probability that in a sequence of Bernoulli trials, the pattern SFSF appears infinitely often, is equal to:

(a) 1 (b) $\frac{1}{2}$

(c) $\frac{1}{4}$ (d) 0

47. The pdf of a random variable X is given by

$$\begin{cases} \frac{kx^3}{(1+2x)^6}, & x > 0 \\ 0, & \text{otherwise} \end{cases}.$$

What is the value of k ?

(a) 80 (b) 160

(c) 240 (d) 320

48. A beta distribution of first type with parameters m and n has mean $\frac{1}{3}$ and variance $\frac{2}{63}$. What are the values of m and n respectively?

(a) 2, 4 (b) 4, 2

(c) 2, 2 (d) 3, 6

49. Let (X, Y) be jointly distributed with pdf $f(x, y) = 2, 0 < x < Y < 1$. The marginal pdf of Y is:

(a) $f(y) = 1 - y, 0 < y < 1$ (b) $f(y) = 2y, 0 < y < 1$

(c) $f(y) = 1 - 2y, 0 < y < 1$ (d) $f(y) = 2 - 3y, 0 < y < 1$

50. The distribution function of a random variable X is given by :

$$F(x) = \begin{cases} 0; & x < 0 \\ \frac{x}{5}; & 0 \le x \le 5 \\ 1; & x > 5 \end{cases}$$

What is $P[1{\cdot}5 \le X \le 2{\cdot}5]$ equal to?

(a) 1 (b) $\frac{3}{5}$

(c) $\frac{2}{5}$ (d) $\frac{1}{5}$

52. For a set of n observations $x_1, x_2, \ldots x_n$, consider the following ratios:

1. If $R = \frac{\sum_{i=1}^{n} |x_i - M|}{\sum_{i=1}^{n} |x_i - \bar{x}|}$, where M (median) $\neq \bar{X}$ (mean), then $R < 1$.

2. If $R = \frac{\sum_{i=1}^{n} (x_i - A)^2}{\sum_{i=1}^{n} (x_i - \bar{X})^2}$, where A (assumed mean) $\neq \bar{X}$ (mean), then $R > l$.

3. If $R = \frac{\sum_{i=1}^{n} (x_i - M)^2}{\sum_{i=1}^{n} (x_i - \bar{X})^2}$, where M (median) $\neq \bar{X}$ (mean), then $R > 1$.

Which of the statements given above are correct?

(a) 1 and 2 only (b) 2 and 3 only

(c) 1 and 3 only (d) 1, 2 and 3

52. Let X_i be i.i.d. random variables where i = 1, 2, 3, ... n with c.d.f. F(x) and p.d.f. f(x). Then the p.d.f. where gz(x), where $Z = \min \{X_1, X_2, \ldots X_n\}$ is :

(a) $n[F(x)]^{n-1} f(x)$ (b) $n[1 - F(x)]^{n-1} f(x)$

(c) $[1 - F(x)]^{n-1} f(x)$ (d) $[F(x)]^{n-1} f(x)$

53. Which one of the following non-parametric tests is analogou.s to a Chi-square test of goodness of fit?

(a) Mann-Whitney test (b) Kolmogorov-Smirnov test

(c) Wilcoxon test (d) Median test

54. If it is desired to test $H_0 : \sigma^2 = \sigma_0^2$; in a normal distribution $N(0, \sigma^2)$, then the appropriate test would be :

(a) t-test (b) Chi-square test

(c) F-test (d) Normal test

55. Let $\beta_n = E[|x|^n]$ be the nth absolute moment about origin. Consider the following statements for non-degenerate random values:

1. $\beta_k^{\frac{1}{k}} > \beta_{k+1}^{\frac{1}{k+1}}$ for $k = 1, 2, 3, ...$

2. $\beta_1 \le \beta_2^{\frac{1}{2}} \le \beta_3^{\frac{1}{3}} \le ... \le \beta_n^{\frac{1}{n}}$

Which of the statements given above is/are correct?

(a) 1 only (b) 2 only

(c) Both 1 and 2 (d) Neither 1 nor 2

56. Consider the following data .in respect of COVID-19. Among 1482 persons in a locality exposed to COVID-19, 368 persons were attacked with the virus. Among 1482 persons, 343 persons were vaccinated and among them only 35 persons were attacked with the virus. Which of the following statements is/are correct?

1. Vaccination and attack are positively associated.
2. Vaccination may be a preventive measure.

Select the correct answer using the code given below:

(a) 1 only· (b) 2 only

(c) Both 1 and 2 (d) Neither 1 nor 2

57. Which one of the following is correct regarding non-parametric methods?

(a) Sign test uses rank only

(b) Wilcoxon test uses both sign and rank

(c) Mann-Whitney test is a one-sample test

(d) Kruskal-Wallis test is a two-sample test

58. Suppose a person has 10 black, 8 red, 5 green, 12 orange and 15 blue balls. The Chi-square value obtained after testing null hypothesis Consider the following expressions : that the colours of the ball occur with equal frequency is:

(a) 6·9 (b) 5·8

(c) 5·6 (d) 5·4

59. The 95% Confidence Interval for population mean, if a random sample of size 100 is taken from $N(\mu, 25)$ and sample mean is 5·96 is $(Z = 1{\cdot}96)$

(a) [5·4 7, 6·45] (b) [4·98, 6·94]

(c) [5, 6] (d) [4·1, 6·99]

60. If X has uniform distribution in [0, 1], then pdf of $(-2 \log X)$ is :

(a) Uniform (b) $\beta\left(\frac{1}{2}, \frac{1}{2}\right)$

(c) $\chi^2_{n/2}$ degrees of freedom (d) Exponential with $\theta = 1/2$

61. Consider the following expressions:

    1. $E^2x^2 = (Ex)^2$
    2. $E^n = (1 + \Delta)^n$
    3. $E^nE^m f(x) = \Delta^{n+m} f(x)$

    where n, m are positive integers.

    How many of the above expressions are correct?

    (a) Only one expression (b) Only two expressions
    (c) Only three expressions (d) All four expressions

62. It is given that f(0) = 5, f(1) = 1, f(2) = 9, f(3) = 25, f(4) = 55. What is the approximate value of f(5) obtained by using Newton-Gregory forward interpolation?

    (a) 108 (b) 110
    (c) 112 (d) 115

63. If $y_{10} = 3$, $y_{11} = 6$, $y_{12} = 11$, $y_{13} = 18$ and $y_{14} = 27$, then what is y_4 equal to?

    (a) 3 (b) 4
    (c) 9 (d) 27

64. If Δ and ∇ are the forward and the backward difference operators respectively, then what is $\Delta - \nabla$ equal to ?

    (a) $-\Delta\nabla$ (b) $\Delta\nabla$
    (c) $\Delta + \nabla$ (d) $\frac{\Delta}{\nabla}$

65. Consider the data f(1) = 12, f(2) = 40, f(3) = 90, f(4) = 168, f(5) = 280, and f(6) = 432. The polynomial which conforms to the data, is:

    (a) $f(x) = x^3 + 5x^2 + 5x + 1$ (b) $f(x) = x^3 + 4x^2 + 6x + 1$
    (c) $f(x) = x^3 + 5x^2 + 4x + 2$ (d) $f(x) = x^3 + 5x^2 + 6x$

66. If $u = \Delta[f(x-1)/\Delta g(x-1)]$, $v = \nabla[f(x)\,\Delta g(x)]$ and $w = \Delta[f(x-1)\,\nabla g(x)]$ with difference interval equal to 1, then which one of the following is correct?

    (a) Only u = v (b) Only v = w
    (c) Only u = w (d) u = v = w

67. Consider the following expressions:

    1. $\mu = \sqrt{1 + \frac{\delta^2}{4}}$
    2. $\Delta = \frac{\delta^2}{2} + \delta\sqrt{1 + \frac{\delta^2}{4}}$
    3. $\nabla = -\frac{\delta^2}{2} + \sqrt{1 + \frac{\delta^2}{4}}$

How many expressions given above are correct?

(a) Only one expression (b) Only two expressions

(c) All three expressions (d) No expression

68. For the data f(20) = 512, f(30) = 439, f(40) = 346 and f(50) = 243, consider the following statements:

1. The function f(x) can be approximated by a polynomial of degree 2.
2. The value of f(25) can be obtained as 477 approximately by using Newton-Gregory forward difference interpolation formula.

Which of the statements given above is/are correct?

(a) 1 only (b) 2 only

(c) Both 1 and 2 (d) Neither 1 nor 2

69. What is $\Delta^2\left(\frac{a^{4x}}{(a^2-1)^2}\right)$ equal to ?

[with the interval of differencing as 1]

(a) $(a^2+1)^4 a^{4x}$ (b) $\frac{a^{4x}}{(a^2+1)^2}$

(c) $(a^2+1)^2 a^{4x}$ (d) $\frac{a^{4x}}{(a^2+1)^4}$

70. What is $\Delta E^2 ((3x-3)^{(-2)})$ at x = 1 equal to?

[with the interval of differencing as 1]

(a) $-\frac{1}{30}$ (b) $\frac{1}{30}$

(c) $-\frac{1}{270}$ (d) $\frac{1}{270}$

71. On which type of ROM can data be written only once?

(a) PROM (b) EPROM

(c) EEPROM (d) EROM

72. What is the correct sequence of a cycle of a process in execution ?

(a) Ready → Waiting → Executing → Terminated → Blocked

(b) Ready → Waiting → Executing → Blocked

(c) Waiting → Ready → Executing → Blocked

(d) Waiting → Ready → Executing → Terminated

73. By using which of the following units is data processing performed by a computer system?

1. Monitor
2. Memory unit
3. CPU

Select the correct answer using the code given below:

(a) 1 and 2 only (b) 2 and 3 only

(c) 1 and 3 only (d) 1, 2 and 3

74. Consider the following statements in respect of machine cycle:

 1. It consists of four phases, namely fetching, decoding, executing and storing.
 2. It is a cycle in which machine language instructions are executed.
 3. If a program consists of 6 machine language instructions, 6 sellarate machine cycles would be executed to run the program.

 Which of the statements given above are correct?

 (a) 1 and 2 only (b) 2 and 3 only

 (c) 1 and 3 only (d) 1, 2 and 3

75. Which one of the following provides application independent security and privacy over the internet ?

 (a) IP security protocol (b) Secure socket layer

 (c) Internet protocol (d) Transmission control protocol

76. Which of the following is/are non-volatile?

 1. DRAM
 2. SRAM
 3. EPROM

 Select the correct answer using the code given below:

 (a) 1 only (b) 3 only

 (c) 1 and 3 (d) 2 and 3

77. Consider the following network topologies:

 1. Bu's
 2. Star
 3. Ring
 4. Mesh

 In which of the above does the failure of one computer not affect the other computer in the network?

 (a) 1, 2 and 4 (b) 1, 3 and 4

 (c) 3 and 4 only (d) 1 and 2 only

78. Consider the following terms :

 1. Shared region
 2. Cache memory
 3. Message passing
 4. Shared memory

Which of the above are related to interprocess communication?

(a) 1 and 2 only (b) 1, 2 and 3

(c) 2 and 4 only (d) 3 and 4 only

79. Which of the following are the goals of an operating system?

1. Efficient use of CPU
2. Efficient use of memory
3. Efficient use of I/0 devices

Select the correct answer using the code given below:

(a) 1 and 2 only (b) 2 and 3 only

(c) 1 and 3 only (d) 1, 2 and 3

80. Which of the following properties of transaction mechanism in a database system are correct ?

1. Atomicity
2. Durability
3. Isolation
4. Security

Select the correct answer using the code given below:

(a) 1, 2 and 3 (b) 1, 2 and 4

(c) 1,3 and 4 (d) 2, 3 and 4

GENERAL STATISTICS
Paper I 2021

Time Allowed : Two Hours | *Maximum Marks: 200*

INSTRUCTIONS

1. IMMEDIATELY AFTER THE COMMENCEMENT OF THE EXAMINATION, YO SHOULD CHECK THAT THIS TEST BOOKLET *DOES NOT* HAVE ANY UNPRINTED OR TORN OR MISSING PAGES OR ITEMS, ETC. IF SO, GET IT REPLACE BY A COMPLETE TEST BOOKLET.
2. **Please note that it is the candidate'sresponsibility to encode and fill in the Roll Number and Test Booklet Series A, B, C or D carefully and without any omission or discrepancy at the appropriate places in the OMR Answer Sheet. Any omission/discrepancy will render the Answer sheet liable for rejection.**
3. You have to enter your Roll Number on the Test Booklet in the Box provided alongside. *DO NOT* write *anything else* on the Test Booklet.
4. This Test Booklet contains **80** items (questions). Each item comprises four responses (answers). You will select the response which you want to mark on the Answer Sheet. In case you feel that there is more than one correct response, mark the response which you consider the best. In any case, choose *ONLY ONE* response for each item.
5. You have to mark all your responses *ONLY* on the separate Answer Sheet provided. See directions in the Answer Sheet.
6. All items carry equal marks.
7. Before you proceed to mark in the Answer Sheet the response to various in the Test Booklet, you have to fill in some particulars in the Answer Sheet as per intructions sent to you with your Admission Certificate.
8. After you have complited filling in all your responses on the Answer Sheet and the examination has concluded, you should hand over to the Invigilator *only the Answer Sheet*. You are permitted to take away with you the Test Booklet.
9. Sheets for rough work are appended in the Test Booklet at the end.
10. **Penalty for wrong answers:**

    THERE WILL BE PENALTY FOR WRONG ANSWERS MARKED BY A CANDIDATE IN THE OBJECTIVE TYPE QUSTION PAPERS.

    (i) There are four alternatives for the answer to every question. For each question for which a wrong answer has been given by the candidate, **one-third** of the marks assigned to that question will be deducted as penalty.

    (ii) If a candidate gives more than one answer, it will be treated as a **wrong answer** even if one of the given answers happens to be correct and there will be same penalty as above to that question.

    (iii) If a question is left blamk,i.e., no answer is given by the candidate, there will be **no penalty** for that question.

DO NOT OPEN THIS TEST BOOKLET UNTIL YOU ARE TOLD TO DO SO

Consider the following for the next three (03) itmes that follow:

Let the joint p.d.f. of X and Y be

$$f(x, y) = \begin{cases} 6(1 - x - y), & x > 0, y > 0, x + y < 1 \\ 0, & \text{otherwise.} \end{cases}$$

1. What is the value of E(XY)?

   (a) 10 (b) 20

   (c) 1/10 (d) 1/20

2. What is the value of Cov(X, Y)?

   (a) 1/40 (b) 1/80

   (c) – 1/40 (d) – 1/80

3. What is the eqation of line of regression of X and Y?

   (a) X = (3 – 5Y)/15 (b) X = (1 – Y)/3

   (c) X = (5 – 3Y)/15 (d) X = (1 – Y)/5

Consider the following for the next two (02) items that follow:

Let the joint density function of X and Y be

$$f(x, y) = \begin{cases} 8xy, & 0 < x < y < 1 \\ 0, & \text{otherwise.} \end{cases}$$

4. What is $E[Y | X = x]$ equal to?

   (a) $\frac{1}{5}\left(\frac{1-x^3}{1+x^2}\right)$ (b) $\frac{2}{5}\left(\frac{1+x^3}{1-x^2}\right)$

   (c) $\frac{2}{3}\left(\frac{1-x^3}{1+x^2}\right)$ (d) $\left(\frac{1+x^3}{1+x^2}\right)$

5. What is the value of $[Y^2 |_{X=0.5}]$?

   (a) 0.5 (b) 0.525

   (c) 0.6 (d) 0.625

6. How large a sample must be taken in order that the probability will be at least 0.95 and the sample mean will be within 0.5-neighbourhood of the population mean, provided population standard deviation is 1?

   (a) 80 (b) 79

   (c) 74 (d) Cannot be determined

7. Let $A_1, A_2, A_3, \ldots$ be a sequence of events and let E = lim sup An. If $\sum_{n=1}^{\infty} P(A_n) < \infty$, then P(E) is equal to

   (a) 1 (b) 1/2

   (c) 1/4 (d) 0

8. Consider the following statements in respect of characteristic function of a random variable:

1. It always exists.
2. It is uniformly continuous on R.
3. It is not independent of change of origin and scale.
4. If characteristic function of sum of two random variables is same as the product of their individual characteristic functions, then the variables are independent.

Which of the above statements are correct?

(a) 1, 2 and 3 only (b) 1, 2 and 4 only

(c) 1, 3 and 4 only (e) 2, 3 and 4 only

9. Whst is the value of

$$\lim_{n\to\infty}\sum_{j=n}^{4n}\binom{4n}{j}\left(\frac{1}{4}\right)^{j}\left(\frac{3}{4}\right)^{4n-j}?$$

(a) 0 (b) 1/4

(c) 1/2 (d) 3/4

10. For a sequence of Bernoulli trials, the fraction of successes f/n is a consistent estimator of the probability of success p. This follows from

(a) Central limit theorem (b) De Moivre-Laplace theorem

(c) Law of large numbers (d) Chebyshev's theorem

11. Consider a random sample of size 4 from a population having density function

$$f(x)=\begin{cases}2x, & 0<x<1\\ 0, & \text{otherwise}\end{cases}$$

If the four ordered observations are $x_1 < x_2 < x_3 < x_4$, then the $P\left[\frac{1}{2} < x_3\right]$ is

(a) $\frac{15}{16}$ (b) $\frac{243}{256}$

(c) $\frac{1}{2}$ (d) $\frac{247}{256}$

12. Consider the following conditions in respect of attributes A and B:

1. $(AB) \le (A)$
2. $(AB) \le (B)$
3. $(AB) \ge (A) + (B) - N$

Which of the above conditions are required for the consistency of data on the two attributes A and B?

(a) 1 and 2 only

(b) 2 and 3 only

(c) 1 and 3 only

(d) 1, 2 and 3

13. Consider the following statements:
    1. Mean deviation is minimum when the deviations are taken from the median.
    2. If the units of measurements of variables of two series are not the same, their variabilitie can be compared by standard deviations.
    3. A series with smaller coefficient of variation is more consistent.

    When of the above statement is/are correct

    (a) 1 and 2 only (b) 2 and 3 only
    (c) 1 and 3 only (d) 3 only

14. Consider the following statements:
    1. (X, Y) possesses a bivariate normal distribution iff every linear combination of X and Y is a normal variate.
    2. If the marginal of X and Y are normal, then it always implies that (X, Y) is bivariate normal.

    Which of the above statements is/are correct?

    (a) 1 only (b) 2 only
    (c) Both 1 and 2 (d) Neither 1 nor 2

15. If (X, Y) ~ BVN (0, 1, 1, ρ) then what is the value of E{max(X, Y)]?

    (a) $\sqrt{\pi\rho}$ (b) $\sqrt{\frac{\rho}{\pi}}$
    (c) $\sqrt{\pi(1-\rho)}$ (d) $\sqrt{\frac{1-\rho}{\pi}}$

16. Let random variales X and Y have joint p.d.f $f(x, y) = \frac{1}{3}; 0 \le x \le 1, 0 \le y \le 2$. What is the value of E(XY)?

    (a) 2/3 (b) 5/3
    (c) 2/9 (d) 5/9

17. If x is a standard normal variate, then the third degree orthogonal polynomial is

    (a) $x^3 + x^2 - 1$ (b) $x^3 + 3x + 4$
    (c) $x^3 - 3x$ (d) $x^3 + x^2 - 6$

Consider the following for the next three (03) items that follow:

Let (X, Y) follows Bivariate Normal distribution with joint p.d.f.

$$f(x, y) = k\exp\left[-\frac{8}{27}\{(x-7)^2 - 2(x-7)(y+5) + 4(y+5)^2\}, (xy) \in \mathbb{R}^2\right]$$

18. What are the values of V(X) and V(Y) respectively?

    (a) 9/4 and 9/16 (b) 9/16 and 9/32
    (c) 9/4 and 9/32 (d) 9/16 and 9/16

19. What is the approximate value of k?

    (a) $0.31/\pi$ (b) $0.41/\pi$
    (c) $0.51/\pi$ (d) $0.61/\pi$

20. What is the line of regression of Y on X?

(a) $Y = 6.75X - 0.25$ (b) $Y = 0.25X - 6.75$

(c) $Y = 6.25X + 0.45$ (d) $Y = 6.25X + 0.45$

21. If $\{x_n : n \geq 1\}$ is a sequence of independent and identically distributed random variables with mean $\frac{1}{2}$, then the probability of the event $\left\{|X_n| > \frac{n}{2} \text{ for infinitely many } n\right\}$

(a) is equal to 0. (b) is equal to $\frac{1}{2}$.

(c) lies strictly between $\frac{1}{2}$ and 1. (d) is equal to 1.

22. Suppose n is a natural number and the random variable Y is distributed on $\{-n, -n+1, ..., -1, 0, 1, 2, 3, ..., n-1, n\}$ with the property that for every

$k \in \{1, 2, 3, ..., n\}$,

$\text{Prob}(Y = k) = 2\,\text{Prob}(Y = -k) > 0$.

Then for $y \in \{1, 4, 9, ..., n^2\}$, $E(Y | Y^2 = y)$ is equal to

(a) $-\sqrt{\frac{y}{3}}$ (b) $-\sqrt{\frac{y}{2}}$

(c) $\frac{\sqrt{y}}{3}$ (d) $\frac{y}{2}$

23. Suppose a random variable X has mean 12 and the bound given by Chebychev's inequaltiy for the probability $\text{Prob}(2 < X < 22) \geq \frac{3}{4}$. Then $E(X^2)$ is equal to

(a) 17 (b) 37

(c) 112 (d) 169

24. To find out the prevalence of a vrirus in a city's population of size 1,00,000, a blood test was carried out on 200 randomly selected citizens. If the test retruned 8 positive results, the distribution of number of affected persons in a random sample of size 500 from the population can approximately be taken as

(a) Poisson (40) (b) Poisson (20)

(c) Poisson (8) (d) Poisson (16/5)

25. Suppose $(X_1, X_2, ..., X_n)$ are independent and indetically distributed random variables with finite second moment and for some $x \in \mathbb{R}$, Prob $(X_1 + X_2 ... + X_n \in x\sqrt{n})$ converges to $\Phi(2)$. If thee variance of the common distribution of $X_1, X_2, ...$ is 4, then Prob $(X_1 + X_2 ... + X_n \leq \frac{1}{x}\sqrt{n})$

(a) does not converge (b) converges to 0

(c) converges to Φ (1/2) (d) converges to Φ (1/8)

26. If $\{X_n : n \geq 1|$ is a sequence of independent and indentically distributed random variables with

$E(X_1) = 1$, $E(X_1^4) < \infty$ and $\frac{X_1^2 + X_2^2 + X_3^2 + ... + X_n^2 - 5n}{\sqrt{12n}} \xrightarrow{d} N(0, 1)$ then $V(X_1)$ equals

(a) 4 (b) 5

(c) $\sqrt{12}$ (d) 12

27. Let X have a continuous distribution function F. Consider the following statements:

Statement-1: Y = – log F(X) is exponentially distributed.

Statement-2: F(X) is uniformly distributed in [0, 1].

Which one of the following is correct in respect of the above statements?

(a) Both Statement-1 and Statement-2 are true and Statement-2 is the corret explanation for Statement-1.

(b) Both Statement-1 and Statement-2 are true, but Statement-2 is not the correct explanation for Statement-1.

(c) Statement-1 is true, but Statement-2 is false.

(d) Statement-1 is false, but Statement-2 is true.

28. Let Y_1 and Y_2 be the independent random variables defined as $Y_1 = 2X_1 + 3X_2$ and $Y_2 = X_1 + 2X_2$ where X_1, X_2 are independent random variables. Further Var $(Y_1) = 72$ and Var $(Y_2) = 25$, then what is Var $\left(\frac{2}{3}X_1 - 4X_2\right)$ equal to?

(a) 10 (b) 22

(c) 60 (d) 68

29. 16 persons amongst whom are A and B, are seated at a round table. What is the probability that there are 4 persons between A and B?

(a) $\frac{11}{240}$ (b) $\frac{11}{480}$

(c) $\frac{2}{15}$ (d) $\frac{1}{15}$

30. X has a Binomial distribution with parameters n and p. If the skewness and kurtosis of X are given by $\gamma_1 = 1/6$ and $\gamma_2 = -1/12$, then what are the value of n and p respectively?

(a) 9 and 2/3 (b) 18 and 1/3

(c) 18 and 2/3 (d) 9 and 1/3

31. Consider the following frequency distribution:

Class	Frequency
1– 5	10
6 – 10	15
11 – 15	25
16 –20	25
21 – 25	15
26 – 30	10

With reference to the above freqency distribution, match List I with List II and select the correct answer using the code given below:

List I (Characteristics	List II (Numerical values)
A. First decile	1. 5
B. First quartile	2. 5.5
C. Median	3. 10
D. Quartile deviation	4. 10.5
	5. 15
	6. 15.5

Code:

	A	B	C	D
(a)	2	4	6	1
(b)	1	3	5	2
(c)	2	4	5	3
(d)	1	3	4	2

32. In the case of three variables x_1, x_2 and x_3 given that every pair-wise simple correlation coefficient equals r, what is the partial correlation coefficient $r_{12.3}$ equal to?

(a) r
(b) $\frac{1}{r+1}$
(c) $\frac{r}{r+1}$
(d) $\frac{r}{1-r}$

33. Consider the following statements:

1. Mean and variance of chi-square distribution are not same.
2. Sum of two chi-square variates is also a chi-square variate.

Which of the above statements is/are correct?

(a) 1 only
(b) 2 only
(c) Both 1 and 2
(d) Neither 1 nor 2

34. The correlation coefficient of a random sample of size 11 from a bivariate normal population is found to be 0.6. The value of the t-statistic used to test for significance of the population correlation coefficient is

(a) 2.25
(b) 2.8
(c) 6.75
(d) 8.44

35. Based on two samples of sizes 4 and 3 respectively from two variables X and Y, the ordered combined sample formed out as $x_3 < x_2 < y_1 < y_2 < x_4 < y_3 < x_1$. The value of the Mann-Whitney statistic to test for identicality of their distributions is

(a) 5
(b) 7
(c) 10
(d) 11

36. The variance of the Mann-Whitney statistic used to test for identicality of two distributions based on independent samples of sizes 15 and 20 respectively, is

(a) 28 (b) 532

(c) 875 (d) 900

37. In estimating μ based on a random sample from N(μ, σ²) distribution, the sample mean is more asymptotically efficient than the sample median for al values of

(a) μ and σ^2 (b) σ^2, i and only if $\mu = 0$

(c) μ, if and only if $\sigma^2 = 1$ (d) σ^2, if and only if $\mu \neq 0$

38. Let X be a random variable with probabilities as given below:

Value	2	– 2	...	$(-1)^{i+1} \frac{2!}{i!}$	...
Probability	$\frac{1}{2}$	$\left(\frac{1}{2}\right)^2$	....	$\left(\frac{1}{2}\right)^i$	....

What is E(X) equal to?

(a) 1 (b) e^{-1}

(c) $e - 1$ (d) $1 - e^{-1}$

39. If the mean deviation of x from its mean is 5, then the mean deviation of $y = 2x + 3$ from its mean is

(a) 17 (b) 13

(c) 10 (d) 5

40. Lifetimes in days, in oder of observed falures, for a robust component are recorded below:

198, 211, 216, 219, 224, 225, 230, 236, 243, 252, 253, 264, 268, 271, 272, 275, 282, 284, 288, 291, 294, 295

1. The given sample is random with median lifetime 257.50.
2. Mean number of runs is 13 with standard deviation 1.396.

Which of the above statements is/are correct?

(a) 1 only (b) 2 only

(c) Both 1 and 2 (d) Neither 1 nor 2

41. Which one of the following statements is correct about Newton's divided difference formula?

(a) It is a special case of Newton's forward difference formula.

(b) It is not applicable if values of the arguments are uniformly distributed.

(c) It is applicable whether or not the values of the arguments are uniformly distributed.

(d) The roles of argument and the entry can be interchanged in this formula.

42. What is the approximate value of y for $\frac{dy}{dx} = x + y$ obtaned by using Runge-Kutta method of fourth order when x = 0.1 and given that y(0) = 1?

(a) 1.1103 (b) 1.2124

(c) 1.3236 (d) 1.4125

43. $\Delta^3 y^2$ is equal to

(a) y_2 (b) $\Delta^2 y_2$

(c) $\Delta^3 y_5$ (d) y_5

44. Consider the following data:

x	0	1	2	5
f(x)	2	3	12	147

What is the degree of the Lagrange's interpolation polynomial that represents the above data?

(a) 4 (b) 3

(c) 2 (1)

45. Th number of subintervals requird in Simpson's three-eighth rule is a multiple of

(a) 2 (b) 3

(c) 4 (d) 5

46. Consider the following statements:

1. In interpolation, to find a tabulated value near the begining of the table, Newton's forward formula is used.
2. To find an interpolated value near the centre of the table, Bessel's formula is used.
3. For unequal subintervals, Lagrange's interpolation formula is used.

Which of the above statements are correct?

(a) 1 and 2 only (b) 2 and 3 only

(c) 1 and 3 only (d) 1, 2 and 3

47. Runga-Kutta method of fourth order means that its local truncation error denoted bye is

(a) $e = ch^4 + O(h^5)$ (b) $e = ch^5 + O(h^6)$

(c) $e = ch^3 + O(h^4)$ (d) $e = ch^2 + O(h^3)$

48. Consider the following data:

x	–1	0	1	2
f	4	2	2	4

The interpolating polynomial for the above data is

(a) $2x^2 - x + 2$ (b) $x^2 + x - 2$

(c) $x^2 - x + 2$ (d) $2x^2 + x - 2$

49. The second divided difference of $f(x) = \frac{1}{x}$, with arguments a, b, c is given by

(a) $f[a, b, c] = abc$
(b) $f[a, b, c] = \frac{1}{a} + \frac{1}{b} + \frac{1}{c}$
(c) $f[a, b, c] = \frac{1}{a+b+c}$
(d) $f[a, b, c] = \frac{1}{abc}$

50. What is the second approximation to y when x = 0.2 for $\frac{dy}{dx} = x - y$ obtained by using Picard's method [given that y(0) = 1]?

(a) 0.8278
(b) 0.8387
(c) 0.8327
(d) 0.8297

51. In the context of database management system, which one of the following data models enables us to arrange data files in the tree structure?

(a) Network model
(b) Relational model
(c) Hierarchical model
(d) None of the above

52. Which of the following is/are an advantage/advantages of star topology?

1. If the hub fails, the overall network will not be affected.
2. It requires more amount of cable for connecting the nodes.
3. It allows easy error detection and correction.

Select the correct answer using the code given below:

(a) 1 only
(b) 2 only
(c) 3 only
(d) 2 and 3 only

53. Which one of the following is not correct about Python language?

(a) It is an interpreted language.
(b) It is a platform dependent language.
(c) The syntax of this language is clear.
(d) It is free and open source.

54. Which one of the following protocols is commonly used to retrieve e-mail from a mail server?

(a) FTP
(b) IMAP
(c) HTML
(d) TELNET

55. Which one of the following is not a real-time operating system?

(a) MTOS
(b) LINUX
(c) Lynx
(d) RTX

56. In which one of the following techniques is the virtual address used to map the physical address of the data?

(a) Segmentation
(b) Swapping
(c) Scheduling
(d) Paging

57. Which one of the following is not a system software?

(a) Linker (b) Operating system

(c) Word processor (d) Assembler

58. Which one of the following binary numbers gives output as 100101 by performing AND operating with a binary number 101101?

(a) 101101 (b) 100101

(c) 111010 (d) 110011

59. Which of the following are output devices?

1. Printer
2. Speaker
3. Plotter
4. Webcam

Select the correct answer using the code given below

(a) 1 and 2 only (b) 1, 2 and 3 only

(c) 3 and 4 only (d) 1, 2, 3 and 4

60. Which one of the following is not a Raster Image format?

(a) JPEG (b) TIFF

(c) GIF (d) SVG

61. It is given that

$$\det A = \begin{vmatrix} f(1) & f(2) & f(5) \\ 1 & 2 & 5 \\ 1 & 1 & 1 \end{vmatrix} = 60.$$

What is the value of second divided difference f[1, 2, 5]?

(a) – 5 (b) – 1/5

(c) 5 (d) 1/5

62. For a polynomial f(x) of degree 2, its values at 110, 120, 130, 140 and 150 are respectively 8, 3, 0, – 1, 0. What is f(100) equal to?

(a) 5 (b) 10

(c) 15 (d) 20

63. Consider the following statements:

1. The hypothesis of Simpson's three-eighth rule is that the integrand is a polynomial of degree 3 on each sub-interval $[x_0 + (i-1)h, x_0 + ih]$ for $1 \le i \le n$.
2. To approximate $\int_a^b f(x)\,dx$ by Trapezoidal rule, one divides the inerval [a, b] into any number of (finitely many) sub-intervals of equal size.

Which of the above statements is/are correct?

(a) 1 only (b) 2 only

(c) Both 1 and 2 (d) Neither 1 nor 2

64. Consider the following data:

Marks below	Number of Students
40	250
60	370
80	470
100	540
120	590

The approximate number of students securing marks between 60 and 70 obtained by using Newton's forward interpolation formuala is

(a) 54 (b) 58

(c) 62 (d) 66

65. Consider the data f(1) = 0.98, f(2) = 1.5, f(3) = 4.7, f(5) = 9.9. From the given data, one can obtain f(2.9) using which of the following formulae?

1. Lagrange's interpolation formula
2. Newton's divided difference formula

Select the correct answer using the code give below:

(a) 1 only (b) 2 only

(c) Both 1 and 2 (d) Neither 1 nor 2

66. Consider the following data:

x	1	2	4
f(x)	2	17	257

An approximation to f(3) is given by

(a) 92 (b) 102

(c) 165 (d) 182

67. What is the value of $\frac{\Delta^2}{E}(x^3)$ for $h = 1$?

(a) 6x (b) 3x

(c) 2x (d) x

68. The value of y_4 in the solution of the equation $\frac{dy}{dx} = x^2 + y^2$ with $h = 0.1$, $y(0) = 0$ for $0 \le x \le 0.4$ obtained by Euler's method is approximately equal to

(a) 0.02 (b) 0.005

(c) 0.009 (d) 0.014

69. Consider the following data:

x	0	1	2	4	5	6
f(x)	1	14	15	5	6	19

The value of f(3) obtained using Newton's divided differene formula is

(a) 1 (b) 5

(c) 10 (d) 15

70. Which one of the following holds for every $n \geq 0$?

(a) $\Delta^n x^{(n)} = nh^n$ (b) $\Delta^n x^{(n)} = n(n-1) h^n$

(c) $\Delta^n x^{(n)} = n!\, h$ (d) $\Delta^n x^{(n)} = n!\, h^n$

71. Which one is responsible for determining MAC address?

(a) ICMP (b) IP

(c) ARP (d) FTP

72. There are 4 chips. What is the number of data lines required for Read/Write operations of memory chip containing 2048 locations and each location is of 2 bytes?

(a) 11 (b) 16

(c) 2 (d) 12

73. A major security problem for operating system is

(a) Authentication problem (b) Physical problem

(c) Human problem (d) None of the above

74. Consider the following types of memory in computer systems:

1. Cache memory
2. ROM
3. Optical disks
4. Registers

Which of the above are types of internal process memory?

(a) 1 and 2 only (b) 1, 2 and 4 only

(c) 1 and 4 only (d) 2, 3 and 4 only

75. Consider the following fragments:

1. Replication of a bug
2. Understanding the bug
3. Testing the bug
4. Fixing the bug

Which of the above are parts of debugging process?

(a) 1, 2 and 4 only (b) 1 and 2 only

(c) 1, 2, 3 and 4 (d) None of the above

76. Binary equivalent of Gray coded number 1010110 will be
    - (a) 10101110
    - (b) 11011000
    - (c) 11001011
    - (d) 01010001
77. Which one of the following memory locations is first referred to by the CPU while searching for data?
    - (a) ROM
    - (b) Secondary memory
    - (c) Main memory
    - (d) Cache memory
78. The hexadecimal equivalent of $(6251)_8$ is
    - (a) CA8
    - (b) BA9
    - (c) CA9
    - (d) CA0
79. Which one of the following is an example of Embedded operating systems?
    - (a) Linux
    - (b) Window 2000
    - (c) Window CE
    - (d) MTOS
80. What is the output of lexical analyzer?
    - (a) Parse tree
    - (b) List of tokens
    - (c) Intermediate code
    - (d) Machine code

GENERAL STATISTICS
Paper I 2019

Time Allowed : Three Hours

Maximum Marks: 200

INSTRUCTIONS

1. IMMEDIATELY AFTER THE COMMENCEMENT OF THE EXAMINATION, YOU SHOULD CHECK THAT THIS TEST BOOKLET DOES NOT HAVE ANY UNPRINTED OR TORN OR MISSING PAGES OR ITEMS, ETC. IF SO, GET IT REPLACED BY A COMPLETE TEST BOOKLET.
2. Please note that it is the candidate's responsibility to encode and fill in the Roll Number and Test Booklet Series A, B, C or D carefully and without any omission or discrepancy at the appropriate places in the OMR Answer Sheet. Any omission/discrepancy will render the Answer Sheet liable for rejection.
3. You have to enter your Roll Number on the Test Booklet in I the Box provided alongside. DO NOT write anything else on the Test Booklet.
4. This Test Booklet contains 80 items (questions). Each item comprises four responses (answers). You will select the response which you want to mark on the Answer Sheet. In case you feel that there is more than one correct response, mark the response which you consider the best. In any case, choose ONLY ONE response for each item.
5. You have to mark all your responses ONLY on the separate Answer Sheet provided. See directions in the Answer Sheet.
6. All items carry equal marks.
7. Before you proceed to mark in the Answer Sheet the response to various items in the Test Booklet, you have to fi ll in some particulars in the Answer Sheet as per instructions sent to you with your Admission Certificate.
8. After you have completed filling in all your responses on the Answer Sheet and the examination has concluded , you should hand over to the Invigilator only the Answer Sheet. You are permitted to take away with you the Test Booklet.
9. Sheets for rough work are appended in the Test Booklet at the end.
10. Penalty for wrong answers :

    THERE WILL BE PENALTY FOR WRONG ANSWERS MARKED BY A CANDIDATE IN THE OBJECTIVE-TYPE QUESTION PAPERS.

(i) There are four alternatives for the answer to every question. For each question for which a wrong answer has been given by the candidate, one·thlrd of the marks assigned to that question will be deducted as penalty.

(ii) If a candidate gives more than one answer, it will be treated a s a wrong answer even if one of the given answers happens to be correct and there will be same pen alty as above to that question.

(iii) If a question is left blank, i.e ., no answer is given by the candidate, there will be no penalty for that question.

DO NOT OPEN THIS TEST BOOKLET UNTIL YOU ARE TOLD TO DO SO

1. Consider the following statements:

1. For ordinal and ratio scale data, median is a recommended measure of location.
2. Pie diagrams and bar diagrams are recommended graphs for nominal data.
3. For interval scale data, the recommended graph is histogram and the recommended measure of variability is standard deviation.

Which of the above statements are correct?

(a) 1 and 3 only (b) 2 and 3 only

(c) 1 and 2 only (d) 1, 2 and 3

2. The joint distribution of two random variables X and Y is given below :

X \ Y	–1	1
0	α_1	α_2
1	α_3	α_4

where $\alpha_i \geq 0$, for all i and $\sum_1^4 \alpha_i = 1$.

Which of the following are correct?

1. $E(X') = \alpha_3 + \alpha_4$, forallr
2. $E(XY) = \alpha_4 - \alpha_3$
3. $E(XY)^{2n} = \alpha_3 + \alpha_4$ for all n

Select the correct answer using the code given below.

(a) 1 and 2 only (b) 1 and 3 only

(c) 2 and 3 only (d) 1, 2 and 3

3. For a group of 7 -year-old boys

Body Height: $\overline{X}_1 = 115$ cm, $s_1 = 6.5$ cm

Body Weight: $\overline{X}_2 = 23$ kg, 52 = 2.7 kg

where X is the mean of the group and s is the group's standard deviation.

Which one of the following is correct?

(a) Boys are five times as variable in body weight than in body height

(b) Boys are twice as variable in body weight than in body height

(c) Boys are $\frac{2}{5}$ times as variable in body weight than in body height

(d) Boys are $\frac{2}{5}$ times as variable in body height than in body weight

4. If for two attributes A and B, (A) = 50, (B) = 60, (AB) = 40, N = 100, then

(a) A and B are independent

(b) A and B are positively associated

(c) A and B are negatively associated

(d) nothing definite can be said about the association between A and B without further information

5. If x = 4y + 5 and y = kx + 4 are the lines of regression of x on y and that of y on x respectively, then which one of the following is true?

(a) $k \geq 1$ (b) $k \leq -1$

(c) $-1 \leq k \leq 0$ (d) $0 \leq k \leq \frac{1}{4}$

6. The regression lines of Y on X and of X on Y are respectively $Y = aX + b$ and $X = cY + d$. If rXY is the correlation coefficient between X and Y, and $\frac{s_X}{s_Y}$ is the ratio of standard deviation of X to standard deviation of Y, then the pair $\left(r_{XY}, \frac{s_Y}{s_Y}\right)$ would assume the value

(a) $\left(\sqrt{ac}, \sqrt{\frac{c}{a}}\right)$ (b) $\left(\sqrt{\frac{c}{a}}, \sqrt{ac}\right)$

(c) $\left(\frac{bd}{\sqrt{ac}}, \sqrt{ac}\right)$ (d) $\left(\sqrt{ac}, \sqrt{\frac{a}{c}}\right)$

7. Let X, Y, Z be independently and identically distributed standard normal variates and $(X + \alpha z, Y + \alpha Z)$ follows bivariate normal distribution with correlation coefficient 0·25. Then the absolute value of a is

(a) $\frac{1}{\sqrt{2}}$ (b) $\frac{1}{\sqrt{3}}$

(c) $\frac{1}{\sqrt{2}+1}$ (d) $\frac{1}{\sqrt{3}+1}$

8. If r is the observed correlation coefficient in a sample of n pairs of observations from a correlated bivariate normal population, then the statistic

$$\frac{1}{2}\log_e\left(\frac{1+r}{1-r}\right)$$

is approximately normal with variance

(a) $\frac{1}{n-1}$ (b) $\frac{1}{n}$

(c) $\frac{1}{n-2}$ (d) $\frac{1}{n-3}$

9. Consider the pairs of observations on X and Y as (– 1, – 2), (0, – 1), (1, 0), (2, 1). If the correlation coefficient between X and Y is denoted by r and that between X^2 and Y^2 by s, then which one of the following is correct?

(a) $r > 0$ but $s < 0$ (b) $r > 0$ and $s > 0$

(c) $r < 0$ but $s > 0$ (d) $r < 0$ and $s < 0$

10. The coefficient of correlation between X and Y is 0.6. Their covariance is 4.8. If the variance of X is 9, then the standard deviation of Y is

(a) 7.21 (b) 5.23

(c) 3.22 (d) 2.67

11. A stick of length 1 is tossed at random on a plane that is ruled with a series of parallel lines at a distance 2l apart. What is the probability that the stick will intersect one of the lines?

(a) $\frac{1}{2\pi}$ (b) $\frac{3}{2\pi}$

(c) $\frac{1}{\pi}$ (d) $\frac{2}{3\pi}$

12. Two cannons A_1 and A_2 fire at the same target. Cannon A_1 fires on an average 9 projectiles in the time in which cannon A_2 fires 10 projectiles. But on an average 7 out of 10 projectiles from cannon A_1 and 6 out of 10 projectiles from cannon A_2 strike the target. If in the course of shooting, the target is struck by one projectile, then the probability that it was struck by a projectile from cannon A_1 is

(a) $\frac{20}{41}$ (b) $\frac{21}{41}$

(c) $\frac{6}{19}$ (d) $\frac{63}{190}$

13. 5% of patients suffering from a certain disease are selected to undergo a new treatment that is believed to increase the recovery rate from 30% to 50%. A person is randomly selected from these patients after the completion of the treatment and is found to have recovered. What is the probability that the patient received the new treatment?

(a) 0.03 (b) 0.08

(c) 0.80 (d) 0.30

14. A discrete random variable X takes four values –1.5, –1, 2·5 and 3 with respective proaties $\frac{1}{6}, \frac{1}{5}, \frac{1}{2}$ and $\frac{1}{12}$. Then what is E (|X|) equal to?

(a) 0 (b) $\frac{1}{4}$

(c) $\frac{3}{2}$ (d) 2

15. If the probability of having a male or a female child is 0.50, then what is the probability that family's seventh child is their second daughter?

(a) $\frac{3}{64}$ (b) $\frac{15}{64}$

(c) $\frac{21}{64}$ (d) $\frac{1}{64}$

16. Let X be a Poisson random variable with p.m.f.

$$P(X = k) = \begin{cases} \frac{e^{-\lambda}\lambda^k}{k!}, k = 0, 1, 2, ...; & \lambda > 0 \\ 0; & \text{otherwise} \end{cases}$$

If $Y = X^2 + 3$, then what is $P(Y = y)$ equal to?

(a) $\frac{e^{-\lambda}\lambda^{\sqrt{y-3}}}{\sqrt{(y-3)!}}$ for $y = \{3, 4, 7, 12, ..\}$ (b) $\frac{e^{-\lambda}\lambda^{-\sqrt{y-3}}}{\sqrt{(3-y)!}}$ for $y = \{3, 4, 7, 12, ..\}$

(c) $\frac{e^{-\lambda}\lambda^{\sqrt{3-y}}}{\sqrt{(3-y)!}}$ for $y = \{4, 7, 12, ..\}$ (d) $\frac{e^{-\lambda}\lambda^{-\sqrt{3-y}}}{\sqrt{(3-y)!}}$ for $y = \{4, 7, 12, ..\}$

17. A person purchases a weekly lottery ticket until he wins the lottery. If p is the probability of winning the lottery, then the expected number of weeks required to win the lottery is

(a) $\frac{1}{p}$ (b) $\frac{1}{p} - 1$

(c) $\frac{1}{1-p}$ (d) $\frac{1}{1-p} - 1$

18. Consider the following statements:

1. Binomial distribution with mean $a > 0$ and variance $b > 0$ is such that $\frac{a^2}{(a-b)^2}$ is an integer.
2. Binomial distribu tion with mean 3.5 and variance 1.75 is bimodal.
3. For a binomial distribution, with mean and variance equal to 4 and $\frac{4}{3}$ respectively, $P(X \geq 1) > 0{\cdot}99$.
4. Sum of two independent binomial variates is a binomial variate.

Which of the above statements are correct?

(a) 1 and 3 (b) 1, 2 and 4

(c) 2 and 3 only (d) 2, 3 and 4

19. r is given to be the correlation coefficient between two random variables X and Y. If Z = aY + b, where a($\neq$ 0) and b are real numbers, then the correlation coefficient between X and Z is

(a) r (b) $r|a|$

(c) $\left(\frac{a}{|a|}\right)|r|$ (d) $\left(\frac{a}{|a|}\right)r$

20. Let f (x, y) = 4xy, $0 \leq x \leq 1$, $0 \leq y \leq 1$ be the joint p.d.f. of (X, V). Then the marginal distribution of X is

(a) $f_X(x) = 4x; 0 \le x \le 1$ (b) $f_X(x) = 2x; 0 \le x \le 1$

(c) $f_X(x) = \frac{x}{2}; 0 \le x \le 1$ (d) $f_X(x) = x; 0 \le x \le 1$

21. Consider the following statements:

1. Correlation coefficient is a measure of proportion or percentage in a relationship.
2. Statistic Z^2 is an equivalent measure of the statistic χ^2.
3. t-distribution becomes mesokurtic when degrees of freedom approach a very large value.
4. $(1 - \alpha)$ significant points of $F(n_2, n_1)$ distribution are same as reciprocal of $(1 - \alpha)$ significant points of $F(n_1, n_2)$ distribution.

Which of the above statements are correct?

(a) 2 and 3 only (b) 2 and 4 only

(c) 3 and 4 only (d) 1, 2, 3 and 4

22. Consider the following statements

1. A type I error of 0·05 means that 5 times out of 100, one can reject a true null hypothesis.
2. The smaller the type I error rate, the more correct is the inference.
3. Type I error is sensitive to the number of subjects in a sample.
4. Type I error is completely under the control of the experimenter.

Which of the above statements is/are correct?

(a) 1 and 3 only (b) 2 and 4 only

(c) 4 only (d) 1, 2, 3 and 4

23. Let W_1 and W_2 denote the standard errors of the sample means $\bar{X}_1$ and $\bar{X}_2$ of two independent random samples. The standard error of $T = (\bar{X}_1 - \bar{X}_2)$ is

(a) 0 (b) $|W_1 - W_2|$

(c) $\sqrt{|W_1^2 - W_2^2|}$ (d) $\sqrt{(W_1^2 + W_2^2)}$

24. Two independent groups A and B consist of 100 people each who have a disease. A serum is given to group A but not to group B; otherwise the two groups are treated identically. It is found that in groups A and B, 75 and 65 people respec tively, recover from the disease. Given $Z_{0.05} = 1·645$ and $Z_{0.10} = 1·28$.

Consider the following statements:

1. The results are due to chance only at 5% level of significance.
2. The serum is effective at 10% level of significance.
3. Assuming that the serum has no effect, 70 people are expected to recover in group A.
4. The standard deviation of the difference in proportions is given by 0.06.

Which of the above statements are correct?

(a) 1, 3 and 4 (b) 1, 2 and 3

(c) 1, 2 and 4 (d) 2, 3 and 4

25. Let X_1, X_2, X_3, X_4, X_5 be a random sample of size 5 from a population having standard normal distribution. If

$$\bar{X} = \frac{1}{5}\sum_{i=1}^{5} X_i \text{ and } T = \sum_{i=1}^{5}(X_i - \bar{X})^2$$

then $E(T^2 \bar{X}^2)$ is equal to

(a) 3 (b) 3.6

(c) 4.8 (d) 5.2

26. For $\chi^2 = 2.38$ and N = 200. the coefficient of contingency C for the given data is

(a) 0.01 (b) 0.1084

(c) 0.1096 (d) 0.1840

27. Which of the following is/are *not* needed for the validity of χ^2 test?

1. The sample observations should be independent.
2. Constraints on the cell frequencies should not be linear.
3. N. the total frequency, should be reasonably large.
4. None of the theoretical frequencies should be less than 5.

Select the correct answer using the code given below.

(a) 1 and 2 (b) 2 only

(c) 2 and 3 (d) 4

28. Suppose that the five random variables $X_1, X_2, ..., X_5$ are independent and each has a standard normal distribution. A constant C such that the random variable

$$\frac{C(X_1 + X_2)}{(X_3^2 + X_4^2 + X_5^2)^{\frac{1}{2}}}$$

will have a t-distribution, has value

(a) $\frac{\sqrt{3}}{2}$ (b) $\sqrt{\frac{3}{2}}$

(c) $\frac{3}{2}$ (d) $\sqrt{\frac{2}{3}}$

29. If X is an F(m, n) random variable, where m > 2 and n > 2, then $E(X) . E(X)\left(\frac{1}{X}\right)$ equals

(a) $\frac{n(n-2)}{m(m-2)}$ (b) $\frac{m(m-2)}{n(n-2)}$

(c) $\frac{mn}{(m-2)(n-2)}$ (d) $\frac{m(n-2)}{N(m-2)}$

30. What is the probability that the sample median based on a random sample of size 3 drawn from a distribution with p.d.f.

$$f(x) = \begin{cases} 2X, & 0 < X < 1 \\ 0, & \text{otherwise} \end{cases}$$

exceeds $\frac{1}{2}$?

(a) $\frac{3}{4}$ (b) $\frac{13}{16}$

(c) $\frac{27}{32}$ (d) $\frac{29}{32}$

31. Let X be a random variable with p.d.f.

$$f(x) = \begin{cases} \frac{2x}{\pi^2}, & 0 < x < \pi \\ 0, & \text{otherwise} \end{cases}$$

Let Y = sin X, then for $0 < y < 1$, the p.d.f. of Y is given by

(a) $\frac{2\pi}{\sqrt{1-y^2}}$ (b) $\frac{\pi}{2}\sqrt{1-y^2}$

(c) $\frac{2}{\pi}\sqrt{1-y^2}$ (d) $\frac{2}{\pi\sqrt{1-y^2}}$

32. Suppose that r balls are drawn one at a time without replacement from a bag containing n white and m black balls. What is the variance of the number of black balls drawn?

(a) $\frac{mr(m+n-2)}{(m+n)(m+n+1)}$ (b) $\frac{mnr(m+n-r)}{(m+n)(m+n+1)}$

(c) $\frac{mn(m+n)^2}{(m-1)(m+n+r)}$ (d) $\frac{(m+n)(m+n-r)}{(m+n)^2}$

33. The number of items produced in a factory during a week is a random variable with mean 50. If the variance of a week's production is known to be 25, then the probability that this week's production will be between 40 and 60 is at least

(a) 0·50 (b) 0·60

(c) 0·75 (d) 0·80

34. The smallest value of k in Chebyshev's inequality, for which the probability that a random variable will take a value in between $\mu - k\sigma$ and $\mu + k\sigma$ is at least 0.99, is given by

(a) 9.5 (b) 10

(c) 10.5 (d) 11

35. The round-off error to the second decimal place has the uniform distribution on the interval (- 0·05, 0·05). What is the probability that the absolute error in the sum of 1000 numbers is less than 2?

[Given $\Phi(2{\cdot}19) = 0.985$)]

(a) 0·92 (b) 0·95

(c) 0.97 (d) 0·99

36. If X and Yare independent N(0, 1), then what is E[Max(X, Y)] equal to?

(a) $\frac{1}{\sqrt{2\pi}}$ (b) $\frac{1}{\sqrt{\pi}}$

(c) $\frac{1}{\sqrt{2}}$ (d) $\frac{2}{\sqrt{\pi}}$

37. Let X be a continuous random variable with p.d.f.

$$f(x) = \begin{cases} ax, & 0 \le x < 1 \\ a, & 1 \le x \le 2 \\ -ax + 3a, & 2 < x \le 3 \\ 0, & \text{elsewhere} \end{cases}$$

What is the value of the constant a?

(a) 1 (b) $\frac{1}{2}$

(c) $\frac{1}{3}$ (d) 1

38. If the probability density function of the normal distribution of X is

$$f(x) = k\exp\left(-\frac{1}{8}x^2 + 2x\right), -\infty < x < \infty$$

then the mean and variance of the distribution are respectively

(a) 8 and 2 (b) 4 and 2

(c) 8 and 4 (d) 4 and 4

39. The random variable X has p .d.f.

$$f(x) = \begin{cases} \frac{3x^2}{2}, & -1 < x < 1 \\ 0, & \text{otherwise} \end{cases}$$

What are the values of E(|X|) and var (|X|) respectively?

(a) $\frac{1}{4}$ and $\frac{1}{80}$ (b) $\frac{3}{4}$ and $\frac{1}{80}$

(c) $\frac{1}{4}$ and $\frac{3}{80}$ (d) $\frac{3}{4}$ and $\frac{3}{80}$

40. Let X and Y be two i.i.d. random variables with p.d.f. $f(x) = 2e^{-2x}, x \ge O$. The distribution of Z = X – Y is

(a) exponential (b) beta

(c) Laplace (d) Cauchy

41. A bus that manages the transfer of data and addresses among various **components is**

(a) address bus (b) control bus

(c) data bus (d) None of the a bove

42. Which of the following codes is/ are positional weighted code(s)?

1. Gray code
2. BCD code

3. ASCll code
4. Excess-3 code

Select the correct answer using the code given below.

(a) and 4 (b) 1 and 2 only

(c) 1, 2 and 3 (d) 2 only

43. When $(217)_{10}$ is divided by $(12)_{10}$, then the quotient and remainder in binary system will be respectively

(a) 11010 and 1001 (b) 10100 and 0001

(c) 10010 and 0001 (d) 10010 and 0010

44. A software development module that arranges the object code of all the modules that have been generated by the language translators into a single program, is

(a) editor (b) debugger

(c) linker (d) loader

45. Antivirus is a software that comes in the category of

1. system software
2. application software
3. utility software
4. debugger

Select the correct answer using the code given below.

(a) 2 (b) 3 and 4 only

(c) 3 only (d) 1, 3 and 4

46. Which of the statements regarding Network Protocol are not correct?

1. Identification of type of physical connection cannot be done by Network Protocol.
2. Error detection and correction are done by Network Protocol.
3. Message formatting cannot be done by Network Protocol.
4. Network Protocol does initiation and termination.

Select the correct answer using the code given below.

(a) 1 and 4 (b) 1 and 3 only

(c) 2, 3 and 4 (d) 1, 2 and 3

47. A software that gathers information about a person and organization without their knowledge is called

(a) firmware (b) adware

(c) virus (d) spyware

48. Consider the following statements in respect of subroutine:

1. It reduces the length of code.
2. It is a program stored somewhere else in memory and called to execute it.
3. It does not require the use of stack for its execution.

Which of the above statements is/ are not correct?

(a) 1 and 2 (b) 3 only

(c) 2 and 3 (d) 1 and 3

49. If someone wants to reduce the cost of developing and maintaining a computer software, which operating system(s) should be installed?

(a) Windows only (b) Linux only

(c) Mac (d) Both Windows and Linux

50. Which one of the following protocols is used to send email messages?

(a) TCP (b) SMTP

(c) POP (d) UDP

51. Consider the following table :

x	2	3	4	5	6
y	45	49.2	54.1	k	67.4

What is the value of k in the above table?

(a) 60·05 (b) 61·05

(c) 62·05 (d) 63·05

52. What is the value of

$\Delta^{10}[(1 - ax)(1 - bx^2)(1 - cx^3)(1 - dx^4)]$?

(a) 0 (b) 1O!

(c) abcd × (10)! (d) abcd

53. What are the values of $\Delta^5 O^3$ and $\Delta^3 O^5$ respectively?

(a) 0 and 0 (b) 144 and 0

(c) 0 and 150 (d) 0 and 96

54. For interval of differencing as unity, consider the following observations:

f(0) = 41, f(l) = 61, f(5) = 20 and f(6) = 50

What is the value of the sum

$S = \sum_{k=0}^{4} \Delta^2 f(k)$?

(a) – 10 (b) 10

(c) 50 (d) Cannot be determined

55. Which one of the following is equal to $1 + x + x^2 + x^3$?

(a) $x^{(3)} + 3x^{(2)} + 4x^{(l)} + 1$ (b) $x^{(3)} + x^{(2)} + 3x^{(l)} + 1$

(c) $3x^{(3)} + 4x^{(2)} + x^{(1)} + 1$ (d) $x^{(3)} + 4x^{(2)} + 3x^{(l)} + 1$

56. Given that f(x) is a polynomial of third degree with the values f(– 2) = – 33, f(– 1) = m_1, f(0) = 5, f(l) = 9, f(2) = m_2 and f(3) = 47. What are the values of m_1 and m_2 respectively?

(a) – 10 and 19 (b) – 10 and 21
(c) – 5 and 19 (d) – 5 and 21

57. Gauss forward interpolation formula involves

(a) even differences above the central line and odd differences on the central line
(b) even differences below the central line and odd differences on the central line
(c) odd differences below the central line and even differences on the central line
(d) odd differences above the central line and even differences on the central line

58. The third divided difference of the polynomial $2x^2 + 1$ over the points 0, 1, 3, 6 is

(a) 0 (b) 1
(c) 2 (d) 4

59. It is given that a curve passes through the points (0, 18), (1, 10), (3, – 18) and (6, 90). What is the slope of the curve at x = 2 (using Lagrange's formula)?

(a) – 16 (b) – 8
(c) 1 (d) 0

60. Consider the following table where y = f(x):

x	10	15	20
y	1754	2648	3564

What is the value of x for y = 3000 obtained by applying inverse interpolation (iterative method), with h = 5?

(a) 15.90 (b) 16.10
(c) 16.93 (d) 17.02

61. Which one of the following translates IP address to readable manner such as website URLs?

(a) DNS (b) SMTP
(c) DHCP (d) POP

62. Which one of the following is content based addressable memory?

(a) ROM (b) Cache memory
(c) Associative memory (d) SRAM

63. Which one of the following systems does not share common memory and common bus?

(a) Tightly coupled system (b) Distributed system
(c) Batch system (d) Multiprogramming system

64. Which one of the following network cables is capable for faster data transmission?

(a) Thin Ethernet cable (b) Thick Ethernet cable
(c) Fiber optic cable (d) UTP cable

65. Which one of the following techniques, a hacker uses for listening to private voice or data transmission often using wiretap?

(a) Spoofing (b) Snooping

(c) Eavesdropping (d) Piggybacking

66. The name of the network developed by the Government of India in public interest for various government activities is

(a) ARPANET (b) NICNET

(c) Quicknet (d) None of the above

67. Which one of the following communication media supports higher Internet bandwidth?

(a) UTP cable (b) Coaxial cable

(c) Fiber optic cable (d) Thin Ethernet

68. A technique used by an operating system for efficient management of memory space of a computer system is

(a) paging (b) swapping

(c) caching (d) debugging

69. Which of the following are the functions of an operating system?

1. Memory management
2. Device management
3. Security management

Select the correct answer using the code given below.

(a) 1 and 2 only (b) 2 and 3 only

(c) 1 and 3 only (d) 1, 2 and 3

70. Which type of memory is suitable for mobile phones, digital cameras and ipods?

(a) Programmable ROM (b) Flash memory

(c) RAM (d) Optical disk

71. The value estimated for ln2, obtained by applying trapezoidal rule to

$$\int_1^2 \frac{1}{x}\,dx$$

with two equal divisions of [1, 2), is

(a) $\frac{1}{2}$ (b) $\frac{17}{24}$

(c) $\frac{19}{24}$ (d) 1

72. Simpson's one-third rule for evaluation of

$$\int_a^b f(x)\,dx$$

requires the interval [a, b) to be divided into

(a) an even number of subintervals of equal width

(b) an odd number of subintervals of equal width

(c) any number of subintervals of equal width

(d) any number of subintervals

73. Consider the following table:

x	– 1	0	1	2	3	4	5
f(x)	2	1	2	5	10	17	26

The value of the integral

$$\int_{-1}^{5} f(x)\, dx$$

when computed by Simpson's $\frac{3}{8}$th rule is

(a) 48 (b) 47

(c) 46 (d) 45

74. Consider the initial value problem $y' = y + 2x - 1$ with $y(0) = 1$ over the interval $0 \le x \le 1$. The value of the solution $y(0.2)$, obtained using Euler's method with $h = 0.1$, is

(a) 0 (b) 1

(c) 1·020 (d) 1·062

75. The third approximation of the initial value problem

$$\frac{dy}{dx} = x + y,\ y(0) = 1$$

obtained using Picard's method, is

(a) $1 + x + x^2 + \frac{x^3}{3} + \frac{x^4}{24}$

(b) $1 + x + x^2 + \frac{x^3}{6}$

(c) $1 + x^2 + \frac{x^3}{6}$

(d) $x + \frac{x^2}{2} + \frac{x^3}{3}$

76. The values of the function f(x) for different values of x are f(l) = 4, f(2) = 5, [(7) = 5 and f(8) = 4. Then f(x) attains

(a) maximum value at x = 4.5

(b) minimum value at x = 4.5

(c) neither maximum nor minimum for any x

(d) minimum value at x = – 4.5

77. Let

$$f(x) = \log_{10}(1 + x)$$

with $x_0 = 1$ and $x_1 = 1.1$. What is the approximate value of f(1.04) obtained by using linear interpolation?

[Given that $\log_{10} 2 = 0{\cdot}30\,1030$ and $\log_{10} 2.1 = 0.322219$]

(a) 0·309506 (b) 0·095603

(c) 0·390506 (d) 0·090356

78. What is the approximate value of y when x = 1.1 for

$$\frac{dy}{dx} = 3x + y^2$$

obtained by using Runge-Kutta method of second-order formula?

[Given that y = 1.2 when x = 1]

(a) 1.722 (b) 1.644

(c) 1.044 (d) 1·022

79. If δ is the central difference operator, then what is

$$\frac{1}{2}\delta^2 + \delta\sqrt{1 + \frac{\delta^2}{4}}$$

equal to?

(a) E + 1 (b) ∇

(c) Δ (d) $\Delta + 1$

80. The third divided difference of the function $f(x) = x^3 - 2x$ with the arguments 2, 4, 9, 10 is equal to

(a) 23 (b) 21

(c) 15 (d) 1

GENERAL STATISTICS
Paper I 2018

Time Allowed : Three Hours | *Maximum Marks: 200*

INSTRUCTIONS

1. IMMEDIATELY AFTER THE COMMENCEMENT OF THE EXAMINATION, YOU SHOULD CHECK THAT THIS TEST BOOKLET DOES NOT HAVE ANY UNPRINTED OR TORN OR MISSING PAGES OR ITEMS, ETC. IF SO, GET IT REPLACED BY A COMPLETE TEST BOOKLET.
2. Please note that it is the candidate's responsibility to encode and fill in the Roll Number and Test Booklet Series A, B, C or D carefully and without any omission or discrepancy at the appropriate places in the OMR Answer Sheet. Any omission/discrepancy will render the Answer Sheet liable for rejection.
3. You have to enter your Roll Number on the Test Booklet in I the Box provided alongside. DO NOT write anything else on the Test Booklet.
4. This Test Booklet contains 80 items (questions). Each item comprises four responses (answers). You will select the response which you want to mark on the Answer Sheet. In case you feel that there is more than one correct response, mark the response which you consider the best. In any case, choose ONLY ONE response for each item.
5. You have to mark all your responses ONLY on the separate Answer Sheet provided. See directions in the Answer Sheet.
6. All items carry equal marks.
7. Before you proceed to mark in the Answer Sheet the response to various items in the Test Booklet, you have to fi ll in some particulars in the Answer Sheet as per instructions sent to you with your Admission Certificate.
8. After you have completed filling in all your responses on the Answer Sheet and the examination has concluded , you should hand over to the Invigilator only the Answer Sheet. You are permitted to take away with you the Test Booklet.
9. Sheets for rough work are appended in the Test Booklet at the end.
10. Penalty for wrong answers :

    THERE WILL BE PENALTY FOR WRONG ANSWERS MARKED BY A CANDIDATE IN THE OBJECTIVE-TYPE QUESTION PAPERS.

(i) There are four alternatives for the answer to every question. For each question for which a wrong answer has been given by the candidate, one·thlrd of the marks assigned to that question will be deducted as penalty.

(ii) If a candidate gives more than one answer, it will be treated a s a wrong answer even if one of the given answers happens to be correct and there will be same pen alty as above to that question.

(iii) If a question is left blank, i.e ., no answer is given by the candidate, there will be no penalty for that question.

DO NOT OPEN THIS TEST BOOKLET UNTIL YOU ARE TOLD TO DO SO

1. Let A_1, A_2, A_3, and A_4 be independent events 3. such that $P(A_1) = \frac{1}{2}$, $P(A_2) = \frac{1}{4}$, $P(A_3) = \frac{1}{8}$ and $P(A_4) = 16$.

What is $P(A_1 \cup A_2 \cup As \cup A_4)$ equal to?

(a) $\frac{15}{16}$ (b) $\frac{1023}{1024}$

(c) $\frac{709}{1024}$ (d) $\frac{315}{1024}$

2. A lot of 15 mobiles contains 4 defective mobiles. The mobiles are taken out one by one at random and examined. The examined ones are not put back. The probability that the ninth mobile examined is the last defective is

(a) $\frac{56}{195}$ (b) $\frac{8}{195}$

(c) $\frac{1}{7}$ (d) $\frac{2}{65}$

3. Let X be a random variable having probability density function

$$f(x) = \begin{cases} \frac{x}{2}, & 0 < x \le 1 \\ \frac{1}{2}, & 1 < x \le 2 \\ \frac{3-x}{3}, & 2 < x \le 3 \end{cases}$$

What is $P(1.5 < X \le 2.51\ X > 1)$ equal to ?

(a) $\frac{3}{8}$ (b) $\frac{1}{2}$

(c) $\frac{5}{8}$ (d) $\frac{1}{4}$

4. The first of three urns contains 7 white and 10 black balls; the second urn contains 5 white and 12 black balls; and the third urn contains 17 white balls only. A person chooses an urn at random and draws a ball from it. The ball is white. What are the probabilities that the ball drawn is from the first, second and third urns respectively?

(a) $\frac{7}{29}, \frac{6}{29}, \frac{18}{29}$

(b) $\frac{7}{29}, \frac{5}{29}, \frac{20}{29}$

(c) $\frac{7}{29}, \frac{5}{29}, \frac{17}{29}$

(d) None of the above

5. Let X and Y be jointly distributed with pdf

$$f(x, y) = \begin{cases} \frac{1+xy}{t}, & |x|<1, |y|<1 \\ 0, & \text{otherwise} \end{cases}$$

Which of the following statements is/are correct?

1. X and Y are independent.
2. X^2 and Y^2 are independent.

Select the correct answer using the code given below:

(a) 1 only

(b) 2 only

(c) Both 1 and 2

(d) Neither 1 nor 2

6. Let X be a random variable with pdf

$$f(x) = \begin{cases} \frac{2}{x^3}, & x \geq 1 \\ 0, & x < 1 \end{cases}$$

Which one of the following statements is correct?

(a) Both mean and variance exist.

(b) Mean exists but variance does not exist.

(c) Both mean and variance do not exist.

(d) Variance exists but mean does not exist.

7. Let X be a random variable following Binomial distribution with parameters $n = 13$ and $p = 0.3$. Consider the following statements:

1. Mode of the distribution of X is 3.
2. Distribution is negatively skewed.

Which of the above statement(s) is/are correct?

(a) 1 only

(b) 2 only

(c) Both 1 and 2

(d) Neither 1 nor 2

8. If X follows Normal distribution with mean 4 and variance 100, then the distribution of

$$Y = \frac{1}{2}\left(\frac{X-4}{10}\right)^2 \text{ is}$$

(a) Exponential with mean 4

(b) Chi square with one degree of freedom

(c) Gamma distribution with parameter 1/2

(d) Normal with mean 4 and variance 10

9. Let X and Y be independent gamma $G(\alpha_1, \beta)$ and $G(\alpha_2, \beta)$ random variables respectively. Then $X|(X+Y)$ is distributed as

(a) $G(\alpha_1 + \alpha_2, \beta)$ (b) $\beta_1(\alpha_1, \alpha_2)$

(c) $U(0, 1)$ (d) $G(\alpha_1, \alpha_2)$

10. For exponential distribution $f(x) = \theta e^{-\theta x}; x > 0$, consider the following statements:

1. Variance is greater than mean if $0 < \theta < 1$.
2. Variance is equal to mean if $\theta = 1$.
3. Variance is less than mean if $\theta > 1$.

Which of the above statements are correct ?

(a) 1 and 3 only (b) 2 and 3 only

(c) 1 and 2 only (d) 1, 2 and 3

11. A rod of length 2l is broken into two pieces at random. The mean and variance of the length of the shorter of the two pieces are respectively

(a) $\frac{1}{2}, \frac{l^2}{3}$ (b) $l, \frac{l^2}{3}$

(c) $\frac{1}{2}, \frac{l^2}{12}$ (d) $l, \frac{l^2}{12}$

12. The joint distribution -function of X and Y is given by

$$F(x, y) = \begin{cases} (1-e^{-x})(1-e^{-y}); & \text{for } x . 0, y > 0 \\ 0; & \text{otherwise} \end{cases}$$

What is the value of $P(|X - Y| \leq 10)$?

(a) $(1 - e^{-10})$ (b) $\frac{1}{2}(1-e^{-10})$

(c) $\left(1-\frac{e^{-10}}{2}\right)$ (d) None of the above

13. The joint density function of X and Y is given by

$$f(x, y) = \begin{cases} 2e^{-x}\, e^{-2y}; & 0 < x < \infty, 0 < y < \infty \\ 0; & \text{otherwise} \end{cases}$$

What is the value of $P(X < Y)$?

(a) 1/3 (b) 1/2

(c) 1/4 (d) 1/6

14. Thejoint pdf of X and Y is given by

$$f(x, y) = \begin{cases} \frac{1}{3}(x+y); & 0 < x < 1, 0 < y < 2 \\ 0; & \text{elsewhere} \end{cases}$$

What is the value of E[3X(X + 2Y)]?

(a) $\frac{9}{2}$ (b) $\frac{29}{6}$

(c) $\frac{31}{6}$ (d) $\frac{11}{2}$

15. The joint probability distribution of X and Y is given by

Y \ X	–1	0	1
–1	1/6	1/3	1/6
0	0	0	0
1	1/6	0	1/6

Consider the following statements:

1. X and Y are independent random variables.
2. Cov(X, Y) = 0.

Which of the statement(s) given above is/are correct?

(a) 1 only (b) 2 only

(c) Both 1 and 2 (d) Neither 1 nor 2

16. If the pdf of X is given by

$$f(x) = \begin{cases} 1+x, & -1 < x \le 0 \\ 1-x, & 0 < x < 1 \\ 0, & \text{elsewhere} \end{cases}$$

The random variables are defined as U = X and V = X^2.

Consider the following statements:

1. Cov(U, V) = O.
2. U and V are independent random variables.

Which of the above statement(s) is/are correct?

(a) 1 only (b) 2 only

(c) Both 1 and 2 (d) Neither 1 nor 2

17. Suppose X and Yare two independent normal random variables with means 10, 5 and variances 9, 4 respectively. Define Z = 4X – 5Y. The moment generating function of Z [i.e. $M_Z(t)$] is given by

(a) $\exp[15t + 22t^2]$ (b) $\exp[15t - 22t^2]$

(c) $\exp[15t + 122t^2]$ (d) $\exp[15t - 122t^2]$

18. A fair die is thrown repeatedly until 3 or 4 appears. Let X denote the number of throws required. The probability genrating function of X when |s| < 3/2 is given by the expression

(a) $P(s) = \frac{2s}{3-s}$ (b) $P(s) = \frac{2s}{3-2s}$

(c) $P(s) = \frac{3-s}{2s}$ (d) $P(s) = \frac{3-2s}{2s}$

19. The number of a utomobiles sold weekly at a certain dealership is a random variable with expected value 16 and variance 9. The probability that next week's sales are between 10 and 22 is at least

(a) 0.50 (b) 0.56

(c) 0.75 (d) 0.95

20. The pdf of random variable X is given by

$$f(x) = \begin{cases} \frac{kx^3}{(1+2x)^6}; & x > 0 \\ 0; & \text{otherwise} \end{cases}$$

The distribution of random variable $Y = \frac{2X}{1+2X}$ is β distribution of first kind with parameters:

(a) $m = 4, n = 2$ (b) $m = 5, n = 1$

(c) $m = 3, n = 3$ (d) $m = 5, n = 2$

21. Consider the following statements:

1. The weight of strawberry measured in interval scale. box is
2. Number of students admitted in each 11M in the year 2007 is cross-sectional data.
3. Bar code for items in departmental store is measured in nominal scale.

Which of the statements given above are correct?

(a) 1 and 2 only (b) 1 and 3 .only

(c) 2 and 3 only (d) 1, 2 and 3

22. The minimum value of Var(Y – aX), for all the values of 'a' is given by

(a) $\rho^2 \frac{Var(Y)}{Var(X)}$ (b) $\rho^2 \frac{Var(X)}{Var(Y)}$

(c) ρ^2 Var (Y) (d) $(1 - \rho^2)$ Var (Y)

23. For a certain frequency distribution, the numerical computation yields the following:

Mean = 62, Median = 65, Coefficient of skewness = – 0.3

The standard deviation is equal to

(a) 10 (b) 30

(c) 90 (d) 300

24. The data relating to smoking habits of father and son are given below:

1. Father is a smoker and so is son : 50
2. Father is a smoker, but not the son : 10
3. Father is not a smoker, but son is a smoker : 10
4. Father is not a smoker, son is not a smoker : 30

The coefficient of association between smoking habits offather and son is

(a) 0 (b) $\frac{7}{8}$

(c) $\frac{-7}{8}$ (d) $\frac{1}{4}$

25. Consider the following statements:

1. Two attributes A and B are said to be positively associated if the presence of one attribute A is accompanied by the presence of the other attribute B.
2. Two attributes A and B are said to be negatively associated if the presence of an attribute A ensures the absence of the other attribute B or vice versa.
3. Two attributes A and B are called independent in case the presence or absence of one attribute has linear relationship with the presence of the other attribute.

Which of the statements given above are correct?

(a) 1, 2 and 3 (b) 1 and 2 only

(c) 1 and 3 only (d) 2 and 3 only

26. If the joint pdf of (X, Y) is

$$f(x, y) = \begin{cases} \frac{1}{3}x^2 e^{-y(1+x)}; & x \geq 0, y \geq 0 \\ 0; & \text{otherwise} \end{cases}$$

then the regression equation of Y on X is

(a) $y = \frac{1}{1+x}$ (b) $y = \frac{x^2}{1+x}$

(c) $y = 1 + x$ (d) $y = \frac{x^2}{2(1+x)^2}$

27. Let (X, Y) ~ BVN($\mu_1, \mu_2, \sigma_1^2, \sigma_2^2, \rho$).

Consider the following statements :

1. X and Y are independent if and only if $\rho = 0$.
2. Every linear combination of X and Y is a normal variate.
3. The regression equation of Y on X and the regression equation of X on Y are linear and homoscedastic.

Which of the statements given above are correct?

(a) 1 and 2 only (b) 2 and 3 only

(c) 1 and 3 only (d) 1, 2 and 3

28. The correlation coefficient between the marks obtained in Mathematics and Statistics in First Semester Examination for a given set of 60 students is 0.65. After re-evaluation the marks in Mathematics of all the 60 students increased by 3 marks. The coefficient of correlation between the original marks in Statistics and the revised marks in Mathematics will be

(a) 0.60 (b) 0.65

(c) 0.70 (d) Almost 1

29. If the correlation coefficient of zero order in a set of 3 variates were equal to ρ each, then the multiple correlation $R^2_{1.23}$ is equal to

(a) ρ (b) $\frac{2\rho^2}{1-\rho}$

(c) $\frac{\rho^2}{1+\rho}$ (d) $+1$

30. If r is the coefficient of correlation for a sample of N independent observations from a bivariate normal population with population coefficient of correlation zero, then $E(1-r^2)^{-1}$ is

(a) $\frac{(N-3)}{(N-4)}$ (b) $\frac{2(N-3)}{(N-4)}$

(c) 0 (d) 1

31. If the relation $ax_1 + bX_2 + cX_3 = 0$ holds for all sets of values of x_1, x_2 and x_3, then the partial correlation coefficient $r_{12.3}$ is

(a) 0 (b) 1

(c) −1 (d) 0.5

32. If X_1, X_2, X_3 and X_4 are four uncorrelated random variables each with variance σ^2, then what is the value of the correlation coefficient between U and V where $U = X_1 + X_2 + X_3$ and $V = X_1 + X_2 + X_4$?

(a) 0 (b) 1

(c) $\frac{1}{3}$ (d) $\frac{2}{3}$

33. Let $(X_1, X_2, X_3, ..., X_n)$ be a random sample of size n from a uniform distribution U[− 3, 3). The large sample distribution of $\sqrt{n}\,\bar{X}$ is

(a) N(0, 1) (b) N(0, 3)

(c) $U\left[-\frac{3}{\sqrt{n}}, \frac{3}{\sqrt{n}}\right]$ (d) $U\left[-\frac{3}{n}, \frac{3}{n}\right]$

34. A normal population has a mean 0.1 and standard deviation 2·1. What is the probability that the mean of a sample of size 900 will be negative?

[Given $P(0 < Z < 1{\cdot}43) = 0.4236$)

(a) 0·0764 (b) 0·6408

(c) 0·6074 (d) 0·7046

35. Suppose that five random variables $(X_1, X_2, X_3, X_4, X_5)$ are independent and each has standard normal distribution. The random variable $\frac{C(X_1 + X_2)}{(X_3^4 + X_4^2 + X_5^2)^{1/2}}$ will have a t-distribution if the constant C is equal to

(a) $\frac{\sqrt{3}}{2}$ (b) $\sqrt{\frac{3}{2}}$

(c) $\frac{3}{2}$ (d) $\sqrt{\frac{2}{3}}$

36. If X is an F(m, n) random variable, where m > 2 and n > 2, then E(X) $E\left(\frac{1}{X}\right)$ equals

(a) $\frac{n(m-2)}{m(m-2)}$ (b) $\frac{m(m-2)}{n(n-2)}$

(c) $\frac{mn}{(m-2)(n-2)}$ (d) $\frac{m(n-2)}{n(m-2)}$

37. Which one of the following non-parametric tests is analogous to chi-square test of goodness of fit?

(a) Mann-Whitney test (b) Kolmogorov-Smirnov test

(c) Wilcoxon test (d) Median test

38. Consider the following statements:

1. Normal distribution is a particular case of chi-square distribution with 1 degree of freedom.
2. All moments of order less than n of t-distribution with n degrees of freedom exist.
3. If a statistic t follows Student's t-di stribution with n degrees of freedom, then t^2 follows F-distribution with (1, n) degrees of freedom.

Which of the statement(s) given above is/are correct?

(a) 1 only (b) 1 and 2 only

(c) 2 and 3 only (d) 1, 2 and 3

39. For a random sample of size 2 from N(0, σ^2) population, what is the value of E[$X_{(1)}$], where $X_{(1)}$ is first order statistic?

(a) $\frac{2\sigma}{\sqrt{\pi}}$ (b) $\frac{\sigma}{\pi}$

(c) $-\frac{\sigma}{\sqrt{\pi}}$ (d) $-\frac{\sigma}{\sqrt{2\pi}}$

40. If X_i, i = 1, 2, 3, ... , n are independent and identically distributed random variables with cdf F(x) = x, $0 \le x \le 1$, then the pdf g(r) of the range R = $X_{(n)} - X_{(1)}$ is

(a) $n(n-1)r^{n-2}(1-r)$ (b) $n(n-1)1, (1-r)^{n-2}$

(c) nr^{n-1} (d) $(n-1)r^{n-2}$

41. Given the data f(1) = 12, f(2) = 40, f(3) = 90, f(4) = 168, f(5) = 280, f(6) = 432. The degree of the polynomial f(x) is at least

(a) 2 (b) 3

(c) 4 (d) 5

42. The polynomial function f(x) = x^3 represented as factorial polynomial f(x) = $Ax^{(3)} + Bx^{(2)} + Cx +$ D when interval of differencing is h = 2. The values of A, B, C and D are respectively

(a) 1, 2, 6 and 0 (b) 1, 6, 4 and 0

(c) 2, 4, 6 and 0 (d) 2, 2, 6 and 1

43. **The nth divided difference of an nth degree**

(a) A variable (b) A constant

(c) Zero (d) None of the above

44. **The Runge-Kutta method of order four is used to solve the initial value problem $\frac{dy}{dx} = f(x)$, $y(0) = 0$ with step size h. Then the solution at $x = h$ is given by**

(a) $y(h) = \frac{h}{6}\left[3f(0) + f\left(\frac{h}{2}\right) + 3f(h)\right]$ (b) $y(h) = \frac{h}{6}[f(0) + 5f(h)]$

(c) $y(h) = \frac{h}{6}\left[f(0) + 3f\left(\frac{h}{2}\right) + 2f(h)\right]$ (d) $y(h) = \frac{h}{6}\left[f(0) + 4f\left(\frac{h}{2}\right) + f(h)\right]$

45. **The images f(n) of $n \in \{1, 2, 3, ..., 99\} \setminus \{50\}$ are given. If you have to estimate the image of 50 using forward difference table, then your hypothesis is**

(a) f is a polynomial of degree 50

(b) f is a polynomial of degree 99

(c) f is a polynomial of degree 98

(d) f is a polynomial of degree not more than 97

46. **Consider the following table:**

x	1	2	3	4	5
f(x)	2	5	7	α	32

The missing term (l in the above table is

(a) 14 (b) 15

(c) 16 (d) 17

47. **If $u_{10} = 9$, $u_{20} = 39$, $u_{30} = 74$, $u_{40} = 116$ and $u_{50} = 167$, then the value of $E^{3/2}(u_{10})$ is**

(a) 35.75 (b) 45.75

(c) 55.75 (d) 65.75

48. **The value of k that satisfies the equation $\Delta^2(1 + k\Delta^3)\, 0^5 = 630$ IS**

(a) 4 (b) 5

(c) 6 (d) 7

49. **Consider the following statements (Given that interval of differencing is 1):**

1. $(E - 2)^2 (x2^x) = 0$.
2. $(E - 3)^3 (x3^x) \neq 0$

Which of the statement(s) given above is/are correct?

(a) 1 only (b) 2 only

(c) Both 1 and 2 (d) Neither 1 nor 2

50. The following table gives the population (in lakhs) of a town in certain years.

Year	Population (in lakhs)
1971	0.9
1981	1.2
1991	1.5
2001	1.9
2011	2.5

The population P_{2006} (in lakhs) in 2006 is estimated by Newton's forward difference formula. Which one of the following is correct?

(a) $P_{2006} < 2$ (b) $2 < P_{2006} < 2.1$

(c) $2.1 < P_{2006} < 2.2$ (d) $2.2 < P_{2006} < 2.3$

51. Consider the following table:

x	2	3	α	5
f(x)	4	5	16	25

The missing value a of the argument in the above table is estimated by Lagrange interpolation formula. Which one of the following is correct?

(a) $3.5 < \alpha < 4$ (b) $\alpha = 4$

(c) $4 < \alpha < 4.2$ (d) $4.2 < \alpha < 4.5$

52. If δ and μ are the central differ ence and average operator respectively, then δ [f(x)g(x)]is equal to

(a) $\mu f(x)\, \mu g(x) + \delta f(x)\, \delta g(x)$ (b) $\delta f(x)\, \delta g(x) - \delta f(x)\, \mu g(x)$

(c) $\mu f(x)\, \delta g(x) - \mu g(x)\, \delta f(x)$ (d) $\mu f(x)\, \delta g(x) + \mu g(x)\, \delta f(x)$

53. If $f(x) = \frac{1}{x}$, then the third divided difference $\underset{b,c,d}{\overset{3}{\Delta}} f(a)$ is equal to

(a) $\frac{1}{abcd}$ (b) $-\frac{1}{abcd}$

(c) $\frac{a-d}{ad}$ (d) $\frac{1}{ad} - \frac{1}{bc}$

54. The equality $f(n^2) = n^3$ holds for n = 1, 2, 3. Then f(3) is given by Lagrange's interpolation as.

(a) 4·9 (b) 5·1

(c) 5·3 (d) 5·5

55. The central difference δ is equivalent to which of the following?

1. $2 \sinh\left(\frac{hD}{2}\right)$
2. $E^{-1/2} \Delta$
3. $\Delta(1 + \Delta)^{-1/2}$

Select the correct answer using the code given below:

(a) 1 and 2 only (b) 2 and 3 only

(c) 1 and 3 only (d) 1, 2 and 3

56. Consider the following statements regarding quadrature formulae:

1. Geometrically Simpson's one-third rule implies that we have re placed the graph of the given function by nl2 arcs of second degree polynomials.
2. Weddle's rule gives an exact result when f(x) is a polynomial of degree 6 or less.

Which of the statement(s) given above is/are correct?

(a) 1 only (b) 2 only

(c) Both 1 and 2 (d) Neither 1 nor 2

57. If an integral is computed using Simpson's three-eighth rule dividing the range into three equal parts, then the value of the integral $\int_0^{\frac{1}{2}}$ is

(a) $\frac{3(1+\sqrt{2})}{32}$ (b) $\frac{5+3\sqrt{3}}{32}$

(c) $\frac{3+5\sqrt{3}}{32}$ (d) $\frac{3\sqrt{3}}{8}$

58. The formula a $\alpha f\left(-\frac{1}{2}\right)+\beta f(0)+\gamma f\left(\frac{1}{2}\right)$ which approximates the integral $\int_{-1}^{1}$ f(x) dx is exact for every polynomial of degree less than 3. Then which one of the following is correct?

(a) $\alpha=\gamma=\frac{4}{3}, \beta=-\frac{2}{3}$ (b) $\alpha=\gamma=\frac{1}{3}, \beta=0$

(c) $\alpha=\gamma=\frac{4}{3}, \beta=1$ (d) $\alpha=\beta=\gamma$

59. If the integral is computed using Trapezoidal rule by dividing the range into ten equal parts, then the value of $\int_0^{10} 2^x$ belongs to

(a) (1400, 1450) (b) (1450, 1500)

(c) (1500, 1550) (d) (1550, 1600)

60. For the initial value problem $\frac{dy}{dx}=\frac{y}{x^2}$, y(1) = 1, approximations y_1 and y_2 are computed using Picard's method with $y_0 = y(1)$. Then the constant terms of $y_1(x)$ and $y_2(x)$ are respectively

(a) 1, 1 (b) 2, 2

(c) $2, \frac{3}{2}$ (d) None of the above

61. Consider the following statements:

1. ALU is a component of Control Unit.
2. CPU is a component of Control Unit.
3. Control Unit is not a component of ALU.
4. ALU is a component of CPU.

Which of the above statement(s) is/are correct?

(a) 4 only (b) 3 and 4 only

(c) 1 and 3 only (d) 2, 3 and 4

62. Conversion of octal number 325·12 into its decimal number will be

(a) 532·123 (b) 213.15625

(c) 213.56121 (d) 124.123

63 A system consists of 1024 memory locations and each location can store 8 bits. How many number of address lines are required to address?

(a) 8 (b) 10

(c) 16 (d) 1024

64. The core component of UNIX is

(a) Command shell (b) Kernel

(c) Directories and programs (d) None of the above

65. Consider signed magnitude, 1's complement and 2's complement repr esentation of negative integers in computers. Generally 2's complement is used because

1. More numbers can be stored in 2's complement
2. Arithmetic operations can be performed faster
3. It is easy to represent negative numbers in 2's complement

Which of the above are correct?

(a) 1 and 3 only (b) 2 and 3 only

(c) 1 and 2 only (d) 1, 2 and 3

66. Which one of the following is the correct normalised form for 11·234 ?

(a) 11·234 (b) ·11234E + 2

(c) ·011234E + 1 (d) 1·1234E x 10

67. The maximum decimal integer number that can be stored in memory of 8 bit word processor computer is

(a) $(128)_{10}$ (b) $(127)_{10}$

(c) $(129)_{10}$ (d) $(130)_{10}$

68. Which of the following are not bitwise operators?

1. &&
2. &
3. »
4. !
5. %

Select the correct answer using the code given below :

(a) 2 and 3 only (b) 1, 3, 4 and 5

(c) 1,2 and 5 (d) 1, 4 and 5

69. Which type of memory is the auxiliary memory?

(a) SRAM (b) Magnetic tape

(c) Flash ROM (d) Cache memory

70. Which one of the following statements is correct?

(a) Compiler translates and executes instructions simultaneously.

(b) Interpreter translates and executes the instructions simultaneously.

(c) Interpreter can only translate machine language programs.

(d) None of the above

71. Consider the following code:

```
While (x! = y)
{
    if(x > y)
    x = x - y
    else
    y = y - x
}
```

What does the above code do ?

(a) It computes x mod y using repeated subtraction

(b) It computes x ÷ y using repeated subtraction

(c) It computes the greatest common divisor of x and y

(d) It computes the least common multiple of x and y

72. Consider the following statements:

1. Array is a collection of data elements of same type.
2. Strings are character arrays in which each character is stored using one byte precedence? in memory.
3. Array can store different types of elements.
4. Strings can be data array also.

Which of the above statements are correct?

(a) 1 and 3 only (b) 1 and 2 only

(c) 3 and 4 only (d) 1, 2, 3 and 4

73. Consider the following statements:

1. Weighted 4-bit BCD code is known as 1246 weighted code.
2. Octal system is also known as base-8 system.
3. Octal system is known as base-2 system.
4. Weighted 4-bit BCD code is known as 8421 weighted code.

Which of the above statement(s) is/are correct?

(a) 2 only (b) 3 and 4 only
(c) 1 and 2 only (d) 2 and 4 only

74. The maximum permissible integer in a computer with n-bit word processor and one word per integer is equal to

(a) $2^n - 1$ (b) $2^{n-1} - 1$
(c) $2^{n-1} + 1$ (d) $2n + 1$

75. Which operators follow right to left order of precedence?

1. Unary operator
2. Assignment operator
3. Logical operator
4. Bit manipulation operator

Select the correct answer using the code given below:

(a) 1 and 2 only (b) 1, 2 and 4
(c) 3 and 4 only (d) 1 only

76. Compiler can diagnose

(a) Grammatical errors only
(b) Logical errors only
(c) Both grammatical and logical errors
(d) Neither grammatical errors nor logical errors

77. A software program that cannot be changed easily and is stored in a ROM is known as

(a) Hardware (b) Firmware
(c) Linker (d) Editor

78. A computer program can run successfully even if there is

(a) Syntax error (b) Logical error
(c) Run-time error (d) None of the above

79. A disc storage has 16 data-recording s urfaces. Number of tracks per surface is 256 and number of sectors per track is 16. Bytes per sector are 512. What is storage capacity of the disc system?

(a) 3325652 bytes (b) 3256662 bytes
(c) 33554432 bytes (d) 335444332 bytes

80. Which one of the following is a low-level programmivg language?

(a) FORTRAN (b) Machine language
(c) COBOL (d) C

GENERAL STATISTICS
Paper I 2017

Time Allowed : Three Hours | *Maximum Marks: 200*

INSTRUCTIONS

1. IMMEDIATELY AFTER THE COMMENCEMENT OF THE EXAMINATION, YOU SHOULD CHECK THAT THIS TEST BOOKLET DOES NOT HAVE ANY UNPRINTED OR TORN OR MISSING PAGES OR ITEMS, ETC. IF SO, GET IT REPLACED BY A COMPLETE TEST BOOKLET.
2. Please note that it is the candidate's responsibility to encode and fill in the Roll Number and Test Booklet Series A, B, C or D carefully and without any omission or discrepancy at the appropriate places in the OMR Answer Sheet. Any omission/discrepancy will render the Answer Sheet liable for rejection.
3. You have to enter your Roll Number on the Test Booklet in I the Box provided alongside. DO NOT write anything else on the Test Booklet.
4. This Test Booklet contains 80 items (questions). Each item comprises four responses (answers). You will select the response which you want to mark on the Answer Sheet. In case you feel that there is more than one correct response, mark the response which you consider the best. In any case, choose ONLY ONE response for each item.
5. You have to mark all your responses ONLY on the separate Answer Sheet provided. See directions in the Answer Sheet.
6. All items carry equal marks.
7. Before you proceed to mark in the Answer Sheet the response to various items in the Test Booklet, you have to fi ll in some particulars in the Answer Sheet as per instructions sent to you with your Admission Certificate.
8. After you have completed filling in all your responses on the Answer Sheet and the examination has concluded , you should hand over to the Invigilator only the Answer Sheet. You are permitted to take away with you the Test Booklet.
9. Sheets for rough work are appended in the Test Booklet at the end.
10. Penalty for wrong answers :

    THERE WILL BE PENALTY FOR WRONG ANSWERS MARKED BY A CANDIDATE IN THE OBJECTIVE-TYPE QUESTION PAPERS.

(i) There are four alternatives for the answer to every question. For each question for which a wrong answer has been given by the candidate, one·thlrd of the marks assigned to that question will be deducted as penalty.

(ii) If a candidate gives more than one answer, it will be treated a s a wrong answer even if one of the given answers happens to be correct and there will be same pen alty as above to that question.

(iii) If a question is left blank, i.e ., no answer is given by the candidate, there will be no penalty for that question.

DO NOT OPEN THIS TEST BOOKLET UNTIL YOU ARE TOLD TO DO SO

1. Leelas has appeared in an examination which follows multiple choice questions, each having five possible answers. The probability that she knows an answer is 0.75. If she does not know an answer, she wil guess, with the conditional probability $\frac{1}{5}$ of being correct. The conditional probability that Leela knows the answer, given that she give the correct answer, is

(a) 0.25 (b) 0.80

(c) 0.90 (d) 0.84

2. Consider a sequence of Bernoulli trials with probability of success $\frac{1}{3}$ for each trial. Let X denote the length of run of either successes or failure starting with the first trial. Then the value of E(X) is

(a) 2 (b) 2.5

(c) 3 (d) 3.5

3. The probability that a death occurs due to heart failure is 0.45 and the probability that a death occurs due to cancer is 0.02.

Consider the following statements:

1. The probability that the death is either due to heart failure or due to cancer is 0.67.
2. The probability that the death is due to some other cause (but not these two) is 0.55.

Which of the statements is/are correct?

(a) 1 only (b) 2 only

(c) Both 1 and 2 (d) Neither 1 nor 2

4. Let X, a continous random variable, follow U(0, 1) distribution. Then, we assert that

1. $P(X \geq 0.27) = 0.73$
2. $P(0.27 , X < 1.27) = 0.73$

Which of the above assertions is/are correct?

(a) 1 only (b) 2 only

(c) Both 1 and 2 (d) Neither 1 nor 2

5. Let X be the number of phone calls recieved at a call centre during business hours and Y be the number of calls received outside business hours, on a partiular day. Assume that X and Y are independent, and follow the Poisson distribution with means λ_1 and λ_2 respectively, where $\lambda_1 \neq \lambda_2$. Then the conditional distribution of X, given the total number of calls recieved that day

(i.e., X + Y), is

(a) Binomial (b) Poisson

(c) Discrete Uniform (d) Negative Binomial

6. A and B are events such that P(A) = **, P(B) = ** and $P(A \cap B)$ = **. Then consider the following:

1. $P(A \cap \bar{B}) = \frac{1}{4}$

2. $P(\bar{A} \cap \bar{B}) = \frac{1}{2}$

3. $P(B|\bar{A}) = \frac{1}{3}$

Which of the above statement are correct?

(a) 1 and 2 only (b) 2 and 3 only

(c) 1 and 3 only (d) 1, 2 and 3

8. A man buys 10 bulbs, each with independent exponentially distributed lifetimes with the same mean, with the intention of using one bulb at a time and replacingit with another as soon as it fails. The distribution of the total duration of the 10 bulbs taken together is

(a) Exponential (b) Normal

(c) Beta (d) Gamma

9. In a continuous distribution, the probability density function is given by

$$f(x) = \begin{cases} y_0 x(2-x); & 0 \le x \le 2 \\ 0 & \text{otherwise} \end{cases}$$

where y_0 is a constant

Its first moment about the origin is given by

(a) 1 (b) 2

(c) 3 (d) 4

10. Let X and Y be independent random variables, each having the uniform distribution on [–1, 2]. Then Var (X + Y) is equal to

(a) $\frac{3}{2}$ (b) $\frac{5}{2}$

(c) 4 (d) 6

11. In an examination, marks obtained by the students in Physics, Mathematics and Statistics denoted by X, Y and Z are normally distributed with mean 50, 52 and 48 respectively and with standard devitation 15, 12 and 16 respectively. The distribution of (X + Y + Z) is

(a) N(3350, 53) (b) N(55, 350)

(c) N(150, 625) (d) N(625, 150)

12. A drunkard takes a forward step with probability p and a backward step with probability q. After taking 11 steps, the probability that he is one step away from the starting point is

(a) $p^6 + q^6$ (b) $2(p^6 + q^5)$

(c) $462\ p^6q^5$ (d) $462(pq)^5$

13. **Consider n independent Poisson variables $X_1, X_2, X_3, ..., X_n$ with parameters $\lambda_1, \lambda_2, \lambda_3, ... \lambda_n$ respectively and $S_n = X_1 + X_2 + X_3 + ... + X_n$.**

Statement I:

S_n has a Poisson distribution with parameter $\sum_{j=1}^{n} \ddot{e}_i$

Statement II:

The mgf of S_n is $e^{\sum_{i=1}^{n} \lambda_i (e^t - 1)}$

Which one of the following is correct in respect of the above statements?

(a) Both Statement I and Statement II are true and Statement II is the correct explanation of Statement I

(b) Both Statement I and Statement II are true but Statement II is ***not*** the correct explanation of Statement I

(c) Statement I is true but Statement II is false

(d) Statement I is false but Statement II is true

14. **If the distribution function of a random variable X is given by F(x) = sin x, where $0 < x < \frac{\pi}{2}$, then the probability density function at $x = \frac{\pi}{6}$ has the value**

(a) $\frac{1}{2}$ (b) $\frac{\sqrt{3}}{2}$

(c) $\frac{1}{\sqrt{2}}$ (d) $\frac{1}{3}$

15. **If X and Y are independent identically distributed $N(0, \sigma^2)$ random variables, then which of the following are correct?**

1. $\frac{X^2 + Y^2}{\sigma^2}$ follows a Chi-square distribution with 2 degree of freedom.
2. $\frac{X}{Y}$ follows a standard Cauchy distribution.
3. $\frac{(X + Y)^2}{\sigma^2}$ follows a Chi-square distribution with 2 degree of freedom.
4. $(X - Y)$ and $(X + Y)$ are independent

Select the correct answer using the code given below:

(a) 1 and 2 only (b) 2, 3 and 4 only

(c) 1, 2 and 4 only (d) 1 and 4 only

6. **A and B are events such that $P(A) = \frac{1}{4}, P(B) = \frac{1}{3}$ and $P(A \cap B) = \frac{1}{12}$. Then consider the following:**

1. $P(A \cap \bar{B}) = \frac{1}{4}$

2. $P(\bar{A} \cap \bar{B}) = \frac{1}{2}$

3. $P(B|\bar{A}) = \frac{1}{3}$

Which of the above statements are correct?

(a) 1 and 2 only
(b) 2 and 3 only
(c) 1 and 3 only
(d) 1, 2 and 3

7. Consider a game where the player tosses a six-sided die. If the face that comes up is 6, the player wins ₹ 36, otherwise he loses ₹ k^2, where k is the face that comes up (k = 1, 2, 3, 4, 5). What amount in rupees can the player expect to win at this game if the die is fair?

(a) $\frac{19}{6}$
(b) $-\frac{19}{6}$
(c) $\frac{3}{2}$
(d) $-\frac{3}{2}$

8. A man buys 10 bulbs, each with independent exponentially distributed lifetimes with the same mean, with the intention of using one bulb at a time and replacing it with another as soon as it falls. The distribution of the total duration of the 10 bulb taken together is

(a) Exponential
(b) Normal
(c) Beta
(d) Gamma

9. In a continuous distribution, the probability density function is given by

$$f(x) = \begin{cases} y_0 x(2-x); & 0 \le x \le 2 \\ 0 & \text{otherwise} \end{cases}$$

where y_0 is a constant.

Its first moment about the origin is given by

(a) 1
(b) 2
(c) 3
(d) 4

10. Let X and Y be independent random variables, each having the uniform distribution on [–1, 2]. Then Var (X + Y) is equal to

(a) $\frac{3}{2}$
(b) $\frac{5}{2}$
(c) 4
(d) 6

11. In an examination, marks obtained by the students in Physics, Mathematics and Statistics denoted by X, Y and Z are normally distributed with mean 50, 52 and 48 respectively and with standard deviation 15, 12 and 16 respectively. The distributionof (X + Y + Z) is

(a) N(350, 53)
(b) N(55, 350)
(c) N(150, 625)
(d) N(625, 150)

12. A drunked takes a forward step with probability p and a backward step with probability q. After taking 11 steps, the probability that he is one step away from the starting point is

(a) $p^6 + q^6$
(b) $2(p^6 + q^5)$
(c) $462p^6q^5$
(d) $462(pq)^5$

13. Consider n independent Poisson variables $X_1, X_2, X_3, ..., X_n$ with parameters $\lambda_1, \lambda_2, \lambda_3, ..., \lambda_n$ respectively and $S_n = X_1 + X_2 + X_3 + ... + X_n$.

Statement I

S_n has a Poisson distribution with parameter $\sum_{j=1}^{n} \lambda_1$

Statement II

The mgf of S_n is $e^{\sum_{j=1}^{n} \lambda_i (e^t - 1)}$

Which one of the folowing is correct in respect of the above statements?

(a) Both Statement I and Statement II are true and Statement II is the correct explanation of Statement I

(b) Both Statement I and Statement II are true but Statement II is not the correct explanation of Statement I

(c) Statement I is true but Statement II is false

(d) Statement I is false but Statement II is true

14. If the distribution function of a random variable X is given by $F(x) = \sin x$, where $0 < x < \frac{\pi}{2}$, then the probability density function at $x = \frac{\pi}{6}$ has the value

(a) $\frac{1}{2}$ (b) $\frac{\sqrt{3}}{2}$

(c) $\frac{1}{\sqrt{2}}$ (d) $\frac{1}{3}$

15. If X and Y are independent identically distributed $N(0, \sigma^2)$ random variables, then which of the following are correct?

1. $\frac{X^2 + Y^2}{\sigma^2}$ follows a Chi-square distribution with 2 degrees of freedom.
2. $\frac{X}{Y}$ follows a standard Cauchy distribution.
3. $\frac{(X+Y)^2}{\sigma^2}$ follows a Chi-square distribution with 2 degrees of freedom.
4. $(X - Y)$ and $(X + Y)$ are independent.

Select the correct answer using the code given below:

(a) 1 and 2 only (b) 2, 3 and 4 only

(c) 1, 2 and 4 only (d) 1 and 4 only

16. Player A writes a '+' sign on a magic slate. The slate is then passed on to players B, C and D in succession, each of whom may rub the slate and change the sign to '–' with probability ** before passing the slate to the next person. D hands the slate to the referee. The probability that the referee sees as '+' sign is

(a) $\frac{13}{27}$ (b) $\frac{7}{27}$

(c) $\frac{10}{27}$ (d) $\frac{4}{27}$

17. For a random variable X, $P(X = 0) = 1 - \frac{1}{k^2}$ and $P(X = +1) = P(X = -1) = \frac{1}{2k^2}$ where k is a constant greater than 1. Then which one of the following is correct?

(a) $P(|X| \geq k\sigma) < \frac{1}{k^2}$ (b) $P(|X| \geq k\sigma) = \frac{1}{k^2}$

(c) $P(|X| \geq k\sigma) > 1 - \frac{1}{k^2}$ (d) $P(|X - 1| \geq k\sigma) = \frac{1}{k^2}$

18. For the sequence $\{X_k\}$ of independent random variables the following are defined:
$P(X_k = \pm 2^k) = 2^{-(2k+1)}$, $P(X_k = 0) = 1 - 2^{-2k}$
Which of the following are not correct?

1. Weak law of large numbers holds because $E(X_k) = 0$ and $\lim_{n\to\infty} \frac{B_n}{n^2} = 0$ where $B_n = \text{Var}\left(\sum_{i=1}^{n} X_i\right)$
2. Weak law of large numbers holds by Khinchin's theorem because $E(X_k)$ is finite.
3. Weak law of large numbers holds sincd X_k are identically distributed.

Select the correct answer using the code given below:

(a) 2 and 3 only (b) 1 and 2 only

(c) 1 amd 3 only (d) 1, 2 and 3

19. Let X and Y be two random variables. Which one of the following conditions is sufficient for the relation Var(X – Y) = Var(X) + Var(Y) to hold?

(a) X, Y are statistically independent

(b) X, Y are identically distributed

(c) X = Y

(d) For any X and Y

20. Suppose U and V are independently and uniformly distributed on the interval (0, 1). Then the distribution of max (U, V) is

(a) Beta (1, 1) (b) Beta (2, 2)

(c) Beta (1, 2) (d) Beta (2, 1)

Consider the following for the next three (03) items:

The distribution of marks obtained by 500 candidates in a Statistics paper in a certain examination is as follows:

Marks more than	Number of Candidates
0	500
10	460

20	400
30	200
40	100
50	30

21. If 60% of the candidates pass the paper, then the minimum marks obtained by a pass candidate is

(a) 20 (b) 25

(c) 30 (d) 35

22. The value of semi-interquartile range is

(a) 4.25 (b) 8.125

(c) 16.25 (d) 32.5

23. The value of mode of frequency distribution is

(a) 23.13 (b) 24.43

(c) 25.83 (d) 26.13

24. In a series of 2n observation, half of then equal to k and the remaining half equal to – k. If the standard deviation of the observations is 2, then |k| is equal to

(a) $\sqrt{2}$ (b) 2

(c) $\sqrt{\frac{2}{n}}$ (d) $\frac{1}{n}$

25. If σ_x^2, σ_y^2 and σ_{x-y}^2 are the variance of X, Y and X – Y respectively, then what is the coefficient of correlation between X and Y?

(a) $\frac{\sigma_x^2 + \sigma_y^2 - \sigma_{x+y}^2}{2\sigma_x \sigma_y}$ (b) $\frac{\sigma_x^2 + \sigma_y^2 - \sigma_{x-y}^2}{2\sigma_x \sigma_y}$

(c) $\frac{\sigma_x^2 + \sigma_y^2}{2\sigma_x \sigma_y}$ (d) $\frac{\sigma_x^2 - \sigma_y^2}{2\sigma_x \sigma_y}$

26. For a distribution of 10 observations, calculations showed that the first two moments about the origin are 3 and 46 respectively. It was however discovered that the observation 12 was wrongly written as 22. Then the correct value of mean and variance are respectively

(a) 2, 12 (b) 2, 8

(c) 4, 12 (d) 4, 8

27. Given that x_1 and x_2 are two independent observation drawn from a normal population P_1 and y_1 and y_2 are another two independent observations drawn from a second normal population P_2. In order that $Z = \frac{(x_1 - x_2)^2}{(y_1 - y_2)^2}$ follows F-distribution with (1, 1) degrees of freedom, which one of the following must be true?

(a) P_1 has $N(\mu_1, \sigma_1^2)$ and P_2 has $N(\mu_1, \sigma_2^2)$

(b) P_1 has $N(0, \sigma_1^2)$ and P_2 has $N(\mu_1, \sigma_2^2)$

(c) P_1 has $N(\mu_1, \sigma_1^2)$ and P_2 has $N(\mu_2, \sigma_2^2)$

(d) P_1 has $N(\mu_1, \sigma^2)$ and P_2 has $N(\mu_2, \sigma^2)$

28. What is the probability that the sample median based on a random sample of size 3, drawn from a distribution with pdf

$$f(x) = \begin{cases} 2x & 0 < x < 1 \\ 0 & \text{otherwise} \end{cases} \quad \text{exceeds } \frac{1}{2}?$$

(a) $\frac{13}{32}$ (b) $\frac{17}{32}$

(c) $\frac{27}{32}$ (d) $\frac{29}{32}$

29. Consider the following statements:

1. If $F(n_1, n_2)$ represents an F variate with n_1 and n_2 degrees fo freedom, then $F(n_2, n_1)$ is dstributed as $\frac{1}{F(n_1, n_2)}$ variate.
2. In $F(n_1, n_2)$ distribution if $n_2 \to \infty$, then n_1F follows t-distrbution with n_1 degrees of freedom.
3. If a statistic t follows Student's t-distribution with n degrees of freedom, then t^2 follows F-distribution with (1, n) degrees of freedom.

Which of the above statements are correct?

(a) 1 and 2 only (b) 2 and 3 only

(c) 1 and 3 only (d) 1, 2 and 3

30. A continuous random variable X has the density function

$$f(x) = \begin{cases} \frac{3x^2}{\theta^3} & 0 \le x \le \theta \text{ for some } \theta > 0 \\ 0 & \text{otherwise.} \end{cases}$$

Then the ratio of the median for the distribution is

(a) $2^{-1/3}$ (b) $2^{1/3}$

(c) $\frac{\theta}{2^{1/3}}$ (d) θ

31. Consider the following statements on the use of F-distribution:

1. It is used to test the equality of variances of two normal populations.
2. It is used to test the equality of variances of several normal populations.
3. It is used to test for the equality of means of several normal populations with identical variances.
4. It is used to rest for the independence of two attributes in a contingency table.

Which of the above statements are correct?

(a) 1 and 3 only (b) 2 and 3 only

(c) 1 and 4 only (d) 1, 3 and 4 only

32. Suppose for a given data, the linear, parabolic, power function and exponential models fitted by the principle of least squares respectively are given below:

M_1: $Y = 3.77 + 0.92X$

M_2: $Y = 1.21 + 0.40X + 0.04X^2$

M_3: $Y = 2.58X^{0.5}$

M_4: $Y = 2.64e^{0.0625X}$

If for any model, $\hat{Y}_i$ denotes the estimated value of Y_i and $\sum_i (Y_i - \hat{Y}_i)^2$ computed for models M_1, M_2, M_3 and M_4 are 19.37, 5.73, 4.81 and 11.58 respectively, then which one of the following shall be taken as the best possible estimate of Y for X = 16?

(a) 18.49 (b) 17.85

(c) 10.32 (d) 7.18

33. If X_1, X_2, X_3 and X_4 are four uncorrelated variables each with varance σ^2, then what is the value of the correlation coefficient between $U = X_1 + X_2 + X_3$ and $V = X_1 + X_2 + X_4$?

(a) 0 (b) $\frac{1}{3}$

(c) $\frac{2}{3}$ (d) 1

34. Given that X, Y and Z = X + 2Y are variables such that Var (X) = 4, Var(Y) = 3 and Var(Z) = 4.

Consider the following statements in respect of the above:

1. The covariance between X and Y is –3.
2. The correlation between X and Y is $-\frac{\sqrt{3}}{2}$.
3. The regression coefficient of Y on X is $-\frac{3}{4}$.
4. The covariance between X and Z is – 2.

Which of the above statements are correct?

(a) 1, 2 and 3 only (b) 1, 3 and 4 only

(c) 2 and 4 only (d) 1, 2, 3 and 4

35. Suppose X, Y and Z are independent random variables such that X follows a standard normal distribution; Y and Z follow Chi-square distribution with n_1 and n_2 degrees of freedom respectively.

Consider the following statements in respect of the above:

1. X^2 follows Chi-square distribution with one degree of freedom.
2. $\frac{X}{\sqrt{Y/n_i}}$ follows Student's t-distribution with n_1 degrees of freedom.

3. $\dfrac{(Y/n_1)}{(Z/n_2)}$ follows F-distribution with (n_1, n_2) degrees of freedom.

4. Y + Z follows Cauchy distribution.

Which of the above statements are correct?

(a) 1, 2 and 3 only (b) 2, 3 and 4 only

(c) 1 and 4 only (d) 1, 2, 3 and 4

36. IfX follows (6, 6) distribution, then consider the following statements:

1. Mean of X is greater than 1.
2. Median of X is equal to 1.
3. Mode of X lies between 0 and 1.

Which of the above statements are correct?

(a) 1 and 2 only (b) 2 and 3 only

(c) 1 and 3 only (d) 1, 2 and 3

37. An analysis of monthly wages of workers of two factories A and B belonging to the same group gave the following results:

Statistic	Factory A	Factory B
Number of workers	50	60
Average daily wages	₹ 186	₹175
Variance of wages	81	100

Then the combined variance is given by

(a) 101.36 (b) 111.36

(c) 121.36 (d) 131.36

38. Chi-square test can be applied to test the

1. Goodness of fit
2. Equality of two population variances
3. Independence of attributes

Which of the above are correct?

(a) 1 and 2 only (b) 2 and 3 only

(c) 1 and 3 only (d) 1, 2 and 3

39. Let f(x, y) = $Ce^{-\frac{Q}{2}}$ where Q = 2x2 + y2+ 2xy – 22x – 14y + 65 be the pdf of a bivariate normal BN(μ_1, σ_1^2, σ_2^2, ρ) distribution. Then ρ = Corr(X, Y) is

(a) 1 (b) – 1

(c) $\dfrac{1}{2}$ (d) $-\dfrac{1}{\sqrt{2}}$

40. Let (X, Y) be a bivariate normal $BN\left(1, 2, 16, 25, \frac{3}{4}\right)$, then $E(X|Y = 7)$ is

(a) 1 (b) 2

(c) 4 (d) $\frac{91}{16}$

41. The polynomial of least degree interpolation of the data (0, 4), (1, 5), (2, 8), (3, 13) is

(a) 4 (b) 3

(c) 2 (d) 1

42. If $x_0 = 2$, $x_1 = 3$ and $x_2 = 5$ and $f(x_0) = 1$, $f(x_1) = 2$ and $f(x_2) = 6$, then the approximate value of f(4) using Lagrange's interpolation formula is

(a) 5.66 (b) 4.66

(c) 3.66 (d) 2.66

43. If h is the increment in the variable x, then $\left(\frac{\Delta^2}{E}\right)x^2$ is equal to

(a) 2h (b) $2h^2$

(c) $2h^3$ (d) None of the above

44. Consider the following statements:

1. Lagrange's interpolation formula is applicable only when arguments are equispaced.
2. The sum of Lagrangean coefficients is unity.

Which of the above statements is/are correct?

(a) 1 only (b) 2 only

(c) Both 1 and 2 (d) Neither 1 nor 2

45. Consider the followig statements:

1. Simpson's one-third rule follows from Romberg's method with n = 2.
2. Weddle's rule follows from Romberg' method with n = 4.

Which of the above statements is/are correct?

(a) 1 only (b) 2 only

(c) Both 1 and 2 (d) Neither 1 nor 2

46. Consider the following:

x	0	1	2	3	4
f(x)	5	1	9	25	55

The estimation of f(5) using Newton-Gregory interpolation is

(a) 71 (b) 87.5

(c) 95 (c) 115

47. What is the function whose first difference is $9x^2 + 11x + 5$ with interval of difference equal to 1?

(a) $x^3 + 2x^2 - x$ + cosnstant
(b) $2x^3 - 3x^2 + x$ + constant
(c) $3x^3 + x^2 + x$ + constant
(d) $9x^3 + 20x^2 + 5x$ + constant

48. What is the value of

$\Delta^3[(1 - x)(1 - 2x)(1 - 3x)]$

with interval of difference equal to 1?

(a) – 36
(b) – 12
(c) 0
(d) 6

49. The error in evalunting $\int_1^2 x^2\,dx$ using Simpson's one-third rule by dividing the interval (1, 2) into four equal parts is

(a) 0
(b) 1.5
(c) 1.52
(d) 1

50. Consider the following statements for numerical solution of first order differential equations:

1. Euler's method is slow for large x-increment and inaccurate for small x-increment.
2. Modified Euler's method has an error of order h^2.
3. Picard's method is an iterative method.

Which of the above statements is/are correct?

(a) 1 and 3 only
(b) 2 and 3 only
(c) 1 and 2 only
(d) 3 only

51. Consider the following:

x	1	2	3	4
f(x)	46	66	81	93

The value of f(3.5) using Newton's Backward Difference Interpolation formula is

(a) 86.25
(b) 87.25
(c) 88.25
(d) 89.25

52. Let the factorial polynomial be

$f(x) = x^{(3)} + 2x^{(2)} - 4x + 9$. When the interval of differencing is 1, then mode of f(x) is

(a) $-\frac{4}{3}$
(b) – 2
(c) 1
(d) None of the above

53. Consider the following statements with standard notation:

1. $E = 1 + \Delta$
2. $E = e^{hD}$
3. $\nabla = 1 - E^{-1}$

Which of the above are correct?

(a) 1 and 2 only
(b) 2 and 3 only
(c) 1 and 3 only
(d) 1, 2 and 3

54. If δ is the central difference operator, μ is the average operator, Δ is the forward difference operator and ∇ is the backward difference operator, then $\Delta + \nabla$ equal to

(a) ** (b) $\mu + \delta$

(c) $2\mu\delta$ (d) $\mu\delta$

55. What is $f(3) + \Delta f(2) + \Delta^2 f(1) + \Delta^2 f(1)$ equal to? (Take the interval of differencing to be unity)

(a) $f(4)$ (b) $\Delta f(4)$

(c) $\Delta^2 f(4)$ (d) $\Delta^3 f(4)$

56. Using Picard's method to compute y(0.2), correct up to two decimal places, where y(x) is the solution of $\frac{dy}{dx} = x - y$, $y(0) = 1$. The value of y(0.2) is

(a) 0.82 (b) 0.83

(c) 0.84 (d) 0.86

57. Milne's method for numerial solution of a differential equation is based on

(a) Prediction only (b) Correction only

(c) Both prediction and correction (d) Neither on prediction nor on correction

58. The sum to 10 terms of the series

$$\frac{1}{2\times 3}\times 2 + \frac{2}{3\times 4}\times 4 + \frac{3}{4\times 5}\times 8 + \frac{4}{5\times 6}\times 16 + \ldots \text{ is}$$

(a) $\frac{253}{3}$ (b) $\frac{256}{3}$

(c) $\frac{509}{3}$ (d) $\frac{512}{3}$

59. A cubic polynomial takes the following values:

x	0	1	2	3
f(x)	1	0	1	10

Then f(4) equal to

(a) 6 (b) 19

(c) 27 (d) 33

60. The iterative formula for the solution of differential equation $\frac{dy}{dx} = f(x, y)$, $y(x_0) = y_0$ by Euler's method is

(a) $y_{n+1} = y_0 + hf(x_0, y_n)$ (b) $y_{n+1} = y_0 + hf(x_0, y_n)$

(c) $y_{n+1} = y_0 + hf(x_n, y_n)$ (d) $y_{n+1} = y_n + hf(x_n, y_n)$

61. Consider the following:

1. Break
2. If
3. Do-while
4. Continue

While of the above are jump control statements?

(a) 1 and 4 only (b) 2 and 3 only

(c) 1, 3 and 4 only (d) 3 and 4 only

62. Which one of the following is the correct sequence of stages in problem solving?

(a) Precise formulation, Analysis, Computation of the problem

(b) Designing, Coding, Analysis, Debugging the program

(c) Coding, Precise formulation, Computation, Debugging the problem

(d) Coding, Compilation, Designing, Debugging and Executing the program

63. An operating system is crucial for the operation of a computer system becuase it

1. controls the hardware of the computer.
2. runs the antivirus software.
3. manages files and directories.
4. allows Google search.

Which of the above are the most crucial funnctions of an operating system?

(a) 1 and 2 only (b) 2 and 4 only

(c) 1 and 3 only (d) 1, 2, 3 and 4

64. What is the decimal equivalent of the hexadecimal number FFFE?

(a) 25535 (b) 32766

(c) 65244 (d) 65534

65. Consider the following statements:

1. A compiler checks the source code for syntax errors and if it is error-free, creates an object code.
2. Linking means resolving library references to embed necessary routines.

Which of the above statements is/are correct?

(a) 1 only (b) 2 only

(c) 1 only (d) 2 only

67. Consider the following:

1. Computer port
2. Modem type
3. Modem speed
4. Modem size

Which of the above factors are important when using a modern for data communication?

(a) 1 and 2 only (b) 2 and 3 only

(c) 1 and 3 only (d) 1 and 4 only

68. The size of memory in any system is decided/calculated by the

(a) Number of data lines

(b) Number of address lines

(c) Number of bits in a single memory location

(d) Number of bits in a single word

69. What is the function of a Firewall?

1. To autheticate user before access
2. To block traffic intended for a particular IP address
3. To create a wall to prevent unauthorised access for network

Select the correct answer using the code given below:

(a) 1 and 2 only (b) 2 and 3 only

(c) 1 and 3 only (d) 1, 2 and 3

70. Machhine language programs are very efficient becuase

(a) they are easy to develop

(b) their object code is very small in size

(c) they are directly executed by CPU

(d) they are easily understood by programmers

71. Consider the following statements in respect of a mouse:

1. It controls the two-dimensional movement of the cursor on the displayed screen.
2. It is usually of two different types, mechanical and optical.
3. It can be used as an alternate to the keyboard for all purposes.
4. It is an input device.

Which of the above statements are correct?

(a) 3 and 4 only (b) 1 and 4 only

(c) 1, 2 and 4 only (d) 1, 2 and 3 only

72. Which one of the following hardware components is normally used to accommodate the secondary cache?

(a) Motherboard (b) Processor

(c) RAM (d) Any secondary storage device

73. The file manager is responsible for

1. Naming files
2. Saving files
3. Deleting files

Which of the above are correct?

(a) 1 and 2 only (b) 2 and 3 only

(c) 1 and 3 only (d) 1, 2 and 3

74. Collecting the data and converting it into information is called

(a) Compiling (b) Processing

(c) Importing (d) Exporting

75. SSL in Linux provides

1. Password protection
2. Logging
3. Security

Which of the above is/are correct?

(a) 1 and 2 only (b) 2 and 3 only

(c) 3 only (d) 1, 2 and 3

76. Consider the following statements:

Statement I:

Intranet is a wide area network that uses TCP/IP protocol and it is a private network of an organization.

Statement II:

With advancements in computer security, cryptography and firewalls, the Internet is completely seure.

Which one of the following is correct in respect of the above statements?

(a) Both Statement I and Statement II are true and Statement II is the correct explanation of Statement I

(b) Both Statement I and Statement II are true but Statement II is not the correct explanation of Statement I

(c) Statement I is true but Statement II is false

(d) Statement I is false but Statement II is true

77. What is the purpose of the Memory Address Register?

(a) To store the address of the next location in the main memory

(b) To store the address of the next location in the secondary memory

(c) To store the address of the next location in the cache memory

(d) To store the address of an output device to which the data is to be ssent

78. Consider the following statemetns:

1. C is a high level language.
2. C is an assembly language.
3. A compiler translates a high-level language program to a machine language program.
4. An assembler translates an assembly language program to a machine language program.

Which of the above statements are correct?

(a) 1 and 3 only (b) 2, 3 and 4 only

(c) 3 and 4 only (d) 1, 3 nad 4 only

79. Cache memory is used to transfer data between the

(a) Main memory and secondary memory

(b) Processor and an input device

(c) Main memory and processor

(d) Processor and an output device

80. Consider the following statements:

1. If-then-else is a sequence structure.
2. Sequence structures require decision-making
3. If-then-else is a selection structure.
4. In repetition structures, the same set of statements are excuted several times.
5. Do-while is a type of selection structure.

Which of the above statements are correct?

(a) 1 and 2 only (b) 3 and 4 only

(c) 1, 2 and 5 only (d) 4 and 5 only

GENERAL STATISTICS
Paper I 2016

Time Allowed : Three Hours | *Maximum Marks: 200*

INSTRUCTIONS

1. IMMEDIATELY AFTER THE COMMENCEMENT OF THE EXAMINATION, YOU SHOULD CHECK THAT THIS TEST BOOKLET DOES NOT HAVE ANY UNPRINTED OR TORN OR MISSING PAGES OR ITEMS, ETC. IF SO, GET IT REPLACED BY A COMPLETE TEST BOOKLET.
2. Please note that it is the candidate's responsibility to encode and fill in the Roll Number and Test Booklet Series A, B, C or D carefully and without any omission or discrepancy at the appropriate places in the OMR Answer Sheet. Any omission/discrepancy will render the Answer Sheet liable for rejection.
3. You have to enter your Roll Number on the Test Booklet in I the Box provided alongside. DO NOT write anything else on the Test Booklet.
4. This Test Booklet contains 80 items (questions). Each item comprises four responses (answers). You will select the response which you want to mark on the Answer Sheet. In case you feel that there is more than one correct response, mark the response which you consider the best. In any case, choose ONLY ONE response for each item.
5. You have to mark all your responses ONLY on the separate Answer Sheet provided. See directions in the Answer Sheet.
6. All items carry equal marks.
7. Before you proceed to mark in the Answer Sheet the response to various items in the Test Booklet, you have to fi ll in some particulars in the Answer Sheet as per instructions sent to you with your Admission Certificate.
8. After you have completed filling in all your responses on the Answer Sheet and the examination has concluded , you should hand over to the Invigilator only the Answer Sheet. You are permitted to take away with you the Test Booklet.
9. Sheets for rough work are appended in the Test Booklet at the end.
10. Penalty for wrong answers :

    THERE WILL BE PENALTY FOR WRONG ANSWERS MARKED BY A CANDIDATE IN THE OBJECTIVE-TYPE QUESTION PAPERS.

(i) There are four alternatives for the answer to every question. For each question for which a wrong answer has been given by the candidate, one·thlrd of the marks assigned to that question will be deducted as penalty.

(ii) If a candidate gives more than one answer, it will be treated a s a wrong answer even if one of the given answers happens to be correct and there will be same pen alty as above to that question.

(iii) If a question is left blank, i.e ., no answer is given by the candidate, there will be no penalty for that question.

DO NOT OPEN THIS TEST BOOKLET UNTIL YOU ARE TOLD TO DO SO

1. Let (X, Y) be jointly distributed with density

$$f(x,y) = \begin{cases} e^{-y}, & 0 < x < y < \infty \\ 0, & \text{otherwise} \end{cases}$$

Consider the following:

1. E(X) = 1
2. E(Y) = 2
3. E(XY) = 2

Which of the above are correct ?

(a) 1 and 2 only (b) 2 and 3 only

(c) 1 and 3 only (d) 1, 2 and 3

2. Let X have a Bernoulli distribution with mean 0-4. What is the variance of (2X – 3)?

(a) 0.24 (b) 0.48

(c) 0.6 (d) 0.96

3. If in 6 trials, X is a binomial variate which follows the relation 9P(X = 4) = P(X = 2), then what is the probability of success?

(a) 1/8 (b) 1/4

(c) 3/8 (d) 3/4

4. X_1 and X_2 are independent Poisson variables such that $P(X_1 = 2) = P(X_1 = 1)$ and $P(X_2 = 2) = P(X_2 = 3)$. What is the variance of $(X_1 - 2X_2)$?

(a) 14 (b) 4

(c) 3 (d) 2

5. For the distribution

$$f(x) = \frac{1}{\beta(p, q)} \frac{x^{p-1}}{(1+x)^{p+q}}, 0 < x < \infty, p > 0,$$

q > 0; what is the harmonic mean ?

(a) $\frac{p}{p+q}$ (b) $\frac{1}{p}$

(c) $\frac{p-1}{q}$ (d) $\frac{p+1}{q-1}$

6. A Poisson variable X has mean equal to $\frac{1}{2}$. Consider the following for Y = 2X :

1. $E(Y) = 1$
2. $Var(Y) = 4$
3. $\mu_3(Y) = 4$
4. $\mu_4(Y) = 28$

Which of the above is/are correct ?

(a) 1 only (b) 2 and 4 only

(c) 1 and 3 only (d) 1, 2 and 3 only

7. Let the random variable X have the distribution P(X = 0) = P(X = 3) = p, maximum value of V(X) ?

(a) 3 (b) 4

(c) 5 (d) 6

8. Let X be a Poisson variate with parameter λ such that P(X = 2) = 2P(X = 4) + 20P(X = 6). What is the coefficeint of skewness?

(a) $\frac{1}{\sqrt{3}}$ (b) 1

(c) $\frac{1}{2}$ (d) $-\frac{1}{\sqrt{3}}$

9. Let X be a random variable with probability generating function $P(s) = \sum_k p_k s^k$. What is the probability generating function of Y = 2X?

(a) $P(\sqrt{s}) + P(-\sqrt{s})$ (b) $\frac{P(\sqrt{s}) - P(-\sqrt{s})}{2}$

(c) $P(\sqrt{s}) - P(-\sqrt{s})$ (d) $\frac{P(\sqrt{s}) + P(-\sqrt{s})}{2}$

10. A simple random sample of size 10 is selected with replacement from a population of size 100. What is the expected number of unique elements in the sample?

(a) $100 \times \left(\frac{99}{100}\right)^{10}$ (b) $100 \times \left[1 - \left(\frac{99}{100}\right)^{10}\right]$

(c) $100 \times \left(\frac{9}{10}\right)^{10}$ (d) $100 \times \left(1 - \frac{9}{10}\right)^{10}$

11. 10 balls are placed in 10 boxes independently at random. Assuming that all 10 boxes were initially empty, what is the expected number of boxes that remain empty?

(a) $\left(\frac{9}{10}\right)^{9}$ (b) $\frac{9^9}{10^{10}}$

(c) $\frac{9^{10}}{10^9}$ (d) $\left(\frac{9}{10}\right)^{10}$

12. To compare the lifetimes of bulbs produced by two companies, A and B, one bulb of each company was selected at random and thier lifetimes were observed. Assume that the bulbs have exponentially distributed lifetimes with mean 1000 days and 800 days for company A and B, respectively. What is the probability that the bulb from B fails first?

(a) $\frac{4}{9}$ (b) $\frac{5}{9}$

(c) $\frac{25}{81}$ (d) $\frac{25}{41}$

13. The lifetime of a bulb is exponentially distributed with mean 100 hours. The bulb remains switched on for exactly 4 hours every day and remains switched off the remaining time. What is the probability that the bulb stops working on or before the 25th day ?

(a) $\frac{1-e^{-1}}{1-e^{-\frac{1}{25}}}$ (b) $1-e^{-\frac{1}{25}}$

(c) $1-e^{-1}$ (d) e^{-1}

14. Suppose X follows the N(0, σ^2) distribution and conditional on X = Y has the N(ρx, σ^2) distribution. What is Cov(X, Y) equal to?

(a) ρ (b) ρ^2

(c) $\rho\sigma^2$ (d) $\rho^2\sigma^2$

15. Suppose $X_1, X_2, X_3, \ldots, X_n$ are independent standard normal random variables and $T_n = \sum_{i=1}^{n} X_i^2$. Consider the following:

1. The distribution of T_n is χ_n^2.
2. The asymptotic distribution of $\sqrt{n}\left(\frac{T_n}{n}-1\right)$ is N(0, σ^2) for some $\sigma^2 > 0$.

Which of the above is/are correct?

(a) 1 only (b) 2 only

(c) Both 1 and 2 (d) Neither 1 nor 2

16. Consider the following statements:

Statement I: **For a Laplace distribution**

$$f(x) = \frac{1}{2}e^{-|x|}, -\infty < x < \infty,$$

$$f(x) = \frac{1}{2\pi}\int_{-\infty}^{\infty} e^{-itx}\,\psi(t)\,dt \text{ for all } x \in R',$$

where $\psi(t)$ is the characteristic function.

Statement II: $\psi(t)$ is absolutely integrable.

Which one of the following is correct in respect of the above statements?

(a) Both Statement I and Statement II are true and Statement II is the correct explanation of Statement I.

(b) Both Statement I and Statement II are true but Statement II is ***not*** the correct explanation of Statement I.

(c) Statement I is true but Statement II is false.

(d) Statement I is false but Statement II is true.

17. Let X_1 and X_2 be the number of eggs laid by two insects which follow independent Poisson distributions with parameters λ_1 and λ_2, respectively. The conditional distribution of X_1 given $X_1 + X_2$ will be

(a) Poisson (b) Geometric

(c) Binomial (d) Negative Binomial

18. Suppose 5 tickets are drawn at a time from a box containing n tickets numbered 1, 2, 3, .., n. Let X be the sum of the numbers of the 5 tickets drawn.

Consider the following statements:

1. $E(X) = \dfrac{5(n+1)}{2}$
2. $V(X) = \dfrac{5(n+1)(n-5)}{2}$

Which of the above is/are correct?

(a) 1 only (b) 2 only

(c) Both 1 and 2 (d) Neither 1 nor 2

19. If X and Y are two independent random variables with Binomial distributions having integer parameters m and n and the same probability parameter p, then consider the following statements:

1. $m + n - X - Y$ has a Binomial distribution.

2. The conditional distribution of X given the sum $X + Y$ is a hyper-geometric distribution.

3. The conditional distribution of X given the sum $X + Y$ is again a Binomial distribution.

Which of the above statements is/are correct?

(a) 1 only (b) 2 only

(c) 1 and 2 only (d) 1 and 3 only

20. If X has a uniform distribution over the interval (0, 1) then for any real numbers a and b, $0 < a < b < 1$, what is $P\left[a < X < b \middle| X > \dfrac{a > b}{2}\right]$ equal to?

(a) $\dfrac{b-a}{2-a-b}$ (b) $\dfrac{2(b-a)}{b+a}$

(c) $\dfrac{2(b-a)}{2-a-b}$ (d) $\dfrac{b-a}{b+a}$

21. Let X be a random variable with density $f(x) = \dfrac{1}{2}e^{-|x|}, -\infty < x < \infty$. What is the expected value of [X], where [.] denotes the greatest integer function?

(a) $\dfrac{1}{2}$ (b) 0

(c) $-\dfrac{1}{2}$ (d) -1

22. Let X and Y independently and identically distributed as lognormal with parameters μ and σ^2. What are the mean and variance of $\log\left(\frac{X}{Y}\right)$ respectively?

(a) 0 and σ^2 (b) 0 and $2\sigma^2$

(c) 2μ and σ^2 (d) 2μ and $2\sigma^2$

23. The joint probability density of X anf Y is given as

$$f(x, y) = \begin{cases} \frac{x+2y}{3} & \text{for } 0 < X < 1, 0 < y < 1 \\ 0, & \text{otherwise} \end{cases}$$

What is the value of $\left(Y \le \frac{1}{2} \middle| X = \frac{1}{2}\right)$?

(a) $\frac{1}{6}$ (b) $\frac{1}{3}$

(c) $\frac{2}{3}$ (d) $\frac{5}{6}$

24. A and B are two events such that P(A) = P(A) = P(A | B) = $\frac{1}{4}$ and P(B | A) = $\frac{1}{2}$. Which of the following are correct?

1. A and B independent events.

2. P(A) < P(B)

3. $P(\bar{A} \mid B) = \frac{3}{4}$

4. A and B are mutually exclusive events.

Select the correct answer using the code given below:

(a) 1, 2 and 3 only (b) 1, 2 and 4 only

(c) 2, 3 and 4 only (d) 1, 3 and 4 only

26. Which of the following tests shold be employed for deciding whether or not two samples come from the same skewed parent population?

1. Paired t-test

2. Unpaired t-test

3. Run test

4. Sign test

Which of the above statements are correct?

(a) 1 and 3 only (b) 3 and 4 only

(c) 2, 3 and 4 only (d) 1, 3 and 4 only

27. Consider the following relations (with usual notations) where X ~ N(μ, σ^2):

1. $\chi^2_{(2)} = \frac{(\bar{X} - \mu)^2}{\sigma^2}$

2. $t = \frac{(\bar{X} - \mu)\sqrt{n}}{s}$

Which of the above is/are correct?

(a) 1 only (b) 2 only

(c) Both 1 and 2 (d) Neither 1 nor 2

28. In a trivariate distribution, if $r_{12} = r_{23} = r_{31} = \rho \neq 1$, then what is the value of $R_{1.23}$?

(a) $\frac{\rho}{\sqrt{1+\rho}}$ (b) $\frac{1}{\sqrt{1+\rho}}$

(c) $\frac{\sqrt{2}\rho}{\sqrt{1+\rho}}$ (d) $\frac{1}{1+\rho}$

29. If Y = aX + 3 and X = 2Y + 6 are the regression lines of Y on X and X and Y respectively, then which one of the following is correct?

(a) $0.5 \leq a \leq 1$ (b) $a > 1$

(c) $0 \leq a \leq 0.5$ (d) $-0.5 \leq a \leq 0$

30. Let the regression lines of Y on X and X on Y be Y = aX + b and X = cY + d respectively. Consider the following statements:

1. The ratio of the variance of X and Y is $\frac{c}{a}$.

2. The correlation coefficient between X and Y is $\sqrt{ac}$.

3. The values of $\bar{X}$ and $\bar{Y}$ are $\frac{cb+d}{1-ac}$ and $\frac{ad+b}{1-ac}$ respectively.

Which of the above are correct?

(a) 1 and 2 only (b) 2 and 3 only

(c) 1 and 3 only (d) 1, 2 and 3

31. If $\bar{X}$ and S^2 are the mean and variance of a random sample of size n from a normal population with mean μ and standard deviation σ, then the random variable $Y = \frac{(n-1)S^2}{\sigma^2}$ follows

(a) χ^2 with (n – 2) d.f. (b) t with (n – 1) d.f.

(c) χ^2 with (n – 1) d.f. (d) t with (n – 2) d.f.

32. In measuring reaction time, an experimenter estimates that the standard deviation is 0.09 s. What should be the value of sample size n so that the experimenter is 95% confident that the error of his estimate of the mean reaction time will not exceed 0.02 s?

(a) $0 < n < 50$ (b) $n \geq 78$

(c) $50 \leq n \leq 77$ (d) $n < 77$

33. Consider the 2 × 2 contingency table on two attributes A and B:

	A_1	A_2
B_1	10	20
B_2	30	40

Which is the value of χ^2 for testing the independence of the attributes A and B?

(a) 0.79 (b) 0.81

(c) 0.83 (d) 0.85

34. Consider the following statements :

1. X_1 and X_2 are independent σ^2 variates with n_1 and n_2 d.f. respectively, then $Y = \frac{X_1}{X_2}$ follows $\beta_2\left(\frac{n_1}{2}, \frac{n_2}{2}\right)$ distribution.

2. X_1 and X_2 are independent χ^2 variates with n_1 and n_2 d.f. respectively, then $Z = \frac{X_1}{X_1 + X_2}$ follows $\beta_1\left(\frac{n_1}{2}, \frac{n_2}{2}\right)$ distribution.

3. X_1 and X_2 are independent standard normal distribution, then $W = X_1^2 + X_2^2$ follows $X^2_{(2)}$ distribution.

Which of the above statements is/are corr ect ?

(a) 1 and 2 only (b) 2 and 3 only

(c) 3 only (d) 1, 2 and 3

35. Which of the following are correct in respect of a frequency distribution ?

1. Arithmetic mean is less than harmonic mean.

2. $\beta_2 > 1$

3. $\beta_2 - \beta_1 - 1 \geq 0$

4. Karl Pearson's coefficient of skewness lies between – 1 and +1.

Select the correct answer using the code given below :

(a) 1 and 2 only (b) 2 and 3 only

(c) 3 and 4 only (d) 1 and 4 only

36. If $r_{12.3}$ is the correlation coefficient between the variables X_1 and X_2 after eliminating the linear effect of X_3, then which of the following are correct ?

1. $r_{12.3} = \frac{r_{12} - r_{13}\, r_{23}}{\sqrt{(1 - r_{13}^2)(1 - r_{23}^2)}}$

2. $r_{12}^2 + r_{23}^2 + r_{31}^2 - 2r_{12}\, r_{23}\, r_{31} \leq 1$

3. $r_{12.3}^2 = b_{12.3}\, b_{21.3}$, where b's are partial regression coefficients

(a) 1 and 2 only (b) 2 and 3 only

(c) 1 and 3 only (d) 1, 2 and 3

37. The following information was obtained in a survey of 100 workers of a factory:

All men workers were more than 20 years old. There were 50 women workers in the sample. Altogether 60 workers were over 20 years. 25 of the women workers were married, while 15 of the married workers were over 20 years old and 10 of the married women workers were over 20 years old.

From the above information, what is the number of married workers ?

(a) 20 (b) 25

(c) 30 (d) 40

38. **To find out the mean yield per plant, 64 plants were selected at random from a field. The mean yield and standard deviation were found to be 10 and 2, respectively.**

(For $\alpha = 0.05$ and 63 degrees of freedom, the critical value of t is 2) What is the 95% confidence interval for the population mean ?

(a) (9.5, 10.5) (b) (9.75, 10.25)

(c) (6.0, 4.0) (d) (8.0, 12.0)

39. **The burning time of a certain kind of rocket has a probability distribution with mean burning time 5 minutes, variance 0.5 square minutes and coefficient of kurtosis 4. What is the distribution of burning time of these kind of rockets?**

(a) Uniform (b) Mesokurtic

(c) Leptokurtic (d) Platykurtic

40. **Consider the following statements :**

Statement I:

It is not possible to determine the total number of birds in a forest by standard sampling technique.

Statement II:

It is not possible to construct the sampling frame for such populations. respect of the above two statements ?

(a) Both Statement I and Statement II are true and Statement is the correct explanation for Statement I.

(b) Both Statement I and Statement II are true but Statement II is not the correct explanation for Statement I.

(c) Statement I is true but Statement II is false.

(d) Statement I is false but Statement II is

41. **A statistician mailed a survey questionnaire to a random sample of 100 teachers from each of 4 types of schools. The number of responses received is summarized in the following table:**

Type of School	Number of responses	Number of non-responses
Government Primary	23	77
Government Secondary	30	70
Private Primary	43	57
Private Secondary	29	71

Before analysing the data collected, the statistician wants to test whether the probability of non-response was the same for all types of schools. What is the appropriate test for this purpose?

(a) Sign test (b) Goodness-of-fit test

(c) Test for independence (d) ANOVA F-test

42. **If X and Y are standard normal variates with correlation coefficient between them, then what is the correlation coefficient between X^2 and Y^2?**

(a) $2\rho - 1$ (b) ρ^2

(c) ρ (d) $\sqrt{\rho}$

43. If X is random variable having Poisson distribution with parameter λ, then what is the m.g.f. of $Y = X - 2$?

(a) $e^{\lambda e^t - 2t - \lambda}$ (b) $e^{\lambda e^t - t - 1}$

(c) $e^{\lambda(e^t - t - 1)}$ (d) $e^{\lambda(e^t - 1)}$

44. If the random variables X, Y and Z have the means $\mu_x = 5$, $\mu_y = 7$ and $\mu_z = 4$; variances $\sigma_x^2 = 10$, $\sigma_y^2 = 20$; Cov(XY) = 1, Cov(XZ) = – 3 and Cov(YZ) = 2, then what is the covariance of $U = X + 4Y + 2Z$ and $V = 3X - Y$

(a) – 76 (b) 82

(c) 82 (d) 76

45. Consider the following statements :

1. Mean and variance are equal for Poisson distribution.
2. Mean is less than variance for Binomial distribution.
3. Mean is less than variance Chi-square distribution.

Which of the above statements are correct?

(a) 1 and 2 only (b) 1 and 3 only

(c) 1 and 3 only (d) 1, 2 and 3

46. The probability of a random variable X is given by

$$P(X = r) = \binom{n}{r} p^r q^{n-r}; r = 0, 1, 2, ..., n;$$

$$p + q = 1, p > 0$$

What is the coefficient of skewness of the random variable X?

(a) $\frac{1+2p}{\sqrt{npq}}$ (b) $\frac{1-2p}{\sqrt{npq}}$

(c) $\frac{p}{\sqrt{nq}}$ (d) $\frac{1+p}{\sqrt{nq}}$

47. Consider the following statements:

$P: X + Y = 2, 2X + 3Y = 4$

$Q: X - 2Y = 3, 2X - 3Y = 5$

$R: X + 2Y = 5, 2X - 3Y = 3$

Which of the above is/are valid pair(s) of regression equations?

(a) P only (b) Q only

(c) P and Q only (d) P, Q and R

48. In a Chi-square test, the contingency table has 4 rows and 4 columns. What is the number of degrees of freedom?

(a) 3 (b) 4

(c) 8 (d) 9

49. Consider the following statement:

Statement I

The correlation coefficient between two variables X and Y is the geometric mean of the two regression coefficients β_{YX} and β_{XY}.

Statement II

The arithmetic mean of the two regression coefficients β_{YX} and β_{XY} is greater than or equal to the correlation coefficient between the variables X and Y.

Which one of the following is correct in respect of the above two statements ?

(a) Both Statement I and Statement II are true and Statement II is the correct explanation for Statement I.

(b) Both Statement I and Statement II are true but Statement II is not the correct explanation for Statement I.

(c) Statement I is true but Statement II is 52. false.

(d) Statement I is false but Statement II is true.

50. For a given data (X_i, Y_i); i = 1, 2, 3, ... , n; using the principle of least-squares, two models, say M_1 and M_2 are fitted. Let M_1 be $Y = f_1(X)$ and let M_2 be $Y = f_2(X)$. Suppose Xo is a value of X for which the predicted value of Y is to be determined.

Define $E_1 = \sum_{i=1}^{n}[Y_i - f_1(X_i)]^2$ **and**

$E_2 = \sum_{i=1}^{n}[Y_i - f_2(X_i)]^2$. **Then which one of the following is the criterion for choosing the estimated value of Y for $X = X_0$?**

(a) Put $X = X_0$ in that model for which Y value obtained is the least.

(b) Put $X = X_0$ in that model for which Y value obtained is the greatest.

(c) Put $X = X_0$ in that model for which E value obtained is the least.

(d) Put $X = X_0$ in that model for which E value obtained is the greatest.

51. Consider the following statements:

1. Divided difference of kth order involves k arguments.

2. Divided difference is a symmetric function of its argument values.

3. Divided difference can be expressed as the ratio of two determinants of (n + 1) order each.

4. Divided difference is applicable even when arguments are not equispaced.

Which of the above statements are correct?

(a) 2, 3 and 4 only (b) 1,3 and 4 only

(c) 1, 2 and 4 only (d) 1, 2 and 3 only

52. What is the third order divided difference with arguments 2, 4, 9 and 10 of the function $f(x) = x^3 - 2x$?

(a) 1 (b) 2

(c) 3 (d) 4

53. If $\Delta^n 0^m = \Delta^n x^m |_{x=0}$, then what is the value of $\Delta^3 0^6$?

(a) 500 (b) 515

(c) 530 (d) 540

54. What is the function whose first difference is $3x^2 + 7x + 10$ (assuming h = 1)?

(a) $3x^{(3)} + 7x^{(2)} + 10x + c$

(b) $x^{(3)} + 7x^{(2)} + 10x + c$

(c) $x^{(3)} + 5x^{(2)} + 10x + c$

(d) $3x^{(3)} + 5x^{(2)} + 10x + c$

55. It is given that $u_1 = 1$, $u_2 + U_3 = 6$ and $u_4 + u_5 + u_6 + u_7 + u_8 = 30$. approximate value of when computed by using Lagrange's interpolation formula?

(a) 7 (b) 6

(c) 5 (d) 4

56. Let $f(x) = 5x^3 - 13x^2 + 11x + 4$. If the interval of differencing is 1, then consider the following statements:

1. $\Delta^3 f(x) = 30$ for all x

2. $\Delta^2 f(x) = 34$ for x = 1

3. $\Delta f(x) = 4$ for x = 1

Which of the above statements are correct ?

(a) 1 and 2 only (b) 1 and 3 only

(c) 2 and 3 only (d) 1, 2 and 3

57. What is $\frac{1}{(E^2 - 4)}(9x^2)$ equal to ?

(a) $-3x^2 - \frac{20x}{3} - 4$ (b) $-4x^2 - 3x + \frac{20}{3}$

(c) $-3x^2 - 4x - \frac{20}{3}$ (d) $-3x^2 - 4x + \frac{20}{3}$

58. Which of the following statements are correct?

1. Weddle's rule requires at least six consecutive values of the function.

2. If f(x) is a polynomial of 4th degree, then Weddle's

3. In general, Weddle's rule is more accurate than Simpson's rule. below :

(a) 2 and 3 only (b) 1 and 3 only

(c) 1 and 2 only (d) 1, 2 and 3

59. The solution of the initial value problem $y' = f(t, y)$, $y(t_0) = y_0$ is to be obtained by the Euler's method with step length h. The truncation error of the Euler's method is Euler's bounded by

(a) $\frac{h^2}{2} \max|y''(x)|$ (b) $\frac{h^2}{2} \max|y'''(x)|$

(c) $h^2 \max|y''(x)|$ (d) $h \max|y''(x)|$

60. Consider the following data :

X	– 2	– 1	0	1	2
f(x)	– 11	– 8	– 5	– 2	1

(a) 4 (b) 3

(c) 2 (d) 1

61. Consider the following data:

x	3	6	9	12
y(x)	– 1	1	2	3

What is the value of $\int_3^{12} y(x)\,dx$, when computed by Simpson's $\frac{1}{3}$ rule?

(a) 10 (b) 9

(c) 6 (d) 3

62. The error in fourth order Runge-Kutta formula for solving the differential equation $\frac{dy}{dx}$ = f(x, y) is of the order

(a) (equal interval)^2 (b) (equal interval)^3

(c) (equal interval)^4 (d) (equal interval)^5

63. The values of the function f(x) for values of x are given as f(l) = 4, f(2) = 5, f(7) = 5, f(8) = 4. Which one of the following is correct in respect of f(x) when it is computed by using Lagrange's formula ?

(a) f(x) is maximum when x = 4.5

(b) f(x) is minimum when x = 4.5

(c) f(x) is maximum when x = 4

(d) f(x) is minimum when x = 4

64. Consider the following data :

x	1.35	1.36	1.37	1.38
$\log_{10}$ x	0.1303	0.1335	0.1367	0.1399

What is the value of x when x = 10 $logj_{10}$ x and computed using Stirling's formula?

(a) 1.3609 (b) 1.3709

(c) 1.3809 (d) 1.3909

65. If y = (a + bx)2^X with difference interval h = 1, then what is ($\Delta^2 - 2\Delta + 1$) y equal to?

(a) 4 (b) 2

(c) 1 (d) 0

66. A computer linked to the Internet is identified by 'X', while a web page is identified by 'Y'. What are X and Y, respectively ?

(a) IP address and Search Engine Google

(b) IP address and URL

(c) URL and Search Engine

(d) Browser and IP address

67. Consider the following statements:

1. Intranet is a wide area network, using TCP/IP protocol like the Internet.
2. Intranet is a private network of an organisation.
3. Hackers are known to have logged on computers breaching password security.

Which of the above statements are correct?

(a) 1 and 2 only (b) 2 and 3 only

(c) 1 and 3 only (d) 1, 2 and 3

68. Computation of X > P + Q AND I = J is equivalent to

(a) ((X > P) + Q) AND (I = J)

(b) (X > P) + (Q AND I = J)

(c) (X > P) + (Q AND I) = J

(d) ((X > (P + Q))) AND I = J)

69. Consider the following statements :

1. A function is a subroutine that may include one or more statements designed to perform a specific task.
2. A compiled and linked program is called executable code.

Which of the above statements is/are correct ?

(a) 1 only (b) 2 only

(c) Both 1 and 2 (d) Neither 1 nor 2

70. Consider the following statements :

Statement I :

Debugging is a three-stage process consisting of detection, isolation and correction of errors in a computer program.

Statement II :

Compiler can detect and isolate all errors in a computer program.

Which one of the following is correct in respect of the above two statements ?

(a) Both Statement I and Statement II are true and Statement II is the correct explanation for Statement I.

(b) Both Statement I and Statement II are true but Statement II is not the correct explanation for Statement I.

(c) Statement I is true but Statement II is false.

(d) Statement I is false but Statement II is true.

71. Consider the following statements:

1. Fixed point numbers are numbers in which the decimal point is assumed to be in a fixed position.
2. Integer arithmetic can be considered as special case of fixed point arithmetic.
3. Fixed point arithmetic tends to be more suitable for business data processing.
4. Floating point arithmetic tends to important for scientific computing.

Which of the above statements are correct?

(a) 2 and 4 only (b) 1, 3 and 4 only
(c) 1, 2 and 3 only (d) 1, 2, 3 and 4

72. Flash memory is a

1. slow-write and fast-read memory
2. fast-write and fast-read memory
3. non-volatile memory
4. removable and portable memory

Which of the above are correct?

(a) 1 and 3 only (b) 2 and 4 only
(c) 1, 3 and 4 only (d) 2, 3 and 4 only

73. Consider the following in respect of scripting languages:

1. They assume availability of collection of programs.
2. They assume availability of high speed efficient compiler
3. They combine components to perform complex task.
4. They do not support strong data typing.

Which of the above statements are correct ?

(a) 1, 2 and 3 only (b) 1, 2 and 4 only
(c) 2, 3 and 4 only (d) 1, 3 and 4 only

74. Consider the following statements:

1. Browser, e-mail and ftp are parts of an operating system.
2. Wireless LAN can be established using CDMA or infrared as medium.
3. Optical fibre offers higher bandwidth and is cheaper than coaxial cables.
4. Server is a powerful computer that can be accessed over a computer network.

Which of the above statements are correct?

(a) 1 and 2 only (b) 2 and 4 only
(c) 1 and 3 only (d) 1, 2 and 4 only

75. Consider the following statements:

1. Routers are special purpose computers which interconnect networks.
2. ISPs are dedicated, special service providers.

3. OSPs are operating service providers.

Which of the above statements is/are correct?

(a) 1 and 3 only (b) 1 only

(c) 2 and 3 only (d) 1, 2 and 3

76. The primary purpose of a firewall in a network is to

(a) execute antivirus program on each e-mail attachment and stop objectionable messages

(b) permit any safe packets to the destination computer in the network

(c) prevent operations of machine BOTS

(d) stop excessive downloading of data by network users

77. Which of the following statements are correct?

1. Scanner resolution is measured in dpi.
2. Processor speed is measured in GHz.
3. An LCD monitor uses less power than an LED monitor.
4. Laser printers use the same technology as photocopiers.

Select the correct answer using the code given below:

(a) 1, 2 and 3 only (b) 1, 3 and 4 only

(c) 1, 2 and 4 only (d) 2, 3 and 4 only

78. Which key is used to convert an ASCII code to the corresponding character (if displayable) ?

(a) Alt key (b) Shift key

(c) Ctrl key (d) Esc key

79. Which of the following are statistical softwares ?

1. Minitab 2. GIMP

3. R 4. SPSS

Select the correct answer using the code given below :

(a) 1, 2 and 3 only (b) 1, 3 and 4 only

(c) 1, 2 and 4 only (d) 2, 3 and 4 only

80. Which of the following statements are correct ?

1. SQL is used for database management.
2. Spreadsheets are good for manipulating huge tables.
3. Presentation softwares can handle text, tables, images and videos.

Select the correct answer using the code given below :

(a) 1 and 2 only (b) 2 and 3 only

(c) 1 and 3 only (d) 1, 2 and 3

GENERAL STATISTICS
Paper I 2015

Time Allowed : Three Hours | *Maximum Marks: 200*

INSTRUCTIONS

Please read each of the following instructions carefully before attempting the questions:

There are EIGHT questions divided under TWO sections. Candidate has to attempt FIVE questions in ALL. Questions no. 1 and 5 are compulsory and out of themremaiazing, THREE are to be attempted choosing at least ONE from each section. The number of marks carried by a question/part is indicated against it. Unless otherwise mentioned, symbols and notation~ have ~heir usual standard meanings. Assume suitable data, if necessary, and indicate the same clearly, Candidates should attempt questions / parts as per the instructions given in the section. All parts and sub-parts of a question are to be attempted together in the answer book. Attempts of questions shall be counted in chronological order. Unless struck off, attempt of a questiol'- shall be counted even it attempted partly. Any page or portion of the page left blank in the answer book must be clearly struck off. Answers must be written in ENGLISH only. Required tables (Normal Distribution table and 't' table) are attached with the question paper.

SECTION A

1. Answer all of the following: **5×8=40**

(a) For random variables X, Y, show that

$$V[Y] = E_X [V(Y|X)] + V_X\{E(Y|X)].$$

(b) Prove that for r = 1, 2, ..., n

$$\frac{1}{\Gamma(r)}\int_{\mu}^{\infty} t^{r-1} e^{-t}\, dt = \sum_{x=(}^{r-1} \frac{e^{-\mu}\mu^{x}}{x!}$$

(c) Let X have pdf

$$f(x) = \begin{cases} \dfrac{1}{3}, & -1 < x < 2 \\ 0, & \text{otherwise} \end{cases}$$

Obtain the cdf of $Y = X^2$.

(d) Let X be a random variable with $E(X) = 3$, $E(X)^2 = 13$. Use Chebyshev' inequality to obtain $P(-2 < X < 8)$.

(e) Using Central Limit Theorem, show that

$$e^{-n} \sum_{k=0}^{n} \frac{n^k}{k!} = \frac{1}{2}$$

2. (a) Let C be a circle of unit area with centre at origin and let S be a square of unit area with $\left(\frac{1}{2}, \frac{1}{2}\right), \left(\frac{1}{2}, -\frac{1}{2}\right), \left(-\frac{1}{2} \cdot \frac{1}{2}\right)$ and $\left(-\frac{1}{2}, -\frac{1}{2}\right)$ as the four vertices. If X and Y be two independent standard normal variates, show that

$$\iint_C \phi(x)\, \phi(y)\, dx\, dy \geq \iint_S \phi(x)\, \phi(y)\, dx\, dy$$

where $\phi(.)$ is the pdf of N(0, 1) distribution.

(b) Let X follow log-normal parameters μ and σ^2. Find tribulation of $Y = aX^b, a > 0, -\infty < b < \infty$.

(c) Let $\{X_n\}$ be a sequence of pairwise, uncorrelated random variables with $E(X_i) = \mu_i$ and $V(X_i) = \sigma_i^2, i = 1, 2, ...$

If $\sum_{i=1}^{n} \sigma_i^2 \to \infty$ as $n \to \infty$, then show that

$$\sum_{i=1}^{n} \left[\frac{X_i - \mu_i}{\sum_{j=1}^{n} \sigma_j^2}\right] \xrightarrow{P} 0 \text{ as } n \to \infty.$$

3. (a) Let $X_1, X_2, ..., X_n$ be independent Poisson variates with $E(X_i) = \mu_i$. Find the conditional distribution of $X_1, ... X_n \left| \sum_{i=1}^{n} X_i = y \right.$.

(b) Let Y_1 denote the first order statistic in a random sample of size n from a distribution that has the pdf $f(x) = \begin{cases} e^{-(x-\theta)}, & \theta < x < \infty \\ 0, & \text{otherwise} \end{cases}$ Obtain the distribution of $Z_n = n(Y_1 - \phi)$.

(c) Two points are chosen at random on a line of unit length. Find the probability than each of the 3 line segments will have length greater than $\frac{1}{4}$.

4. (a) Obtain the characteristic function of X whose pdf is

$$f(x) = \frac{\lambda}{\pi}, \frac{1}{\lambda^2 + (x-\mu)^2}, -\infty < x < \infty$$

(b) Let $\{X_n\}$ be a sequence cf random variables with

$$P(X = \pm n^{\alpha}) = \frac{1}{2} n^{-\alpha}$$

$P(X_n = 0) = 1 - n^{-\alpha}$

For what values of α does weak law of large numbers (WLLN) hold?

(c) Three urns U_1, U_2 and U_3 each contain 5 black, balls and 7 white balls initially. A ball is drawn at random from U_1 and 2 balls of the drawn colour are added to U_2. Then a ball is drawn at random from U_2 and 3 balls of the drawn colour are added to U_3. Find the probability of drawing a white ball from U_3.

SECTION B

5. Answer *all* of the following: **5×8=40**

(a) Let (X, Y) be distributed as bivariate normal BVN $\left(3, 1; 13, 25; \frac{3}{5}\right)$. Calcuate P(4 < Y 11.84 | X = 7)

(b) With 3 variables X_1, X_2 and X_3, it is given that r13 = 0.71, R1.23 = 0.78. Find r12..

(c) Suppose the given values of x_i are such that $a \le x_i \le b$ for i = 1, 2, ..., n. Show that

$$0 \le s^2 \le \frac{(b-a)^2}{4}$$

(d) Let X have F(m, n) distribution.

Obtain $E(X^{-r})$, r > 0.

(e) If X follows binomial $b(a_1, p_1$. distribution and Y follows $b(n_2, p_2)$, provide an appropriate exact test at level α for $H_0: p_1 = p_2$ against $H_1: p_1 > p_2$.

6. (a) By using Euler – Mac;arom formula, find the sum $\frac{1}{51^2} + \frac{1}{53^2} + \ldots + \frac{1}{99^2}$.

(b) Given the random samples

X: 1,. 5, 7, 9, 15, 17, 21, 23

Y: 2, 6, 10, 12, 18, 20, 26, 28, 32

from the population having the distribution function respectively as F_1 and F_2, test the hypothesis

$H_0: F_1 = F_2$

against $H_1: F_1 \ne F_2$

at 5% level of significance by the Wald – Wolfowitz run test. It is given that the critical number of runs at sample sizes (8, 9) at 5% level is 5.

(c) Compute Yule's coefficient of association (Q) and Yule's coefficient of coligation (Y) for the following table:

		Disease on-set	
		Yes	No
Medicine used	A	19	587
	B	193	2741

7. (a) By making use of the difference table and a suitable interpolation formula, find the number of students who obtained less than 45 marks in an examination, form the following table:

Marks	30–40	40–50	50–60	60–70	70–80
Number of Students	31	42	51	35	31

(b) Consider the two samples as follows:

Sample I = 6, 7, 8, 10, 12, 14, 16, 23

Sample II = 9, 11, 13, 15, 17, 18, 19, 20, 24

Test whether the samples have come from the same populations using Wilcoxon-Mann-Whitney (WMW) test an 10% level of significance. [You can use normal approximation].

(c) For 20 pairs for heights of father (X) and sor (Y) measured in cm, the following data were obtained:

$$\overline{x} = 168.17, \Sigma(x_i - \overline{x})^2 = 777.80$$

$$\Sigma(y_i - \overline{y})^2 = 939.42, y = 9.25 + 0.932x$$

Test whether the cut on the X-ais can be assumed to be zero, at 5% level of significance. 40

7. (a) Compute the value of $\int_4^{5.2} \ln \Sigma\, dx$ by Simposon's $\frac{1^{rd}}{3}$ rule. Given that ln 4.0 = 1.39, ln 4.2 = 1.43, ln 4.4 = 1.48 ln 4.6 = 1.53, ln 4.8 = 1.57, ln 5.0 = 1.61, ln 5.2 = 1.65.

(b) Let $X_1, X_2, ..., X_{12}$ be a random sample from a normal $N(\mu_1, \sigma^2)$ distribution and $Y_1, Y_2, .., Y_0$ be another random sample from normal $N(\mu_2, \sigma^2)$, independently of each other. Carry out an appropriate test for testing

H_0: $\mu_1 = \mu_2$

against H_1: $\mu_1 \neq \mu_2$

at 5% level of significance. It is given that $\overline{x} = 2$, $s_x^2 = 16$, $\overline{y} = 8$ and $s_y^2 = 15$.

(c) Fit the exponertial curve y = a + bx to the following data:

x: 0	2	4
y: 5.01	10	31.62

GENERAL STATISTICS
Paper I 2014

Time Allowed : Three Hours

Maximum Marks: 100

QUESTIONS PAPER SPECIFIC INSTRUCTIONS

Please read each of the following instructions carefully before attempting question.

There are EIGHT questions divided under TWO sections. Candidate has to attempt FIVE questions in ALL. All the parts in the ONLY question in Section A are compulsor. Questions no. 1 and 5 are compulsory and out of the least ONE from each Section. The number of marks carried by a question/part is indicated against it. Unless otherwise mentioned, symbols and notations have their usual standard meanings. Assume suitable data, if necessary and indicate the same clearly. Camdidates should attempt questions/part as per the instructions given in the Section. All parts and sub-parts of a question are to be attempted together in the answer book. Attempts of questions shall be counted in chronological order. Unless struck off, attempt of a question shall be counted even if attempted partly. Any page or portion of the page left blank in the answer book must be clearly struck off. Answers must be written in ENGLISH only. A Normal Distribution table and a 't' table are attached with the question paper.

SECTION A

1. Answer all of the following: **5×8=40**

(a) A positive integer X is selected at random from the first 50 natural number. Calculate $P\left(X+\frac{96}{X}>50\right)$. 8

(b) Suppose that all the four outcomes O_1, O_2, O_3 and O_4 of an experiment are equally likely. Define $A = \{O_1, O_4\}$, $B = \{O_2, O_4\}$ and $C = \{O_3, O_4\}$. What can you say about the pairwise independence and mutually independece and mutually independence of the events A, B and C? 8

(c) The marginal distribution of X and Yare given in the following table:

x \ y	1	2	Total
3			$\frac{1}{4}$
4			$\frac{3}{4}$
Total	$\frac{1}{2}$	$\frac{1}{2}$	1

If the covariance between X and Y is zero, find the cell probabilities and see whether X and Y are independent.

(d) Show that for 40,000 throws of a balanced coin, the probability is at least 0.99 that the proportion of heads will fall between 0.475 and 0.525. 8

(e) If $f_X(x)$ be the probability density function of a $N(\mu, \sigma^2)$ distributuion, then show that

$$\int_L^U x f_x(x)\, dx = \mu[\Phi(U') - \Phi(L')] - [\phi(U') - \phi(L')]$$

where $L' = \frac{L-\mu}{\sigma}$, $U' = \frac{U-\mu}{\sigma}$ and $\phi(z)$ and $\Phi(z)$ are the probability density function and distribution function of the standard normal distribution respectively. 8

2. (a) $X_1, X_2, \ldots, X_N$ are independently, identically distributed random variables. Define $S_N = X_1 + X_2 + \ldots + X_N$, where N is a random variable independent of X_i, i = 1, 2, ... N.

Show that the moment generating function (mfg) of S_N is

$$M_{S_N}(t) = M_N(\log M_X(t))$$

where $M_Y(t)$ is the mgf of a random variable Y.

Hence find the mgf of S_N when N follows a Poisson distribution with parameter λ and X_i follows an exponential distribution with mean parameter θ, i = 1(1) N. 15

(b) If $f_X(x)$ be the probability density function of a lognormal distribution, show that

$$\int_L^U x^k f_x(x)\, dx = e^{k\mu + \frac{1}{2}k^2\sigma^2} [\Phi(U_k) - \Phi(L_k)]$$

where $L_k = \frac{\log L - \mu}{\sigma} - k\sigma$ and

$U_k = \frac{\log U - \mu}{\sigma} - k\sigma$ and $\Phi(z)$ is the distribution. Hence find E(X) and V(X). 15

(c) In a lottery 1000 tickets are sold and the cost of a ticket is ₹ 10. The iottery offers a first prize of ₹1,000, two second prizes of ₹500 each, and three third prizes fo ₹100 each. A person purchases a ticket. If X denots the amount he may get, find E(X) and V(X). 10

3. (a) n balls are distributed among r cells at random, each cell being free to receive any number of balls. Calculate the probability that a particular cell contains k balls ($k \le n$) when (i) balls are distinguishable. 15

(b) Write down the probability mass function of a trinomial distribution. Obtain the moment generating function of the distribution. Show that the correlation coefficient of any two variables is negative. Why? 15

(c) Prove that two events cannot be incompatible and independent simultaneously. 10

4. (a) $\{X_n\}$ is a sequence of independent random variables. Show that $X_n \xrightarrow{P} X \Rightarrow X_n \xrightarrow{L} X$ where X is a random variable. Is the converse true? 15

(b) There are three indentical bags U_1, U_2 and U_3. U_1 contains 3 red and 4 black balls; U_2 contains 4 red and 5 black balls; U_3 contains 4 red and 4 black balls. One bag is chosen at random; a ball is drawn at random from the chosen bag and it is found to be red. Find the probability that the first bag is chosen. 15

(c) Let P(s) be the probability generating function associated with a non-negative, integer valued random variable X. Show that

$$\sum_{n=0}^{\infty} s^n P(X \le n) = \frac{P(s)}{1-s}.$$ 10

Section B

5. **Answer *all* of the following:** 5×8=40

(a) The runs scored by two batsmen A and B in five cricket matches were as follows:

Batsman A:	50	60	100	70	20
Batsman B:	120	100	30	20	40

Discuss the consistency and efficiency of the batsmen. 8

(b) Given the following correlation matrix of order 3 × 3

$$R = \begin{bmatrix} 1 & 0.5708 & 0.6735 \\ & 1 & 0.4487 \\ & & 1 \end{bmatrix}$$

Calcuate (i) $r_{12.3}$ (ii) $r_{1.23}$. 8

(c) Consider two samples as follows:

Sample 1: 1, 4, 7, 9, 16, 17, 22, 24

Sample 2: 2, 6, 10, 12, 18, 20, 26, 28, 32

Test whether the exampls have come from the same population by Wilcoxon-Mann-Whitney test. [Given value of Z for a = 0.05 = 1.645, where Z is N(0, 10] 8

(d) Define power of a test and discuss its role in selecting the test. Describe a test procedure for testing equality of means of two independent normal populations, when standard deviations are equal but unknown for small samples. 8

(e) Given the following values of the function y = f(x); evaluate f(4) and also find x for which f(x) = 25.

f(1) = 10, f(2) = 15, f(3) = 42. 8

6. (a) Describe a test procedure for testing the null hypothesis H_0: $\mu_x - \mu_y = \delta_0$ (a particular value) for a bivariate normal population

$B_N(\mu_x, \mu_y, \sigma_x^2, \sigma_y^2\ \rho)$ when (i) σ_x^2, σ_y^2 and ρ are known; (ii) σ_x^2, σ_y^2 and ρ are known. 15

(b) Let $X_1, X_2, \ldots X_n$ be n independently distributed random variables following an exponential distribution with mean parameter θ. Obtain the distributions of (i) Maximum $(X_1, X_2, \ldots X_n)$; (ii) Minimum $(X_1, X_2, \ldots, X_n)$ and (iii) Median for $n = 2m + 1, (m > 0)$. 15

(c) A medicine supposed to have effect in preventing TB was treated on 500 individuals and their records were compared with the records of 500 untreated individuals as follows. Study the effectiveness of medicine by calculating (i) Yule's coefficient of association (ii) Yule's coefficient of colligation. 10

	NO-TB	TB
Treated	252	248
Untreated	224	276

7. (a) Distinguish between inter-class correlation and intra-class correlation.

The height (in cm) of three brothers belonging to each of three families are recorded below. Compute the intra-class correlation coefficient. 15

Family	Heights of brothers (in cm)		
I	158.0	161.5	161.3
II	166.6	170.7	169.4
III	163.6	163.3	164.1

(b) Discuss the role of asymptotic relative efficiency in judging the relative preference of two test.

Following are the yields (in kg) of a crop recorded from an experiment with median (M) = 20:

15.4, 16.4, 17.8, 18.2, 19.2, 20.9, 22.7, 23.6, 24.5 Test the null hypothesis

$H_0: M = 20$ against $H_1: M \neq 20$ at $\alpha = 0.05$.

[You are given $P[X \leq 4] = 0.50$] 15

(c) The force of mortality is defined as $\mu_x = -\frac{1}{l_x}\frac{dl_x}{dx}$ when l_x is number of persons at exact age x (in years) in any year of time. Given the following table, find a value of μ_{50}. 10

Age(x) :	50	51	52	53
l_x:	73,499	72,724	71,753	70,599

8. (a) Explain the procedure for testing the hypothesis of equality of variances of two independent normal populations when population means are unkown. Write down the sampling distribution of the statistic. A sample of size 10 is drawn from each of two uncorrelated normal populations. Sample means and variances are:

1st population: mean = 7, variance = 26

2nd population: mean = 4, variance = 10

Test at 5% level of significance whether the first population has greater standard deviation than that of the second populatio.

[Given $F_{0.05; 9,9} = 3.18$] 15

(b) Let X follow a binomial distribution B(n, P). Explain the test procedure for

$H_0: P = P_0$ against H1: $P > P_0$

when the sample size is (i) small, and (ii) large. It is desired to use sample proportion p as an estimator of the population proportion P, with probability 0.95 or higher, that p is within 0.05 o P. How large should sample size (n) be? 15

(c) Using Euler's method, compute the values of y correct upto 4 places of decimal for the differential equation $\frac{dy}{dx} = x + y$ with initial $x_0 = 0$, $y_0 = 1$, taking $h = 0.05$. 10

GENERAL STATISTICS
Paper I 2013

Time Allowed : Three Hours | Maximum Marks: 200

INSTRUCTIONS

The candidates should attempt FIVE questions in ALL including Question No. 1 and 5 which are compulsory. The remaining THREE questions should be answered by choosing at least ONE question each from Section A and Section B. The number of marks carried by each question is indicated at the end of the question. Answers must be written in ENGLISH. (Symbols and abbreviations are as usual) Any essential data assumed by candidates for answering questions must be clearly stated.

SECTION A

1. Answer all of the following: **5×8=40**

(a) If the probability for n independent events are $p_1, p_2, \ldots, p_n$, then prove that:

(i) none of the events will occur

(ii) at least one event will occur

(iii) at most one event will occur 8

(b) Let X have the density function,

$$f(x) = \begin{cases} c(1-x^2), & |x|<1 \\ 0, & \text{otherwise} \end{cases}$$

(i) Find the constant c.

(ii) Find the distribution function.

(iii) Compute $P[X \geq -1/2]$. 8

(c) Compute the factorial moments $\mu_{(r)}$ and the cumulants k_r, r = 1, 2, ..., of Poisson distribution with parameter m. 8

(d) Let X be a random variable with E[X] = 4 and E[X²] = 20. Use Chebyshev's inequality to determine a lower bound for the probability $P[0 < X < 8]$. 8

(e) Show that convergence in probability implies convergence in distribution. 8

2. (a) A fair die is rolled twice. Let A be the event that the first throw shows a number ≤ 2, and B be the event that the second throw shows at least 5. Show that $P(A \cup B) = \frac{5}{9}$. 10

(b) Prove that for among the discrete distributions, the geometric distribution has the lack of memory property. 10

(c) Let X be a continuous random variable and have F(x) as the distribution function. If E[X] exists, then show that:

$$E[X] = \int_0^{\infty} (1 - F(x))\, dx - \int_{-\infty}^{0} F(x)\, dx$$ 10

(d) For a random vector $(X_1, X_2, ..., X_p)$, let Cor $(X_i, X_j) = \rho$, $i \neq j$.

Show that:

$$\rho \ge \frac{1}{(p-1)}$$ 10

3. (a) Let P(z) be the probability generating function of the random variable X whose probability distribution is $Pr[X = n] = p_n$, n = 0, 1, 2, ... Find the generating function of (i) $Pr[X > n]$, (ii) $Pr[X < n]$ and (iii) $Pr[X = 2n]$. 10

(b) Find the density funciton of X whose characteristic function $\phi(t)$ is given by:

$$\phi(t) = \begin{cases} 1 - |t|, & |t| \le 1 \\ 0, & |t| > 1 \end{cases}$$ 10

(c) Let (X, Y) have a joint probability mass function $f(x, y) = \frac{xy}{36}$, x = 1, 2, 3; y = 1, 2, 3 = 0, elsewhere.

Find the marginal mass functions of X and Y. 10

(d) Find the distribution of the ratio iid random variables with density function:

$f(x) = e^{-x}, 0 < x < \infty$

$= 0$, elsewhere. 10

4. (a) If $X \sim N(0, 1)$ obtain the distribution of X^2. 10

(b) Let $\{X_n\}$ be a sequence of iid random variables with common finite mean $\mu = E(X)$.

Show that:

$$\frac{\rho_n}{n} \xrightarrow{P} \mu \text{ as } n \to \infty.$$ 10

(c) Let $\{X_n\}$ be iid with density function $f(x) = \lambda e^{-\lambda x}$, $x > 0$ and 0, elsewhere. Let $Y_n = \underset{1 \le i \le n}{\text{Min}} \{X_n\}$ be the first order statistic. Find the limiting distribution of Y_n. 10

(d) State and prove Lindeberg-Levy Central limit theorem. 10

SCTION B

5. Answer all of the following: **8×5=40**

(a) For the following frequency distribution on 229 values:

Class	Frequency
0–10	12
10–12	30
20–30	x
30–40	65
40–50	y
50–60	25
60–70	18

the median is found to be 46. Find the values of x and y. 8

(b) Out of 200 persons appeared for an examination, 80% were males and the rest were females. Among 30 married males, 14 were successful; 110 unmarried males were successful. In respect of 10 married females, 4 were successful; 20 unmarried females were successful. Compute Yule's coefficient of association between success in the examination and the marital status for males as well as females. 8

(c) Describe the run test for randomness. For the sequence of outcomes of 14 tosses of a coin,

H T T H H H T H T T H H T H,

test whether the outcomes are in random order.

(Given the lower and upper critical values $R_L = 3$, $R_U = 12$ at 0.05 significance level.) 8

(d) Find the missing value in the table by assuming a polynomial form for y;

x	0	1	2	3	4
y	1	2	4	–	16

8

(e) Evaluate the follwong by taking seven ordinates of the integrand:

$$\int_0^1 \frac{dx}{1+x^2}.$$ 8

6. (a) The values of two random samles are arranged below in an incareasing order with X denoting the value of sample 1 and Y denoting the value of sample 2:

X X X Y X Y Y Y X X Y X X X Y X X Y Y

Use Wald-Wolfowitz run test to test whether the two samples may be regarded as coming from a common population. 10

(b) Given the two regression lines between X and Y, $2Y - X - 50 = 0$, $3Y - 2X - 10 = 0$, compute the means of X and Y and the correlation coefficient between X and Y. 10

(c) From along series of annual river flows, the variance is found out to be 49 units. For a new sample of 25 years, the variance is calculated as 81 units. Can we regard that the sample variance is significant?

(Given the chi-square value at 5% level of significance as 37.7) 10

(d) Find the weighted arithmetic mean of the first 'n' natural numbers, the weights being the corresponding numbers. 10

7. (a) For a trivariate population, it is given that:

$\sigma_1 = 3, \sigma_2 = 4, \sigma_3 = 5, r_{12} = 0.7, r_{13} = 0.6, r_{23} = 0.4$

Compute all partial and multiple correlation coefficients. 10

(b) Define correlation ratio. Discuss its properties and usefulness. 10

(c) Obtain 100(1 – α)% confidence interval for the ratio of population variances by using two independent random samples from $N(\mu_1, \sigma_1^2)$ and $N(\mu_2, \sigma_2^2)$ under the assumption that the population means are (i) known and (ii) unknown. 10

(d) The memory capacities of nine students were tested before and after some training. The data are given below. Test whether the training was effective:

Student Number	1	2	3	4	5	6	7	8	9
Before Training	10	15	9	3	7	12	16	17	4
After Training	12	17	8	5	6	11	18	20	3

(Given t-value at 8 d.f. = 2.36) 10

8. (a) Prove that independent variables are uncorrelated. Establish that the converse is false. 10

(b) The proportion of defective telephone instruments from the All-India basis was observed to be at 0.01. A new manufacturer of telephone instruments wants to estimate the proper-tion of defectives in his production lot. How many telephones should be sampled in order to estimate the fraction defective within 0.01 with 90% confidence? 10

(c) Use Simpson's one-third rule to estimate approximately the area of the cross section of a river 80 feet wide, the depth d (in feet) at a distance x from one bank being given by the following table:

x:	0	10	20	30	40	50	60	70	80
d:	0	4	7	9	12	15	14	8	3

10

(d) Solve the equation:

$$\frac{dy}{dx} = 1 - y, \; y = 0 \text{ when } x = 0$$

Use Euler algorithm and tabulate the solution at x = 0.1, 0.2, 0.3 10

GENERAL STATISTICS
Paper I 2012

Time Allowed : Three Hours | *Maximum Marks: 200*

INSTRUCTIONS

Please read each of the following instructions carefully before attempting the questions:

Candidates should attempt FIVE questions in ALL including Question Nos. 1 and 5, which are compulsory. The remaining THREE questions should be answered by choosing at least ONE question each from Section-A and Section-B. The number of marks carried by each question is indicated against each. Answers must be written only in ENGLISH. (Symbols and abbreviations are as usual, unless otherwise indicated.) Any essential data assumed by candidates for answering questions must be clearly stated. A Normal Distribution Table and a 't' Table are attached with this question paper. All parts and sub-parts of a question being attempted must be completed before moving on to the next question.

SECTION A

1. (a) You arc given the following information

   (i) In random testing, you test positive for a disease.

   (ii) In 5% of cases, the test shows positive even when the subject does not have the disease.

   (iii) In the population at large, one person in 1000 has the disease.

   What is the conditional probability that you have the disease given that you have been tested positive, assuming that if someone has the disease, he will test positive with probability I?

   (b) Items from a large lot are examined one by one until r items with a rare manufacturing defect are found. The proportion of items with this type of defect in the lot is known to be p. Let X denote the number of items needed to be examined. Derive the probability distribution of X, and find E(X).

   (c) A 4-digit number is formed by selecting 4 digits from the set (0, 1, 2, ..., 9) at random, 0 at the left-most position(s) being permissible. Find the probabilities that-

   (i) all 4 digits will be alike;

   {ii) 3 will be alike, 1 diffe rent;

(iii) there will be 2 pairs of identical digits;

(iv) 2 will be alike, 2 different;

(v) all 4 will be different.

(d) 12.3% of the candidates in a public examination score at least 70%, while another 6.3% score at most 30%. Assuming the underlying distribution to be normal, estimate the percentage of candidates scoring 80% or more.

(e) Let $\{X_n\}$ be a sequence of random variables with

$$P\{X_n = -2^n\} = P\{X_n = +2^n\} = \frac{1}{2}, = 1, 2, \cdots$$

Examine if the sequence obeys Weak Law of large numbers and Central Limit Theorem.

8×5=40

2. (a) Of three independent events A, Band C, A only happens with probability $\frac{1}{4}$, B only happens with probability $\frac{1}{8}$ and C only happens with probability $\frac{1}{12}$. Find the probability that at least one of these three events happens.

(b) For the Cauchy distribution given by

$$f(x) = \frac{k}{\sigma^2 + \{x - \mu\}^2}, -\infty < x < \infty$$

where k is a const ant to be suitably chosen, derive the expression for the distribution function. Hence obtain a measure of central tendency and a measure of dispersion. What are the points of inflexion of the distribution?

{c) The ith box contains 2i white balls and 6 – 2i black balls, i == 1 (1)3. A fair die is cast once. 3 balls are taken at random from box 1, box 2 or box 3 according as the die shows up face 1, any of 2 and 3, or any of 4, 5 and 6, respectively. Let X denote the number of white balls drawn. Find E(X).

(d) Write down the probability mass function of geometric distribution. State and prove its 'lack of memory property'. Find also the mean and the variance of the distribution. 10×4=40

3. (a) Two persons Amal and Bimal come to the club at random points of time between 6 p.m. and 7 p.m., and each stays for 10 minutes. What is the chance that they will meet?

(b) Show that in a sequence Bernoullian trials with probability $p = \frac{1}{2}$, the most number of s uccesses is s, corresponding probability is

$$p_s = \frac{1 \cdot 3 \cdot 5 \cdot \ldots .\ 2s - 1}{2 \cdot 4 \cdot 6 \cdot \ldots\ 2s} < \frac{1}{\sqrt{2s + 1}}$$

(c) Find E(X) and V(X) for the random variable X having the probability density function

$$f(x) = \begin{cases} c \cdot \frac{1}{\sigma\sqrt{2\pi}} e^{-\frac{1}{2\sigma^2}\{x - \mu\}^2}, & \mu - k\sigma \le x \le \mu + k\sigma \\ 0, & \text{otherwise} \end{cases}$$

where c is a constant to be suitably chosen.

(d) Let X be a random variable with F (x) as the distribution function. m is a suitable measure of central tendency and M is the mean square error about m. Show that

$F(m + c) - F(m - c) \geq 1 - M/c^2 \ \forall \ c > 0$ 10×4=40

4. (a) An urn contains a white and b black balls. After a ball is drawn at random, it is to be returned to the urn if it is white; if it is black, it is to be replaced by a white ball from another urn. What is the probability of drawing a white ball from the urn after the foregoing operation has been repeated n times?

(b) For a discrete random variable X assuming the values 0, 1, 2, ···, the probability mass function satisfies the recursion relation

$$f(x) = \frac{\alpha + \beta x}{x} f(x - 1), x = 1, 2, ...$$

Find the mean and the mean deviation about the mean of X.

(c) Let $X_1, X_2, \cdots, X_n$ be random variables such that $E(X_1) \mid = \mu$, $E(X_r \mid X_{r-1}) = X_{r-1}$, r = 2(1) n. Also

$E(X_1 - \mu)^2 = E[(X_r - X_{r-1})^2 \mid X_{r-1}] = \sigma^2$, r =2(1)n

Find $E(X_n)$ and $V(X_n \}$.

(d) The continuous random variable X has the distribution function F(x). X_1 and X_2 are two randomly selected values of X. Show that

$$E \mid X_1 - X_2 \mid = 4 \int_{-\infty}^{\infty} x \left[F(x) - \frac{1}{2} \right] dF(x)$$ 10×4=40

SECTION B

5. (a) The three sides x_1, x_2 and x_3 (in decimeter} of a solid rectangular parallelopiped satisfy the relation $x_1 + 2x_2 + 4x_3 = 12$. Exploiting the inequality relation between two wellknown measures of central tendency, determine the maximum possible volume of this parallelopiped .

(b) In respect of the following observations, arranged in a non-decreasing sequence

8, 10, 10, X, 12, 14, 14, 16

where x is unknown, indicate, with a brief justification, if the following statements are correct :

(i) x is necessarily larger than the standard d eviation of the entire set including x.

(ii) The mean deviation about the median is necessarily smaller than that about the mean.

(c) Solve the linear difference equation with p + q = 1 and initial conditions $u_0 = 0$ and $u_{a+b} = I$.

(d) (i) In a ticket counter, at some point of time the sequence of males (M) and females (F) was found as

MMFMFFFMFMMFFFFMFMMMM

Use runs test to examine if the sequence is random (5% critical value of the number r of runs with $n_1 = 11$, $n_2 = 10$ is 6).

(ii) Name two non-parametric tests for comparing locations of two correlated populations.

(e) 125 out of 285 college-going male students in 1995 from a city were found to be smokers. Another sample of 325 such students from the same city in 2012 included 95 smokers. Examine at 5% level of significance if smoking habit among college-going students is on the decrease in this city. 8×5=40

6. (a) Show, by proving all intermediate results, that for a set of n unsorted data, the measure of skewness based on mean, median and standard deviation, necessarily lies between -3 and +3.

(b) Scores in a UPSC examination in Statistics Paper-I and Pa per-II awarded to 10 candidates were as under :

Candidate	A	B	C	D	E	F	G	H	I	J
Score in Paper-I	91	65	80	120	80	140	105	80	42	72
Score in Paper-II	86	38	75	135	85	135	94	101	45	65

Calculate Spearman's rank correlation coefficient between the scores in the two papers.

(c) Solve the equation f(x) = 0 by using a suitable interpolation formula on the following values:

x	3	4	5	6
f(x)	–2.8	–1.2	–0.3	1.8

(d) Let (X, Y) follow the bivariate normal distribution $N_2(0, 0, 1, 1, p)$. Show that the expected value of the absolute difference between X and Y is $2\sqrt{(1-P)/\pi}$. . 10×4=40

7. (a) Consider a 3-point symmetrical distribution having the values $x_0 - h, x_0, x_0 + h$ with the corresponding relative frequencies f, 1-2f and f. Calculate the coefficient of kurtosis b_2 and find its limiting values as $f \to 0$ and $f \to \frac{1}{2}$. Hence comment on the suitability of b_2 as a measure of unimodality versus bimodality.

(b) For a set of 10 pairs of observations (x_i, y_j), $i = 1\,(1)1\,0$, the following calculations are available

$\Sigma x_i = 61, \Sigma x_f = 412, \Sigma y_i = 45, \Sigma y_i^2 = 308$

and $\Sigma x_i y_i = 295$

Examine at 5% level of significance if the two variables are uncorrelated in the population.

(c) An unknown function u_x has been tabulated below for some selected values of x. Use Newton's divided difference formula on these to find an approximate value of u_3:

X	0	2	5	10
u_x	3	19	73	223

(d) Define partial correlation coefficient $r_{12.3}$ between x_1 and x_2 eliminating from each the effect of x_3. Derive the expression for $r^{12.3}$ and comment on its usefulness in multivariate data a nalysis. 10×4=40

8. (a) Mention two measures-one of skewness and the other of kurtosis-based on central moments. State and prove an inequality relation involving these two measures and a constant term. Give an example of a distribution for which equality holds in this relation.

(b) The speed y (in km/hr) of a car at different points of time x between 10:00 a.m. and 10:40 a.m. on some day was recorded as follows:

Time x (a.m.)	10:00	10:10	10:20	10:30	10:40
Speed y (in km/hr)	24·2	35·0	41·3	42·8	39·2

Calc ulate the approximate distance covered by the car between 10:00 a.m. and 10:40 a. m. on that day using Simpson's one-third formula for numerical integration.

(c) Indicate how you would test the hypothesis that the means of k independent normal populations are identical, clearly mentioning the null and the alternative hypotheses, the assumptions made, the test statistic used, and the critical region.

(d) Ten short-distance runners were put to a rigorous training for two months. Times taken by them to clear 100 metres before and after the training were as follows :

Sl. No. of runner	1	2	3	4	5	6	7	8	9	10
Time (in sec) before training	10.6	10.9	10.1	10.5	11.0	11.2	10.7	10.2	10·9	10.6
Time (in sec) after training	10.1	10.7	9.9	10.0	11.1	10.9	10.6	10.3	10.5	10.8

Use Wilcoxon's paired sample signed rank test to examine at 1% level if the training was at all effective. [The critical value of Wilcoxon's statistic at 1% level of significance for $n = 10$ is 5]

10×4=40

GENERAL STATISTICS
Paper I 2011

Time Allowed : Three Hours | Maximum Marks: 200

INSTRUCTIONS

Candidates should attempt FIVE questions in ALL including Questions No. 1 and 5 which are compulsory. The remaining THREE questions should be answered by choosing at least ONE question each from Section A .and Section B. The number of marks carried by each question is indicated against each. Answers must be written only in ENGLISH. (Symbols and abbreviations. are as usual) Any essential data assumed by candidates for answering questions must be clearly stated. A normal distribution table and a 't' table are attached with this question paper.

SECTION A

1. Answer any five of the following:

(a) Verify the following identities: 8×5=40

(i) $P(A \cup B) = P(A) + P(B \cap A^c)$

(ii) $P(A \cup B \cup C) = P(A) + P(B) + P(C) - P(A \cap B) - P(B \cap C) - P(A \cap C) + P(A \cap B \cap C)$

(b) A fair die is thrown until a 6 appears. Specify the sample space. What is the probability that it must be thrown at least 3 times ?

(c) $P(A) = 1/3$ and $P(B^c) = 1/4$. Can A and B be disjoint ? Explain.

(d) Show that $E(X - a)^2$ is minimized for $a = E(X)$, assuming that the first 2 moments of X exist.

(e) Let

$$\frac{1}{\Gamma(n)\,\beta^n} x^{n-1} e^{-x/\beta}, x > 0, n > 0, \beta > 0.$$

Show that f(x) is a probability density 'function Obtain V(X).

(f) Show that $f(x) = \frac{a}{x^3}$, $a < x$, $(a > 0)$ is a probability density function for an appropriate value of a. Upto what order do the moments of this p.d.f. exist ?

2. (a) Let $E|X|^n < \infty$. Prove that $E|X|^k < \infty$ for $k \leq n$.

(b) Show that the sum of two independent Poisson random variables with parameters A and 11 respectively is a Poisson random variable with parameter λ and μ respectively is a Poisson random variable with parameter $\lambda + \mu$.

(c) Let the joint p.d.f. of (X, Y) be

$f(x, y) = e^{-y}, 0 < x < y < \infty.$

Obtain the probability $P(X + Y \leq 1)$.

(d) Let $X_1, X_2, ..., X_n$ be a sequence of i.i.d.r.v.s with $E(X_i) = 0$ and $V(X_i) = 1$. Show that the sequence

$S_n^2 = \frac{1}{n}\sum_{i=1}^{n} X_i^2$ tends to 1 in probability. 10×4=40

3. (a) Let X_1 and X_2 be two independent exponentially distributed random variables with the same mean θ. Define $V = \max(X_1, X_2)$ and $W = \min(X_1, X_2)$ Show that V-W and 2W are independent and identically distributed random variables.

(b) Let X be a positive valued random variable. Prove that

$$P(X \geq r) \leq \frac{E(X)}{r}, r > 0.$$

Hence deduce the Chebychev's inequality.

(c) Let X have the continuous c.d.f. F(x). Define U = F(x). Show that both - log U arid -log (1 - U) are exponential random variables:

(d) Obtain the median and the quartiles of the Cauchy distribution with p.d.f.

$$f(x) = \frac{1}{\pi(1 + x^2)}, -\infty < x < \infty.$$ 10×4=40

4. (a) Let Z be a random variable with p.d.f. f(z). Let z_σ be its upper a[th] quantile. Show that if X is a random variable with p.d.f. $\frac{1}{\sigma}f\left(\frac{x-\mu}{\sigma}\right)$ $\sigma z_\alpha + \mu$ is the upper ath quantile of X.

(b) Let (X, Y) have a bivariate distribution with finite moments upto order 2. Show that

(i) $E(E(X|Y)) = E(X)$, and

(ii) $V(X) \geq V(X||Y)$:

(c) Show that a.c.d.f. can. have at most a countable number of jumps.

(d) Consider the following bivariate p.m.f .. of (X, Y):

$$p(0, 10) = p(0, 20) = \frac{2}{18};$$

$$p(1, 10) = p(1, 30) = \frac{3}{18};$$

$$p(1, 20) = \frac{4}{18}; p(2, 30) = \frac{4}{18}$$

Obtain the conditional mass functions $p(y \mid x = 2)$, and $p(y \mid x = 1)$ 10×4=40

SECTION B

5. Answer any *five* of the following: **8×5=40**

(a) Tabulate the exact null distribution of Wilcoxon rank sum statistic for $n_1 = n_2 = 3$.

(b) Let (X, Y) have the uniform distribution over the range $0 < y < x < 1$. Obtain the conditional mean and variance of X given Y = y.

(c) Let the temperature before and after administration of aspirin be

Patient	Before	After
1	100.0	98.1
2	102.1	97.2
3	100.6	98.6
4	100.1	99.1
5	101.5	97·6
6	102	98.6
7	99.9	98.2
8	102.7	98.1
9	100.4	98.2
10	100.8	97.1

Test by the sign test; whether aspirin is effective in reducing temperature. What is the p-value of the calculated statistic?

(d) Use Simpson's rule with five ordinates to compute an approximation to π with the help of the integration of the function $(1 + x^2)^{-1}$ from 0 to 1.

(e) Use mathematical induction to prove

$$f_{x+ah} = \sum_{i=0}^{\infty} \binom{n}{i} \Delta^i f_x.$$

(f) Let $D_n = \sup_{-\infty<x<\infty} |F_n(x) - F(x)|$ be the

Kolmogorov statistic. Show that

$$D_n^+ = \max_{0 \le i \le n} \sup_{x(i) \le x < x_{(i+1)}} \left\{ \frac{i}{n} - F(x) \right\}$$

where $x_{(1)}, x_{(2)}, \ldots, x_{(n)}$ are the order statistics of the data.

6. (a) Let X and Y be two random variables with correlation coefficient 0.9. Can a third random variable Z have correlation coefficient – 0.9 with both X and Y? Give reasons for your answer.

(b) Show that the square of the one sample t-statistic has the F-distribution. What are its degrees of freedom ?

(c) Define the correlation ratio η_1 of X on Y. If ρ is the usual correlation coefficient between X and Y, then show that $0 \le \rho^2 \le \eta_1^2 \le 1$.

(d) Prove that the sum of two independent chi-squared random variables is also chi-squared.

10×4=40

7. (a) Apply the Wilcoxon two-sample test to the following data on the first breakdown. times of two brands of computers:

Brand A	98,	102,	47,	85,	99,	140,	130
Brand B	95,	125,	160,	155,	148.		

Use 1.96 as the critical point for the appropriate test.

(b) Describe a test of independence of two normal random variables based on r, the sample correlation coefficient using the t-distribution. If n = 10 and r = 0.9, then carry out the test.

(c) Show that the best predictor of Y, in terms of minimum MSE, is linear in X, if (X, Y) have bivariate normal distribution.

(d) Explain the Wald- Wolfowitz run test for randomness in a sequence of two types of symbols. Find $E_{H_0}(R)$ where R denotes the number of runs of elements of one kind. 10×4=40

8. (a) The following are the frequencies in the given intervals :

(0-2]	(2-5]	(5-10]	(10-15]	(15-18]	(18- 20]
43	85	151	112	72	34

Draw the histogram of this data. Calculate the mean of the data from the frequency table.

(b) Let $X_1, X_2, \ldots, X_n$ be independent $N(0, \sigma^2)$ random variables. Obtain the mean and variance of $\sum_{i=1}^{n} X_i^2$. What is its probability distribution?

(c) From a bivariate data set of 4995 observations, the following quantities have been calculated:

$\Sigma x = -2353$, $\Sigma y = -1400$, $\Sigma x^2 = 9508$

$\Sigma y^2 = 70802$, $\Sigma xy = 8805$.

Obtain the estimated linear regression of X on Y.

(d) Explain how to carry out the chi-squared test for

$H_0: \sigma^2 = \sigma_0^2$ on the basis of a random sample $X_1, X_2, \ldots, X_n$ from $N(\mu, \sigma^2)$ population. 10×4=40

GENERAL STATISTICS
Paper I 2010

Time Allowed : Three Hours

Maximum Marks: 200

INSTRUCTIONS

Candidates should attempt FIVE questions in ALL including Questions No. 1 and 5 which are compulsory. The remaining THREE questions should be answered by choosing at least ONE question each from Section A .and Section B. The number of marks carried by each question is indicated against each. Answers must be written only in ENGLISH. (Symbols and abbreviations. are as usual) Any essential data assumed by candidates for answering questions must be clearly stated. A normal distribution table and a 't' table are attached with this question paper.

SECTION A

1. Answer any five of the following: **8×5=40**

(a) An unbiased die rolled twice. Let A be the event that the first throw shows a number ≤ 2, and B be the event that the second throw shows at least 5.

Show that $P(A \cup B) = \frac{5}{9}$.

(b) Let $\{A_n\}$ be a non-decreasing sequence events. Show that:

$$\lim_{n\to\infty} P(A_n) = P\left(\lim_{n\to\infty} A_n\right)$$

(c) Let X be a random variable defined on (Ω, A, P). Defint; a point function

$F(x) = P\{\omega: X(\omega) \leq x\}$, for all $x \in R$.

Show that the function F is indeed a distribution function.

(d) Let $k > 0$. be a constant, and

$$f(x) = \begin{cases} kx(1-x), & 0 < x < 1 \\ 0, & \text{otherwise} \end{cases}$$

obtain $P(X > 0.3)$.

(e) Let X be a random variable with E(X) = 0 and Var (X)= σ^2.

Show that:

$$P(X \geq x) \leq \frac{\sigma^2}{\sigma^2 + x^2} \text{ if } x > 0$$

and $P(X \geq x) \leq \dfrac{x^2}{\sigma^2 + x^2}$ if $x < 0$.

(f) Let $X_1, X_2, \ldots\ldots,$ be independent and identically distributed random variables with common p.d.f.

$$f(x) = \begin{cases} \dfrac{1+\delta}{x^2+\delta}, & x \geq 1 \\ 0, & x < 1 \end{cases}, \delta > 0.$$

Show that law of large numbers holds.

(a) Let $\{X_n, Y_n\}$, n = 1, 2, ... be a sequence of random variables. Then

$|X_n - Y_n| \xrightarrow{P} 0$ and $Y_n \xrightarrow{\alpha} Y \Rightarrow X_n \xrightarrow{\alpha} Y$.

Prove it.

(b) Let $\beta_n = E|X|^n < \infty$. Show that for arbitrary k, $2 \leq k \leq n$,

$$\beta_{k-1}^{\frac{1}{k-1}} \leq \beta_k^{\frac{1}{k}}$$

(c) Let (X, Y) be jointly distributed with p.d.f.

$$f(x, y) = \begin{cases} 2, & 0 < x < y < 1 \\ 0, & \text{otherwise} \end{cases}$$

Find marginal probability density functions of X andY. ·

(d) Let $X_1, X_2, \ldots\ldots, X_m$ be i.i.d. random variables with common p.m.f.

$$P(X = k) = \binom{n}{k} p^k (1-p)^{n-k}, k = 0, 1, 2, \ldots, n, 0 < p < 1.$$

Obtain the p.m.f. of $S_m = X_1 + X_2 + \ldots + X_m$. 10×4=40

3. (a) Let X have a geometric distribution, then for any two non-negative integers m and n,

$P(X > m + n/X > m) = P(X \geq n)$. Prove it.

(b) Let X be a random variable with a continuous distribution function F. Show that F(X) has the uniform distribution on (0, 1).

(c) Let X be a Poisson random variable with parameter A. Show that

$$P(X \leq K) = \frac{1}{K!} \int_{\lambda}^{\infty} e^{-x} x^K \, dx.$$

(d) How large a sample must be taken in order that the probability will be at least 0.95 that $\overline{X}_n$ will be within 0.5 of μ. (μ is unknown and a = 1). 10×4=40

4. (a) Let Fn(x) be the distribution function defined by

$$F_n(x) = \begin{cases} 0, & \text{for } x \le -n \\ \dfrac{x+n}{2n}, & \text{for } -n < x < n \\ 1, & \text{for } x \ge n \end{cases}$$

Is the $\lim_{n\to\infty} F_n(x)$ a distribution function? If not, why?

(b) If X_l can have only two values with equal probabilities i^{α} and - i^{α}, show that law of large numbers can be applied to the independent variables $X_1, X_2, \ldots\ldots$, if $\alpha < \frac{1}{2}$.

(c) If $A_1, A_2, \ldots\ldots$, be a sequence of events on the probability space (S, B, P) and let $A = \overline{\lim}\, A_n$. If $\sum_{n=i}^{\infty} P(A_n) < \infty$, then P(A) = 0.

Prove it.

(d) Let $\{X_k\}$ be independent random variables with p.m.f.

$$P(X_k = k^{\lambda}) = P(X_k = -k^{\lambda}) = \frac{1}{2}, \; k = 1, 2, \ldots..$$

Show that this sequence $\{X_k\}$ obeys central limit theorem, for $\lambda > 0$. 10×4=40

SECTION B

5. **Answer any *five* of the following:** **8×5=40**

(a) Show that for any discrete distribution, standard deviation is not less than mean deviation from mean.

(b) Let (X, Y) be jointly distributed with density function

$$f(x, y) = \begin{cases} x + y, & 0 < x < 1; \quad 0 < y < 1 \\ 0, & \text{otherwise} \end{cases}$$

Obtain correlation coefficient between X and Y.

(c) For the 2 x 2 table

a	b
c	d

prove that Chi-square test of independence gives

$$\chi^2 = \frac{N(ad - bc)}{(a + c)\,(b + d)\,(a + b)\,(c + d)},$$

N = a + b + c + d

(d) The following data repesent lifetimes (hours) of batteries for two different brands:

Brand A:	40	30	40	45	55	30
Brand B:	50	50	45	55	60	40

Test whether two brands are the same.

(e) Estimate U_2 from the following table:

x:	1	2	3	4	5
U_x:	7	–	13	21	37

(f) Evaluate loge 7 by Simpson's $\frac{1}{3}$rd rule.

6. (a) A cyclist pedals from his house to his college at a speed of 10 km per hour and back from the college to his house at 15 km per hour. Find the average speed.

(b) The random variables X and Y are jointly normally distributed a!ld U and V are defined by $U = X \cos \alpha + Y \sin \alpha$, $V = Y \cos \alpha - X \sin \alpha$. Show that U and V will be uncorrelated if

$$\tan 2\alpha = \frac{2\gamma\sigma_x \sigma_y}{\sigma_x^2 - \sigma_y^2}$$

(c) The following values of the function f(x) for values of x are given:

f(1) = 4, f(2) = 5, f(7) = 5, f(8) = 4.

Find the value of f(6) and also the value of x for which f(x) is maximum or minimum.

(d) If third differences are constant, prove that

$$\int_{-1}^{1} f(x)\,dx = \frac{2}{3}\left[f(0) + f\left(\frac{1}{\sqrt{2}}\right) + f\left(-\frac{1}{\sqrt{2}}\right)\right].$$ 10×4=40

7. (a) The first three moments of a distribution apout the value 1 are 2, 25 and 80. Find its mean, standard deviation and the moment-measure of skewness.

(b) You are working as a purchase manager for a company. The following information has been supplied to you by two manufacturers of electric bulbs.

	Company A	Company B
Mean life (in hours)	1300	1288
Standard deviation (in hours)	82	93
Sample size	100	100

Which brand of bulbs are you going to purchase if you desire to take a risk of 5% ?

(c) Describe clearly sign test. State its asymptot. relative efficiency with respect to t-test.

(d) The observed-values of a function are respectively 168, 120, 72 and 63 at the four positions 3, 7, 9 and 10 of the independent variable. What is the best estimate you can give for the value of the function at the position 6 of the independent variable? 10×4=40

8. (a) Show that for discrete distribution $\beta_2 > 1$.

(b) Find the most likely price in Mumbai corresponding to the price of Rs. 70 at Kolkata from the followmg:

	Kolkata	Mumbai
Average price	65	67
Standard deviation	2.5	3.5

Correlation coefficient between the prices of commodities in the two cities is 0.8.

(c) Show that for t-distribution with n degrees of freedom, mean deviation about mean is given by

$$\frac{\sqrt{n}\,\Gamma\left[\left(\frac{n-1}{2}\right)\right]}{\sqrt{\pi}\,\Gamma\left(\frac{n}{2}\right)}$$

(d) If $f(x) = \frac{1}{x^2}$, find the divided differences f(a, b) and f(a, b, c). 10×4=40

GENERAL STATISTICS
Paper I 2010

Time Allowed : Three Hours | *Maximum Marks: 200*

INSTRUCTIONS

Candidates should attempt FIVE questions in ALL including Questions No. 1 and 5 which are compulsory. The remaining THREE questions should be answered by choosing at least ONE question each from Section A and Section B. The number of marks carried by each question is indicated against each. Answers must be written only in ENGLISH. (Symbols and abbreviations are as usual) Any essential data assumed by candidates for answering questions must be clearly stated.

SECTION A

1. Answer any five of the following: **5×8=40**

(a) Prove that for $n \geq 2$,

$$\sum_{j=1}^{n} p[A_j] \geq P\left[\bigcup_{j=1}^{n}\right] \geq \sum_{j=1} P[A_j] - \sum_{1 \leq k \leq n} P[A_j \cap A_k]$$

(b) A die is rolled twice. Let A, B, C denote the events respectively that the sum of scores is 6, the sum of scores is 7, and the first score is 4. Are A and C independent? Are B and C independent ?

(c) Given the distribution function

$$F(x) = \frac{1}{2} + \frac{x}{2(1+|x|)} \quad -\infty < x < \infty$$

find its probability density function.

(d) Let X have the probability density function

$$f(x) = \begin{cases} (\alpha+1)\,x^{\alpha}, & 0 < x < 1, \alpha > 1 \\ 0, & \text{otherwise} \end{cases}$$

Find the mean, geometric mean and harmonic mean.

(e) (i) Let X be a random variable such that $P[X < 0] = 0$ and $E[x]$ exist. Show that $P(X < 2E[x]) \geq \frac{1}{2}$.

(ii) Let E[X] = 0 and $E[X^2]$ be finite. Show that $P(X^2 \leq 9E[X^2]) > \frac{8}{9}$.

(f) Let (X_n) be a sequence of random variables such that

$$P(X_n = 1) = \frac{1}{n} = 1 - P(X_n = 0), n \geq 1.$$

Show that $X_n \to 0$ in prob. and $X_n \to 0$ a.s.

2. (a) Given the joint density of (X_1, X_2)

$$f(x_1, x_2) = \begin{cases} \frac{1}{8}(x_1^2 - x_2^2)\, e^{-x}\, 1, & 0 < x_1 < \infty, |x_2| < x_1 \\ 0, & \text{otherwise} \end{cases}$$

Find the marginal densities of X_1 and X_2. Also find $E[X_1]$.

(b) Suppose that the random variable X has a normal distribution with mean μ and variance σ^2. Let ϕ be the distribution function of a standard normal variate. Find the density of $\phi\left(\frac{X-\mu}{\sigma}\right)$. Also find $E\left[\phi\left(\frac{X-\mu}{\sigma}\right)\right]$.

(c) Find the generating function of X whose probability density function is

$P[X = r] = pq^{r-1}, r = 1, 2, \ldots, 0 \leq p \leq 1, q = i - p.$

(d) Explain "Memoryless property" of a distribution. Show that the exponential distribution has memoryless property. 4×10=40

3. (a) Let

$$P_{X,Y}(u, v) = e^{-\lambda_1 - \lambda_2 - \mu + \lambda_1 u + \lambda_2 u + \lambda_2 v + \mu uv}$$

be the probability generating function of the random variables X and Y.

(i) Find the marginal densities of X and Y.

(ii) Obtain the generating function of

$Z = X + Y.$

(iii) Interpret the case when $\mu = 0$.

(b) Let $X \sim BIN(100, 0.2)$. Compute $P[10 \leq X \leq 30]$.

(c) The joint density of (X, Y) is

$$f(x, y) = \begin{cases} x^2 + \frac{xy}{3}, & 0 < x < 1, 0 < y < 2 \\ 0, & \text{otherwiese.} \end{cases}$$

Find the conditional densities and $E[X|Y = 1.5]$.

(d) Find the density, if its characteristic function is

$$\phi(t) = \begin{cases} 1 - |t|, & |t| < 1 \\ 0, & \text{otherwiese.} \end{cases}$$

4×10=40

4. (a) Let $X_1, X_2, ..., X_n$ be a sequence of iid N(0, 1) variables. Find the limiting distribution of

$$\frac{(X_1 + X_2 + ... + X_n)}{X_1^2 + X_2^2 + ... + X_n^2}$$

(b) Show that

$$\sum_{k=0}^{n} \frac{e^{-n} n^k}{k!} \to \frac{1}{2}, \text{ as } n \to \infty$$

(c) Let (X_n) be iid with density function

$$f_n(x) = \begin{cases} \frac{1}{|x|^5}, & |x| > 1 \\ 0, & \text{otherwise.} \end{cases}$$

Examine whether Law of Large Numbers holds good for (X_n).

(d) If the exponent of a bivariate normal density function is

$$-\frac{2}{3}(x^2 + 9y^2 - 3xy - 13x + 60y + 103],$$

find its means, variances, conditional means, conditional variances and correlation coefficient.

4×10=40

SECTION B

5. **Answer any *five* of the following :** **5x8=40**

(a) Explain the advantages of fitting orthogonal polynomials to a given paired data over the other methods.

(b) Show that the mean and variance computed for a random sample drawn from a normal distribution are independent.

(c) The data on lives of two models of refrigerators are given below:

Life	Number of Model A	Number of Model B
0-2	5	2
2-4	16	7
4-6	13	12
6-8	7	19
8-10	5	9
10-12	4	1

Which model is more reliable ?

(d) Two drugs were given to two batches of 6 students. The numbers of days to get a complete cure are given below :

Drug A	6	7	8	9	12	16
Drug B	10	11	13	14	15	17

Using Mann — Whitney test decide whether the median days for cure by the two drugs are equal. (Table values of U - Statistic at 0·05 level are : $U_{5,5} = 2$, $U_{5,6} = 3$, and $U_{6,6} = 5$.)

(e) Given the following data:

x:	0	1	3
f(x):	1	3	55

find a polynomial P(x) of degree 2 or less so that P(x) = f(x) at the tabulated values of x. Hence approximate f(2).

(f) A train travels y(t) kilometers at time t = 0(1)6. Using the following table of values for (t, y(t)), compute the speed and acceleration of the train at t = 1.

t:	0	1	2	3	4	5	6
y(t):	0	1	8	27	64	125	216

6. (a) Let the correlation coefficient between X_i and X_j be p for i, j = 1, 2, ... , n, i ≠ j. Show that the square of the multiple correlation coefficient satisfies

$$R^2 = \frac{(p-1)\rho^2}{1+(p-1)\rho}.$$

(b) A manufacturer of alkaline batteries expects that only 5% of his products are defective. A random sample of 300 batteries contained 10 defectives. Can we conclude the proportion of defectives in the entire lot is less than 0.5 at 5% level of significance ?

(c) The two regression lines between X and Y are 8X – 10Y + 66 = 0, 40X – 18Y = 214. The vanance of X is 9. Find $\overline{X}, \overline{Y}$, σ_y, and ρ.

(d) Explain the method of testing nonnality by using chi-squared test. 4×10=40

7. (a) If Cov $(X_i, X_j) = r_{ij}$, i, j = 1, 2, 3, i ≠ j, then show that

(i) $r_{12} + r_{23} + r_{13} \geq -\frac{3}{2}$

(ii) $r_{12}^2 + r_{23}^2 + r_{13}^2 \leq 1 + 2r_{12}\, r_{23}\, r_{13}$

(b) (i) Show that the arithmetic mean of (positive) regression coefficients is greater than the correlation coefficient.

(ii) What 1s the value of the product of geometric mean of variances and the geometric mean of regression coefficients ?

(c) Define 'minimum mean square error' and 'best linear predictor'. Show that they coincide for the normal distribution.

(d) Two set of students were given different teaching methods. Their IQ's are given below:

Set I	77	74	82	73	87	69	66	80
Set II	72	68	76	68	84	68	61	76

Test whether the two teaching methods differ significantly at 5% level of significance.

(Assume critical value of test statistic to be 1.96) 4×10=40

8. (a) A sample of 100 records on lengths of stay of patients in a hospital gave a standard deviation of days of stay as 4.9. In order to estimate the mean number of days of stay within 0.25 day with 95% confidence, what should be the sample size ?

(b) Find the value of

$$\int_0^1 \frac{1}{1+x^2}$$

by taking 5 subintervals and using the Trapezoidal rule.

(c) Define correlation ratio η· Show that

$0 \leq \rho^2 \leq \eta^2 \leq 1.$

(d) Ten experts have given scores of effectiveness on two teams A and B as given below.

Expert	Score on A	Score on B
1	7	9
2	4	5
3	8	8
4	9	8
5	3	6
6	6	10
7	8	9
8	10	8
9	9	4
10	5	9

Are the distribution of scores for group A above that of group B? 4×10=40

STATISTICS-II

STATISTICS
Paper- II 2023

Time Allowed : Three Hours | *Maximum Marks: 200*

INSTRUCTIONS

1. IMMEDIATELY AFTER THE COMMENCEMENT OF THE EXAMINATION, YOU SHOULD CHECK THAT THIS TEST BOOKLET DOES NOT HAVE ANY UNPRINTED OR TORN OR MISSING PAGES OR ITEMS, ETC. IF SO, GET IT REPLACED BY A COMPLETE TEST BOOKLET.
2. Please note that it is the candidate's responsibility to encode and fill in the Roll Number and Test Booklet Series Code A, B, C or D carefully and without any omission or discrepancy at the appropriate places in the OMR Answer Sheet. Any omission/discrepancy will render the Answer Sheet liable for rejection.
3. You have to enter your Roll Number on the Test Booklet in the Box provided alongside. DO NOT write anything else on the Test Booklet.
4. This Test Booklet contains 80 items (questions). Each item comprises four responses (answers). You will select the response which you want to mark on the Answer Sheet. In case you feel that there is more than one correct response, mark the response which you consider the best. In any case, choose ONLY ONE response for each item.
5. You have to mark all your responses ONLY on the separate Answer Sheet provided. See directions in the Answer Sheet.
6. All items carry equal marks.
7. Before you proceed to mark in the Answer Sheet the response to various items in the Test Booklet, you have to fill in some particulars in the Answer Sheet as per instructions sent to you with your Admission Certificate.
8. After you have completed filling in all your responses on the Answer Sheet and the examination has concluded, you should hand over to the Invigilator *only the Answer Sheet*. You are permitted to take away with you the Test Booklet.
9. Sheets for rough work are appended in the Test Booklet at the end.
10. Penalty for wrong answers :

THERE WILL BE PENALTY FOR WRONG ANSWERS MARKED BY A CANDIDATE IN THE OBJECTIVE TYPE QUESTION PAPERS.

(i) There are four alternatives for the answer to every question. For each question for which a wrong answer has been given by the candidate, one-third of the marks assigned to that question will be deducted as penalty. ·

(ii) If a candidate gives more than one answer, it will be treated as a wrong answer even if one of the given answers happens to be correct and there will be same penalty as above to that question.

(iii) If a question is left blank, i.e., no answer is given by the candidate, there will be no penalty for that question.

DO NOT OPEN THIS TEST BOOKLET UNTIL YOU ARE TOLD TO DO SO

1. The radius ofa circle ia measured with an error of measurement, which is N(0, σ2). Let $x_1, x_2, \ldots x_n$ be n measurements of the radius. Let $\overline{X} = \frac{\sum_{i=1}^{n} x_i}{n}$ be the sampe mean and $S^2 = \frac{\sum_{i=1}^{n}(x_i - \overline{x})^2}{n-1}$ be the sample variance. What is the unbiased estimate of the area of the circle?

   (a) $\pi(\overline{x})^2$ (b) $\pi\frac{\sum_{i=1}^{n} x_i^2}{n}$

   (c) $\pi\left(\frac{\sum_{i=1}^{n} x_i^2}{n} - S^2\right)$ (d) $\pi[(\overline{x})^2 - S^2]$

2. Let 2.5, – 2.0, 1.5, 3.5, 0.5 be the observations of a random sample of size 5 from the continuous distributions with pdf $f(x) = \frac{1}{8}e^{-|x-2|} + \frac{3}{4\sqrt{2\pi}}e^{-\frac{1}{2}(x-\theta)^2}$; x, θ ∈ E and θ is unknown. The the method of moment estimators of θ belongs to the interval:

   (a) (0.60, 0.70) (b) (0.70, 0.80)

   (c) (0.80, 0.90) (d) (0.90, 0.99)

3. Consider the followidg statéments:

   Statement-I

   The method of momeñts provides cñnaiatent estimators of population moments.

   Statement-II

   From the Weak Law of Large Numbers, it follows that $\frac{1}{n}\sum_{i=1}^{n} x_i^j \xrightarrow{P} E(X_j)$ provided $E(X_j)$ exists.

   Which one of the following is correct in respect of the above Statements?

   (a) Statement-I and Statement-II are individually correct and Statement-II is the correct explanation of Statement-I.

   (b) Statement-I and Statement-II are individually correct but Statement-II is *not* the correct explanation of Statement-I.

   (c) Statement-I is correct but Statement-II is incorrect.

   (d) Statement-I is incorrect but Statement-II is correct.

4. Let X be a random variable which assumes only two values 1 and 0, respectively representing occurrence of success or failure in an experiment with only two outcomes. The probability of getting success in the experiment is p(θ) defined as:

$$p(\theta) = \begin{cases} \theta, & \text{if } \theta \text{ is rational} \\ 1-\theta, & \text{if } \theta \text{ is algebraic irrational} \end{cases}$$

Define an estimator, $T = \frac{\sum_{i=1}^{n} x_i}{n}$ = Sample proportion of success.

Which one of the following is correct?

(a) T is MLE as well as consistent for θ.

(b) T is unbiased and consistent for θ.

(c) T is MLE but not consistent for θ.

(d) T is consistent but not MLE tending to θ.

5. Let {6, 11, 4, 13, 5} be a random sample from the exponemential distribution $f(x, \theta) = e^{-(x-\theta)}$, $x \geq \theta$, $\theta \in (-\infty, 3]$ is unknown. Then the Maximum Likelihood Estimate of e^{θ} is:

(a) e^3 (b) e^4

(c) $e^{7.8}$ (d) e^6

6. Let {1, 0, 0, 0, 1, 1} be a random sample from a binomial b(1, θ), $0 < \theta < 1$. Then UMVUE of $\theta(1 + \theta)$ is:

(a) 0.7 (b) 0.6

(c) 0.5 (d) 0.3

7. Consider the following statements regarding unbiased estimators of parameter θ:

   1. Let T_0 be an UMVUE of θ and T_1 is any other unbiased estimator of θ with efficiency 0.64, then the correlation coefficient between T_0 and T_1 is 0.8.
   2. Let T_0 be an MVUE of $g(\theta)$ and T_1 is any other unbiased estimator with efficiency less than 1, then any unbiased linear combinatio of T_0 and T_1 will also be MVUE of $g(\theta)$.

Which of the above statements is/are correct?

(a) 1 only (b) 2 only

(c) Both 1 and 2 (d) Neither 1 nor 2

8. Let $x_1, x_2, ... x_n$ be a random sample from U(θ – 0.5, θ + 0.5), $\theta \in R$. Which of the following statements is/are correct?

   1. $(X_{(1)}, X_{(n)})$ is sufficient as well as complete.
   2. $\frac{(X_{(1)} + X_{(n)})}{2}$ is MLE for θ.

Select the correct answer using the code given below:

(a) 1 only (b) 2 only

(c) Both 1 and 2 (d) Neither 1 nor 2

9. Let {4.5, 3.8, 2.5, 5.2} be a random sample from N(μ, 1) distribution. If the parametric space for parameter μ is $\Omega = \{-2, -1, 1, 2\}$, then the MLE of μ is:

(a) 5.2 (b) 4

(c) –2 (d) 2

10. Let {2.5, 4.0, 7.1, 6.3, 8.9, 5.1} be a random sample from the distribution with pdf $f(x, \theta) = \theta 2^{\theta} x^{-(\theta+1)}$, $x > 2, \theta > 2$. The Cramer-Rao Lower Bound for the variance of an unbiased estimate of ln θ is:

(a) 6 (b) $\frac{\theta^2}{6}$

(c) $\frac{6}{\theta^2}$ (d) $\frac{1}{6}$

11. Let $X \sim U(7, 7 + \theta)$, $\theta > 0$; U being Uniform distribution. Define $T = a(X - b)^2$. Then the statistic T becomes unbiased for θ^2 if:

(a) a = 3, b = 0 (b) a = 7, b = 0

(c) a = 3, b = 7 (d) a = 7, b = 7

12. Let $X_1, X_2, ..., X_n$ be iid exponential variates with mean $\lambda > 0$. Define $T = \sum_{i=1}^{n} x_i$, a sufficient statistic for λ. Then pivotal statistic to construct confidence intervall for λ is:

(a) $2\lambda + T$ (b) $\frac{2T}{\lambda}$

(c) $\frac{2\lambda}{T^2}$ (d) $\frac{\lambda}{2T^2}$

13. If we have a sample of size n = 5, then the number of distinct bootstrap samples with replacement of size 5 is:

(a) 625 (b) 306

(c) 252 (d) 126

14. Consider the following distributions:

1. Bernoulli distribution b(1, θ)
2. Poisson distribution P(θ)
3. Cauchy distribution C(θ, 1)
4. Logistic distribution with location parameter θ

How many of the above distrbution possess Monotone Likelihood Ratio property?

(a) Only one (b) Only two

(c) Only three (d) All four

15. Let X follow normal distribution $N(\mu, \sigma^2)$. Consider the hypotheses for the test as $H_0: \mu = 2$ versus $H_1: \mu = 3$. Which one of the following statements is correct?

(a) H_0 is sample but H_1 is composite.

(b) Both H_0 and H_1 are simple.

(c) H_0 is composite but H_1 is simple.

(d) Both H_0 and H_1 are composite.

16. In which one of the following cases, MLE for a parameter θ need not be unique based on a random sample of size n?

(a) $U(0, \theta)$ (b) $U(\theta - 0.5, \theta + 0.5)$

(c) $f(x, \theta) = e^{-(x-\theta)}, x \geq \theta$ (d) $f(x, \theta) = (1 + \theta) x^{\theta}, 0 < x < 1$

17. Let X be an random variable with pdf $f(x, \theta) = 2\theta + 1 - \theta, 0 < x < 1, -1 \leq \theta \leq 1$. Based on a samp le size one, the Uniformly Most Powerful (UMP) critical region for testing $H_0: \theta = 0$ versus $H_1: \theta > 0$ at level $\alpha = 0.05$ is given by:

(a) $x \geq \frac{1}{20}$ (b) $x \leq \frac{1}{20}$

(c) $x \leq \frac{19}{20}$ (d) $x \geq \frac{19}{20}$

18. Consider the following statements:

Statement-I

If T is MLE of θ, then log T is MLE of log θ.

Statement-II

If T is MLE of θ, then distribution of T will be normal in case of large sample size.

The properties of MLE associated with Statement-I and Statement-II are respectively:

(a) Asymptotic property and consistency property

(b) Invariance property and asymptotic property

(c) Consistency property and efficiency property

(d) Invariance property and consistency property

19. In a test of randomness of a given set of observations {7, 19, 3, 1, 8, 5, 10, 4}, when the null hypothesis of randomness of the observations is true, then the expeted number of runs U and its variance are respectively:

(a) $4, \frac{12}{7}$ (b) $5, \frac{12}{7}$

(c) $4, \frac{20}{7}$ (d) $5, \frac{20}{7}$

20. Let $x_1, x_2, ..., x_n$ be a random sample from a population with probability density function

$$f(x, \theta) = \begin{cases} e^{-(x-\theta)}; & x > \theta \\ 0, & \text{otherwise} \end{cases}$$

For parameter θ, consider the following statements:

1. Min (x_1, x_2, x_n) is a sufficient statistic of θ.

2. $\overline{x} = \frac{1}{n}\sum_{i=1}^{n} x_i$ is a minimum variance bound estimator of θ.

Which of the statements given above is/are correct?

(a) 1 only (b) 2 only

(c) Both 1 and 2 (d) Neither 1 nor 2

21. Let $x_1, x_2, ..., x_n$ be a random sample from Normal distribution $N(\mu, \sigma^2)$. Assume that μ is known and σ is unknown. Define an estimator T as $T = k\sqrt{\frac{\sum_{i=1}^{n}(x_i - \mu)^2}{n}}$. Then the constant k for T to be unbiased estimator of σ is:

(a) $\sqrt{2}\frac{\Gamma\left(\frac{n}{2}\right)}{\Gamma\left(\frac{n+1}{2}\right)}$ (b) $\sqrt{\frac{n}{2}}\frac{\Gamma\left(\frac{n+1}{2}\right)}{\Gamma\left(\frac{n}{2}\right)}$

(c) 1 (d) $\sqrt{\frac{n}{2}}\frac{\Gamma\left(\frac{n}{2}\right)}{\Gamma\left(\frac{n+1}{2}\right)}$

22. Let $x_1, x_2, x_3, ..., x_n$ be a random sample from a Normal distribution $N(\mu, \sigma^2)$. suppose both m and s are unknown. Which of the following are jointly sufficient statistic for (μ, σ)?

1. $\left\{\sum_{i=1}^{n} x_i, \sum_{i=1}^{n} x_i^2\right\}$
2. $\left\{\sum_{i=1}^{n} x_i, \sum_{i=1}^{n} (x_i - \overline{x})^2\right\}$
3. $\left\{\sum_{i=1}^{n} x_i^2, \sum_{i=1}^{n} (x_i - \overline{x})^2\right\}$

Select the correct answer using the code give below:

(a) 1 and 2 only (b) 2 and 3 only

(c) 1 and 3 only (d) 1, 2 and 3

23. Let $x_1, x_2, ... x_n$ be a random sample from a Cauchy distrbution having pdf $f(x, \theta) = \frac{1}{\pi[1 + (x + \theta)^2]}$; $-\infty < x, \theta < \infty$:

Consider the following statements:

1. $\overline{X}$ is unbiased for q but not consistent estimator for θ.
2. Sample median is consistent estimator fro θ.

Which of the statements given above is/are correct?

(a) 1 only (b) 2 only

(c) Both 1 and 2 (d) Neither 1 nor 2

24. Let $x_1, x_2, ... x_n$ be a random sample from a Poisson distribution with mean $\theta > 0$. Then minimum variance unbiased estimator for $P(x = k)$ is:

(a) $T_1 = \begin{cases} 1; & \text{if } x = k \\ 0; & \text{otherwise} \end{cases}$ (b) $T_2 = \begin{cases} k; & \text{if } x = 0 \\ 0; & \text{otherwise} \end{cases}$

(c) $T_3 = \begin{pmatrix} \sum_{i=1}^{n} x_i \\ k \end{pmatrix} \dfrac{(n-1)\left(\sum_{i=1}^{n} x_i - k\right)}{n\left(\sum_{i=1}^{n} x_i\right)}$ (d) $T_4 = \begin{pmatrix} \sum_{i=1}^{n} x_i \\ k \end{pmatrix} \left(1 - \dfrac{1}{n}\right)^{\left(\sum_{i=1}^{n} x_i - k\right)}$

25. Let $x_1, x_2, \ldots x_n$ be a random sample with density function $f(x, \theta) = \theta e^{-\theta x}$; $x > 0$. The best critical region for testing $H_0: \theta = \theta_0$ against $(> \theta_0)$ is:

(a) $x : \sum_{i=1}^{n} x_i \leq \dfrac{1}{2\theta_0} \chi^2_{1-a, 2n}$ (b) $x : \sum_{i=1}^{n} x_i \geq \dfrac{1}{2\theta_0} \chi^2_{1-\alpha, 2n}$

(c) $x : \sum_{i=1}^{n} x_i \geq \dfrac{1}{2\theta_0} \chi^2_{\alpha, 2n}$ (d) $x : \sum_{i=1}^{n} x_i \leq \dfrac{1}{2\theta_0} \chi^2_{\alpha, 2n}$

26. Let X be a random variable with $N(\theta, 1 + a\theta^2)$, $a > 0$. The locally Most Powerful Test for testing H0: $\theta = 0$ against $H_1: \theta > 0$ is

(a) $\varphi(x) = \begin{cases} 1; & \sum_{i=1}^{n} x_i > \dfrac{Z_\alpha}{\sqrt{n}} \\ 0; & \text{otherwise} \end{cases}$ (b) $\varphi(x) = \begin{cases} 1; & \overline{X} > \dfrac{Z_{1-\alpha}}{n} \\ 0; & \text{otherwise} \end{cases}$

(c) $\varphi(x) = \begin{cases} 1; & \overline{X} > \dfrac{Z_\alpha}{n} \\ 0; & \text{otherwise} \end{cases}$ (d) $\varphi(x) = \begin{cases} 1; & \overline{X} > \dfrac{Z_\alpha}{\sqrt{n}} \\ 0; & \text{otherwise} \end{cases}$

where Z_α is the upper α% value of N(0, 1)

27. Let. $x_1, x_2, \ldots x_n$ be a random sample from Normal distribution $N(\mu, \sigma^2)$. The Mean Squared Error (MSE) of the estimator $T = \sum_{i=1}^{n} (x_i - \overline{x})^2$ where $\overline{x} = \dfrac{\sum_{i=1}^{n} x_i}{n}$ for estimating σ^2 is:

(a) $(n^2 - 1)\sigma^4$ (b) $(n^2 + 1)\sigma^4$

(c) $((n + 1)^2 + 1)\sigma^4$ (d) $((n + 1)^2 + 1)\sigma^4$

28. Let $x_1, x_2, \ldots x_n$ be a random sample from Normal distribution $N(\theta, \theta^2)$. Then sufficient statistic for θ is:

(a) $\sum_{i=1}^{n} x_i$ only (b) $\sum_{i=1}^{n} x_i^2$ only

(c) $\sum_{i=1}^{n} x_i + \sum_{i=1}^{n} x_i^2$ only (d) $\left(\sum_{i=1}^{n} x_i, \sum_{i=1}^{n} x_i^2\right)$

29. Let $x_1, x_2, \ldots x_n$ be a random sample from a Poisson distribution with parameter $\lambda > 0$. Which of the following statements are correct in respect of Likelihood Ratio Test (LRT)?

   1. The LRT for testing H_0; $\lambda = \lambda_0$ against H_1: $\lambda > \lambda_0$ produces UMP test identical to the test obtained by NP theory of testing.
   2. The LRT for testing H_0: $\lambda = \lambda_0$ against H_1: $\lambda < \lambda_0$ produces UMP test identical to the test obtained by NP theory of testing.
   3. The LRT for testing H_0: $\lambda = \lambda_0$ against H_1: $\lambda \neq \lambda_0$ produces UMPU test identical to the test obtained by NP theory of testing.

   Select the correct answer using the code given below:

   (a) 1 and 2 only (b) 2 and 3 only

   (c) 1 and 3 only (d) 1, 2 and 3

30. In SPRT, to test $H_0 = X \sim f(x, \theta_0)$ versus $H_1 = X \sim f(x, \theta_1)$, Z is defined as $Z = \log\left\{\frac{f(x,\theta)}{f(x,\theta_0)}\right\}$ and $h(\theta)$ is non-zero solution of the equation $E(e^{zh(\theta)}) = 1$. Under H_0, the OC function $L(\theta)$ becomes:

   (a) α (b) β

   (c) $1-\alpha$ (d) $1-\beta$

Consider the following for the next two (02) items that follows:

Let X be a random variable with pmf

$$P(x) = \begin{cases} \dfrac{3+2\theta+\mu}{15}, & x = 1 \\ \dfrac{5+\theta-2\mu}{15}, & x = 2 \\ \dfrac{7-3\theta+\mu}{15}, & x = 3 \end{cases}$$

where $\theta \geq 0$, $\mu \geq 0$ are unknown constants and $\theta + \mu \leq 2$.

For testing H_0: $\theta + \mu = 1$ versus H_1: $\theta = \mu = 0$, the null hypothesis is rejected if $x = 2$ or 3.

31. The size of the test based on a single observation is:

   (a) $\frac{2}{5}$ (b) $\frac{11}{15}$

   (c) $\frac{4}{5}$ (d) $\frac{13}{15}$

32. The test is

   (a) biased with power $\frac{3}{5}$ (b) biased with power $\frac{2}{5}$

   (c) unbiased with power $\frac{4}{5}$ (d) unbiased with power $\frac{13}{15}$

Consider the following for the next two (02) items that follow:

Let $x_1, x_2, \ldots x_n$ be a random sample from the distribution having pdf $f(x, \theta) = 3\theta^3(x+\theta)^{-4}$; $0 < x < \infty$, $\theta > 0$.

33. What is $E\left(\frac{\partial^2 \ln f}{\partial \theta^2}\right)$ equal to?

(a) $-\frac{3}{5\theta^2}$ (b) $-\frac{4}{5\theta^2}$

(c) $\frac{3}{5\theta^2}$ (d) $\frac{4}{5\theta^2}$

34. The C-R bound for unbiased estimator of θ^3 will be:

(a) $\frac{3n}{5\theta^2}$ (b) $\frac{5\theta^5}{3n}$

(c) $\frac{5\theta^4}{n}$ (d) $\frac{5n}{\theta^4}$

Consider the following for the next two (02) items that follow:

Let $x_1 = \frac{17}{3}, x_2 = \frac{10}{3}, x_3 = \frac{13}{3}$, $x_4 = 4$ be the observed values of a random sample of size 4 from the distribution having pdf $f(x, \theta) = \frac{1}{3}\left[\frac{1}{2\theta}e^{-\frac{x}{2\theta}} + \frac{1}{\theta^2}e^{-\frac{x}{\theta^2}} + e^{-x}\right]; x > 0, \theta > 0$

35. What is E(X) equal to?

(a) $\frac{\theta^2 + \theta + 1}{3}$ (b) $\frac{\theta^2 + 2\theta + 1}{3}$

(c) $\frac{\theta^2 + 2\theta + 2}{3}$ (d) $\frac{\theta^2 + 3\theta + 1}{3}$

36. The method of moment estimate of θ is:

(a) $\sqrt{13} - 1$ (b) $\sqrt{13} + 1$

(c) 1 (d) 3

37. The size of the randomized test is within the interval:

(a) (0.05, 0.20) (b) (0.30, 0.50)

(c) (0.60, 0.80) (d) (0.80, 0.90)

38. The power of the randomized test is within the interval:

(a) (0.50, 0.70) (b) (0.60, 0.75)

(c) (0.70, 0.85) (d) (0.80, 0.99)

Consider the following for the next two (02) items that follow:

Let X be a random variable whose pmf under H_0 and H_1 is given as under:

x :	0	1	2	3	4
$P(x\|H_0)$:	0.1	0.2	0.3	0.3	0.1
$P(x\|H_1)$:	0.2	0.3	0.1	0.2	0.2

Test is conducted based on a single observed value of X to test $H_0: X \sim P(x|h_0)$ versus $H_1: X \sim P(x|H_1)$. The null hypothesis is rejected if X = 0 is observed. Further, null hypothesis is rejected when head 'H' is observed on tossing of an unbiased coin when X = 4 is observed.

39. The size of the test is:
    (a) 0.15 (b) 0.20
    (c) 0.30 (d) 0.60
40. The power of the test is:
    (a) 0.15 (b) 0.30
    (c) 0.40 (d) 0.70

Consider the following for the next two (02) items that follow:

Let $x_1, x_2, \ldots x_n$ be a random sample from Poisson distributiuon with mean $\lambda > 0$.

41. If $T_1 = \sum_{i=1}^{n} x_i$ and $T_2 = \left(x_1, \sum_{i=2}^{n} x_i \right)$ are the statistics, then which of these statistics is/are sufficient for λ?
    (a) T_1 only (b) T_1 only
    (c) Both T_1 and T_2 (d) Neither T_1 and T_2
42. If $T_3 = (x_1, x_2, x_3, \sum_{i=4}^{n} x_i)$ and $T_4 = (x_1 + x_2 + x_3 + x_4, \sum_{i=5}^{n} x_i)$ are the statistics, then which of these statistics is/are sufficient for λ?
    (a) T_3 only (b) T_4 only
    (c) Both T_3 and T_4 (d) Neither T_3 and T_4

Consider the following for the next two (02) items that follow:

Let $x_1, x_2, \ldots x_n$ be a random sample from Normal distribution $N(0, \theta)$, $\theta > 0$.

43. Consider the following statements in respect of x_1:
    1. x_1 is unbiased of θ.
    2. x_1 is complete statistic for θ.
    3. x_1 is sufficient for θ.

    How many of the above statements are correct?
    (a) Only one (b) Only two
    (c) All three (d) None
44. Consider the following statements in respect of x_1^2:
    1. x_1^2 is complete for θ.
    2. x_1^2 is sufficient for θ.

    Which of the statements given above is/are correct?
    (a) 1 only (b) 2 only
    (c) Both 1 and 2 (d) Neither 1 nor 2

45. Let $X_1, X_2, \ldots X_n$ be iid random variables with $N(\theta, 1)$. The UMPU test of size α for testing $H_0: \theta = \theta_0$ against $H_1: \theta \neq \theta_0$ is given by

$$\varphi(x) = \begin{cases} 1: & \sum_{i=1}^{n} x_i < c_i \text{ or } \sum_{i=1}^{n} X_i > c_2 \\ 0; & \text{otherwise} \end{cases}$$

What are the values c_1 and c_2?

(a) $\left(n\theta_0 - \sqrt{nZ}_{\left(\frac{\alpha}{2}\right)}, n\theta_0 + \sqrt{nZ_{\left(\frac{\alpha}{2}\right)}}\right)$ (b) $\left(n\theta_0 - \sqrt{n}Z_\alpha, n\theta_0 + \sqrt{nZ_{1-\alpha}}\right)$

(c) $\left(n\theta_0 - \sqrt{n}Z_{1-\alpha}, n\theta_0 + \sqrt{nZ_\alpha}\right)$ (d) $\left(n\theta_0 - \sqrt{n}Z_{1-\left(\frac{\alpha}{2}\right)}, n\theta_0 + \sqrt{nZ_{\left(\frac{\alpha}{2}\right)}}\right)$

46. Let $x_1, x_2, \ldots x_9$ be a random sample from Normal distribution $N(\mu, \sigma^2)$, μ and σ are unknown parameters, $\mu \in R$, $\sigma > 0$. The observed values of $\bar{x} = \frac{\sum_{i=1}^{9} x_i}{9} = 9.8$ and $\frac{1}{8}\sum_{i=1}^{9}(x_i - \bar{x})^2 = 1.69$. If LRT is used to test $H_0: \mu - 8.8$ versus $H_1: \mu > 8.8$, then what is the calculated value of the statistic

(a) 1.86 (b) 2.31

(c) 2.90 (d) 3.36

47. Let $x_1, x_2, \ldots x_9$ be a random sample from $e^{-(x-\theta)}$, $x \geq \theta$, $\theta > 0$. What is the confidence coefficient of the interval $\left(x_{(1)} - \frac{\ln 4}{n}, x_{(1)} + \frac{\ln 2}{n}\right)$ for θ, where $x_{(1)} = \min(x_1, x_2, \ldots x_n)$?

(a) 0.5 (b) 0.75

(c) 0.95 (d) 0.99

48. Consider the following statements:

1. If an MVB estimator T exists for θ, then Likelihood equation will have a solution eqal to the estimator T.
2. MVB estimator for location parameter θ in the Cauchy distribution does not exist for θ.

Which of the statements given above is/are correct?

(a) 1 only (b) 2 only

(c) Both 1 and 2 (d) Neither 1 nor 2

49. Consider the following statements:

1. If a sufficient estimator exists, it is a function of the maximum likelihood estimator.
2. If a sufficient estimator exists, it is always unique.

Which of the statements given above is/are correct?

(a) 1 only (b) 2 only

(c) Both 1 and 2 (d) Neither 1 nor 2

50. Consider the following statements about Likelihood Ratio Test (LRT) as:

1. LRT is generally Uniformly Most Powerful (UMP), if a UMP test exists.
2. Under certain conditions, LRT is consistent.

Which of the statements given above is/are correct?

(a) 1 only (b) 2 only

(c) Both 1 and 2 (d) Neither 1 nor 2

51. If Y is $N_3(\mu, \Sigma)$ where $\mu' = (3, -2, 1)$ and $\Sigma = \text{diag}(2, 4, 3)$, then the distribution of $Y' \Sigma^{-1} Y$ is:

(a) $\chi^2(3, 2.9167)$ (b) $\chi^2(3, 1.45835)$

(c) $\chi^2(3, 1.45835)$ (d) $\chi^2(3, 1.944)$

52. Three different methods of analysis are used to determine the amount of a certain constituent in a sample. Five different under each of these methods. Various sum of squares are obtained as

TSS = 97.6,

SSA (Analysts) = 4.27,

SSB (Methods) = 79.6.

What is the value of MSF, the Mean Sum of Squares due to error?

(a) 2.89 (b) 1.96

(c) 1.72 (d) 1.53

53. Let $\mathbf{Y} = \begin{pmatrix} y_1 \\ y_2 \\ y_3 \end{pmatrix} \sim N_3(\mathbf{0}, \mathbf{I}_3)$ and

$$\mathbf{A} = \frac{1}{3}\begin{pmatrix} 2 & -1 & -1 \\ -1 & 2 & -1 \\ -1 & -1 & 2 \end{pmatrix}.$$

What is the value of Var (Y'AY)?

(a) 1 (b) 2

(c) 4 (d) 6

54. Let $\mathbf{Y} = \begin{pmatrix} y_1 \\ y_2 \\ y_3 \end{pmatrix} \sim N_3(\mathbf{0}, \mathbf{I}_3)$ and

$$\mathbf{A} = \begin{pmatrix} \frac{1}{3} & 0 & -\frac{\sqrt{2}}{3} \\ 0 & 0 & 0 \\ -\frac{\sqrt{2}}{3} & 0 & \frac{2}{3} \end{pmatrix}.$$

What is the value of Var (Y'AY)?

(a) Exp (1) (b) N(0, 3)

(c) $\chi^2_{(1)}$ (d) $\chi^2_{(3)}$

55. Let Y1, Y2, ... Yn be an iid N(0, 1) variates and

$$Y = \begin{bmatrix} Y_1 \\ Y_2 \\ Y_3 \\ \cdot \\ \cdot \\ Y_n \end{bmatrix}$$. If quadratic forms $\mathbf{Y'A_1Y}$ and

$Y'A_2Y$ are independently Chi-square distributed, then:

(a) $\mathbf{A_1A_2 = I}$ (b) $\mathbf{A_1A_2 = 0}$

(c) $\mathbf{A_1A_2 = nI}$ (d) $\mathbf{A_1A_2 = n^{-1}I}$

Consider the following for the next two (02) items that follow:

Let X_i, Y_i, Z_i, where i = 1, 2, 3 be nine independent observations with common variance σ^2, and $E(X_i) = \theta_1$, $E(Y_i)\ \theta_2$ and $E(Z_i) = \theta_1 - \theta_2$; i = 1, 2, 3. Let $X = \sum_{i=1}^{3} X_i$, $Y = \sum_{i=1}^{3} Y_i$ and $Z = \sum_{i=1}^{3} Z_i$.

56. What is the BLUE of θ_1 equal to?

(a) $\frac{1}{9}[2X + 3Y - Z]$ (b) $\frac{1}{9}[3X + Y - 2Z]$

(c) $\frac{1}{9}[2X + Y + Z]$ (d) $\frac{1}{9}[2X + Y - Z]$

57. What is the BLUE of θ_2 equal to?

(a) $\frac{1}{9}[X + 3Y - 2Z]$ (b) $\frac{1}{9}[3X + Y - 2Z]$

(c) $\frac{1}{9}[2X + Y - Z]$ (d) $\frac{1}{9}[X + 2Y - Z]$

Consider the following for the next three (03) items that follow:

In a Simple Linear Regression Model $y_i = \beta_0 + \beta_1 x_i + \varepsilon_i$; i = 1, 2, ... n where $E(\varepsilon_i) = 0$, Var $(\varepsilon_i) = \sigma^2$ and Cov $(\varepsilon_i, \varepsilon_j) = 0$, $i \neq j$.

58. What is Var $(\hat{\beta}_0)$ equal to?

(a) $\dfrac{\sigma^2}{\sum_{i=1}^{n}(x_i - \bar{x})^2}$ (b) $\dfrac{n\sigma^2}{\sum_{i=1}^{n}(x_i - \bar{x})^2}$

(c) $n\sigma^2 + \dfrac{\sigma^2(\bar{x})^2}{\sum_{i=1}^{n}(x_i - \bar{x})^2}$ (d) $\dfrac{\sigma^2}{n} + \dfrac{\sigma^2(\bar{x})^2}{\sum_{i=1}^{n}(x_i - \bar{x})^2}$

59. What is Cov $(\hat{\beta}_0, \hat{\beta}_1)$ equal to?

(a) $\dfrac{\bar{x}\sigma^2}{\sum_{i=1}^{n}(x_i - \bar{x})^2}$

(b) $-\dfrac{\bar{x}\sigma^2}{\sum_{i=1}^{n}(x_i - \bar{x})^2}$

(c) $\sigma^2 \sum_{i=1}^{n} (x_i - \bar{x})^2$

(d) 0

60. What is Var $(\hat{\beta}_1)$ equal to?

(a) $\dfrac{\sigma^2}{\sum_{i=1}^{n}(x_i - \bar{x})^2}$

(b) $\dfrac{n\sigma^2}{\sum_{i=1}^{n}(x_i - \bar{x})^2}$

(c) $\dfrac{(n-1)\,\sigma^2}{\sum_{i=1}^{n}(x_i - \bar{x})^2}$

(d) $\sigma^2 \sum_{i=1}^{n} (x_i - \bar{x})^2$

61. For a two-away classification with one observation per cell, if p and q are the levels of the two factors A and B, then the degrees of freedom for error are:

(a) $pq - 1$
(b) $p(q - 1)$
(c) $q(p - 1)$
(d) $(p - 1)(q - 1)$

62. Let A be a matrix of order $n \times p$. Then any generalized inverse of A is of order:

(a) $p \times n$
(b) $n \times n$
(c) $n \times p$
(d) $p \times p$

63. Consider the following statements in respect of a symmetric matrix A:

1. A generalized inverse of a symmetric matrix is not necessarily symetric.
2. A symmetric generalized inverse of A can always be found.

Which of the statements give above is/are correct?

(a) 1 only
(b) 2 only
(c) Both 1 and 2
(d) Neither 1 nor 2

64. Let **A** be an $n \times p$ matrix of rank r. Let $\mathbf{A}^-$ be any generalized inverse of **A**. Which of the statements given below is/are correct?

1. rank $(\mathbf{AA}^-)$ = rank $(\mathbf{A}^-\mathbf{A})$ = rank $(\mathbf{A}) = r$
2. $(\mathbf{A}^-)'$ is a generalized inverse of $\mathbf{A}'$

Select the correct answer using the code given below:

(a) 1 only
(b) 2 only
(c) Both 1 and 2
(d) Neither 1 nor 2

65. Consider the following ANOVA table:

Source of variation	Degrees of freedom	Sum of squares	Mean sum of squares	Test statistic
Treatments	m	p	r	5.22
Error	12	q	25	
Total	14	561		

What are the values of p, q and r respectively?

(a) 261, 300, 130.5 (b) 300, 261, 130.5

(c) 250, 300, 128.5 (d) 261, 300, 128.5

66. Which one of the following is ***not*** a fundamental principle of official statistics?

(a) Professional standard and ethics (b) Accountability and transparency

(c) Confidentiality and coordination (d) Pricin and advertisement

67. With regard to the conduct of the census, which of the following, as per the Census Act 1948, is correct?

(a) The Census must be conducted every ten years.

(b) The Central Government may notify whenever it may consider it necessary or desirable to take a Census.

(c) The Central Government may conduct after amending the periodicity clause.

(d) The Registrar General of India, who is the Census Commissioner, may decide and his decision will be final

68. Consider the following pairs:

1. Marine Hospital – Union List
2. Public Health – State List
3. Sanitation – State List
4. Population Control – Concurrent List

How many pairs given above are correctly matched?

(a) Only one (b) Only two

(c) Only three (c) All four

69. Which of the following Agencies/Organizations generate labour force data?

1. National Sample Survey Office
2. Labour Bureau and the Directorate General of Employment and Training
3. Office of Registrar General of India

Select the correct answer using the code give below:

(a) 1 and 2 only (b) 2 and 3 only

(c) 1 and 3 only (d) 1, 2 and 3

70. Which of the following Index Numbers are prepared and published by the Government of India?

1. Index number of agricultural production
2. Index numbers of foreign trade
3. Annual indices of industrial production

Select the correct answer using the code given below:

(a) 1 and 2 only (b) 2 and 3 only

(c) 1 and 3 only (d) 1, 2 and 3

71. Consider the following statements in respect of GDP:

1. GDP is composed of goods and services produced for sale in the market.
2. GDP includes some non-market production as well (such as defence services and education services).
3. Not all productive work is included in GDP.
4. Volutary work is not included in GDP.

How many statements given above are correct?

(a) Only one (b) Only two

(c) Only three (d) All four

72. Marshall and Edgeworth price index number formula utilizes the weights as:

(a) Quanntities of the base year only

(b) Quantities of the given year only

(c) Combined quatities of the base year and given year

(d) Neither quantities of base year nor quantites of given year

73. Consider the following in respect of an NSSO survey:

1. Collecting data from the respondents – Field Operations Division
2. Formulating sample design for a survey – Survey, Designn and Research Division
3. Disseminating the data to public – Field Operations Division
4. Preparing survey reports – Survey Coordination Division

How many of the pairs given above are correctly matched?

(a) Only one pair (b) Only two pairs

(c) Only three pairs (d) All four pairs

74. Periodic Labour Force Survey is conducted by:

(a) Labour Bureau, Ministry of Labour and Employment

(b) Office of Economic Adviser, Ministry of Commerce and Industry

(c) National Statistical Office

(d) None of the above

75. Which of the following Census tables are covered in the Census of India?
    1. Social and cultural tables
    2. Migration tables
    3. Fertility tables

    Select the correct answer using the code given below:

    (a) 1 and 2 only (b) 2 and 3 only
    (c) 1 and 3 only (d) 1, 2 and 3

76. Which of the following are International Statistical Organizations?
    1. Economic and Social Commission for Asisa and the Pacific
    2. North Atlantic Treaty Organization
    3. The Asian Development Bank
    4. The International Labour Organization

    Select the correct answer using the code given below:

    (a) 1, 2 and 3 (b) 1, 2 and 4
    (c) 1, 3 and 4 (d) 2, 3 and 4

77. Consider the following statements regarding Global Hunger Index (GHI):
    1. GHI is a 100 point scale, where 0 (zero) is the best score and 100 is the worst score.
    2. GHI consists of four indicators that together capture the multidimensional nature of hunger.

    Which of the statemetns given above is/are correct?

    (a) 1 only (b) 2 only
    (c) Both 1 and 2 (d) Neither 1 nor 2

78. Consider the following statements:
    1. The population census is a Union subject and is listed at serial number 69 of the Eigth Schedule of the Constitution of India.
    2. The responsibility of conducting the census rests with the office of the Registrar General and Census Comminssioner of India, Ministry of Home Affairs, Government of India.

    Which of the statements given above is/are correct?

    (a) 1 only (b) 2 only
    (c) Both 1 and 2 (d) Neither 1 nor 2

79. Which of the following are monthly High Frequency Indicators (HFIs)?
    1. Consumer Price Index
    2. Rail Freight Traffic
    3. E-way Bills
    4. Population

Select the correct answer using the code give below:

(a) 1, 2 and 3 (b) 1, 2 and 4

(c) 1, 3 and 4 (d) 2, 3 and 4

80. Which of the following Goods and Services arfe omitted from GDP?

1. Household production such as preparing meals, gardening, etc.
2. Leisure time activities.
3. Helping children with homework and similar activities

Select the correct answer using the code given below:

(a) 1 and 2 only (b) 2 and 3 only

(c) 1 and 3 only (d) 1, 2 and 3

STATISTICS
Paper- II 2022

Time Allowed : Three Hours | *Maximum Marks: 200*

INSTRUCTIONS

1. IMMEDIATELY AFTER THE COMMENCEMENT OF THE EXAMINATION, YOU SHOULD CHECK THAT THIS TEST BOOKLET DOES NOT HAVE ANY UNPRINTED OR TORN OR MISSING PAGES OR ITEMS, ETC. IF SO, GET IT REPLACED BY A COMPLETE TEST BOOKLET.
2. Please note that it is the candidate's responsibility to encode and fill in the Roll Number and Test Booklet Series Code A, B, C or D carefully and without any omission or discrepancy at the appropriate places in the OMR Answer Sheet. Any omission/discrepancy will render the Answer Sheet liable for rejection.
3. You have to enter your Roll Number on the Test Booklet in the Box provided alongside. DO NOT write anything else on the Test Booklet.
4. This Test Booklet contains 80 items (questions). Each item comprises four responses (answers). You will select the response which you want to mark on the Answer Sheet. In case you feel that there is more than one correct response, mark the response which you consider the best. In any case, choose ONLY ONE response for each item.
5. You have to mark all your responses ONLY on the separate Answer Sheet provided. See directions in the Answer Sheet.
6. All items carry equal marks.
7. Before you proceed to mark in the Answer Sheet the response to various items in the Test Booklet, you have to fill in some particulars in the Answer Sheet as per instructions sent to you with your Admission Certificate.
8. After you have completed filling in all your responses on the Answer Sheet and the examination has concluded, you should hand over to the Invigilator ***only the Answer Sheet***. You are permitted to take away with you the Test Booklet.
9. Sheets for rough work are appended in the Test Booklet at the end.
10. Penalty for wrong answers :

THERE WILL BE PENALTY FOR WRONG ANSWERS MARKED BY A CANDIDATE IN THE OBJECTIVE TYPE QUESTION PAPERS.

(i) There are four alternatives for the answer to every question. For each question for which a wrong answer has been given by the candidate, one-third of the marks assigned to that question will be deducted as penalty. ·

(ii) If a candidate gives more than one answer, it will be treated as a wrong answer even if one of the given answers happens to be correct and there will be same penalty as above to that question.

(iii) If a question is left blank, i.e., no answer is given by the candidate, there will be no penalty for that question.

DO NOT OPEN THIS TEST BOOKLET UNTIL YOU ARE TOLD TO DO SO

1. Let $Y = X\beta + \varepsilon$, where Y is $n \times 1$ vector of response, X is $n \times k$ ($n > k$) matrix of predictors, β is $k \times 1$ vector of unknown coefficients to be estimated and ε is $n \times 1$ vector of random errors. Further ε is $N(0, \sigma^2 I)$. The distribution of $\hat{Y}$ is:

(a) $N(X\beta, \sigma^2)$ (b) $N(X\beta, X(X'X)^{-1} X' \sigma^2)$

(c) $N(X\beta, (X'X)^{-1} \sigma^2)$ (d) $N(X\beta, (X'X)^{-1} X' \sigma^2)$

2. An ecologist takes data (X_i, Y_i); $i = 1, 2, 3, \ldots n$ where X_i is the size of an area and Y_i is the number of moss plants in the area. We model the data by $Y_i \sim$ Poisson (θX_i); Y_i's are 5. independent. The least square estimator and the MLE of θ are respectively :

(a) $\left(\frac{\sum_{i=1}^{n} Y_i}{\sum_{i=1}^{n} X_i}, \frac{\sum_{i=1}^{n} X_i Y_i}{\sum_{i=1}^{n} X_i^2}\right)$ (b) $\left(\frac{\sum_{i=1}^{n} X_i Y_i}{\sum_{i=1}^{n} X_i^2}, \frac{\sum_{i=1}^{n} Y_i}{\sum_{i=1}^{n} X_i}\right)$

(c) $\left(\frac{\overline{Y}}{\overline{X}}, \frac{\text{Cov}(X, Y)}{V(X)}\right)$ (d) $\left(\frac{\text{Cov}(X, Y)}{V(X)}, \frac{\overline{Y}}{\overline{X}}\right)$

3. Let A be any $n \times m$ matrix with A^- as any generalized inverse of it. Further, let $H = AA^-$ and $T = A^- A$. Then which one of the following is correct?

(a) Only H is an idempotent matrix

(b) Only Tis an idempotent matrix

(c) Both H and T are idempotent matrices

(d) Neither H nor T is an idempotent matrix

4. Let A be a matrix of order $n \times p$ with A^- as any generalized inverse of it. Let $(A'A)^-$ be any generalized inverse of $A'A$, then which of the following are correct?

1. $(A') = (A^-)'$
2. $A^- = (A'A)^- A'$
3. Rank $(A^- A) =$ rank (AA^-)

Select the correct answer using the code given below:

(a) 1 and 2 only (b) 2 and 3 only

(c) 1 and 3 only (d) 1, 2 and 3

5. Let A be any matrix of order $n \times m$. Consider the following statements for its Moore-Penrose inverse A^+:

1. $A^+ = (A'A)^+ A'$
2. A^+ is unique

Which of the above statements is/are correct ?

(a) 1 only (b) 2 only

(c) Both 1 and 2 (d) Neither 1 nor 2

6. Let X_i, Y_i and Z_i; i = 1, 2, 3 be nine independent observations with common variance σ^2, and $E(X_i) = \theta_1$, $E(Y_i) = \theta_2$, $E(Z_i) = \theta_1 - \theta_2$; i = 1, 2, 3. If $\hat{\theta}_1$ and $\hat{\theta}_2$ denote the BLUEs of θ_1 and θ_2 respectively, then which one of the following is correct ?

   (a) $V(\hat{\theta}_1) > V(\hat{\theta}_2)$ (b) $V(\hat{\theta}_1) = V(\hat{\theta}_2)$

   (c) $V(\hat{\theta}_1) < V(\hat{\theta}_2)$ (d) $V(\hat{\theta}_1) \geq V(\hat{\theta}_2)$

7. Consider two-way classified data with 5 levels of factor A, 6 levels of factor B and 4 observations per cell. The degrees of freedom for error are :

   (a) 120 (b) 100

   (c) 96 (d) 90

8. For a two-way classified random effect model with p levels of factor A and q levels of factor B having m observations per cell, the estimate of variance component $\hat{\sigma}_A^2$ is given by :

   (a) $\dfrac{MSA - MS(AB)}{qm}$ (b) $\dfrac{MSB - MS(AB)}{pm}$

   (c) $\dfrac{MSA - MSB}{pq}$ (d) $\dfrac{MSA + MSB}{pq}$

Consider the following for the next ***two (02)*** *items :*

The moisture content of three types of cheese made by two methods was recorded. Two pieces of cheese were measured for each type and for each method. Let the method be designated as factor A and type as factor B. The sum of squares for factor A, factor B and error are respectively 0.114075, 25.900117 and 0·661950.

9. The mean squares for method and error are respectively :

   (a) 0.114075 and 0.110325 (b) 0.057037 and 0.110325

   (c) 0.114075 and 0.08274375 (d) 0.057037 and 0.08274375

10. 10. The values ofF-statistic for factors A and B are respectively :

    (a) 1.034 and 78.2539 (b) 0.51699 and 117.381

    (c) 1.034 and 117.381 (d) 0.51699 and 78.2539

11. Let y represent tensile strength of a cable of diameter X mm. If $Y = CX^2$ for some constant C and density function of X is given by

$$f(x) = \begin{cases} \dfrac{1}{\theta}, & 5 < x < 5 + \theta \\ 0, & \text{otherwise} \end{cases}$$

    what is the unbiased estimate of θ^2?

    (a) $3X - 5$ (b) $X^2 - 5$

    (c) $3(X - 5)^2$ (d) $3(X^2 - 5)$

12. Which of the following assertions is/are correct?

    1. Maximum Likelihood Estimate of Poisson mean λ, is unbiased, sufficient and consistent estimate for θ.

    2. For $X \sim U(0, \theta)$, maximum likelihood estimate of θ is a biased, consistent and sufficient estimate for θ.

Select the correct answer using the code given below:

(a) 1 only (b) 2 only

(c) Both 1 and 2 (d) Neither 1 nor 2

13. Consider the following statements:

1. For an exponential random variable with mean θ, $\left(\frac{n}{n+1}\right)\bar{X}^2$ is unbiased for θ^2.

2. For a Bernoulli random variable with parameter p, $\frac{\left(\sum x_j\right)^2}{n^2}$ is unbiased for p^2.

Which of the statements given above is/are correct?

(a) 1 only (b) 2 only

(c) Both 1 and 2 (d) Neither 1 nor 2

14. Let $X_1, X_2, X_3, \ldots X_n$ be i.i.d. random variables from f(x), where $f(x) = (\theta + 1)\, x^{\theta}; 0 < x < 1, \theta > -1$. The UMVUE of θ is:

(a) $-\frac{(n-1)}{\sum \ln x_i} - 1$ (b) $-\frac{\sum \ln x_i}{(n-1)} - 1$

(c) $\frac{(n-1)}{\sum \ln x_i} - 1$ (d) $-\frac{(n-1)}{\sum \ln x_i} + 1$

15. Let $X_1, X_2, X_3, \ldots X_n$ be i.i.d. random variables with B(n, p). The CR lower bound for the variance of an unbiased estimator of $\frac{p}{1+p}$ is:

(a) $\frac{pq}{mn}$ (b) $\frac{pq}{(1+p)^2\, m}$

(c) $\frac{pq}{(1+p)^4\, mn}$ (d) $\frac{pq}{(1+q)^2\, m}$

16. Suppose waiting time at a vaccination centre queue is modelled by a normal distribution. A random sample of 16 adults showed a mean waiting time of 40 minutes with a standard deviation of 8 minutes. What is the 95% confidence interval for the true waiting time in this queue? [Given that $t_{15,\, 0.025} = 2.13$]

(a) [35·6, 44·4] (b) [25·7, 54·3]

(c) [30·3, 50·7] (d) [35·7, 40·3]

17. Time to failure of an electric tube follows the density function $f(x) = \begin{cases} \frac{1}{\theta} e^{-\frac{x}{\theta}}, & x > 0 \\ 0, & \text{otherwise} \end{cases}$ For testing $H_0 : \theta \geq 5$ against the alternative $H_1 : \theta < 5$, what is the power function of the critical region $C = (\bar{X} \leq k)$ for a sample of size 2?

(a) $1-\left(1+\frac{2k}{\theta}\right)e^{-\frac{2k}{\theta}}$ (b) $1-(\theta+2k)\,e^{-2k\theta}$

(c) $(\theta-2k)\,e^{-2k\theta}$ (d) $1-\left(1-\frac{2k}{\theta}\right)e^{-\frac{2k}{\theta}}$

18. The statistics T = t(x) will be sufficient for parameter θ iff the joint density/mass function of the sample values $x_1, x_2, x_3, \ldots X_n$ can be expressed in the form $f(x;\theta) = g_\theta[t(x)].h(x)$ where $g_\theta[t(x)]$ depends on θ and $t(x_1, x_2, x_3, \ldots x_n)$ and h(x) is independent of θ. This theorem is known as :

(a) Neyman-Pearson theorem (b) Rao-Black:well theorem

(c) Factorization theorem (d) Cramer-Rao theorem

19. Consider a random sample $x_1, x_2, x_3, \ldots X_n$ from normal distribution with zero mean and variance σ^2. For testing the null hypothesis $H_0 : \sigma = \sigma_0$ against the alternative hypothesis $H_1 : \sigma = \sigma_1$ $(\sigma_0 > \sigma_1)$, the best critical region will take the form:

(a) $C = \left\{x : \sqrt{\sum x_i^2} \le a_\alpha\right\}$ (b) $C = \left\{x : \sqrt{\sum x_i^2} \ge a_\alpha\right\}$

(c) $C = \left\{x : \sum x_i^2 \le a_\alpha\right\}$ (d) $C = \left\{x : \sum x_i^2 \ge a_\alpha\right\}$

20. Let $x_1, x_2, x_3, \ldots x_{100}$ be a random sample of size 100 from the population having pdf $f(x) = \theta e^{-x\theta}$; $0 < X < \infty$. 95% confidence limits for θ will be :

(a) $\frac{1}{\bar{x}} \pm \frac{1.96}{\bar{x}}$ (b) $\frac{1}{\bar{x}} \pm \frac{0.196}{\bar{x}}$

(c) $\frac{1}{\bar{x}} \pm \frac{19.6}{\bar{x}}$ (d) $\frac{1}{\bar{x}} \pm \frac{0.0196}{\bar{x}}$

Consider the following for the next two (02) items :

In general linear model $Y = X\beta + \varepsilon$ where Y is n × 1, X is n × k, β is k × 1 and E is n × 1. Further E is $N(0, \sigma^2 I)$. Let e be an n × 1 vector of residuals. Let $P = X(X'X)^{-1}X' = [p_{ij}]$ where $P_{ii} = x_i'(X'X)^{-1}x_i$ and $p_{ij} = x_i'(X'X)^{-1}x_j$; x_i' is the ith row of X. ·

21. What is the range of p_{ii} ?

(a) $0 \le P_{ii} \le 2$ (b) $0 \le P_{ii} \le 0{\cdot}5$ ·

(c) $-1 \le P_{ii} \le 1$ (d) $0 \le p_{ii} \le 1$

22. What is the correlation coefficient between e_i and e_j?

(a) $\frac{p_{ij}}{\sqrt{(1-p_{ii})(1-p_{jj})}}$ (b) $\frac{-p_{ij}}{\sqrt{(1-p_{ii})(1-p_{jj})}}$

(c) $\frac{p_{ii}}{\sqrt{(1-p_{ij})(1-p_{jj})}}$ (d) $\frac{p_{jj}}{\sqrt{(1-p_{ij})(1-p_{ii})}}$

23. Three methods A, B and C of packing frozen foods were compared. The response variable was ascorbic acid (mg/100 g). The data was collected by taking seven observations for each of the methods. The sum of squares due to treatments and that due to total are 147·3456 and 202·3126 respectively. What is the value ofF -statistic ?

(a) 24·1256 (b) 24·0156

(c) 23·5216 (d) 23·1256

Consider the following for the next ***two (02)*** *items that follow:*

Let X_i, Y_i and Z_i where i = 1, 2, 3, 4 be twelve independent observations with common variance σ^2, and $E(X_i) = \theta_1$, $E(Y_i) = \theta_2$ and $E(Z_i) = \theta_1 + \theta_2$; i = 1, 2, 3, 4. Let $X = \sum_{i=1}^{4} X_i$, $Y = \sum_{i=1}^{4} Y_i$ and $Z = \sum_{i=1}^{4} Z_i$.

24. What is the BLUE of θ_1 equal to ?

(a) $\frac{1}{12}[2X - Y + Z]$ (b) $\frac{1}{12}[X - Y + 2Z]$

(c) $\frac{1}{12}[-X + 2Y + Z]$ (d) $\frac{1}{12}[X - 2Y + Z]$

25. What is the BLUE of θ_2 equal to ?

(a) $\frac{1}{12}[2X - Y + Z]$ (b) $\frac{1}{12}[X - Y + 2Z]$

(c) $\frac{1}{12}[-X + 2Y + Z]$ (d) $\frac{1}{12}[X - 2Y + Z]$

26. Consider a one-way classification model $Y_{ij} = \mu + \alpha_i + e_{ij}$ where i = 1, 2, 3, ... k; j = 1, 2, 3, ... n and $e_{ij} \sim N(0, \sigma^2)$. Assume that $N = \sum_{i=1}^{k} n_i$. We are testing the hypothesis $H_0 : \alpha_1 = \alpha_2 = ... = \alpha_k = a$ (say).

Consider the ANOVA table for this classification :

Source	Degrees of freedom
Treatment	u
Error	v
Total	N-1

What are the values of u and v respectively ?

(a) k, N – k – 1 (b) k – 2, N – k + 1

(c) k – 1, N – k (d) k – 3, N – k + 2

27. Consider a two-way classification with r observations per cell $Y_{ijk} = \mu + \alpha_i + \beta_j + \gamma_{ij} + e_{ijk}$, where i = 1, 2, ... p; j = 1, 2, ... q; k = 1, 2, ... r. Consider the ANOVA table for this classification:

Source	Degrees of freedom
Due to α	t
Due to β	u
Interaction	v
Error	w
Total	pqr – 1

What are the values of t, u, v and w respectively ?

(a) p – 1, q – 1, (p – 1) (q – 1), pq (r – 1) (b) q – 1, p – 1, (p – 1) (q – 1), pq (r – 1)

(c) r – 1, q – 1, (r – 1) (q – 1), pq (r – 1) (d) p – 1, r – 1, (r – 1) (p – 1), pq (r – 1)

28. In a Randomized Block Design with 4 blocks and 5 treatments having one missing observation, the error degrees of freedom are:

(a) 12 (b) 11

(c) 10 (d) 9

*Consider the following for the next **two (02)** items that follow:*

Consider the Gauss-Markov linear model

$E(y_1) = \beta_1 - \beta_2$

$E(y_2) = 2\beta_1$

$E(y_3) = \beta_1 + \beta_2$

with $V(y_i) = \sigma^2$, $Cov(y_i, y_j) = 0$ for $i \neq j$.

29. Consider the following statements:

1. The best linear unbiased estimator of β_1 is $\hat{\beta}_1 = \frac{1}{6}(y_1 + 2y_2 + y_3)$.

2. The best linear unbiased estimator of β_2 is $\hat{\beta}_2 = \frac{1}{2}(y_1 + y_3)$.

Which of the statements given above is/are correct?

(a) 1 only (b) 2 only

(c) Both 1 and 2 (d) Neither 1·nor 2

30. The residual sum of squares is given by:

(a) $\frac{1}{3}(y_1 + y_2 + y_3)^2$ (b) $\frac{1}{2}(y_1 + y_2 - y_3)^2$

(c) $\frac{1}{2}(y_1 - y_2 + y_3)^2$ (d) $\frac{1}{3}(y_1 - y_2 + y_3)^2$

*Consider the following for the next **two (02)** items that follow:*

Let X have a pdf of the form $f(x, \theta) = \theta x^{\theta-1}; 0 < x < 1$.

31. What is the significance level of the test to test $H_0 : \theta = 1$ against $H_1: \theta = 2$ using a random sample X_1, X_2 of size 2 by taking the critical region $w = \left\{(x_1, x_2) : \frac{3}{4x_1} \leq x_2\right\}$?

(a) *ln* 3 (b) *ln* 3 – *ln*4

(c) *ln* 4 (d) *ln* 4 – *ln* 3

32. What is the power function of the test to test $H_0: \theta = 2$ against $H_1: \theta = 3$ using a random sample X_1, X_2 of size 2 by taking the critical region $w = \left\{(x_1, x_2) : \frac{3}{4x_1} \leq x_2\right\}$?

(a) $\frac{7}{16} + \frac{9}{8}\ln\left(\frac{3}{4}\right)$ (b) $\frac{7}{16} - \frac{9}{8}\ln\left(\frac{3}{4}\right)$

(c) $\frac{37}{64} + \frac{81}{64}\ln\left(\frac{3}{4}\right)$ (d) $\frac{37}{64} - \frac{81}{64}\ln\left(\frac{3}{4}\right)$

33. Let T_1 be an MVUE of θ and T_2 be any other unbiased estimator of θ, such that the correlation coefficient between T_1 and T_2 is 0·75. What is the efficiency of T_2?

(a) $\frac{\sqrt{3}}{2}$ (b) $\frac{3}{\sqrt{2}}$

(c) $\frac{16}{9}$ (d) $\frac{9}{16}$

34. An MVB estimator for a function of parameter θ, say γ(θ) exists if and only if:

(a) $\frac{\partial}{\partial\theta}(\ln L) = \frac{t-\alpha(\theta)}{\gamma(\theta)}$ (b) $\frac{\partial}{\partial\theta}(\ln L) = \frac{1}{\gamma(\theta)}$

(c) $\frac{\partial}{\partial\theta}(\ln L) = \frac{\alpha(\theta)}{t-\gamma(\theta)}$ (d) there exists a suffucient estimator for γ(θ)

[Here α(θ) is any function of θ]

35. Let $X_1, X_2, X_3, \ldots X_n$ be a random sample from normal population with mean 0 and variance σ^2. Let $T = \frac{\sum x_i^2}{n}$. Then which one of the following is correct?

(a) T is MLE of σ^2 but does not attain CRLB.

(b) T is biased estimator of σ^2 but attains CRLB.

(c) T is MLE of σ^2 and attains CRLB.

(d) T is biased for σ^2 but not MLE of σ^2.

36. Let X_1 and X_2 be two independent variables. Define $T_1 = X_1 + 2X_2$ as statistic for θ in Bernoulli (θ) distribution, where $0 < \theta < 1$ and $T_2 = X_1 + 2X_2$ as statistic for λ. in Poisson (λ.) distribution, where $\lambda > 0$. Then which one of the following is correct ?

(a) T_1 is sufficient for θ and T_2 is sufficient for λ.

(b) T_1 is sufficient for θ but T_2 is not sufficient for λ.

(c) T_1 is not sufficient for θ but T_2 is sufficient for λ.

(d) T_1 is not sufficient for θ as well as T_2 is not sufficient for λ.

37. Let X_1 and X_2 be two iid random variables having the discrete uniform distribution on {1, 2, 3, ..., N}, where N is unknown. Let $T = \max(X_1, X_2)$. Then which one of the following is correct ?

(a) $X_1 + X_2$ is sufficient for N but T is not sufficient for N

(b) Tis sufficient for N but $X_1 + X_2$ is not sufficient for N

(c) Both T and $X_1 + X_2$ are sufficient for N

(d) Neither T nor $X_1 + X_2$ is sufficient for N

38. Consider the problem of testing H_0: μ = 0 against H_1: μ ≠ 0, based on random sample of size n taken from N(μ, σ^2) normal distribution where σ^2 is unknown. Consider the transformation Y = bX, b ≠ 0. Which one of the following statements is correct?

(a) Sample space will change and hence UMPU similar test will change and hence does not remain invariant under the transformation.

(b) Parametric space will change and hence UMPU similar test does not remain invariant under the transformation.

(c) Sample space will change but parametric space remains unchanged and hence UMPU similar test remains invariant under the transformation.

(d) Sample space as well as parametric space remain unchanged and UMPU similar test becomes invariant under the transformation.

Consider the following for the next two (02) items that follow :

Consider the problem of testing H_0: $\theta = \theta_0$ against H_1: $\theta = \theta_1$ for the probability distribution given below:

X	0	1	2	3
$P_{\theta_0}(x)$	1/4	1/4	1/4	1/4
$P_{\theta_1}(x)$	0.20	0.40	0.25	0.15

The null hypothesis is rejected if X = 0 is observed. It is further rejected when tossing of two unbiased coins gives both the heads for X = 1.

39. What is the probability of type-I error of the test?

(a) $\frac{3}{10}$ (b) $\frac{5}{16}$

(c) $\frac{7}{10}$ (d) $\frac{1}{4}$

40. What is the probability of type-II error of the test?

(a) $\frac{3}{10}$ (b) $\frac{5}{16}$

(c) $\frac{7}{10}$ (d) $\frac{1}{4}$

41. Which of the following reasons can result in privacy breaches even in aggregate-level data (not unit level data or micro data) derived from data collected in surveys or census ?

1. Aggregated data given state-wise
2. Dealing with very small areas
3. Dealing with rare sub-populations

Select the correct answer using the code given below:

(a) 1 and 2 only (b) 2 and 3 only

(c) 1 and 3 only (d) 1, 2 and 3

42. Subjects covered under 76th round of NSSO are Disability, Drinking water, Sanitation, Hygiene and Housing conditions. Which agency is responsible for finalising subjects to be covered in NSS survey ?

(a) NSSO (b) CSO

(c) NSC (d) NITI Aayog

43. Which of the following indicators from National Indicator Framework would help in monitoring Goal 4, namely 'Ensure inclusive and equitable quality education and promote lifelong learning opportunity for all' ?

1. Proportion of computer literate adults.
2. Number of persons treated in de-addiction centres.
3. Enrolment ratio of children with disabilities.
4. Percentage of agriculture 'mandis' enrolled in e-market.

Select the correct answer using the code given below:

(a) 2 and 4 only (b) 1 and 3 only

(c) 1, 2 and 3 only (d) 1, 2, 3 and 4

44. Which of the divisions are parts of Central Statistics Office?
    1. National Accounts Division
    2. Economics Statistics Division
    3. Field Operation Division

    Select the correct answer using the code given below :

    (a) 1 and 2 only (b) 2 and 3 only

    (c) 1 and 3 only (d) 1, 2 and 3

45. Consider the following in respect of National and International official statistical systems:
    1. They use absolute numbers, percentages, ratios and pictograms.
    2. They only count physical quantities.
    3. They estimate from sampling where exact counting is not possible.

    Which of the above statements are correct ?

    (a) 1 and 2 only (b) 2 and 3 only

    (c) 1 and 3 only (d) 1, 2 and 3

46. Consider the following in respect of Gross Domestic Product (GDP):
    1. It refers to market value of all final goods and services within a country in a given period.
    2. It is measured at current and constant prices.
    3. It is a measure of economic welfare.

    Which of the above statements is/are correct ?

    (a) 1 only (b) 1 and 2 only

    (c) 2 and 3 only (d) 1, 2 and 3

47. Which one of the following is not a Sustainable Development Goal (SDG)?

    (a) Affordable and clean energy

    (b) Promote regulated use of AI

    (c) Peace, Justice and Strong Institutions

    (d) Climate Action

48. Consider the following pairs:

Index Number	Department I Office
1. Consumer	— Labour Bureau

Price Index (Rural, Urban, Combined)

2. Consumer — National

Price Index (Agricultural Labour Statistical Office

3. Wholesale — Office of Economic

Price Index Adviser

How many pairs are correctly matched ?

(a) None of the pairs (b) Only one pair

(c) Only two pairs (d) All three pairs

49. Which organization at the central level is responsible to coordinate and unifY the activity of death registration in India ?

(a) Ministry of Health and Family Welfare

(b) Office of Registrar General oflndia

(c) National Statistical Office

(d) None of the above

50. Consider the following statements :

1. The basic unit of data collection in the Agriculture Census is operational holding.
2. Population Census comes under Concurrent list.
3. The periodicity of economic census is ten years.

Which of the above statements is/are correct ?

(a) 1 only (b) 3 only

(c) 1 and 3 only (d) 1, 2 and 3

51. Let a random variable X have the following probability distribution under $H_0 : \theta = \theta_0$ against $H_1 : \theta = \theta_1$:

X	−1	1	2
$P_{\theta_0}(x)$	1/3	1/3	1/3
$P_{\theta_1}(x)$	1/4	1/4	1/2

To test sequentially the hypothesis H_0 against H_1, it is decided to continue the procedure as long as ************, where S_n = **. Then the probability under H_1 that the procedure will terminate with the second observation, is :

(a) 1/9 (b) 1/8

(c) 1/3 (d) 1/2

52. A test of level α is said to be an unbiased test if its pow er is:

(a) equal to the level of significance

(b) less than the leyel of significance

(c) greater than probability oftype-11 error

(d) gre ater than the level of significance

53. Consider the following pairs :

1. Like lihood ratio test	—	Construction of tests for a composite hypothesis
2. Most powerful· test	—	Test of confirmation of a set of observations to a given distribution
3. Chi-square test	—	Agreement of a set of observed frequencies with corresponding expected frequencies
4 Run test	—	A distribution free test of randomness

How many pairs are correctly matched ?

(a) Only one pair (b) Only two pairs

(c) Only three pairs (d) All four pairs

54. Consider the following pairs :

1. Power function	—	Uniformly most powerful test
2. Size of the test	—	Larger of the two types of errors
3. Neyman Pearson Lemma	—	Maximum power for a fixed level of Type-I error
4 Randomised tests	—	Tests not based on the sample observations

How many pairs are not correctly matched ?

(a) Only one pair (b) Only two pairs

(c) Only three pairs (d) All four pairs

55. Let $X_1, X_2. X_3, \dots X_n$ be a random sample of size n from $N(\mu, \sigma^2)$ where μ is unknown. Then the most efficient biased estimator for μ is:

(a) $\overline{x}$ (b) $m\overline{x}$

(c) $\frac{n}{n+1}\overline{x}$ (d) $\frac{n+1}{n}\overline{x}$

56. Suppose the survival times of patients of a bladder disorder can be modelled by the exponential distribution such that the average time a patient survives is λ.

Consider the following statements :

1. 50% of patients will die by the time $\lambda. \log_e 2$.
2. 25% of patients will die by the time $\lambda \log_e \left(\frac{4}{3}\right)$.

Which of the above statements is/are correct ?

(a) 1 only (b) 2-only

(c) Both 1 and 2 (d) Neither 1 nor 2

57. Consider the following statements with regard to Maximum Likelihood Estimator :

1. It may not be unbiased.
2. It may not in general be unique.
3. It leads· to a consistent estimate which has an asymptotic norma~ distribution, under some conditions.

Which of the above statements are correct ?

(a) 1 and 2 only (b) 2 and 3 only

(c) 1 and 3 only (d) 1, 2 and 3

58. For independent Poisson random variables with parameter λ, which one of the following is sufficient statistic ?

(a) $(X_1, \Pi_{i=2}^{2} X_i)$ (b) $\frac{X_1}{X_2}$

(c) $\frac{X_1}{\sum_{i=1}^{n} X_i}$ (d) $(X_1, \sum_{i=1}^{n} X_i)$

59. For independent Bernoulli random variables, which of the following is/are sufficient statistic for p, such that

$P(X_i = 1) = p = 1 - P(X_i = 0); i = 1, 2, 3$?

1. $X_1 + X_2 + X_3$
2. $X_1 + 2X_2 + X_3$

Select the correct answer using the code given below:

(a) 1 only (b) 2 only

(c) Both 1 and 2 (d) Neither 1 nor 2

60. Let X — N(μ, σ²) where μ is known. If a confidence interval for σ² is to be determined, then an appropriate pivot is :

(a) $(n-1)\frac{S^2}{\sigma^2}$ (b) $\sum_{i=1}^{n} \frac{(X_i - \mu)^2}{\sigma^2}$

(c) $\frac{(\bar{X} - \mu)\sqrt{n}}{\sigma}$ (d) $\frac{(\bar{X} - \mu)\sqrt{n}}{S}$

61. The mandate of Commission is to : National Statistical

    1. Serve as a model and empowered body for all core statistical securities of the nation.
    2. Evolve, monitor and . enforce statistical priorities and standards.
    3. Ensure statistical coordination.

    Which of the above statements are correct ?

    (a) 1 and 2 only (b) 2 and 3 only
    (c) 1 and 3 only (d) 1, 2 and 3 ·

62. Consumer Price Index (CPI) is calculated for which of the following categories :

    (a) Industrial workers, agricultural labourers and rural labourers and urban non-manual employees
    (b) Organized workers, plantation labourers, unorganized workforce and non-rural migrant population
    (c) Skilled labourers, unskilled workers, cultivators and agricultural workforce
    (d) Office-goers, unemployed persons and housewives

63. Consider the following in respect of Index of Industrial Production (IIP) :

    1. It measures the change in volume of industrial production of a representative basket.
    2. It is used to analyse performance of various sectors of economy.

    Which of the above statements is/are correct ?

    (a) 1 only (b) 2 only
    (c) Both 1 and 2 (d) Neither 1 nor 2

64. Consider the following :

    1. Relevance, impartiality and equal access
    2. Professional standards and ethics
    3. Accountability and transparency
    4. Legislation
    5. International cooperation

    Which of the above are fundamental principles of Official Statistics ?

    (a) 1, 2 and 3 only (b) 2, 3, 4 and 5 only
    (c) 1, 4 and 5 only (d) 1, 2, 3, 4 and 5

65. Consider the following statements:

    1. Laspeyres index uses current period quantity as weights.
    2. Paasche index uses base period quantity as weights.
    3. For the same set of data, Laspeyres index is greater than Paasche index.

    Which of the statements given above are not correct?

    (a) 1 and 2 only (b) 2 and 3 only
    (c) 1 and 3 only (d) 1, 2 and 3

66. The most appropriate method for constructing index numbers is Fisher's Ideal Index method. It is referred to as an ideal because :

   1. It is based on the geometric mean which is considered best average.
   2. It satisfies both time reversal test and factor reversal test.
   3. It takes into account both current and base year quantities as weights.

   Which of the above statements are correct ?

   (a) 1 and 2 only (b) 2 and 3 only
   (c) 1 and 3 only (d) 1, 2 and 3

67. Consider the following statements in respect of index numbers :

   1. They help in framing of economic policies.
   2. They help in assessing the purchasing power of money.
   3. They are used for adjusting national income.

   Which of the statements given above are correct?

   (a) 1 and 2 only (b) 2 and 3 only
   (c) 1 and 3 only (d) 1, 2 and 3

Consider the following data for the next ***three (03)*** *items that follow :*

The sum of the products of prices and quantities for the current year 1 and base year 0 for five items are given below:

$\Sigma p_0q_0 = 782$, $\Sigma p_0q_1 = 1008$, $\Sigma p_1q_0 = 1084$, $\Sigma p_1q_1 = 1329$

68. What is the approximate value of Fisher's Ideal Price Index number P_{01}?

   (a) 125 (b) 128
   (c) 130 (d) 135

69. What is the approximate value of Fisher's Ideal Price Index number P 10 ?

   (a) 64 (b) 74
   (c) 81 (d) 85

70. What is the approximate value of Fisher's Ideal Quantity Index number Q01 ?

   (a) 114 (b) 126
   (c) 134 (d) 144

71. Let $x_1, x_2, x_3, \ldots X_n$ be a random sample taken from Gamma(α, β) having p.d.f.

$$f(x; \alpha, \beta) = \frac{e^{-\frac{x}{\beta}} x^{\alpha-1}}{\beta^\alpha \Gamma(\alpha)}; 0 \le x < \infty; \alpha, \beta > 0$$

   The jointly sufficient statistic for α and β. are respectively:

   (a) $(\Sigma x_i, \Pi x_i)$ (b) $(\Sigma x_i^2, \Pi x_i^2)$
   (c) $(\Sigma x_i^2, \Pi x_i)$ (d) $(\Sigma x_i, \Pi x_i^2)$

Consider the following for the next ***two (02)*** *items that follow :*

Let $X_1, X_2, X_3, \ldots X_n$ be a random sample from uniform distribution $U(0, \theta)$.

Let $T_1 = \frac{2}{n}\sum_{i=1}^{n} X_i$ and $T_2 = \max(X_1, X_2, X_3, \ldots X_n)$.

72. Consider the following statements :

    1. T_1 and T_2 are consistent estimators of θ.
    2. T_1 and T_2 are unbiased estimators of θ.

    Which of the statements given above is/are correct?

    (a) 1 only (b) 2 only

    (c) Both 1 and 2 (d) Neither 1 nor 2

73. Consider the following statements:

    1. T_1 is not sufficient but T_2 is sufficient estimator of θ.
    2. T_1 is the method of moment estimator of θ.

    Which of the statements given above is/are correct?

    (a) 1 only (b) 2 only

    (c) Both 1 and 2 (d) Neither 1 nor 2

*Consider the following for the next **two (02)** items that follow :*

Let $X_1, X_2, X_3, \ldots X_n$ be a random sample from

$$f(x) = \begin{cases} \frac{1}{b-a}, & a \le x \le b \\ 0, & \text{otherwise} \end{cases}$$

74. The estimator for 'a' by method of moments is:

    (a) $\bar{X} - \sqrt{\frac{\Sigma(X_i - \bar{X})^2}{n}}$ (b) $\bar{X} - \sqrt{\frac{2\Sigma(X_i - \bar{X})^2}{n}}$

    (c) $\bar{X} - \sqrt{\frac{3\Sigma(X_i - \bar{X})^2}{n}}$ (d) $\bar{X} - 2\sqrt{\frac{\Sigma(X_i - \bar{X})^2}{n}}$

75. The estimator for 'b' by method of moments is:

    (a) $\bar{X} + \sqrt{\frac{\Sigma(X_i - \bar{X})^2}{n}}$ (b) $\bar{X} + \sqrt{\frac{2\Sigma(X_i - \bar{X})^2}{n}}$

    (c) $\bar{X} + \sqrt{\frac{3\Sigma(X_i - \bar{X})^2}{n}}$ (d) $\bar{X} + 2\sqrt{\frac{\Sigma(X_i - \bar{X})^2}{n}}$

76. Let $X_1, X_2, X_3, \dots X_n$ be iid Bemoulli with parameter p. What is the Cramer-Rao Lower Bound for $\bar{X}$, where $E(\bar{X}) = p$?

(a) $\frac{n}{p}$ (b) $\frac{n}{p(p-1)}$

(c) $\frac{n}{p(1-p)}$ (d) $\frac{p(1-p)}{n}$

77. Let $X_1, X_2, X_3, \dots X_n$ be a random sample of size 2 from Bemoulli distribution with pmf

$$f(x, \theta) = \begin{cases} \theta^x (1-\theta)^{1-x} & x = 0, 1 \\ 0; & \text{otherwise} \end{cases}$$

What is the sufficient statistic for θ?

(a) $X_1 - X_2$ (b) $X_1 X_2$

(c) $X_1 + X_2$ (d)

78. Let $X_1, X_2, X_3, \dots X_n$ be iid random variables with common pmf $P[X_i = k] = \frac{1}{N}$, k = 1, 2, 3, ... N; i = 1, 2, 3, ... n. What is the sufficient statistic for the family of joint pmfs PN?

(a) min $(X_1, X_2, X_3, \dots X_n)$

(b) max $(X_1, X_2, X_3, \dots X_n)$

(c) [min $(X_1, X_2, X_3, \dots X_n)$, max $(X_1, X_2, X_3, \dots X_n)$]

(d) $X_1 + X_2 + X_3 + \dots + X_n$

Consider the following for the next two (02) items that follow :

Let $X_1, X_2, X_3, \dots X_n$ be a random sample of size n from b(1, θ), 0 < θ < 1 (Bemoulli) distribution. Let $Y = \Sigma X_i$ be complete sufficient statistic for θ.

79. UMVUE of θ is:

(a) $\frac{Y}{n}$ (b) $\frac{Y^2}{n}$

(c) $\frac{2Y}{n}$ (d) $\frac{Y}{2n}$

80. UMVUE of θ^2 is :

(a) $\frac{Y(Y-1)}{n(n+1)}$ (b) $\frac{Y(Y-1)}{n(n-1)}$

(c) $\frac{Y(Y+1)}{n(n+1)}$ (d) $\frac{Y(Y+1)}{n(n-1)}$

STATISTICS - II
2021

Time Allowed : Two Hours | *Maximum Marks: 200*

INSTRUCTIONS

1. IMMEDIATELY AFTER THE COMMENCEMENT OF THE EXAMINATION, YO SHOULD CHECK THAT THIS TEST BOOKLET *DOES NOT* HAVE ANY UNPRINTED OR TORN OR MISSING PAGES OR ITEMS, ETC. IF SO, GET IT REPLACE BY A COMPLETE TEST BOOKLET.
2. **Please note that it is the candidate'sresponsibility to encode and fill in the Roll Number and Test Booklet Series A, B, C or D carefully and without any omission or discrepancy at the appropriate places in the OMR Answer Sheet. Any omission/discrepancy will render the Answer sheet liable for rejection.**
3. You have to enter your Roll Number on the Test Booklet in the Box provided alongside. *DO NOT* write *anything else* on the Test Booklet.
4. This Test Booklet contains **80** items (questions).Each item comprises four responses (answers). You will select the response which you want to mark on the Answer Sheet. In case you feel that there is more than one correct response, mark the response which you consider the best. In any case, choose *ONLY ONE* response for each item.
5. You have to mark all your responses *ONLY* on the separate Answer Sheet provided. See directions in the Answer Sheet.
6. All items carry equal marks.
7. Before you proceed to mark in the Answer Sheet the response to various in the Test Booklet, you have to fill in some particulars in the Answer Sheet as per intructions sent to you with your Admission Certificate.
8. After you have complited filling in all your responses on the Answer Sheet and the examination has concluded, you should hand over to the Invigilator *only the Answer Sheet*. You are permitted to take away with you the Test Booklet.
9. Sheets for rough work are appended in the Test Booklet at the end.
10. **Penalty for wrong answers:**

    THERE WILL BE PENALTY FOR WRONG ANSWERS MARKED BY A CANDIDATE IN THE OBJECTIVE TYPE QUSTION PAPERS.

    (i) There are four alternatives for the answer to every question. For each question for which a wrong answer has been given by the candidate, **one-third** of the marks assigned to that question will be deducted as penalty.

    (ii) If a candidate gives more than one answer, it will be treated as a **wrong answer** even if one of the given answers happens to be correct and there will be same penalty as above to that question.

    (iii) If a question is left blamk,i.e., no answer is given by the candidate, there will be **no penalty** for that question.

DO NOT OPEN THIS TEST BOOKLET UNTIL YOU ARE TOLD TO DO SO

1 Consider the model $y_{ij} = \mu + \alpha_i + \beta_j + \varepsilon_{ij}$, $i = 1, 2; j = 1, 2$. For which one of the following choices of λ', the function $\lambda'\beta$ where $\beta' = (\mu, \alpha_1, \alpha_2, \beta_1, \beta_2)$ is not estimable?

(a) (1, 1, 0, 1, 0) (b) (0, 0, 0, – 1, 1)

(c) (0, –1, 1, 0, 0) (d) (1, 1, 1, 1, 1)

2. For the model $y_{ij} = \mu + \tau_i + \varepsilon_{ij}$, $i = 1, 2; j = 1, 2$; consider the following statements:

1. $\mu + \tau_1$ is estimable.
2. $\tau_1 + \tau_2$ is estimable.

Which of the above statements is/are correct?

(a) 1 only (b) 2 only

(c) Both 1 and 2 (c) Neither 1 nor 2

3. Let X_i, Y_i and Z_i; $i = 1, 2, 3$ be nine independent observations with common variance σ^2, and $E(X_i) = \theta_1$, $E(Y_i) = \theta_2$, $E(Z_i) = \theta_1 - \theta_2$; $i = 1, 2, 3$. If $X = \sum_{1.1}^{1} x_1$, $Y = \sum_{1.1}^{2} y_1$ and $Z = \sum_{1.1}^{3} z_1$, then the BLUE of θ1 is given by

(a) $\frac{1}{9}[2X + Y - Z]$ (b) $\frac{1}{9}[X + 2Y - Z]$

(c) $\frac{1}{9}[X + 2Y - 2Z]$ (d) $\frac{1}{9}[X + 3Y - 2Z]$

4. In general regression model

$Y_{n\times1} = X_{n\times k}\, \beta_{k\times1} + \varepsilon_{n\times1}$. Further ε is $N(0, \sigma^2 I)$. The $n \times 1$ vector of ordinary residuals is denoted by $e = Y - \bar{Y}$. The distribution of $\frac{\theta'\theta}{\sigma^2}$ is

(a) $N(0, \sigma^2 \rho)$ (b) $N(X\beta, \sigma^2)$

(c) χ^2_{n-k} (d) χ^2_{n-1}

5. Consider a model

$Y_1 = A + B + C + D + e_1$;

$Y_2 = A + C - B - D + e_2$;

$Y_3 = A + B - C - D + e_3$;

$Y_4 = A + D - B - C + e_4$;

If this model is equivalent to $Y = X\beta + e$, then the matrix $(X'X)^{-1}$ is equal to

(a) $\frac{1}{3} I_e$ (b) $\frac{1}{2} I_e$

(c) $\frac{1}{5} I_e$ (d) $\frac{1}{4} I_e$

6. Consider the following statements:

1. Tukey's test of multiple comparisons reduces the Type-I error in the test.
2. Student-Newman-Keuls test uses stepwise procedure.

Which of the above statements is/are correct?

(a) 1 only (b) 2 only

(c) Both 1 and 2 (d) Neither 1 nor 2

7. Consider the following statements in respect of a symmetric matrix X:

   1. Generalized inverse of X is not necessarily symmetric.
   2. Symmetric inverse of X can always be determined.

   Which of the above statements is/are correct?

   (a) 1 only (b) 2 only

   (c) Both 1 and 2 (d) Neither 1 nor 2

8. Five methods of packing frozen foods were compared by taking six observations for each of the methods used. The response variable was ascorbic acid (mg/100 g). The degrees of freedom for error sum of squares are

   (a) 26 (b) 25

   (c) 24 (d) 20

9. Consider a two-way classification with one observation per cell. The model is

   $y_{ij} = \mu + \alpha_i + \beta_j + e_{ij}$; i = 1, 2, 3, ..., p;

   j = 1, 2, 3, ..., q. Which one of the following parameters is estimable?

   (a) α (b) β

   (c) $\alpha_i - \alpha_u$; i, u = 1, 2, 3, ..., p ($i \neq u$) (d) $\alpha_1 + \alpha_2$

10. Let A be matrix of order 4×7, then any generalized inverse of A is of order

    (a) 4×4 (b) 7×4

    (c) 4×7 (d) 7×7

11. Let X be a discrete random variable with probability distribution

    $$P(X = x) = \begin{cases} \theta & \text{if } x = -1 \\ (1-\theta)^2\,\theta^x & \text{if } x = 0, 1, 2, 3 \end{cases}$$

    where $0 < \theta < 1$. Then

    (a) X is minimal sufficient and complete.

    (b) X is minimal sufficient only.

    (c) X is complete only.

    (d) X is unbiased estimator for θ.

12. Let $X_1, X_2, ..., X_n$ be a random sample from uniform distribution $U(0, \theta)$, $\theta > 0$. Define $U = 2\overline{X}$, such that $\overline{X} = \frac{\sum_{i=1}^{n} X_1}{n}$ and $T = X_{(1)} = \min\{X_1, X_2, ..., X_n\}$. Then $E[U \mid T = t]$ will be

    (a) independent of θ. (b) most efficient for θ.

    (c) a function of θ. (d) MVUE for θ.

13. Lt $X \sim f(x, \theta) = \frac{1}{\theta}\theta^{-\frac{x}{\theta}}; x > 0, \theta > 0$ and $Y \sim f(y, \theta) = \frac{1}{2\theta}\theta^{\frac{y}{\theta}}; y > 0, \theta > 0$. Which one of the following statements is correct?

(a) $X + 2Y$ is sufficient for θ and left tail UMP test is given by $X + 2Y < C$.

(b) $X + 2Y$ is sufficient for θ and right tail UMP test is given by $X + 2Y > C$.

(c) $Y + 2X$ is sufficient for θ and left tail UMP test is given by $Y + 2X < C$.

(d) $Y + 2X$ is sufficient for θ and right tail UMP test is given by $Y + 2X < C$.

14. Consider a Sequential Probability Ratio Test (SPRT) to test H_0: $\theta = \theta_0$ againt H_1: $\theta = \theta_1$ and continue taking obervations as long as $a_m < s_m < r_m$; where $s_m = \sum_{i=1}^{\Omega} X_1$; $a_m = 0.90 + 0.05$ m and $r_m = 2.25 + 0.05m$. On the basis of the data {1, 1, 0, 1, 0, 0} the decision will be

(a) may accept H_1 at 6th stage.
(b) reject H_0 at 4th stage.
(c) may accept H_1 at 3rd stage.
(d) reject H_1 at 3rd stage.

15. Let $X_1, X_2, X_3, ..., X_n$ be i.i.d, random variables from the density function $f(x) = \frac{1}{\alpha}\theta^{\frac{x}{a}}$, $x > 0$, $\alpha > 0$. Then the uniformly minimum variance unbiased estimator of the parameter α is

(a) $n\overline{X}$
(b) $\frac{\overline{X}}{n}$
(c) $\overline{X}$
(d) $\frac{\overline{X}}{n+1}$

16. Let $X_1, X_2, X_3, ..., X_n$ be a random sample of size n taken from normal population ($N(0, \sigma^2)$). Then a central confidence interval for σ^2 (i.e., confidence interval with equal tail probabilities) with confidence coefficient 0.95 for large sample is given by

(a) $\left(\frac{\frac{1}{n}\sum_{i=1}^{n} X_1^2}{1+196\sqrt{\frac{2}{n}}}, \frac{\frac{1}{n}\sum_{i=1}^{n} X_1^2}{1-196\sqrt{\frac{2}{n}}}\right)$

(b) $\left(\frac{\frac{1}{n}\sum_{i=1}^{n} X_1^2}{1+196\sqrt{\frac{2}{\pi}}}, \frac{\frac{1}{n}\sum_{i=1}^{n} X_1^2}{1-196\sqrt{\frac{2}{\pi}}}\right)$

(c) $\left(\frac{\sum_{i=1}^{n} X_1^2}{1+196\sqrt{\frac{2}{n}}}, \frac{\sum_{i=1}^{n} X_1^2}{1-196\sqrt{\frac{2}{n}}}\right)$

(d) $\left(\frac{\sum_{i=1}^{n} X_1^2}{1+1645\sqrt{\frac{2}{n}}}, \frac{\sum_{i=1}^{n} X_1^2}{1-1645\sqrt{\frac{2}{n}}}\right)$

17. Consider the following statements in respect of an estimator T for the parameter θ:

1. T is unbiased for $\theta \Rightarrow T^2$ is unbiased for θ^2.
2. T is consistent for $\theta \Rightarrow T^2$ is consistent for θ^2.

3. T is sufficient for $\theta \Rightarrow T^2$ is sufficient for θ.

Which of the above statements is/are correct?

(a) 2 only
(b) 2 and 3 only
(c) 1 and 3 only
(d) 1, 2 and 3

18. If T_1 and T_2 are two consistent estimators of θ_1 and θ_2 respectively, then consider the following statements:

1. $(T_1 + T_2)$ is also consistent estimator for $(\theta_1 + \theta_2)$.
2. $(T_1 \times T_2)$ is also consistent estimator for $(\theta_1 \times \theta_2)$.

Which of the above statements is/are correct?

(a) 1 only
(b) 2 only
(c) Both 1 and 2
(d) Neither 1 nor 2

19. If x is a random sample of size 1 from Poisson (θ), then 5^x is the unbiased estimator of

(a) 5^θ
(b) $e^{5\theta}$
(c) $e^{4\theta}$
(d) θ^5

20. Let 4, 3, 6, 3, 6, 2, 3, 4, 4, 3, 5 and 5 be a sample of size 12 from the geometric population having pdf

$f(x) = \theta(1-\theta)^{x-1};\ x = 1, 2, 3, \ldots$

The estimator of θ using the method of moment

(a) is 0.25
(b) is 4.
(c) is 48.
(d) does not exist.

21. Consider the following statements in respect of a random sample $x_1, x_2, x_3, \ldots, x_n$ from $N(\theta, 4)$:

1. MLE of θ is $\frac{1}{n}\sum_{i=1}^{n} x_1$.
2. MLE of θ^2 is $\frac{1}{n}\sum_{i=1}^{n} x_1^2$.

Which of the above statments is/are correct?

(a) 1 only
(b) 2 only
(c) Both 1 and 2
(d) Neither 1 nor 2

22. Let $X_1, X_2, X_3, \ldots, X_n$ be i.i.d. random variates from $U(0, \theta)$. If $Y = \max(X_1, X_2, X_3, \ldots, X_n)$, then an unbiased estimator of θ^3 will be

(a) y^3
(b) $\left(\frac{n+3}{n}\right)y^3$
(c) $\frac{y^3}{n}$
(d) $\left(\frac{n}{n+3}\right)y^3$

23. Let $x_1, x_2, x_3, \ldots, x_n$ be random sample from $U(0, \theta)$. If $x_{(1)} \leq x_{(2)} \leq x_{(3)} \leq \ldots, \leq x_{(n)}$ are the order statistics, then which of the following statements is/are correct?

1. $x_{(n)}$ is the MLE for θ.
2. $x_{(n)}$ is the consistent estimator of θ.

Select the correct anser using the code given below:

(a) 1 only (b) 2 only
(c) Both 1 and 2 (d) Neither 1 nor 2

24. If $x_1, x_2, x_3, ..., x_n$ is a random sample from Poisson (θ), then consider the following statements:

1. $\frac{1}{n}\sum_{i=1}^{n} x_i$ is the maximum likelihoood estimator of θ.
2. $\frac{1}{n}\sum_{i=1}^{n} x_i$ is sufficient for estimting θ.

Which of the above statments is/are correct?

(a) 1 only (b) 2 only
(c) Both 1 and 2 (d) Neither 1 nor 2

25. Consider the following statements:

1. Cramer-Rao inequality provides a lower bound to the variance of a sufficient estimator for γ(θ).
2. A minimum variance bound (MVB) estimator for γ(θ) exists if and only if there exists a sufficient estimator for γ(θ).

Which of the above statments is/are correct?

(a) 1 only (b) 2 only
(c) Both 1 and 2 (d) Neither 1 nor 2

26. Let $x_1, x_2, x_3, ..., x_n$ be a random sample from the population with pdf

$$f(x, \theta) = \begin{cases} \frac{1}{\theta}\exp\left(-\frac{x}{\theta}\right); & 0 < x < \infty \\ 0; & \text{otherwise} \end{cases}$$

The Cramer-Rao lower bound to the variance of an unbiased estimator of θ is

(a) θ^2 (b) $\frac{\theta^2}{n}$
(c) $n\theta^2$ (d) $\frac{\theta^2}{n^2}$

27. Let $x_1, x_2, x_3, ..., x_n$ be a random sample from the pmf

$$P[X = x] = \binom{2}{x}(1-\theta)^{2-x}\,\theta^x; 0 \le \theta < 1;$$

$x = 0, 1$ and 2 $T = \sum_{i=1}^{n} x_i$. Which of the following statements is/are correct?

1. T is a complete sufficient statistic for θ.
2. $\frac{T^2 - T}{2n(2n-1)}$ is an UMVUE of θ^2.

Select the correct answer using the code given below:

(a) 1 only (b) 2 only

(c) Both 1 and 2 (d) Neither 1 nor 2

28. Let $x_1, x_2, x_3, ..., x_n$ be a random sample of size 64 drawn from Poisson (λ). If it is given that $\sum_{i=1}^{n} x_i = 256$, then 95% confidence interval of λ is

(a) (3.51, 4.9) (b) (0.08, 7.92)

(c) (3.76, 4.25) (d) (3.02, 4.98)

29. For a likelihood ratio λ, consider the following statements:

1. $0 \leq \leq 1$
2. ($-2 \log \lambda$) following asymptotic Chi-square distribution.
3. Likelihood ratio test is consistent.

Which of the above statements are correct?

(a) 1 and 2 only (b) 1 and 3 only

(c) 2 and 3 only (d) 1, 2 and 3

30. Let $x_1, x_2, x_3, ..., x_n$ be a random sample from normal population with pdf

$$\frac{1}{2\sqrt{\pi}} \exp\left[-\frac{1}{4}(x-\mu)^2\right]; -\infty < x < \infty.$$

The S.P.R.T. for rejecting $H_0 = \mu = 4$ against $H_1 = \mu = 6$ for $\alpha = \beta = 0.05$ is

(a) $\sum_{i=1}^{n} x_i \geq 5n + \log 19$ (b) $\sum_{i=1}^{n} x_i \geq 5n$

(c) $\sum_{i=1}^{n} x_i \geq n$ (d) $\sum_{i=1}^{n} x_i \geq n + \log 19$

31. Let the random variable X have N(0, 1). Then E(|X|) is equal to

(a) $\sqrt{2\pi}$ (b) $\frac{\sqrt{\pi}}{\sqrt{2}}$

(c) $\frac{\sqrt{2}}{\sqrt{\pi}}$ (d) $\frac{\sqrt{2}}{\pi}$

32. Let $X \sim b(1, p)$, $p \in \left[\frac{a}{a+b}, \frac{b}{a+b}\right]$; $b > 0$. Then MLE of p is

(a) $\frac{X+b}{a+b}$ (b) $\frac{(b-a)X-1}{a+b}$

(c) $\frac{(b-a)X+b}{a+b}$ (d) $\frac{(b-a)X+b}{a+b}$

33. Consider the following statements:

1. An unbiased estimator is always unique.
2. Sufficient statistic is always a function of MLE.

3. Consistent estimator need not be unique.
4. UMP test is not unique.

Which of the above statements are correct?

(a) 1 and 2 only (b) 3 and 4 only
(c) 1, 3 and 4 only (d) 1 and 4 only

34. Every similar test for testing under H_0 has a Neyman structure under which one of the following conditions?

(a) Sufficient statistic (b) Consistent statistic
(c) Boundedly complete (d) Boundedly complete sufficient statistic

35. Consider the following statements:

1. Unbiased estimators may not always exist.
2. Unbiased estimators are always unique if they exist.

Which of the above statements is/are correct?

(a) 1 only (b) 2 only
(c) Both 1 and 2 (d) Neither 1 n or 2

36. Consider the following statements:

1. If t is an unbiased estimator of θ, it need not be consistent.
2. If t is a consistent estimator of θ, it will also be an unbiased estimator of θ.

Which of the above statements is/are correct?

(a) 1 only (b) 2 only
(c) Both 1 and 2 (d) Neither 1 nor 2

37. Let $x_1, x_2, x_3, ..., x_n$ be a random sample from the population with pdf

$$f(x, \theta) = \frac{x}{\theta} \exp\left(-\frac{x^2}{2\theta}\right); x > 0 \text{ and } \theta > 0.$$

The estimaror of θ using the method of moments is

(a) $\overline{x}$ (b) $\overline{x}^2$
(c) $\frac{2\overline{x}}{\pi}$ (d) $\frac{2\overline{x}^2}{\pi}$

38. Consider the following statements:

1. An MLE is always unique.
2. An MLE may not be consistent.
3. An MLE may not be unbiased.

Which of the above statements are correct?

(a) 1 and 2 only (b) 2 and 3 only
(c) 1 and 3 only (d) 1, 2 and 3

39. Let $x_1, x_2, x_3, ..., x_n$ be a random sample from Poisson distribution with parameter θ. Then the unbiasd estimate of $e^{-\theta}$ which doesn't attain C – R lower bound is

(a) Σx_i (b) $\bar{x}^2$

(c) $\left(1-\frac{1}{n}\right)^{\Sigma x_i}$ (d) $2\Sigma x_i$

40. A random sample of size n is taken from N(θ, 100) and probability of accepting H_0 when H_1 is true is 0.01. If critical region of size 0.05 is used for testing H_0: θ = 90 against H_1: θ = 100, then the sample size n to be taken, is

(a) 14 (b) 15

(c) 16 (d) 17

41. Let $X_1, X_2, X_3, ..., X_n$ be a random sample from a distribution with pdf

$$f(x, \theta) = \begin{cases} \frac{1}{\theta}; \frac{\theta}{2} \leq x \leq \frac{\theta}{2}, & \theta > 0 \\ 0; & \text{otherwise} \end{cases}$$

For the sufficient statistic for the parameter θ, consider the folllowing statements:

1. Order statistic $(X_{(1)}, X_{(2)}, X_{(3)}, ..., X_{(n)})$ is sufficient for θ.
2. Order statistic $(X_{(1)}, X_{(n)})$ is sufficient for θ.

Which of the above statements is/are correct?

(a) 1 only (b) 2 only

(c) Both 1 and 2 (d) Neither 1 nor 2

42. Let $X_1, X_2, X_3, ..., X_n$ be i.i.d. with probability density function $f(x, \theta) = e^{-(x-\theta)}$; x > θ. Let X(1) = min $(X_1, X_2, X_3, ..., X_n)$. Define the class of estimators $T(X) = X_{(1)} + k$; k ∈ R. The estimator that has smallest mean squared error (MSE) is

(a) $T(X) = X_{(1)} - n$ (b) $T(X) = X_{(1)} + 1$

(c) $T(X) = X_{(1)} + \frac{1}{n}$ (d) $T(X) = X_{(1)} - \frac{1}{n}$

43. Let $x_1, x_2, x_3, ..., x_n$ be a random sample from U(α, β). The MLE of α and β are respectively:

(a) Σx_i and Σx_i^2

(b) Πx_i and Πx_i^2

(c) min $(x_1, x_2, x_3, ..., x_n)$ and max $(x_1, x_2, x_3, ..., x_n)$

(d) $\frac{x_{(n)} - x_{(1)}}{2}$ and $\frac{x_{(n)} + x_{(1)}}{2}$

44. Consider the following statements:

1. A minimum varince bound unbiased estimator (MVBUE) is always uniformly minimum variance unbiased estimator (UMVUE).
2. An MVBUE of a parameter θ must be sufficient statistic for θ.

3. UMVUE is always MVBUE.

Which of the above statments are correct?

(a) 1 and 2 only (b) 2 and 3 only

(c) 1 and 3 only (d) 1, 2 and 3

45. Let $x_1, x_2, x_3, \dots, x_n$ be a random sample from Cauchy's population having pdf

$$f(x, \theta) = \frac{1}{\pi[1 + x(x-\theta)^2]}; -\infty < x < \infty$$

Consider the following statements:

1. Sample mean is a sufficient estimator of θ.
2. Sample mean is a minimum variance bound estimator for θ.

Which of the above statements is/are correct?

(a) 1 only (b) 2 only

(c) Both 1 nor 2 (d) Neither 1 nor 2

46. If $x_1, x_2, x_3, \dots, x_n$ be a random sample from a population following Poisson distribution with parameter λ, then 95% confidence interval for λ (for large n) is

(a) $\overline{x} \pm 1.96\frac{\overline{x}}{n}$ (b) $\overline{x} \pm 1.96\frac{\sqrt{x}}{n}$

(c) $\overline{x} \pm 1.96\frac{\overline{x}}{\sqrt{n}}$ (d) $\overline{x} \pm 1.96\sqrt{\frac{\overline{x}}{n}}$

47. For testing a simple null hypothesi against the simple alternative hypothesis, the test is unbiased if

(a) $\alpha \le \beta$ (b) $\alpha + \beta < 1$

(c) $\alpha + \beta > 1$ (d) $\alpha \ge \beta$

48. Let X and Y be two independent random variables with U(0, θ). We are testing $H_0: \theta = 1$ against $H_1: \theta = 2$. The probability of type-I error and power of the test for the critical region $\left\{\frac{X}{Y} > 0.65\right\}$ are respectively

(a) (0.675, 0.675) (b) (0.625, 0.625)

(c) (0.675, 0.625) (d) 0.625, 0.675)

49. For testing standard normal distribution against double exponential distribution, the critical region C is given by

(a) $C = \{x: k_1, < x < k_2\}$ (b) $C = \{x: k_1 < x \text{ or } k_2 > x\}$

(c) $C = \{x: |x| \ge k_1 \text{ or } |x| \le k_2\}$ (d) $C = \{x: |x| > k_1 \text{ or } |x| < k_2\}$

where k_1 and k_2 are some constants.

50. Suppose the number of failed satellte launches have a Poisson distribution with parameter λ. Failure counts for past 12 months are observed in order to test $H_0: \lambda = 2$, against $H_1: \lambda = 3$, What is the Likelihood Ratio?

(a) $1.5e^{-24}$ (b) $1.5e^{-12}$

(c) $(1.5)^{\sum_{i=1}^{12} x_i} e^{-12}$ (d) $(1.5)^{\sum_{i=1}^{24} x_i} e^{-24}$

Consider the following for the next twp (02) items that follow:

The OC function for testing $H_0: \theta = \theta_0$ against H1: θ = θ1(> θ0) using SPRT for a sampling from N(θ, 1) is $L(\theta) = \dfrac{A^{h(\theta)} - 1}{A^{h(\theta)} - B^{h(\theta)}}$ α and β are the probabilities of type-I and type-II errors respectively.

51. What are A and B respectivley equal to?

(a) $\dfrac{1-\beta}{\alpha}, \dfrac{\beta}{1-\alpha}$ (b) $\dfrac{1-\alpha}{\beta}, \dfrac{\alpha}{1-\beta}$

(c) $\dfrac{\alpha}{1-\beta}, \dfrac{1-\alpha}{\beta}$ (d) $\dfrac{\beta}{1-\alpha}, \dfrac{1-\beta}{\alpha}$

52. What is h (θ) equal to?

(a) $\dfrac{\theta_1 - \theta_0 - 2\theta}{\theta_1 - \theta_0}$ (b) $\dfrac{\theta_1 + \theta_0 - 2\theta}{\theta_1 - \theta_0}$

(c) $\dfrac{\theta_1 - \theta_0 + 2\theta}{\theta_1 - \theta_0}$ (d) $\dfrac{\theta_1 - \theta_0 + 2\theta}{\theta_0 - \theta_1}$

Consider the following for the next two (02) items that follow:

Let X be a binomial random variable with parameters n and θ. The prior distribution of θ is beta disribution of θ is beta distribution of first kind with parameters α and β. Let theposterior distribution of $\theta \mid X = x$ be beta distrinution with parameters p_1 and p_2.

53. What is p_1 equal to?

(a) $n - \alpha - \beta$ (b) $x + \alpha$

(c) $n - x + \beta$ (d) $x - \alpha$

54. What is p_2 equal to?

(a) $n + \alpha + \beta$ (b) $x - \alpha$

(c) $n + x - \beta$ (d) $x + \alpha$

Consider the following for the next two (02) items that follow:

Let a random variable X have a uniform distribution with density function

$$f(x; \mu, \sigma) = \frac{1}{2\sqrt{3}\,\sigma},$$

where $\mu - \sqrt{3}\sigma < x < \mu + \sqrt{3}\sigma$,,

where $-\infty < \mu < \infty$, $\sigma > 0$.

55. What is the MLE estimator for μ?

(a) $x_{(1)}$ (b) $x_{(1)} + x_{(n)}$

(c) $[x_{(1)} + x_{(n)}]/2$ (d) $2[x_{(1)} + x_{(n)}]$

56. What is the MLE estimator of σ?

(a) $x_{(n)}$ (b) $x_{(n)} - x_{(1)}$

(c) $[x_{(n)} - x_{(1)}]/(2\sqrt{3})$ (d) $[x_{(n)} - x_{(1)}]/2$

Consider the following for the next two (02) items that follow:

Let $X_1, X_2, X_3, \ldots, X_n$ be i.i.d random variables from $U(\theta_1, \theta_2)$, $f(x) = \dfrac{1}{\theta_2 - \theta_1}; \theta_1 < x < \theta_2; \theta_i > 0; i = 1, 2.$

57. What is UMVUE of θ_1 equal to?

(a) $\dfrac{n\hat{X}_{(n)} - \hat{X}_{(1)}}{n-1}$ (b) $\dfrac{n\hat{X}_{(1)} - \hat{X}_{(n)}}{n}$

(c) $\dfrac{n\hat{X}_{(1)} - \hat{X}_{(n)}}{n-2}$ (d) $\dfrac{n\hat{X}_{(1)} - \hat{X}_{(n)}}{n-2}$

where $\overline{X}_{(n)} = E(X_{(i)}); i = 1, n.$

58. What is UMVUE of θ_2 equal to?

(a) $\dfrac{n\hat{X}_{(n)} - \hat{X}_{(1)}}{n-1}$ (b) $\dfrac{n\hat{X}_{(1)} - \hat{X}_{(n)}}{n}$

(c) $\dfrac{n\hat{X}_{(1)} - \hat{X}_{(n)}}{n-2}$ (d) $\dfrac{n\hat{X}_{(1)} - \hat{X}_{(n)}}{n-2}$

Consider the following for the next two (02) items that follow:

Let $X_1, X_2, X_3, \ldots, X_n$ be i.i.d. random variables with $N(\mu, \mu)$. In this case, mean = variance = μ ($\mu > 0$)

59. Consider the following statements:

1. $\sum x_i^2$ is sufficient for μ.
2. MLE of μ is $\dfrac{-1 + \sqrt{1 + 4m_2}}{2}$

where $m_2 = \dfrac{\sum x_i^2}{n}$

Which of the above statements is/are correct?

(a) 1 only (b) 2 only

(c) Both 1 and 2 (d) Neither 1 nor 1

60. Consider the following statements:

1. $(\Sigma x_i, x_n)$ is sufficient for μ.
2. Moment estimator of μ is $\overline{X}$

Which of the above statements is/are correct?

(a) 1 only (b) 2 only

(c) Both 1 and 2 (d) Neither 1 nor 2

61. Which survey being conducted by MOSPI in 2019 will be an important tool for measuring paid and unpaid work of both men and women in a society?

(a) Periodic Labour Force Survey

(b) Time Use Survey

(c) Employment and Unemployment Survey of NSSO

(d) Population Census

62. Which of the following are major sources of health indicators in India?

1. National Family Health Survey
2. Periodic Labour Force Survey
3. Population Census
4. NSSO 71st Round – Social Consumption: Education and Health

Select the correct answer using the code given below:

(a) 1 and 2 only (b) 2 and 3 only

(c) 1, 2 and 3 only (d) 1, 3 and 4 only

63. Consider the following statements:

1. Most of the index compliers use Laspeyres' Index Formula for index compilation even though it has inherent upward bias.
2. It is advised that Base Period of an index should be revised as frequently as possible.

Which of the above statements is/are correct?

(a) 1 only (b) 2 only

(c) Both 1 and 2 (d) Neither 1 nor 2

64. Which of the following statements are correct about Sustainable Development Goals (SDGs)?

1. United Nations Development Programme (UNDP) formulated these goals.
2. There are 17 goals.
3. These are intended to be completed by 2030.

Select the correct answer using the code given below:

(a) 1 and 2 only (b) 2 and 3 only

(c) 1 and 3 only (d) 1, 2 and 3

65. 'Wages and salaries' earned by a resident of country 'A' from a resident enterprise of country 'B' is included in

(a) GDP if country A. (b) GDP of country B.

(c) GNI of country A. (d) GNI of country B.

66. Which one of the following is not a component of United Nations' Human Development Index (HDI)?
    (a) Life expectancy at birth
    (b) Infant mortality rate
    (c) Expected and mean years of schoolling
    (d) Per capita income

67. Gross Domestic Product reflects the
    (a) industrial growth scenario of the country.
    (b) trend in agricultural grwoth in the country.
    (c) size of country's economy at market price.
    (d) unduplicated output of the economy at basic price.

68. Poverty line in India was based on the data from which of the following
    1. Consumer Expenditure Surveys of National Sample Survey Office (NSO)
    2. Health Survey of NSSO
    3. National Family Health Survey

    Select the correct answer using the code given below:
    (a) 1 and 3 only (b) 2 and 3 only
    (c) 1 only (d) 3 only

69. The statement "Growth rate of the quarterly estimate of GDP is 10%" means
    (a) economy has grown by 10% from the last month of the year.
    (b) economy has grown by 10% over the same month in the previous year.
    (c) eonomy has grown by 10% over the same quarter in the previous year.
    (d) economy has grown by 10% over the previous quarter in the same year.

70. Which are the division of National Sample Survey Office?
    1. Survey Design and Research Division (SDRD)
    2. Field Operation Division (FOD)
    3. Data Processing Division (DPD)
    4. Survey Coordination Division (SCD)

    Select the correct answer using the code given below:
    (a) 1 and 2 only (b) 3 and 4 only
    (c) 1, 2 and 3 only (d) 1, 2, 3 and 4

71. Merchandise Trade Statistics as collected by Directorate General of Commerical Intelligence and Statistics (DGCI&S) is compled from bills submitted by importers and exporters. Thus, it is an example of

(a) statistics collected through Survey. (b) administrative statistics.
(c) statistics collected through Census. (d) statistics collected through mixed mode.

72. In Indian official statistics, the output of agriculture crops is estimated using which one of the following approaches?
(a) Market arrivals + Farmers retention
(b) Area under crop × productivity × prices
(c) Sample surveys of farmers production
(d) Compilation of village level statistics

73. Which one of the following is not correctly matched?

	Index	Base Year
(a)	CPI-IW	2016
(b)	CPI (R and U)	2012
(c)	CPI-AL/RL	2015
(d)	WPI	2011-12

74. Which one of the following measures is known as National Income?
(a) GDP at market price (b) GVA at basic price
(c) GNI at basic price (d) NNI at basic price

75. Consider the following:
1. GDP
2. IMR
3. Dropout rate
4. CPI
5. WPI

Which of the above are official statistics?
(a) 2, 4 and 5 only (b) 1, 2, 4 and 5 only
(c) 1 and 3 only (d) 1, 2, 3, 4 and 5

76. Who are authorised to compile official statistics in India?
1. Central Goverment
2. State Government
3. Panchayat Raj Institutions/Urban Local Bodies

Select the correct answer using the code given below:
(a) 1 and 2 only (b) 2 and 3 only
(c) 1 and 3 only (d) 1, 2 and 3

77. Collection of statistics for different subject specific areas (such as Agriculture, Labour Health, Commerce) vests with which one of the following agencies?

(a) Ministry of Statistics and Programme Implementation

(b) NITI Aayog

(c) Ministry of Finance

(d) Corresponding Administrative Ministry

78. The National Statistical Commission (NSC) was set up in 2005 through

(a) a Constitutional Amendment.

(b) a Goverment Resolution

(c) an executive order.

(d) an internal notification of the Ministry of Statistics and Programme Implementation.

79. For which of the following purpose is NSSO data not used?

(a) Poverty estimations and fixing poverty line

(b) Estimation of contribution of unorganised sector

(c) Fixing minimum support price of major crops

(d) Employment and unemployment scenario

80. Consider the following statements with regard to Consumer Price Index (CPI):

1. It is measure of the average change in prices over time that consumers pay for a basket of goods and services.
2. It is calculated using prices of a sample of representative items whose prices are collected periodically.
3. It may be interpreted as a measure of both inflation and deflation.

Which of the above statements are correct?

(a) 1 and 2 only (b) 2 and 3 only

(c) 1 and 3 only (d) 1, 2 and 3

STATISTICS - II
2019

Time Allowed : Two Hours | *Maximum Marks: 200*

INSTRUCTIONS

1. IMMEDIATELY AFTER THE COMMENCEMENT OF THE EXAMINATION, YO SHOULD CHECK THAT THIS TEST BOOKLET *DOES NOT* HAVE ANY UNPRINTED OR TORN OR MISSING PAGES OR ITEMS, ETC. IF SO, GET IT REPLACE BY A COMPLETE TEST BOOKLET.
2. **Please note that it is the candidate'sresponsibility to encode and fill in the Roll Number and Test Booklet Series A, B, C or D carefully and without any omission or discrepancy at the appropriate places in the OMR Answer Sheet. Any omission/discrepancy will render the Answer sheet liable for rejection.**
3. You have to enter your Roll Number on the Test Booklet in the Box provided alongside. *DO NOT* write *anything else* on the Test Booklet.
4. This Test Booklet contains **80** items (questions).Each item comprises four responses (answers). You will select the response which you want to mark on the Answer Sheet. In case you feel that there is more than one correct response, mark the response which you consider the best. In any case, choose *ONLY ONE* response for each item.
5. You have to mark all your responses *ONLY* on the separate Answer Sheet provided. See directions in the Answer Sheet.
6. All items carry equal marks.
7. Before you proceed to mark in the Answer Sheet the response to various in the Test Booklet, you have to fill in some particulars in the Answer Sheet as per intructions sent to you with your Admission Certificate.
8. After you have complited filling in all your responses on the Answer Sheet and the examination has concluded, you should hand over to the Invigilator *only the Answer Sheet*. You are permitted to take away with you the Test Booklet.
9. Sheets for rough work are appended in the Test Booklet at the end.
10. **Penalty for wrong answers:**

    THERE WILL BE PENALTY FOR WRONG ANSWERS MARKED BY A CANDIDATE IN THE OBJECTIVE TYPE QUSTION PAPERS.

    (i) There are four alternatives for the answer to every question. For each question for which a wrong answer has been given by the candidate, **one-third** of the marks assigned to that question will be deducted as penalty.

    (ii) If a candidate gives more than one answer, it will be treated as a **wrong answer** even if one of the given answers happens to be correct and there will be same penalty as above to that question.

    (iii) If a question is left blamk,i.e., no answer is given by the candidate, there will be **no penalty** for that question.

DO NOT OPEN THIS TEST BOOKLET UNTIL YOU ARE TOLD TO DO SO

1. If y_1, y_2, y_3 and y_4 are independent with
   $E(y_1) = E(E(y_2) = (\theta_1 + \theta_2)$,
   $E(y_3) = E(y_4) = (\theta_1 + \theta_3)$, and
   $V(y_i) = \sigma^2$, i = 1, 2, 3 and 4. For estimability of parametric function $l'\theta = l_1\theta_1 + l_2\theta_2 + l_3\theta_3$, consider the following conditions:
   1. $l_1 = l_2 + l_3$
   2. $l_2 = l_1 + l_3$
   3. $l_3 = l_1 + l_2$

   Which of the above condition(s) is/are correct?
   (a) 1 only (b) 2 only
   (c) 3 only (d) 1, 2 and 3
2. Let an $n \times 1$ vector $y \sim N(X\beta, \sigma^2 I)$ where X is an $n \times p$ matrix. Let $H = (h_{ij}) = X(X'X)^{-1} X'$ be an $n \times n$ matrix. Let $e = y - \hat{y}$; $\hat{y} = X\hat{\beta}$ be the $n \times 1$ residual vector where $\hat{\beta}$ is the least squares estimate of β. Then which one of the following is not correct?
   (a) Rank (H) = p (b) $0 < h_{ij} < 1; 1 \leq i \leq n$
   (c) $V(\hat{y}) = \sigma^2 H$ (d) $Cov(e_i, e_j) = \sigma^2 h_{ij}$
3. For n observations $(x_1, y_1), (x_2, y_2), ..., (x_n, y_n)$ two models were fitted.
   1. $y_i = \alpha + \beta x_i + \text{error}; i = 1, 2, ..., n$
   2. $y_i = \alpha + \beta x_i + \gamma x_i^2 + \text{error}; i = 1, 2, ..., n$

   Let $\hat{Y}_i$ and $\hat{Y}^*_i$ be the estimated values of y_i from the two models and if $E = \sum_{i=1}^{n}(y_i - \hat{y}_i)^2$ $E^* = \sum_{i=1}^{n}(y_i - \hat{y}^*_i)^2$, then which one fo the following is correct?
   (a) $E \geq E^*$ (b) $E \leq E^*$
   (c) $E = E^*$ (d) It is possible that $E = 0, E^* > 0$
4. Let Y_1, Y_2, Y_3 and Y_4 be uncorrelated observations. It is given that
   1. $E(Y_1) = \beta_1 + \beta_2 + \beta_3 = E(Y_2)$
      $E(Y_3) = \beta_1 - \beta_2 = E(Y_4)$
   2. $V(Y_i) = \sigma^2; i = 1, 2, 3, 4$

   Define $e_1 = \frac{1}{\sqrt{2}}(Y_1 - Y_2)$ and
   $e_2 = \frac{1}{\sqrt{2}}(Y_3 - Y_4)$. Then an unbiased estimator of σ^2 is given by
   (a) $\frac{1}{2}(e_1^2 - e_2^2)$ (b) $\frac{1}{2}(e_1^2 + e_2^2)$
   (c) $e_1^2 + e_2^2$ (d) $\frac{1}{4}(e_1^2 + e_2^2)$

5. Consider the following ANOVA table:

Source of variation	Degrees of freedom	Sum of squares	Mean SS	Test statistic
Treatment	w	x	y	5.22
Error	12	z	25	
Total	14	561		

The values of w, x, y and z that compete the above table are respectively

(a) 2, 261, 130.5, 300
(b) 2, 300, 150, 261
(c) 2, 250, 125, 311
(d)) 2, 311, 155.5,, 250

6. For estimating the mode of a normal distribution, which one fo the following is the most estimator?

(a) Sample mean
(b) Sample median
(c) Sample mode
(d) Largest observatin

7. Let $X_1, X_2, X_3, ..., X_n$ be iid random variables with $E(X_i) = \mu$ and $E(X_i^2) < \infty$. Then the consistent estimator for μ is

(a) $\frac{2i^2}{n(n+1)} \sum x_i$
(b) $\frac{2}{n(n+1)} \sum ix_i$
(c) $\frac{2i}{n(n+1)} \sum x_i$
(d) $\frac{2}{n(n+1)} \sum i^2 x_i$

8. If $X_1, X_2, X_3, ..., X_n$ are iid random variables from $N(\mu, \sigma^2)$, then consider the following statements:

1. $\overline{X} = \frac{1}{n} \sum i^2 x_i$ is an unbiased and consistent estimator of μ.

2. $S^2 = \frac{1}{n-1} \sum (X_i - \overline{X})^2$ is an unbiased and consistent estimator of σ^2.

3. $S_1^2 = \frac{1}{n} \sum (X_i - \overline{X})^2$ is an unbiased and consistent estimator of σ^2.

Which of the above statements are correct?

(a) 1 and 2 only
(b) 1 and 3 only
(c) 2 and 3 only
(d) 1, 2 and 3

9. The maximum likelihood estimators (mle) of the parameters α and λ (λ being large) of the distribution $f(x) = \frac{1}{\Gamma(\lambda)} \left(\frac{\lambda}{\alpha}\right)^{\lambda} e^{-\frac{\lambda x}{\alpha}} x^{\lambda - 1}; 0 < x < \infty, \lambda > 0$ are respectively

[Given that $\frac{\partial}{\partial \lambda} \log \Gamma(\lambda) = \log \lambda - \frac{1}{2\lambda}$]

(a) G and $\dfrac{1}{2\log\left(\dfrac{\overline{x}}{G}\right)}$

(b) $\overline{x}$ and $\dfrac{1}{2\log\left(\dfrac{G}{\overline{x}}\right)}$

(c) $\overline{x}$ and $\dfrac{1}{2\log\left(\dfrac{\overline{x}}{G}\right)}$

(d) G and $\dfrac{1}{2\log\left(\dfrac{G}{\overline{x}}\right)}$

where G is the geometric mean.

10. Let the random variables $X_1, X_2, X_3, ..., X_n$ follow U(θ, θ + 1). Then whch one of the following statements is not correct?

(a) $\left(\overline{X}-\dfrac{1}{2}\right)$ is an unbiased estimate of θ

(b) UMVUE will not exist for θ

(c) Any value of θ in the interval $[X^{-1}_{(n)}, X_{(1)}]$ is an mle

(d) $X_{(1)}$ is an mle which is sufficient for θ

11. Let $X_1, X_2, X_3, ..., X_n$ be a ranom sample from a normal distribution N(μθ); where θ is unknown. Then the statistic

$$T=\sum_{i=1}^{n}(x_i-\mu)^2$$

(a) sufficcient but not complete

(b) complete but not sufficient

(c) both sufficient and complete

(d) neither sufficient nor complete

12. Consider a random sample of size 64 from a normal population with mean μ and standard deviation σ (unknown). The computations obtained from 64 sample observations are

$\overline{x}=60.4$ and $\sum_{i=1}^{64}(x_i-\overline{x})^2=6300$. The 95% confidence interval for μ is

(a) (58.44, 62.36)

(b) (57.95, 62.85)

(c) (50.4, 70.4)

(d) (58.32, 62.48)

13. Let X be a random variable with N(μ, σ²), μ and σ² are unknown. Then, which one of the following is a simple hypothesis?

(a) $\mu=\mu_0, \sigma^2\neq\sigma_0^2$

(b) $\mu=\mu_0, \sigma^2=\sigma_0^2$

(c) $\mu>\mu_0, \sigma^2=\sigma_0^2$

(d) $\mu=\mu_0, \sigma^2<\sigma_0^2$

where μ_0 and σ_0^2 are known

14. Let X be a random variable from U(0, θ). Consider the critical region ω = {x: x > 1} to test H_0: θ = 1 against H_1: θ = 2. The size of the test is

(a) 0.05

(b) 0.01

(c) 0

(d) 0.1

15. Let X and Y be two independent random variables with $U(0, \theta)$. We are testing the hypothesis $H_0: \theta = 1$ against $H_1: \theta = 2$. The probability of type-I error and the power of the test based on the critical region $[X + Y > 0.75]$ are respectively

(a) 0.65, 0.85
(b) 0.35, 0.93
(c) 0.72, 0.93
(d) 0.72, 0.85

16. To obtain a critical region (or cut-off point) in testing a statistial hypothesis, we need the distribution of a test statistic

(a) Under H_0
(b) Without any assumption
(c) Under H_1
(d) All of the above

17. Consider the following statements:

1. A UMP test unbiased.
2. A consistent test is UMP.
3. A UMP test is biased.
4. An unbiased test need not be UMP.

Which of the above statements is/are correct?

(a) 1 only
(b) 2 and 3 only
(c) 1 and 2 only
(d) 1, 2 and 4

18. Let X_1, X_2 be iid random variables from $U(0, \theta)$. The power of the UMP test foro testing $H_0: \theta = 2$ against $H_1: \theta > 2$ and $H_0: \theta = 2$ against $H_1: \theta \neq 2$ is

(a) $1-\left(\frac{2}{\theta_1}\right)^2(1-\alpha)$
(b) α
(c) $1-\left(\frac{\theta_1}{2}\right)^2(1-\alpha)$
(d) $1-\alpha$

(Assume α is the size of the test and θ_1 is any value of θ under H_1)

19. Let $x_1, x_2, x_3, \ldots, x_n$ be a random sample from $N(\mu, 1)$ distribution. For testing $H_0: \mu = \mu_0$ against $H_1: \mu = \mu_1 > \mu_1$, the best critical region by NP lemma is

(a) $\overline{x} \geq \frac{1}{2}(\mu_0 + \mu_1) + \frac{\log k_\alpha}{n(\mu_1 - \mu_0)}$
(b) $\overline{x} \leq \frac{1}{2}(\mu_0 + \mu_1) + \frac{\log k_\alpha}{n(\mu_1 - \mu_0)}$
(c) $\overline{x} \geq \frac{1}{2}(\mu_1 - \mu_0) + \frac{\log k_\alpha}{n(\mu_1 - \mu_0)}$
(d) $\overline{x} \leq \frac{1}{2}(\mu_1 - \mu_0) + \frac{\log k_\alpha}{n(\mu_1 - \mu_0)}$

20. Let $x_1, x_2, x_3, \ldots, x_n$ be a random sample from an exponential distribution with pdf $f(x, \theta) = \frac{1}{\theta}e^{-\frac{x}{\theta}}$, $x > 0$, $\theta > 0$. For testing the hypothesis $H_0: \theta = \theta_0$ against the alternative $H_1: \theta = \theta_1(\theta_0)$, the best critical region of size α is

(a) $\left\{x \mid \sum x_i > \frac{\theta_0}{2}\chi^2_{2n,\alpha}\right\}$ (b) $\left\{x \mid \sum x_i < \frac{\theta_0}{2}\chi^2_{2n,\alpha}\right\}$

(c) $\left\{x \mid \sum x_i > \frac{\theta_0}{2}\chi^2_{2n-1,\alpha}\right\}$ (d) None of the above

21. In general linear regression model $y = X\beta + u$; $u \sim N(0, \sigma^2 I)$, e is an $n \times 1$ residual vector and $\hat{y}$ is the estimated value of y. Define $H = X(X'X)^{-1}X'$. Then which of the following statements are correct?
 1. $V(e) = V(y) + V(\hat{y})$ where V(.) represents var-cow matrix
 2. $Cov(y, \hat{y}) = \sigma^2 H$
 3. $V(e) = \sigma^2(I - H)$

 Select the correct answer using the code given below:

 (a) 1 and 2 only (b) 1 and 3 only
 (c) 2 and 3 only (d) 1, 2 and 3

22. For the Gauss Markov model $y = X\beta + u$; $V(u) = \sigma^2 I_n$. Let rank (X) = r and $l'_i\beta$ are m linearly independent estimable functions of β such that $l'_i\beta = \xi_i$; i = 1, 2, ..., m, where l_i and ξ_i are known. Define RSS_1 as the residual sum of squares subject to the conditions $l'_i\beta = \xi_i$; i = 1, 2, .., m and RSS as the unconditional residual sum of squares. Then which of the following statements are correct?
 1. $(RSS_1 - RSS)\sigma^2$ is distributed as a non-central chi square with m degrees of freedom.
 2. RSS_1/RSS is distributed as central F with m and $(n - r)$ degrees of freedom.
 3. $(RSS_1 - RSS)$ and RSS are independently distributed.

 Selected the correct answer using the code given below:

 (a) 1 and 2 only (b) 1 and 3 only
 (c) 2 and 3 only (d) 1, 2 and 3

23. If A^- is any g-inverse of A and $A^-A = H$, then consider the following statements:
 1. H is idempotent
 2. AH = A
 3. rank (A) = rank (H) = trace (H)

 Which of the above statements are correct?

 (a) 1 and 2 only (b) 2 and 3 only
 (c) 1 and 3 only (d) 1, 2 and 3

24. Which of the following are the forms of the central limit theorem?
 1. Lindeberg-Feller theorem
 2. Lyapunov Theorem
 3. Khinchin Theorem

Select the correct answer using the coda given below:

(a) 1 only (b) 1 and 2

(c) 1 and 3 (d) 2 and 3

25. For the linear model $y = X\beta + u$; $E(u) = 0$, $V(u) = \sigma^2 I$, $\hat{\beta} = (X'X)^{-1} X'y$. Which of the following statements are correct?

1. $V(\hat{\beta}) = \sigma^2 (X'X)^{-1}$.
2. $\hat{\beta}$ is the BLUE for β.
3. Residual mean square is an unbiased estimator of σ^2.

Select the correct answer using the code given below:

(a) 1 and 2 only (b) 2 and 3 only

(c) 1 and 3 only (d) 1, 2 and 3

26. Suppose $(x_1, y_1), (x_2, y_2), ..., (x_n, y_n)$ be n observations on certain geographical region, related through the model $y_i = \alpha + \beta x_i + u_i$, $i = 1, 2, ..., n$ where u_i's are the random errors and both x_i and y_i are measured in squares metres. Let $\hat{\alpha}$ and $\hat{\beta}$ be the least squares estimators of α and β respectively. If the results are to be reported in square feet then the values of

(a) $\hat{\alpha}$ may change but $\hat{\beta}$ will not change

(b) $\hat{\beta}$ may change but $\hat{\alpha}$ will not change

(c) both $\hat{\alpha}$ and $\hat{\beta}$ will change

(d) both $\hat{\alpha}$ and $\hat{\beta}$ will not change

27. For the model $y = X\beta + u$ where y is an $n \times 1$ vector, X is an $n \times p$ matrix, β is an $n \times 1$ vector of unknown coefficients and u is the disturbance vector, if $\hat{\beta}$ is the solution of the equation of the equation $X'X\hat{\beta} = X'y$, then which of the following statemewnts is/are correct?

1. If $C'\beta$ is estimable, then $C'\hat{\beta}$ is the BLUE.
2. All linear parametric functions are estimable iff Rank (X) > p.
3. The hypothesis H_0: $L\beta = \xi$ here L is an $r \times p$ matrix and ξ is an $r \times 1$ vector of known constants, may be tested using Snedecor's F statistic.

Select the correct answer using the code given below:

(a) 1 only (b) 2 only

(c) 1 and 3 (d) 2 and 3

28. For 5 observations from a two variable linear regression model, it is observed that $\Sigma x_i = 0$, $\Sigma y_i = 0$, $\Sigma y_i = 5$, $\Sigma x_i y_i = 12$, $\Sigma x_i^2 = 10$, $\Sigma y_i^2 = 20$. The estimated error variance from the above observations, for the model is

(a) 0.1 (b) 0.2

(c) 0.3 (d) 1.0

29. Consider thhe model $E(y_1) = 2\beta_1 + \beta_2$, $E(y_2) = \beta_1 - \beta_2$ and $E(y_3) = \beta_1 - \alpha\beta_2$ with usual assumptions of linear models. The value of α such that the best linear unbiased estimators of β_1 and β_2 are uncorrelated, is

(a) -1 (b) $+1$

(c) 0 (d) $+2$

30. For Gauss-Markov Linear (GML) model $E(y_i) = \alpha_{i1}\beta_1 + \alpha_{i2}\beta_2 + ... + \alpha_{ip}\beta_p$ where $i = 1, 2, 3, ... n$; $V(y_i) = \sigma^2$ and $\text{cov}(y_i, y_j) = 0\ (i \neq j)$

Consider the following statements:

1. If $\alpha_1, \alpha_2, ..., \alpha_p$, are linearly independent ($p \leq n$), then GML model will be of full rank.
2. If all the parameters β's are fixed constants, then GML model is called a fixed effect model.

Which of the above statements is/are correct?

(a) 1 only (b) 1 only

(c) Both 1 and 2 (d) Neither 1 nor 2

31. Let $X_1, X_2, X_3, ..., X_n$ be iid $N(\mu, \sigma^2)$ and $\hat{\mu}$ and $\hat{\sigma}^2$ are the mle of μ and σ^2 respectively. Consider the following statements:

1. $\hat{\mu}$ is an unbiased estimator of μ.
2. $\hat{\sigma}^2$ is an unbiased estimator of σ^2.

Which of the above statements is/are correct?

(a) 1 only (b) 2 only

(c) Both 1 and 2 (d) Neither 1 nor 2

32. Let L be the likelihood function differentiable at least twice and $\theta = \hat{\theta}$ be a solution of the equation $\frac{\partial(\log L)}{\partial\theta} = 0$. IF

$$1 = \left[\frac{\partial^2(\log L)}{\partial\theta^2}\right]_{\theta=\hat{\theta}}$$, then $\hat{\theta}$ is a maximum likelihood estimate of θ if

(a) $1 < 0$ (b) $1 > 0$

(c) $1 = 0$ (d) $1 \geq 0$

33. If X_1, X_2, X_3 be iid random variables with $U(\theta, \theta^2)$; $\theta > 1$. Then maximum likelihood estimator (mle) of θ is

(a) $X_{(1)}$ (b) $\sqrt{X_{(3)}}$

(c) $\sqrt{X_{(1)}}$ (d) $\alpha X_{(1)} + (1-\alpha) X_{(3)}$

34. If t is an unbiased estimator of θ, then the minimum variance bound is attained if

(a) $\frac{\partial^2 \log L}{\partial \theta^2} = \frac{t-\theta}{\lambda}$ (b) $\frac{\partial \log L}{\partial \theta} = \frac{t}{\theta}$

(c) $\frac{\partial^2 \log L}{\partial \theta^2} = \frac{t-\theta}{\theta}$ (d) $\frac{\partial \log L}{\partial \theta} = \frac{t-\theta}{\lambda}$

(where λ is free from sample values but may depend on θ)

35. The estimator whose variance attains the Cramer — Rao lower bound estimating the variance of a normal distribution with mean zero is

(a) $\frac{1}{n-1}\sum(X_i - \bar{X})^2$ (b) $\frac{1}{n}\sum(X_i - \bar{X})^2$

(c) $\frac{1}{n}\sum X_i^2$ (d) $\frac{1}{n-1}\sum X_i^2$

36. Let $X_1, X_2, X_3, ..., X_n$ be iid random variables with U(0, θ). The CR lower bound for any unbiased estimator of θ

(a) does not exist (b) is $X_{(n)}$

(c) is $\frac{\theta}{n}$ (d) is $\frac{1}{\theta}$

37. Let $x_1, x_2, x_3, ..., X_n$ be a random sample from a population with pdf

$$f(x, \theta) = \begin{cases} \frac{1}{\theta}\exp\left(-\frac{x}{\theta}\right); 0 < x < \infty \\ 0; \text{otherwise} \end{cases}$$

The Cramer — Rao lower bound to the variance of an unbiased estimator of θ is

(a) $\frac{\theta}{n}$ (b) θ^2

(c) $\frac{\theta^2}{n}$ (d) θ

38. Let X_1, X_2 be iid random variables with N(θ, 1). Then $E(\bar{X} | X_1)$, where $\bar{X} = \frac{X_1 + X_2}{2}$ is

(a) X_1 (b) θ

(c) $X_1 + \theta$ (d) 55%, 79%

39. Let (X_1, X_2) denote a random sample of size 2 from a binomial distribution with parameters 2 and θ, $0 < \theta < 1$. The sufficient statistic for θ is given by

(a) $X_1 - X_2$ (b) $X_1 + X_2$

(c) $\frac{X_1}{X_2}$ (d) $\frac{X_2}{X_1}$

40. The minimum variance unbiased estimator of θ^2 based on a sample of size n from $N(\theta, 1)$ is

(a) $\bar{X}^2 - \frac{1}{n}$ (b) $\bar{X}^2 + \frac{1}{n}$

(c) $\frac{\sum (X_i - \bar{X})^2}{n}$ (d) $\frac{\sum (X_i - \bar{X})^2}{n-1}$

41. If $X_1, X_2, X_3, ..., X_n$ are iid random variables with $N(\theta, \theta^2)$ then $E\left(\frac{n\bar{X}^2}{n+1} - S^2\right)$, where $S^2 = \frac{\sum (X_i - \bar{X})^2}{n-1}$, is equal to

(a) 0 (b) θ

(c) θ^2 (d) $\frac{\theta}{n}$

42. The family of distributionds θ is

1. Symmetric
2. Complete

Which of the above statements is/are correct?

(a) 1 only (b) 2 only

(c) Both 1 and 2 (d) Neither 1 nor 2

43. If T_1 is a sufficient of θ and T_2 is an unbiased estimator of θ, then an improved estimator of θ is terms of its efficiency is

(a) $E(T_1 T_2)$ (b) $E(T_1 + T_2)$

(c) $E(T_1 | T_2)$ (d) $E(T_2 | T_1)$

44. If, for a given α, $0 \le \alpha \le 1$, non-randomised Neyman-Pearson and likelihood ratio test of a simple hypothesis against a simple alternative exists, then which one of the following is correct?

(a) They are one and the same (b) They are equivalent

(c) They are exactly opposite (d) One cannot say anything about it

45. Let $X_1, X_2, X_3, ..., X_n$ be iid with density $f(x, \mu) = e^{-(x-\mu)}, x \ge \mu$. The MLE of $P(X_1 \ge t)$ for $t > \mu$ is given by

(a) $e^{-(t-\bar{x})}$

(b) $e^{-(t-X_{(1)})}$ where $X_{(1)} = \min (X_1, X_2, X_3, ..., X_n)$

(c) $e^{-(t-X_{(n)})}$ where $X_{(n)} = \min (X_1, X_2, X_3, ..., X_n)$

(d) $e^{-\left(t-\left(\frac{X_{(1)} + X_{(n)}}{2}\right)\right)}$

46. If for an estimator t_n of the parameter θ, $\lim_{n\to\infty} P\{|t_n - \theta| < \varepsilon\} = 1$ for all $\varepsilon > 0$, then

(a) t_n is a consitent estimator of θ
(b) t_n is an unbiased estimator of θ
(c) t_n is a sufficient estimator of θ
(d) t_n is an effiicient estimator of θ

47. Let X be a Bernoulli random variable with parameter p and let h(p) = p(1 – p). Then maximum likelihood estimator of h(p), based on a sample of size n, is

(a) $\sum_{i=1}^{n} X_i \left(1 - \sum_{i=1}^{n} X_i\right)$
(b) $\frac{\bar{X}^2}{n^2}$
(c) $\bar{X}(1 - \bar{X})$
(d) $\frac{\bar{X}}{n}\left(1 - \frac{\bar{X}}{n}\right)$

48. If S(X) is a complete statistic and T(X) is ancillary statistic, then which one of the following statements is correct?

(a) S(X) and T(X) are distributionally dependent
(b) S(X) and T(X) are functionally dependent
(c) S(X) and T(X) are statistically independent
(d) None of the above

49. A statistic T(x) for θ is said to be ancillary if

(a) T(x) is independent of θ
(b) T(x) is dependent on θ
(c) The distribution of T(x) is independent of θ
(d) The distribution of T(x) dependents on θ

50. Suppose T* is the most efficient estimate of θ and T is another estimate whose efficiency is e. Then the correlation coefficient between T* and T will be

(a) – e
(b) e^2
(c) $e^{1/2}$
(d) e

51. Which of the following provides a quick snapshot of manufacturing sector performance in India?

(a) Wholesale Price Index
(b) Annual Survey of Industries
(c) Index of Industrial Production
(d) Wage Rate Index

52. In NSSO survey, a person would be considered as "not in labour force" if he/she

1. is not working
2. is not seeking work.
3. is not available for wor.
4. had a minor accident and so could not go to work for last 7 days.

Select the correct answer using the code given below:

(a) 4 only (b) 1 and 2 only

(c) 1, 2, 3 and 4 (d) 1, 2 and 3 only

53. Which of following are correct regarding Sustainable Development Goals (SDGs) endorsed by UNDP?

 1. SDGs came into effect in January 2016.
 2. SDGs are adopted by more than 150 countries.
 3. SDGs are mandatory to follow by member countries.
 4. SDGs are 17 in number.

 Select the correct answer using the code given below:

 (a) 1, 2 and 3 (b) 2, 3 and 4

 (c) 1, 2 and 4 (d) 1, 3 and 4

54. Which among the followinng is not an activity of CSO?

 (a) Compilation of National Accounts

 (b) Conducting Economic Census

 (c) Conducting Consumer Expenditure Survey

 (d) Training of Statistical Personnel

55. Which of the following is not a function of National Statistical Commission (NSC)?

 (a) To conduct NSSO surveys

 (b) To evolve national policies and prioties relating to the statistical system

 (c) To evolve standard statistical concepts

 (d) To identify the core statistics which are of national importance

56. The principle source of Industrial Statistics in India is

 (a) Index of Industrial Production (IIP)

 (b) Annual Survey of Industries (ASI)

 (c) Economic Census

 (d) Micro, Small and Medium Enterprises (MSME) Census

57. National income estimation is the responsibility of

 (a) NSSO (b) CSO

 (c) Finance Ministry (d) National Income Committee

58. Which of the following activities are undertaken by the office of Registrar General of India?

 1. Conducting population census in India
 2. Conducting Sampling Registration System in India
 3. Preparing and maintaining National Register of Indian Citizens (NRIC)

4. Conducting National Sample Survey Organization (NSSO) surveys
5. Conducting Economic Census

Select the correct answer using the code given below:

(a) 1, 2 and 5 only (b) 1, 2 and 3 only
(c) 1, 2, 3, 4 and 5 (d) 3, 4 and 5 only

59. Indian statistical system is
 1. Centralized
 2. Laterally decentralized
 3. Vertically decentralized

 Which of the above statements is/are correct?

 (a) 1 only (b) 2 only
 (c) 3 only (d) 2 and 3

60. Nodal Ministry of Statistical system in India is
 (a) Ministry of Human Resource Development
 (b) Ministry of Statistics and Programme Implementation
 (c) Directorate of Economics and Statistics, Ministry of Agriculture
 (d) None of the above

61. A test in which probability of rejecting H_0 when it is not true is more than that of rejecting it when it is true, is said to be
 (a) Unbiased (b) Biased
 (c) Consistent (d) Uniformly most powerful

62. Let X be a single observation from f(x). To test H_0: $f(x) = f_0(x)$ for all x against H_1: $f(x) = f_1(x)$ for all x, consider the test with test function

$$\phi(x) = \begin{cases} 1, & \text{if } f_1(x) > kf_0(x) \\ \gamma, & \text{if } f_1(x) = kf_0(x) \\ 0, & \text{if } f_1(x) < kf_0(x) \end{cases}$$

 Suppose that $\gamma > 0$, then which one of the following is correct?
 (a) $\phi(x)$ is a non-randomised test function
 (b) $\phi(x)$ is neither a non-randomised nor a randomised test function
 (c) $\phi(x)$ is a randomised test function
 (d) None of the above

63. Let $X_1, X_2, X_3, .., X_n$ be iid random variables following $N(\theta, 1)$. The unifromly most powerful unbiased test (UMPU test) for testing $H_0: \theta = \theta_0$ against the alternative $H_1: \theta \neq \theta_0$ of size α, is

(a) $\phi(x) = \begin{cases} 1; & \bar{X} < \theta_0 - \frac{Z_{\frac{\alpha}{2}}}{\sqrt{n}} \text{ or } \bar{X} > \theta_0 + \frac{Z_{\frac{\alpha}{2}}}{\sqrt{n}} \\ 0; & \text{otherwise} \end{cases}$

(b) $\phi(x) = \begin{cases} 1; & \bar{X} < \theta_0 - \frac{Z_{\alpha}}{\sqrt{n}} \text{ or } \bar{X} > \theta_0 + \frac{Z_{1-\alpha}}{\sqrt{n}} \\ 0; & \text{otherwise} \end{cases}$

(c) $\phi(x) = \begin{cases} 1; & \bar{X} < \theta_0 - \frac{Z_{\alpha}}{n} \text{ or } \bar{X} > \theta_0 + \frac{Z_{1-\alpha}}{n} \\ 0; & \text{otherwise} \end{cases}$

(d) $\phi(x) = \begin{cases} 1; & \bar{X} < \theta_0 - \frac{Z_{\frac{\alpha}{2}}}{n} \text{ or } \bar{X} > \theta_0 + \frac{Z_{\frac{\alpha}{2}}}{n} \\ 0; & \text{otherwise} \end{cases}$

64. Let X have the distribution

$f(x, \theta) = \theta^x(1-\theta)^{1-x}; x = 0, 1; 0 < \theta < 1$. For testing $H_0: \theta = \theta_0$ against the alternative $H_1: \theta = \theta_1$, if Z $= \log\left\{\frac{f(x, \theta_1)}{f(x, \theta_0)}\right\}$, then E(Z) is equal to

(a) $\theta \log\left\{\frac{\theta_1(1-\theta_0)}{\theta_0(1-\theta_1)}\right\}$

(b) $\theta \log\left\{\frac{1-\theta_1}{1-\theta_0}\right\}$

(c) $\theta \log\left\{\frac{\theta_1(1-\theta_0)}{\theta_0(1-\theta_1)}\right\} + \theta \log\left\{\frac{1-\theta_1}{1-\theta_0}\right\}$

(d) $\theta \log\left\{\frac{\theta_1(1-\theta_0)}{\theta_0(1-\theta_1)}\right\} + \theta \log\left\{\frac{1-\theta_1}{1-\theta_0}\right\}$

65. Two samples of size 15 were selected from $N(\mu, \sigma^2)$. The degrees of freedom for testing the difference between two population means will be

(a) 14
(b) 28
(c) 29
(d) 30

66. If $\bar{X}$ is the mean of a random sample of size n from a distribution with mean μ and variance 1, then an unbiased estimator for μ^2 is

(a) $\bar{X}^2$
(b) $\bar{X}^2 + \frac{1}{n}$
(c) $\bar{X}^2 - \frac{1}{n}$
(d) $\left(\bar{X} - \frac{1}{n}\right)^2$

67. Consider the following statements in respect of iid Poisson (λ) variates $x_1, x_2, x_3, ..., x_n$

1. $T = \Sigma x_i$ is complete sufficient for λ
2. $T = \Sigma x_i$ is the MLE of λ

Which of the above statements is/are correct?

(a) 1 only (b) 2 only

(c) Both 1 and 2 (d) Neither 1 nor 2

68. Let (X_1, X_2) be iid random variables with $N(\theta,1)$. Then number of unbiased estimators of θ is

(a) 1 (b) 3

(c) 5 (d) Infinite

69. Let $x_1, x_2, x_3, ..., x_n$ be a random sample of size n from Cauchy distribution with pdf $f(x, \theta) = \frac{1}{\pi[1+(x-\theta)^2]}, -\infty < x < \infty$. Then the minimum variance bound estimator

(a) is Σxi (b) is $\bar{x}$

(c) is s^2 (d) does not exist

70. Let $x_1, x_2, x_3, ..., x_n$ be a random sample of size n from Bernoulli (p) distribution. The UMVUE of $\frac{1}{p}$

(a) is $\bar{x}$ (b) is $\frac{1}{\bar{x}}$

(c) is $\frac{1}{\Sigma x_i}$ (d) does not exist

71. Let $x_1, x_2, x_3, ..., x_n$ be a random smaple from a uniform population with pdf

$$f(x; \alpha, \beta) = \begin{cases} \frac{1}{\beta - \alpha}, & \alpha \le x \le \beta \\ 0, & \text{otherwise} \end{cases}$$

The sufficient statistic for the parameters

(a) will be x_1 and x_n (b) will be $x_{(1)}$ and $x_{(n)}$

(c) will be $\bar{x}$ and s^2 (d) will not exist

72. If X_1, X_2 be iid $P(\lambda)$ random variables, then which one of the following is correct?

(a) $X_1 + X_2$ is sufficient for λ (b) $X_1 + 2X_2$ is sufficient for λ

(c) $X_1 + X_2$ is unbiased for λ (d) $(X_1 + X_2)/2$ is not UMVUE for λ

73. The uniformly most powerful test for testing $H_0: X \sim f_0(x, \theta)$ against $H_1: X \sim f_1(x, \theta)$ if it exists, then

(a) it is unique (b) it is unique but power is greater than size

(c) it need not beunique (d) None of the above

74. The Bayes estimator of θ, when $X \sim f_\theta(x)$ and θ has prior distribution $\pi(\theta)$, for squared error loss function is

(a) Mean of the distribution, $f_\theta(x)$

(b) Mean of the prior distribution, $\pi(\theta)$

(c) Mean of the posterior distribution, $\pi(\theta|x)$

(d) Median of the posterior distribution, $\pi(\theta|x)$

75. Let $x_1, x_2, x_3, ..., x_n$ be a sample of size n from a population which follows Poisson (λ) distribution. Which of the following statements is/are correct?

1. Cramer – Rao bound to the variance of unbiased estimator of θ is $\frac{\theta}{n}$.
2. $\bar{x} = \frac{1}{n}\sum_{i=1}^{n} x_i$ is a minimum vaiance bound unbiased estimator of θ.

Select the correct answer using the code given below:

(a) 1 only (b) 2 only

(c) Both 1 and 2 (d) Neither 1 nor 2

76. Which one of the following divisions of CSO deals with Environment Statistics?

(a) Economic Statistics Division (b) National Accounts Division

(c) Social Statistics Division (d) Price Statistics Division

77. Which of t he following actions are correctly matched with the fundamental principal of Official Statistics?

1. A media publishes a wrong interpretation of data released by the goverment and so the government brings out an article with the correct interpretation – Prevention of Misuese (Fundamental Principle 4).
2. Government frames Collection of Statistics Act – Sources fo Official Statistics (Principal 5).
3. Unit level data is released and by principle of exclusion, an individual's data is publicly disclosed leading to violation of this fundamental principle – Confidentiality (Principle 6).

Select the correct answer using the code given below:

(a) 1 and 2 only (b) 2 and 3 only

(c) 1 and 3 only (d) 1, 2 and 3

78. The subjects to be covered under 76th round of NSS are

1. Disability
2. Drinking water, sanitation, hygiene and housing condtions
3. Household consumption expenditure

Select the correct answer using the code given below:

(a) 1 and 2 only (b) 1 and 3 only

(c) 2 and 3 only (d) 1, 2 and 3

79. Minimum Support Price (MSP) is recommended by

(a) Directorate of Economics and Statistics

(b) Directorate of Marketing and Inspection

(c) Commission for Agricultural Costs and Prices (CAS)

(d) None of the above

80. Which of the below mentioned data sources can be used as a sampling frame for another survey?

1. Population Census
2. National Famil Healty Survey
3. Situation Assessment Survey
4. Economic Census

Select the correct answer using the code given below:

(a) 2 and 3 only (b) 1 and 4 only

(c) 4 only (d) 1, 2 and 4

STATISTICS - II
2018

Time Allowed : Two Hours

Maximum Marks: 200

INSTRUCTIONS

1. IMMEDIATELY AFTER THE COMMENCEMENT OF THE EXAMINATION, YO SHOULD CHECK THAT THIS TEST BOOKLET *DOES NOT* HAVE ANY UNPRINTED OR TORN OR MISSING PAGES OR ITEMS, ETC. IF SO, GET IT REPLACE BY A COMPLETE TEST BOOKLET.
2. **Please note that it is the candidate'sresponsibility to encode and fill in the Roll Number and Test Booklet Series A, B, C or D carefully and without any omission or discrepancy at the appropriate places in the OMR Answer Sheet. Any omission/discrepancy will render the Answer sheet liable for rejection.**
3. You have to enter your Roll Number on the Test Booklet in the Box provided alongside. *DO NOT* write *anything else* on the Test Booklet.
4. This Test Booklet contains **80** items (questions).Each item comprises four responses (answers). You will select the response which you want to mark on the Answer Sheet. In case you feel that there is more than one correct response, mark the response which you consider the best. In any case, choose *ONLY ONE* response for each item.
5. You have to mark all your responses *ONLY* on the separate Answer Sheet provided. See directions in the Answer Sheet.
6. All items carry equal marks.
7. Before you proceed to mark in the Answer Sheet the response to various in the Test Booklet, you have to fill in some particulars in the Answer Sheet as per intructions sent to you with your Admission Certificate.
8. After you have complited filling in all your responses on the Answer Sheet and the examination has concluded, you should hand over to the Invigilator ***only the Answer Sheet***. You are permitted to take away with you the Test Booklet.
9. Sheets for rough work are appended in the Test Booklet at the end.
10. **Penalty for wrong answers:**

    THERE WILL BE PENALTY FOR WRONG ANSWERS MARKED BY A CANDIDATE IN THE OBJECTIVE TYPE QUSTION PAPERS.

    (i) There are four alternatives for the answer to every question. For each question for which a wrong answer has been given by the candidate, **one-third** of the marks assigned to that question will be deducted as penalty.

    (ii) If a candidate gives more than one answer, it will be treated as a **wrong answer** even if one of the given answers happens to be correct and there will be same penalty as above to that question.

    (iii) If a question is left blamk,i.e., no answer is given by the candidate, there will be **no penalty** for that question.

DO NOT OPEN THIS TEST BOOKLET UNTIL YOU ARE TOLD TO DO SO

1. Consider the model

$Y_1 = \beta_1 + \beta_2 + e_1$

$Y_2 = \beta_1 + \beta_3 + e_2$

$Y_3 = \beta_1 + \beta_2 + e_3$

Then the $\lambda_1\beta_1 + \lambda_2\beta_2 + \lambda_3\beta_3$ is estimable if and only if

(a) $\lambda_1 + \lambda_3 = \lambda_2$ (b) $\lambda_1 + \lambda_2 = \lambda_3$

(c) $\lambda_2 + \lambda_3 = \lambda_1$ (d) $\lambda_1 + \lambda_2 + \lambda_3 = C$

2. Consider the model

$y_1 = \beta_0 + \beta_1 x_i + e_i (i = 1, 2, 3)$

where $x_1 = -1$, $x_2 = 0$ and $x_3 = 1$. The best linear unbiased estimate of β_0 and β_1 is

(a) $\left(\bar{y}, \frac{y_3 - y_1}{2}\right)$ (b) $\left(\frac{y_2 - y_1}{2}, \frac{y_3 - y_1}{2}\right)$

(c) $\left(\bar{y}, \frac{y_2 - y_1}{2}\right)$ (d) $\left(\frac{y_1 + y_2}{2}, \bar{y}\right)$

where $\bar{y} = \frac{y_1 + y_2 + y_3}{2}$.

3. Consider the following statements:
   1. If multicollinearity exists, $(X'X)^{-1}$ cannot be computed.
   2. The method of least squares is a statiscal method.

   Which of the above statemetns is/are correct?

   (a) 1 only (b) 2 only

   (c) Both 1 and 2 (d) Neither 1 nor 2

4. Consider the following statements:
   1. The g-inverse of matrix, if it exits, is unique.
   2. The problem of multicollinearity can be tackled by increasing sample size.

   Which of the above statments is/are correct?

   (a) 1 only (b) 2 only

   (c) Both 1 and 2 (d) Neither 1 nor 2

5. In the context of the linear model $Y = X\beta + \varepsilon$, consider the following statements:
   1. If X is a full rank matrix, then all linear parametric functions are estimable.
   2. Each estimable linear parametric function is of the form $c'X\beta$ for some vector c.

   Which of the above statements is/are correct?

   (a) 1 only (b) 2 only

   (c) Both 1 and 2 (d)) Neither 1 nor 2

6. For a two-way ANOVA with 6 rows, 4 columns and 3 observations per cell, the degrees of freedom for interaction and residual are respectively

(a) 15 and 45 (b) 15 and 48

(c) 24 and 45 (d) 24 and 48

7. As the variability due to chance in an analysis of variance decrease, the F-statistic in the ANOVA

(a) will always increase

(b) will always decrease

(c) will remain constant

(d) requires additional innformation to claim any change

8. When k population mean in an ANOVA are truly different from each other, it is likely that the average error deviation, for a significant F-statistic,

(a) is relatively large compared to the average treatment deviations

(b) is relatively small compared to the average treatment deviations

(c) is relatively to the average treatment deviations

(d) differs significantly between at least two of the pupulations

9. Independent observations are drawn from the model

$y_1 = \beta_0 + \beta_1 x_i + \mu_i; i = 1, 2, 3, ..., 10$

It is given that the errors in the model are independent with mean 0 and variance unity. It is also given that the sum of regressors in the model equals 50 and their sum of squares is 260. The Possible covariance between the least squares estimates of β_0 and β_1 would be

(a) 0 (b) 5

(c) – 0.5 (d) 0.5

10. Let

$$A = \begin{pmatrix} 3 & 2 & 2 \\ 1 & 0 & 1 \\ 4 & 2 & 3 \end{pmatrix}$$

Consider the following matrices:

$$P = \begin{pmatrix} 0 & 1 & 0 \\ \frac{1}{2} & -\frac{3}{2} & 0 \\ 0 & 0 & 0 \end{pmatrix}, Q = \begin{pmatrix} 0 & 0 & 0 \\ 0 & 1 & 0 \\ -2 & \frac{1}{2} & 0 \end{pmatrix}$$

$$\text{and } R = \begin{pmatrix} 0 & \frac{1}{2} & -1 \\ 0 & 0 & 1 \\ 0 & 0 & 0 \end{pmatrix}$$

Which one of the following is correct?

(a) P only does not give generalized inverse of A.

(b) Q only does not give generalized inverse of A.

(c) P and R only do not give generalized inverse of A.

(d) None of the options is correct

11. Consider the following statements:

    1. Scheffe's test of multiple comparisons tests all simple and complex contrasts.
    2. Bartlett's test of multiple comparisons tests simple contrasts
    3. Tukey's test of multiple comparisons reduces the Type-I error in the test.

    Which of the above statements are correct?

    (a) 1 and 2 only (b) 2 and 3 only

    (c) 1 and 3 only (d) 1, 2 and 3

12. Consider the following statements for multiple comparison tests conducted after a significant result is obtained in ANOVA:

    1. The t-test on all pairwise comparisons inflates Type-I error.
    2. Scheffe's test requires equal group sizes for multiple comparisons.
    3. Newman-Keuls test reduces the risk of Type-II error.

    Which of the above statements are correct?

    (a) 1 and 2 only (b) 2 and 3 only

    (c) 1 and 3 only (d) 1, 2 and 3

13. Consider the model

    $E(Y_{ij}) = \mu_i$, $var(Y_{ij}) = \sigma^2$

    $j = 1, 2, 3, ..., n_i = i = 1, 2, 3, ..., p$

    Which of the following is/are correct?

    1. Any linear parametric function is estimable
    2. $\hat{\mu}_i = \frac{\sum_{j=1}^{n} Y_{ij}}{n_i}$

    Select the correct answer the code given below.

    (a) 1 only (b) 2 only

    (c) Both 1 and 2 (d) Neither 1 nor 2

14. Let A be an $n \times p$ matrix and A^- be the generalized inverse of A. Then which of the following statements are correct?

    1. The order of A^- is $p \times n$
    2. (A^-A) and (AA^-) are symmetric matrices.
    3. If the rank of the matrix A is n, then $A^- = (A'A)^{-1}A'$.
    4. If A is non-singular, then $A^{-1} = A^-$.

Select the correct answer using the code given below.

(a) 1, 2 and 3 (b) 1, 3 and 4

(c) 1, 2 and 4 (d) 2, 3 and 4

15. Consider a two-way classification with r observations per cell and interaction present

$y_{ijk} = \mu + \alpha_i + \beta_j + \gamma_{ij} + e_{ijk}$

$i = 1, 2, 3, ..., p; j = 1, 2, 3, ..., q;$

$k = 1, 2, 3, ..., r$

Then the total number of parameters in this model is

(a) $1 + p + q + pq$ (b) $p + q + pq$

(c) pq (d) $p + q + 1$

16. For a sample of unit size from a population with the p.d.f.

$f(x, \alpha) = \frac{1}{\alpha^2}(\alpha - x); 0 < x < \alpha$

consider the following statements:

1. 2x is the maximum likelihood estimator of α.
2. 2x is the unbiased estimator of α.

Which of the above statements is/are correct?

(a) 1 only (b) 2 only

(c) Both 1 and 2 (d) Neither 1 nor 2

17. Let $X_1, X_2, X_3, ..., X_n$ be i.i.d. Bernoulli (p) random variables and $S_n = \sum_{i=1}^{n} X_i$. Then the unbiased estimator of p^3 is

(a) $\frac{S_n^3}{n^3}$ (b) $\frac{S_n(S_n - 1)(S_n - 2)}{n(n-1)(n-2)}$

(c) $\frac{(S_n - 1)(S_n - 2)(S_n - 3)}{n(n-1)(n-2)(n-3)}$ (d) None of the above

18. A sample of n inndependent observations $X_1, X_2, X_3, ..., X_n$ is taken from $N(\mu, \sigma^2)$. For what value of k will

$$T = \frac{k}{(n-1)} \sum_{i=1}^{n-1} (X_{i+1} - X_i)^2$$

be an unbiased estimator of σ^2?

(a) 1 (b) $\frac{1}{2}$

(c) $\frac{1}{3}$ (d) $\frac{1}{4}$

19. Let $(X_1, X_2, X_3, ..., X_n)$ be a random sample from an exponential population with mean $\frac{1}{\theta}$. If Z = $nX_{(1)}$, where $X_{(1)} = \min(X_1, X_2, X_3, ..., X_n)$, then which of the following is/are correct?

1. Z is an unbiased estimator of $\frac{1}{\theta}$.
2. Z is consistent estimator of $\frac{1}{\theta}$.

Select the correct answer using the code given below.

(a) 1 only (b) 2 only

(c) Both 1 and 2 (d) Neither 1 nor 2

20. Let t_1 be a most efficient estimator and t_2 be a less efficient estimator with efficiency e and let be ρ be the correlation coefficient between the two estimators t_1 and t_2. Which one of the following is correct?

(a) $\rho = e$ (b) $\rho = 2e - 1$

(c) $\rho = \sqrt{e}$ (d) $\rho = e^2$

21. A random sample $(X_1, X_2, X_3, ..., X_n)$ is drawn from a Poisson distribution with parameter λ. Which one of the following is an unbiased estimator of λ^2?

(a) $\frac{1}{n}\sum_{i=1}^{n} x_i$ (b) $\frac{1}{n}\sum_{i=1}^{n} x_i^2$

(c) $\frac{1}{n}\sum_{i=1}^{n} x_i(x_i - 1)$ (d) $\frac{1}{n}\sum_{i=1}^{n} x_i(x_i + 1)$

22. Let (X_1, X_2, X_3) be a random sample from binomial (1, p). Which one of the following statistics is not suffficient for p?

(a) $X_1 + X_2 + X_3$ (b) $(X_1, X_2 + X_3)$

(c) $(X_1 + X_2 + X_3)$ (d) $X_1 - X_2 + X_3$

23. Suppose a random sample of size 2 was selected from a population with the p.d.f.

$$f_\theta(x) = f_\theta = \frac{2}{\theta^2}(\theta - x); 0 < x < \theta$$

The maximum likelihood estimator of θ will be

(a) $\frac{(x_1 + x_2) + \sqrt{(x_1 - x_2)^2 + 4x_1x_2}}{4}$ (b) $\frac{(x_1 + x_2) + \sqrt{9(x_1 - x_2)^2 + 4x_1x_2}}{4}$

(c) $\frac{3(x_1 + x_2) + \sqrt{(x_1 - x_2)^2 + 4x_1x_2}}{4}$ (d) $\frac{3(x_1 + x_2) + \sqrt{9(x_1 - x_2)^2 + 4x_1x_2}}{4}$

24. If T is unbbiased for θ and var (T) → 0 as the sample size tends to ∞, then T is consistent from θ. This result follows from

(a) central limit theorem (b) Cramer-Rao inequality

(c) Rao-Blackwell theorem (d) Tchebychev's inequality

25. If one observation from Bernoulli distribution with parameter $p \in \left[\frac{1}{3}, \frac{2}{3}\right]$ is obtained, then the MLE of p is

(a) x
(b) (2x + 1)/3
(c) (x – 1)/3
(d) (x + 1)/3

26. Let Xi ~ N(μ, σ²) where i = 1, 2, 3, ..., n and $\Theta = \{(\mu, \sigma^2); -\infty < \mu < \infty, \sigma^2 > 0\}$ such that μ is known. Then the MLE of σ^2 is

(a) $\frac{\sum_{i=1}^{n}(X_i - \mu)^2}{n}$
(b) $\frac{\sum_{i=1}^{n}(X_i - \mu)^2}{n-1}$
(c) $\frac{n-1}{n^2}\sum_{i=1}^{n}(X_i - \mu)^2$
(d) $\frac{n-1}{n}\sum_{i=1}^{n}(X_i - \mu)^2$

27. Let $(X_1, X_2, X_3, ..., X_n)$ be a random sample of size n from uniform distribution with the p.d.f.

$$f(x) = \begin{cases} \frac{1}{\theta_2 - \theta_1}, & \theta_1 < x < \theta_2 \\ 0, & \text{otherwise} \end{cases}$$

Let T_1 and T_2 be the estimates of θ_1 and θ_2 respectively obtained by method of moments. Which one of the following is correct?

(a) $T_1 = \bar{X} + \sqrt{\frac{3}{n}\sum_{i=1}^{n}(X_i - \bar{X})^2}$ and $T_2 = \bar{X} - \sqrt{\frac{3}{n}\sum_{i=1}^{n}(X_i - \bar{X})^2}$

(b) $T_1 = \bar{X} - \sqrt{\frac{3}{n}\sum_{i=1}^{n}(X_i - \bar{X})^2}$ and $T_2 = \bar{X} + \sqrt{\frac{3}{n}\sum_{i=1}^{n}(X_i - \bar{X})^2}$

(c) $T_1 = \bar{X} + \sqrt{\frac{3}{n}\sum_{i=1}^{n}(X_i - \bar{X})^2}$ and $T_2 = \bar{X} + \sqrt{\frac{3}{n}\sum_{i=1}^{n}(X_i - \bar{X})^2}$

(d) $T_1 = \bar{X} - \sqrt{\frac{3}{n}\sum_{i=1}^{n}(X_i - \bar{X})^2}$ and $T_2 = \bar{X} - \sqrt{\frac{3}{n}\sum_{i=1}^{n}(X_i - \bar{X})^2}$

28. Let $(X_1, X_2, X_3, ..., X_n)$ be i.i.d. random variables with the density function

$f(x, \mu) = e^{-(x-\mu)}, x \geq \mu$

The MLE of is μ given by

(a) $X_{(1)}$
(b) $X_{(n)}$
(c) $\frac{X_{(1)} + X_{(n)}}{2}$
(d) None of the above

29. If T is an MLE of θ and $\phi(\theta)$ is one-to-one function of θ, then θ (t) is the MLE of $\phi(\theta)$. This property is known as

(a) invariance property of MLE (b) asymptotic property of MLE

(c) consistency property of MLE (d) regularity conditions of MLE

30. Which of the following statements are correct?

1. MLE's are consistent
2. MLE's are always unbiased
3. MLE's follow asymptotically normal distributiuon.
4. MLE need not be a unique estimator.

Select the correct answer using the code given below.

(a) 1 and 3 only (b) 1, 3 and 4

(c) 1, 2 and 3 (d) 2, 3 and 4

31. In sampling from a normal population N(θ, 1) with $\overline{X}$ being sample mmean,, which of the following classes describes all MVB estimators of θ?

(a) All estimators of the type $A\overline{X} + B$, where A and B are given constants

(b) $\overline{X}$ only

(c) All the estimators of $f(\overline{X})$, where f is a real-valued function

(d) No estimator attains MVB in this case

32. Let 5, 2, 3, 4, 3, 2, 4, 5, 3, 2 be a sample taken from a normal population with mean 0 and variance σ^2. The minimum variance bound estimator for σ^2 is

(a) 33 (b) 3.3

(c) 1.21 (d) 12.1

33. If $(X_1, X_2, X_3, ..., X_n)$ is a random sample from N(1, σ^2), then which one of the following is unbiased for σ^2 and has variance equal to Cramer-Rao bound?

(a) $\frac{1}{n}\sum_{i=1}^{n}(X_i - 1)^2$ (b) $\frac{1}{n-1}\sum_{i=1}^{n}(X_i - \overline{X})^2$

(c) $\frac{1}{n}\sum_{i=1}^{n}(X_i - \overline{X})^2$ (d) $\frac{1}{n-1}\sum_{i=1}^{n}(X_i - 1)^2$

34. If $(X_1, X_2, X_3, ..., X_n)$ be i.i.d. N(μ, σ^2), with μ known, then C-R bound for estimation of $\sigma^2 = \theta$ will be

(a) $\frac{2\theta}{n}$ (b) $\frac{\theta}{n}$

(c) $\frac{2\theta^2}{n}$ (d) $\frac{\theta^2}{n}$

35. Suppose the p.d.f. is

$$f(x, \theta) = \begin{cases} \dfrac{1}{\theta}, & 0 \le x \le \theta \\ 0, & \text{otherwise} \end{cases}$$

The sufficient statistic for θ based on a random smaple of size n is

(a) $\sum_{i=1}^{n} X_i$ (b) $\bar{X}$

(c) $X_{(1)}$ (d) $X_{(n)}$

36. If $(X_1, X_2, X_3, ..., X_n)$ be a random sample from a popultion with the p.d.f.

$f(x, \theta) = \theta x^{\theta-1}; 0 < x < 1, \theta > 0$

Which one of the following is correct?

(a) $t_1 = \sum_{i=1}^{n} X_i$ is sufficient for θ.

(b) $t_1 = \prod_{i=1}^{n} X_i$ is sufficient for θ.

(c) No sufficient statistic exists for θ.

(d) None of the above

37. Let 5, 3, 3, 6, 2, 5, 4, 3, 6 be a sample of size 10 from a population following Poisson (λ) distribution. The UMVUE of λ is

(a) 40 (b) 8

(c) 4 (d) 3

38. A random sample of 60 schoolchildren gives 40 spectacle users. The 95% confidence limits of the spectacle users of the population of schoolchildren are

(a) 66%, 89% (b) 66%, 79%

(c) 55%, 66% (d) 55%, 79%

39. A sample of size one is drawn from Poisson distribution with parameter θ. To test H_0: λ = 1 against H_1: λ = 2, consider the new randomized test with critical the new randomized test with critical region ω = {x: x > 3}. The probability of Type-I error is

(a) $(3e^2 - 19)/(3e^2)$ (b) $(3e - 5)/3$

(c) $(3e - 8)/(3e)$ (d) $(3e^2 - 16)/(3e^2)$

40. Let $(X_1, X_2, X_3, ..., X_n)$ be a random sample from $N(\mu, \sigma^2)$ distribution, where both μ and σ^2 are unknown. The shortest expected length confidence interval for μ is obtained using

(a) standard normal distribution

(b) t-distribution

(c) F-distribution

(d) Chi-square distribution

41. Let X be a random variable having exponential distribution with mean $\frac{1}{\theta}$. Consider the critical region $\omega = \{x: x > 2\}$ to test $H_0: \theta = 1$ against $H_1: \theta = 2$. The power of the test at $\theta = 2$ is

(a) $(e^2 - 1)/e^2$ (b) $1/e^4$

(c) $(e^4 - 1)/e^4$ (d) $1/e^2$

42. The Neyman-Pearson fundamental lemma gives the method of construction of

(a) uniformly most powerful test

(b) most powerful test

(c) unbiased test

(d) randomized test

43. For the problem of testing $\mu = \mu_0$ against $\mu \neq \mu_0$ in sample $N(\mu, \sigma^2)$ distribution, where both μ and σ^1 are unknown, the likelihood ratio test is equivalent to

(a) uniformly most powerful test

(b) uniformly most powerful similar test

(c) uniformly most powerful invariant test

(d) uniformly most powerful unbiased test

44. Let X_i (i = 1, 2, 3, ..., n) be distributed as $N(\mu_i, 1)$ distribution. The likelihood ratio test for testing $H_0: \mu_1 = \mu_2 = ... = \mu_n = 0$ against $H_1: \mu_i \neq 0$, for some i, is based on the statistic

(a) $\sum_{i=1}^{n}\left(\frac{X_i^2}{\mu_i}\right)$ (b) $\sum_{i=1}^{n} X_i^2$

(c) $\sum_{i=1}^{n}(X_i - \bar{X})^2$ (d) $\sum_{i=1}^{n} X_i$

45. Under the regularity conditions, if λ_n is the likelihood ratio, then the asymptotic distribution of $-2\log \lambda_n$, as $n \to \infty$, is

(a) normal distribution (b) Chi-square distribution

(c) F-distribution (d) t-distribution

46. In a Sequential Probability Ratio Test (SPRT), λ_m denotes the likelihood ratio at mth stage of the experiment; α and β are the probabilities of Type-I and Type-II errors respectively. Which of the following pairs is/are correctly matched?

1. $\lambda_m \geq \frac{1-\beta}{\alpha}$: Terminate the process with the rejection of null hypothesis H_0

2. $\frac{\beta}{1-\alpha} < \lambda_m < \frac{1-\beta}{\alpha}$: Terminate the process with the acceptance of H_0

3. $\lambda_m \leq \frac{\beta}{1-\alpha}$: Continue sampling by taking an additional observation

Selection the correct answer using the code given below.

(a) 1 only (b) 1 and 2

(c) 1 and 3 (d) 2 and 3

47. If N is stopping time for an SPRT, then which one of the following is correct?

(a) $P[N < \infty] = \frac{1}{4}$ (b) $P[N < \infty] = \frac{1}{2}$

(c) $P[N < \infty] = 1$ (d) $P[N < \infty] = \frac{3}{4}$

48. Let $\delta(x)$ be an estimator of θ and $L[\theta, \delta(x)]$ be the loss function associated with $\delta(x)$ at θ. Then the risk $R[\theta, \delta(x)] = E[L(\theta, \delta(x)]$ is mean squared error if the associated loss function is

(a) $L[\theta, \delta(x)] = (\theta - a)^3$ (b) $L[\theta, \delta(x)] = (\theta - a)^2$

(c) $L[\theta, \delta(x)] = |\theta - a|$ (d) $L[\theta, \delta(x)] = \theta(\theta - a)^2$

49. Let $(X_1, X_2, X_3, ..., X_n) \sim N(\mu, 1)$ and let prior distribution of μ be $N(0, 1)$. Let $L(\mu, \delta) = [\mu - \delta(x)]^2$. Then the Bayes' risk associated with δ is

(a) $\frac{\sum_{i=1}^{n} x_i}{n+1}$ (b) $\frac{2}{n+2}$

(c) $\frac{1}{n+1}$ (d) $\frac{\sum_{i=1}^{n} x_i^2}{n}$

50. The Bayes' estimator of a parameter under squared error loss functionis

(a) posterior mean (b) posterior median

(c) posterior mode (d) posterior variance

51. Which one of the following statements is not correct?

(a) If any Bayes' solution is unique, it must be admissible.

(b) A uniformly best decision rule always exists.

(c) Posterior median is the Bayes' estimator under the absolute error loss function.

(d) A Bayes' decision rule, whose risk is constant, is also a minimax decision rule.

52. Let $(X_1, X_2, X_3, ..., X_n)$ denote a random sample from a population with the density $f(x, \theta) = \sqrt{\theta} x^{\sqrt{\theta}-1}, 0 \le x \le 1, \theta > 0$. The MLE of θ is given by

(a) $\frac{\sum_{i=1}^{n} \log x_i}{n}$ (b) $\left(\frac{\sum_{i=1}^{n} \log x_i}{n}\right)^2$

(c) $\frac{n}{\sum_{i=1}^{n} \log x_i}$ (d) $\frac{n^2}{\left(\sum_{i=1}^{n} \log x_i\right)^2}$

53. Let $(X_1, X_2, X_3, ..., X_n)$ be an i.i.d. sequence of random variables $(n > 2)$ from the distribution whose density function is $f(x, \theta)\ x^{\theta-1}, 0 < x < 1, \theta > 0$. If $Z = -\left(\sum_{i=1}^{n} \log X_i\right)$, then an unbiased estimator of θ is

(a) $\frac{n}{Z}$ (b) $\frac{n-1}{Z}$

(c) nZ (d) $(n-1)Z$

54. A statistic $t = t(x_1, x_2, x_3, ..., x_n)$ is sufficient for θ. Consider the following statements:

1. It contains all the information about θ.
2. The likelihood function can be expressed as
$L(x, \theta) = g(t, \theta)\ h(x_1, x_2, x_3, ..., x_n)$
3. The conditional distribution of $x_1, x_2, x_3, ..., x_n$ given t is independent of θ

Which of the above statements are correct?

(a) 1 and 2 only (b) 2 and 3 only

(c) 1 and 3 only (d) 1, 2 and 3

55. Let $(X_1, X_2, X_3, ..., X_n)$ be a random sample from Rayleigh distribution with the p.d.f. $f(x, \theta) = \frac{x}{\theta}\exp\left\{-\frac{x^2}{2\theta}\right\}; x > 0, \theta > 0$. The complete sufficient statistic for θ is

(a) $\sum_{i=1}^{n} x_i$ (b) $\overline{x}$

(c) $\sum_{i=1}^{n} x_i^2$ (d) $\max(x_1, x_2, x_3, ..., x_n)$

56. A single observation X is drawn from B(10, p) distribution. Reject H_0: $p = \frac{1}{2}$ in favour of H_1: $p = \frac{1}{4}$ if $X \le 3$. Then the power of the test is

(a) $369\left(\frac{3^7}{4^{10}}\right)$ (b) $366\left(\frac{3^7}{4^{10}}\right)$

(c) $372\left(\frac{3^7}{4^{10}}\right)$ (d) $375\left(\frac{3^7}{4^{10}}\right)$

57. For testing H_0 against H_1 if $\phi(x)$ is a UMP, then

(a) $\phi(x)$ is always unbiased (b) $\phi(x)$ is never unbiased

(c) $\phi(x)$ has power less than its size (d) None of the above

58. Let X_1 and X_2 be i.i.d. random variables with Poisson. Then $(X_1 + 2X_2)$ is not sufficient becuase

(a) $P(X_1 = 1, X_2 = 1 \mid T = 3)$ depends on λ

(b) $(X_1 + 2X_2)$ is Poisson

(c) $(X_1 + 2X_2)$ is not Poisson

(d) $P(X_1 = 1, X_2 = 1 \mid T = 3)$ is Poisson with parameter one

where $T = (X_1 + 2X_2)$.

59. Let X be the random variable from the p.m.f.

$$f(x\ \phi) = \begin{cases} \left(\frac{\theta}{2}\right)^{|x|} (1-\theta)^{1-|x|}; & x = -1, 0, 1 \text{ and } 0 < \theta < 1 \\ 0; & \text{otherwise} \end{cases}$$

The complete sufficient statistic for θ

(a) is X
(b) is $X - 1$
(c) is $|X|$
(d) does not exist

60. Let $(X_1, X_2, X_3, \ldots, X_n)$ be i.i.d. random variables wioth $N(\theta, 1)$. Then C-R lower bound for the variance of an unbiased estimator of θ^r is

(a) $\frac{\theta^r}{n}$
(b) $\frac{r\theta^{r-1}}{n}$
(c) $\frac{r\theta^{2r-2}}{n}$
(d) $\frac{\theta^r}{n^2}$

61. Which of the following are true for Sustainable Development Goals (SDGs)?

1. It has 8 goals.
2. It has 17 goals.
3. It is recommennded by UNICEF
4. It is recommended by UNDP.
5. Life below water, Life on land, No Poverty and Climate Action are included in SDGs.

Select the correct answer using the code given below.

(a) 1, 3 and 5
(b) 2 and 4 only
(c) 2, 4 and 5
(d) None of the options is correct

62. Which one of the following is not a desirable property of official statistics?

(a) It should be relevant
(b) It should be brought out i n a timely manner.
(c) It should be reliable and credible.
(d) It should be able to disclose an individual unit's data.

63. The reliability of data collected through sample surveys may be measured by

(a) average
(b) standard deviation
(c) coefficient of variation
(d) standard error

64. The Ultimate Stage Unit for data collection in socio-economicd survey of NSSO (National Sample Survey Office) is
   (a) individual
   (b) family
   (c) household
   (d) village/UFS (Urban Frame Survey) block

65. The most common sampling design used by NSSO in its socio-economic surveys is
   (a) simple random sampling
   (b) circular systematic sampling
   (c) probability proportional to size (PPS) sampling
   (d) two-stage stratified sampling

66. Metadata is
   (a) unit level data
   (b) data in tabular format
   (c) raw data (i.e., no data validation has been done)
   (d) data about data/information about data

67. The subject of Statistics comes under which of the following Lists of the Constitution of India?
   (a) Union List
   (b) State List
   (c) Concurrent List
   (d) All of the above

68. Which of the following are the main activities of CSO (Central Statisticsd Office)?
   1. Coordination of statistical activities in the country
   2. Evolving statistical standards
   3. Collecting data through sample
   4. Providing guidance and training in the field of official statistics

   Select the correct answer using the code given below.
   (a) 1, 2 and 3
   (b) 2, 3 and 4
   (c) 1, 2 and 4
   (d) 1, 3 and 4

69. The Collection of Statistics Act, 2008 is applicable on
   1. industrial and business concerns
   2. individual and household
   3. government and private agencies/enterprises

   Which of the above are correct?
   (a) 1 and 2 only
   (b) 1 and 3 only
   (c) 2 and 3 only
   (d) 1, 2 and 3

70. The Dearness Allowance (DA) of Central and State Government employees is linked with
   (a) WPI (Wholesale Price Index)
   (b) CPI (Consumer Price Index) — U&R (Urban and Rural)
   (c) CPI (Consumer Price Index) — IW (Industrial Workers)
   (d) CPI (Consumer Price Index) — AL (Agricultural Labour)/RL (Rural Labour)

71. The retail inflation in India is being measured on which one of the following indices?
    (a) CPI (Consumer Price Index) — IW (Industrial Workers)
    (b) WPI (Wholesale Price Index)
    (c) CPI (Consumer Price Index) — U&R (Urban and Rural)
    (d) CPI (Consumer Price Index) — AL (Agricultural Labour)/RL (Rural Labour)
72. Annual inflation rate can be calculated as
    (a) $\frac{\text{CPI(current year)} - \text{CPI (last year)}}{\text{CPI (last year)}} \times 100$
    (b) CPI(current year) – CPI (last year)
    (c) $\frac{\text{CPI(current year)} - \text{CPI (base year)}}{\text{CPI (base year)}} \times 100$
    (d) CPI(current year) – CPI (base year)
73. Price deflators are used to obtain
    (a) GDP at constant prices
    (b) GDP at current prices
    (c) GDP at basic prices
    (d) GVA at producer prices
74. Which of the following are the sources of industrial data in Indial?
    1. Annual Survey of Industries (ASI)
    2. Economic Census (EC)
    3. Employment, Unemployment Survey of NSSO
    4. Micro, Small and Medium Enterprise (MSME) Survey

    Select the correct answer using the code given below.
    (a) 1 and 2 only
    (b) 2 and 3 only
    (c) 1, 2 and 4 only
    (d) 1, 2, 3 and 4 only
75. Which one of the following is not correct for Minimum Support Price (MSP)?
    (a) MSP is the price at which government purchases food grains
    (b) MSP ensures adequate food grains production in the country
    (c) MSP is a direct benefit transfer.
    (d) MSP is recommended by CACP (Commission for Agricultural Costs and Prices).
76. Which among the following is a data source from where Infant Mortality Rate can be calculated for India?
    (a) NSSO Healty Survey
    (b) Economic Census
    (c) NSSO Disability Survey
    (d) Population Census
77. Which one of the following organizations releases Wholesale Price Index (WPI)?
    (a) Labour Bureau
    (b) NSSO

(c) CSO

(d) Office of Economic Adviser, the Ministry of Commerce a nd Industry

78. The periodicity of Agriculture Census in India is

(a) 5 years (b) 7 years

(c) 10 years (d) 15 years

79. Effective literacy rate is the literacy rate

(a) taking the population from age 7 years and above into account

(b) taking the entire population into account

(c) taking the population from age 7 years to 60 years into account

(d) None of the abov

80. The Human Development Index (HDI) developed by UNDP does not include

(a) life expectancy at birth

(b) gender equality

(c) expected and mean years of schooling

(d) GNI per capita

STATISTICS - II
2017

Time Allowed : Two Hours | *Maximum Marks: 200*

INSTRUCTIONS

1. IMMEDIATELY AFTER THE COMMENCEMENT OF THE EXAMINATION, YO SHOULD CHECK THAT THIS TEST BOOKLET *DOES NOT* HAVE ANY UNPRINTED OR TORN OR MISSING PAGES OR ITEMS, ETC. IF SO, GET IT REPLACE BY A COMPLETE TEST BOOKLET.
2. **Please note that it is the candidate'sresponsibility to encode and fill in the Roll Number and Test Booklet Series A, B, C or D carefully and without any omission or discrepancy at the appropriate places in the OMR Answer Sheet. Any omission/discrepancy will render the Answer sheet liable for rejection.**
3. You have to enter your Roll Number on the Test Booklet in the Box provided alongside. ***DO NOT*** write ***anything else*** on the Test Booklet.
4. This Test Booklet contains **80** items (questions).Each item comprises four responses (answers). You will select the response which you want to mark on the Answer Sheet. In case you feel that there is more than one correct response, mark the response which you consider the best. In any case, choose ***ONLY ONE*** response for each item.
5. You have to mark all your responses *ONLY* on the separate Answer Sheet provided. See directions in the Answer Sheet.
6. All items carry equal marks.
7. Before you proceed to mark in the Answer Sheet the response to various in the Test Booklet, you have to fill in some particulars in the Answer Sheet as per intructions sent to you with your Admission Certificate.
8. After you have complited filling in all your responses on the Answer Sheet and the examination has concluded, you should hand over to the Invigilator ***only the Answer Sheet***. You are permitted to take away with you the Test Booklet.
9. Sheets for rough work are appended in the Test Booklet at the end.
10. **Penalty for wrong answers:**

    THERE WILL BE PENALTY FOR WRONG ANSWERS MARKED BY A CANDIDATE IN THE OBJECTIVE TYPE QUSTION PAPERS.

    (i) There are four alternatives for the answer to every question. For each question for which a wrong answer has been given by the candidate, **one-third** of the marks assigned to that question will be deducted as penalty.

    (ii) If a candidate gives more than one answer, it will be treated as a **wrong answer** even if one of the given answers happens to be correct and there will be same penalty as above to that question.

    (iii) If a question is left blamk,i.e., no answer is given by the candidate, there will be **no penalty** for that question.

DO NOT OPEN THIS TEST BOOKLET UNTIL YOU ARE TOLD TO DO SO

1. The following ANOVA table is obtained for a two-vvariable linear regression:

Source of variation	Degress of freedom	Sum of squares
Regression	1	122.5
Residual	3	77.5
Total	4	200.0

The correlation betweeen the regressor and the regressand is

(a) 0.3875 (b) 0.6125

(c) 0.6225 (d) 0.7826

2. In a2-way ANOVA with 6 rows, 5 columns and 3 observation per cell, what are the degrees of freedom for the sum of squares for interactionn and error respectively?

(a) 20 and 60 (b) 30 and 50

(c) 20 and 40 (d) 15 and 65

3. If Y_1, Y_2, Y_3 and Y_4 are independent with

$E(Y_1) = E(Y_2) = \mu_1 + \mu_2$

$E(Y_3) = E(Y_4) = \mu_1 + \mu_3$

$Var(Y_i) = \sigma^2$; i = 1, 2, 3, 4

the condition of estimability of the parametric function $l_1\mu_1 + l_2\mu_2 + l_3\mu_3$ is

(a) $l_2 = l_3$ (b) $l_2 = l_1 + l_3$

(c) $l_3 = l_1 + l_2$ (d) $l_1 = l_2 + l_3$

4. Let y_i follow

$N(\alpha + \beta x_i, \sigma^2)$; i = 1, 2, 3, ..., n

Let $(\tilde{\alpha}, \tilde{\beta})$ annd $(\hat{\alpha}, \hat{\beta})$, be the least squares and maximum limelihood estimates of (α, β) respectively. Then which one of the following is correct?

(a) $\tilde{\alpha} \neq \hat{\alpha}, \tilde{\beta} \neq \hat{\beta}$ (b) $\tilde{\alpha} = \hat{\alpha}, \tilde{\beta} \neq \hat{\beta}$

(c) $\tilde{\alpha} = \hat{\alpha}, \tilde{\beta} = \hat{\beta}$ (d) $\tilde{\alpha} = \hat{\alpha}, \tilde{\beta} = \hat{\beta}$ only when σ^2 is known

5. In a multiple linear regression model with 5 regressors and 25 observations, the sum of squares due to regressors was 360 and the sum of squares due to errors was 128. For this model, consider the following statements:

   1. Almost 74% of the total variation in the model is explained by the regressors.
   2. The estimated value of the error variance of the m odel is 3.2.

Which of the above statements is/are correct?

(a) 1 only (b) 2 only

(c) Both 1 and 2 (d)) Neither 1 nor 2

6. In the following, the Gauss--Markov model is stated as $Y = X\beta + \varepsilon$ and X^- denotes the g-inverse of the matrix X:

   1. $XX^-X = X$
   2. If X is non-singular, then $X^- = X^{-1}$
   3. X^- is needed when the columns of X are linearly dependent

Where of the above is/are correct?

(a) 1 only (b) 2 only

(c) 1 and 2 only (d) 1, 2 and 3

7. In the Gauss-Markov model $Y = X\beta + \varepsilon$, which of the following assumptions are made?
   1. X is a matrix of full rank
   2. $E(\varepsilon) = 0$
   3. $Var(\varepsilon) = \sigma^2 I$

   Select the correct answer using the code given below.

   (a) 1 and 2 only (b) 2 and 3 only

   (c) 1 and 3 only (d) 1, 2 and 3

8. An experiment was conduct to study the variation in fuel consumption of diesel vehicles. For this purpose, different types of fuel injectors (A) and different qualities of fuel (B) were assigned randomly to the same type of diesel vehicles. The analysis of variance table of the random effect model is given below:

ANOVA Table

Source	Degress of freedom	Sum of squares
A	4	48
B	3	36
A × B	x	96
Error	y	x
Total	59	380

The estimate of component of variance due to interaction $\left(\hat{\sigma}^2_{AB}\right)$ is

(a) 1 (b) 1.6

(c) 5 (d) 8

9. Consider the following two models with $E(\varepsilon) = 0$ and $Var(\varepsilon) = \sigma^2 I$:

   Model A: $Y = X_1\beta_1 + \varepsilon$

   Model B: $Y = X_1\beta_1 + X_2\beta_2 + \varepsilon$

   Which one of the following is correct?

   (a) $R^2_A = R^2_B$ (b) $R^2_A \le R^2_B$

   (c) $R^2_A \ge R^2_B$ (d) $R^2_A \ne R^2_B$

10. Consider a model $Y = X\beta + \varepsilon$, where Y is $n \times 1$, X is $n \times p$ and β is $p \times 1$. Let $H = X(X'X)^- X'$. Which of the following are correct?
    1. $(I_n - H)$ is symmetric
    2. $(I_n - H)$ is idempotent
    3. $(I_n - H)X = 0$
    4. $(I_n - H)X = 0$

    Select the correct answer usin g the code given below:

(a) 1, 2 and 4 (b) 2 and 3 only

(c) 1, 2 and 3 (d) 1 and 3 only

11. let n independent random variables $y_1, y_2, ..., y_n$ be normally distributed with constant annd unknown variance σ^2 and

$$E(y_i) = \sum_{j=0}^{p} \beta_j x_{ij}; x_{i0} = 1$$

The distribution of the test statisitc for testing the hypothesis

$H_0: \beta_1 = \beta_2 = \beta_p = 0$

is

(a) $t_{(n-p)}$ (b) $F_{(p, n-p-1)}$

(c) $F_{(p-1, n-p)}$ (d) $t_{(p-1)}$

12. The following informamtion is given for a two-variable regression model that was run on 22 observations:

$$\sum(y_i - \bar{y})^2 = 500, \sum(x_i - \bar{x})^2 = 125, r_{xy} = 0.6$$

The estimate of error variance will be given by

(a) 1.20 (b) 1.44

(c) 9.00 (d) 16.00

13. The main advantage of having more than one observation per cell in two-way ANOVA is

1. increased degrees of freedom for error SS
2. testing significance of interaction effect

Which of the above is/are correctg?

(a) 1 only (b) 2 only

(c) Both 1 and 2 (d) Neither 1 nor 2

14. For a one-way ANOVA in k classes, each wioth n observations, consider the following:

1. Least significant difference

$$= \sqrt{\frac{2 \times MSE}{n}} \times t_{(n-1)k, a/2}$$

2. Scheffe's critical difference

$$= \sqrt{\frac{2 \times MSE}{n} \times (k-1) \times F_{k-1,(n-1)k, 1-\alpha}}$$

Which of the above is/are correct?

(a) 1 only (b) 2 only

(c) Both 1 and 2 (d) Both 1 nor 2

15. Consider the model $E(y_1) = 2\beta_1 + \beta_2$, and $E(y_2) = \beta_1 - \beta_2$ and $E(y_3) = \beta_1 + \alpha\beta_2$ with $V(y_i) = \sigma^2$ for all i = 1, 2, 3 and Cov $(y_i, y_j) = 0$ for all $i \neq j$. The value of α so that the best linear unnbiased estimators of β_1 and β_2 are uncorrelated is

(a) 0 (b) 2

(c) –2 (d) –1

16. To estimate β in general linear model $Y_{n\times1} = X_{n\times k}\,\beta_{k\times1} + \varepsilon_{n\times1}$, which one of the following assumptions is essential?

(a) $E(\varepsilon) = 0$ (b) $E(\varepsilon\varepsilon') = \sigma^2 I_n$

(c) $\rho(X) = k$ (d) ε follows $N(0, \sigma^2 I_n)$

17. Test for the significane of complete regression is equivalent to

(a) test for the significance of individual regression coefficients

(b) test for the equality between two regressio coefficients

(c) test for the significance of multiple determination

(d) test for the regression coefficient equal to some given value

18. The included explanatory variable in the linear model is irrelevant if

(a) the estimate of the regression coefficient of explanatory variable is less than one

(b) the estimate of the regression coefficient of explanatory variable is greater than one

(c) the calculated statistic of the regression coefficient of explanatory variable is greater than one

(d) the calculated t-statistic of the regression coefficient of explanatory variable is less than one

19. The estimate of error variance in two-variable linear model is

(a) $\frac{e'e}{n-2}$ (b) $\frac{ee'}{n-2}$

(c) $\frac{e'e}{2-n}$ (d) $\frac{ee'}{2-n}$

20. For the linear hypothesis

$H_0: R_{q\times k}\,\beta_{k\times1} = \tau_{q\times1}$

which one of the following represents coefficients of linear restrictions on parameters involved in the model?

(a) R (b) β

(c) r (d) k

21. The following table gives the observed frequencies for the four blood groups along with expected frequencies according to a model:

Blood group	O	A	B	AB
Observed	17	22	15	6
Expected	14	26	12	8

What is the corrected value of chi-square statistic after applyinng Yates' correction for continuity?

(a) 2.4874 (b) 2.2378

(c) 2.5272 (d) 2.7590

22. Which of the following are correct for a test of significance?

 1. Size = 1 – P (TYpe-I error)
 2. Power = 1 – P (Type-II error)
 3. Power = P (Type-II error)
 4. Size = P (Type-I error)

 Select the correct answer using the code given below.

 (a) 1 and 2 (b) 3 and 4

 (c) 1 and 3 (d) 2 and 4

23. If $X_1, X_2, X_3, ..., X_n$ is a random sample of size n from $N(\mu, \sigma^2)$, where μ is known and we definne

$$T = k\sum_{i=1}^{n} |X_i - \mu|$$

 then for what value of k will T be an unbiased estimator of σ?

 (a) 1.25 m (b) 0.8n

 (c) $\frac{1.25}{n}$ (d) $\frac{0.8}{n}$

24. The sample values are drawn from a population with p.d.f $f(x) = (1 + \theta) x^{\theta}; 0 < x < 1, \theta > 0$, and are 0.3, 0.4, 0.5, 0.6, 0.7, 0.8 and 0.9. The estimate of θ by the method of moments is

 (a) 0.4 (b) 0.5

 (c) 0.6 (d) 0.7

25. Consider a population with three kinds of individuals labelled 1, 2 and 3 occurring in the Hardy-Weinberg proportionns $p(1, \theta) = \theta^2$, $p(2, \theta) = 2\,\theta\,(1 - \theta)$ and $p(3, \theta) = (1 - \theta)^2$, where $0 < \theta < 1$. If we observe a sample of three individuals and obtain $x_1 = 1$, $x_2 = 2$ and $x_3 = 1$, then MLE of θ is given by

 (a) $\frac{1}{3}$ (b) $\frac{1}{2}$

 (c) $\frac{2}{3}$ (d) $\frac{5}{6}$

26. Consider the following statements:

 1. The signed-rank test is a non-parametric analogue for the paired t-test.
 2. The Behrens-Fisher problem has no exact solution.
 3. The Mann-Whitney test is a non-parametric two-sample test.

 Which of the above statements are correct?

 (a) 1 and 2 only (b) 2 and 3 only

 (c) 1 and 3 only (d) 1, 2 and 3

27. Consider the following statements:

1. Robustness of a test means relative insensitivity to violation of assumptions.
2. t-test should not be used for sample size 10 if the distribution is clearly skewed.
3. For sample size 100, t-test can be used even if the distribution is non-normal.

Which of the above statements is/are correct?

(a) 2 and 3 only (b) 1 only

(c) 1 and 2 only (d) 1, 2 only

28. If T is an unbiased eastimator of θ, then T^2 is

(a) unbiased estimator for θ^2

(b) biased estimator for θ^2

(c) unbiased estimator for $(\theta^2 + 1)$

(d) biased estimator for $(\theta^2 + 1)$

29. If $X_1, X_2, X_3, ..., X_n$ is a random sample from a normal population $N(\mu, 1)$, the statistic

$$t = \frac{1}{n}\sum_{i=1}^{n} X_i^2$$

is an unbiased estimator of

(a) $\mu^2 + 1$ (b) $\mu + 1$

(c) μ (d) $2\mu + 1$

30. If $X_1, X_2, X_3, ..., X_n$ be a random sample from a population with density

$$f(x, \theta) = \frac{1}{2}e^{-|x-\theta|}, -\infty < x < \infty$$

then the MLE of θ is given by

(a) $\bar{X}$ (b) median $(X_1, X_2, X_3, ..., X_n)$

(c) mode $(X_1, X_2, X_3, ..., X_n)$ (d) standard deviation

31. Let $X_1, X_2, X_3, ..., X_n$ be i.i.d. random variable with $E(X_1) = \theta$. Then for what value of k will

$$T = \frac{k\sum_{i=1}^{n} iX_i}{n(n+1)}$$

be an unbiased estimator of θ?

(a) 1 (b) 2

(c) 3 (d) 4

32. Let $X_1, X_2, X_3, ..., X_n$ be random variables from $N(0, \theta)$ for $\theta > 0$. Then

1. $T_n = \bar{X}_n S_n^2$ is an unbiased estimate of θ^2 where $\bar{X}_n = \frac{1}{n}\sum_{i=1}^{n} X_i$ and $S_n^2 = \frac{\sum_{i=1}^{n}(X_i - \bar{X})^2}{n-1}$

2. T_n is a consistent estimator of θ^2

Which of the above is/are correct?

(a) 1 only
(b) 2 only
(c) Both 1 and 2
(d) Neither 1 nor 2

33. A normal distribution with unspecified mean and variance is fitted to the following frequency distribution:

Class interval	Frequency
10.5-20.5	3
20.5-30.5	5
30.5-40.5	12
40.5-50.5	25
50.5-60.5	23
60.5-70.5	15
70.5-80.5	7
80.5-90.5	2

What are the degrees of freedom for corresponding ch-square test of goodness of fit?

(a) 3
(b) 4
(c) 5
(d) 6

34. The estimate of λ for the exponential distribution $f(x: \lambda) = \lambda e^{-\lambda x}$ for $0 \le x < \infty$ by the method of moments is

(a) $\bar{x}$
(b) $\frac{1}{\bar{x}}$
(c) $\bar{x}^2$
(d) $\frac{1}{\sqrt{\bar{x}}}$

35. Let P be the probability that a coin will fall head in a single toss in order to test the hypothesis $H_0 : p = \frac{1}{2}$ against $H_1 : p = \frac{3}{4}$. The coin is tossed 5 times and H_0 is rejected if more than three heads are obtained. The probability of type-I error is

(a) $\frac{3}{16}$
(b) $\frac{47}{128}$
(c) $\frac{81}{128}$
(d) $\frac{13}{16}$

36. If $x \ge 1$ is the critical region for testing H_0: $\theta = 1$ against the alternative H_1: $\theta = 2$ on the basis of single observation from the pupulation $f(x, \theta) = \theta e^{-\theta x}$, $0 \le x < \infty$, then the values of type-I and type-II errrors will be respectively

(a) $\frac{e-1}{e}, \frac{1}{e^2}$
(b) $\frac{1}{e^2}, \frac{e-1}{e}$
(c) $\frac{e^2-1}{e^2}, \frac{1}{e}$
(d) $\frac{1}{e}, \frac{e^2-1}{e^2}$

37. Let $x_1, x_2, x_3, ..., x_n$ be a ranndom sample from a normal population N(θ, 1). It is desired to test the null hypothesis $H_0: \theta = \theta_0$ against $H_1: \theta = \theta_1$, $(\theta_1 > \theta_0)$. Let a test rejected H_0 when $\overline{x} > \frac{\theta_0 + \theta_1}{2}$. If α and β are type-I and type-II error probabilities of this test, then

(a) $\alpha < \beta$ (b) $\alpha = \beta$

(c) $\alpha > \beta$ (d) $\alpha + \beta > 1$

38. Consider the following statements:

Statement I: UMVU estimator is always unique, if it exists.

Statement II: UMVU estimator is provided by CR lower bound only.

Which one of the following is correct in respect of the above statments?

(a) Both Statement I and Statement II are true and Statement II is the correct explanation of statement I

(b) Both Statement I and Statement II are true but Statement I

(c) Statement I is true but Statement II is false

(d) Statement I is false but Statememt I is true

39. For testing the hypothesis $H_0: \theta = \theta_0$ against the alternative $H_1: \theta = \theta_1$, α and β are the probabilities of type-I and type-II error respectively. Under the SPRT criteria, the values of the constants A and B (B < A) are respectively

(a) $\frac{\alpha}{1-\alpha}, \frac{\beta}{1-\beta}$ (b) $\frac{1-\beta}{\alpha}, \frac{\beta}{1-\alpha}$

(c) $\frac{\beta}{1-\alpha}, \frac{1-\beta}{\alpha}$ (d) $\frac{1-\alpha}{\alpha}, \frac{1-\beta}{\beta}$

40. A test in which decision about H_0 is taken aftet each successive observation is known as

(a) Bayes' test (b) likehood rtio test

(c) sequential probability ratio test (d) Student's ratio test

41. Let three be a population having p.d.f.

$$f(x, \theta) = \begin{cases} e^{-(x-\theta)}; & \theta \le x < \infty \\ 0; & \text{otherwise} \end{cases}$$

The maximum likelihood estimator of θ based on a random sample of size n is

(a) largest sample observation

(b) smallest sample observation

(c) sample median

(d) sample mode

42. If a sufficient statistic t for θ exists, then

1. MLE will be a function of sufficient statistic if it is unique

2. it will have the invariance property

3. $\phi(t)$ will be MLE for $\phi(\theta)$, provided ϕ is a continuous function of θ

Which of the above are correct?

(a) 1 and 2 only (b) 2 and 3 only

(c) 1 and 3 only (d) 1, 2 and 3

43. Regarding optimum properties of MLE under some regulatory conditions, we can say that

1. the likelihood equation has a solution which converges in probability to true value **
2. a consistant solution of likelihood equation does not correspond to the maximum of the likelihood
3. the likelihood equation has one and only one consistent solution

Which of the above are correct?

(a) 1and 2 only (b) 2 and 3 only

(c) 1 and 3 only (d) 1, 2 and 3

44. Let $x_1, x_2, x_3, ..., x_n$ be a ranndom sample of size n from a distibution with p.d.f.

$$f(x, \theta) = \frac{1}{\theta} e^{-\frac{x}{\theta}}; 0 < x < \infty, \theta > 0$$

(a) $\frac{\overline{x}}{\log_e 2}$ (b) $\frac{\log_e 2}{\overline{x}}$

(c) $\overline{x} \log_e 2$ (d) $\log_e 2$

45. The area of critical region depends on the

(a) size of type-I error

(b) size of type-II error

(c) value of statistic

(d) number of observations

46. Let X_1, X_2 be independently and identically distributed Poisson variables with parameter θ. Then $X_1 + 2X_2$ is

(a) sufficient statistic for θ (b) not sufficient statistic for θ

(c) minimal sufficient statistic for θ (d) complete sufficient statistic for θ

47. Let $X_1, X_2, X_3, ..., X_n$ be independently and identically distributed random variables from a distribution with

$$f(x, \theta) = \begin{cases} (\theta + 1)\, x^{\theta}; & 0 < x < 1, \theta > 0 \\ 0; & \text{otherwise} \end{cases}$$

Which of the following statements are correct for θ of the distribution?

1. The method of moments estimate of θ is given by $\frac{2\overline{x} - 1}{1 - \overline{x}}$, where $\overline{x}$ is the sample mean.
2. The estimate of $\frac{1}{\theta}$ obtained by the method of moments is $\frac{1 - H}{H}$, where H is the sample harmonic mean.

3. The maximum likelihood estimate of θ is = $\left(\frac{1+\log G}{\log G}\right)$, where G is the sample geometric mean.

Select the correct answer using the code given blow.

(a) 1 and 2 only (b) 2 and 3 only

(c) 1 and 3 only (d) 1, 2 and 3

48. Regularity conditions of Cramer-Rao inequality are related to
    (a) integrability of functions
    (b) differentiability of functions
    (c) both intregrability and differentiability of functions
    (d) neither integrability nor differeniability of functions

49. The decision criteria in SPRT depend on the functions of
    (a) type-I error
    (b) type-II error
    (c) both type-I and type-II errors
    (d) neither type-I nor type-II error

50. For testing $H_0: \theta = \theta_0$ against the alternative $H_1: \theta = 2\theta_0$, based on a single random observation y from the pupulation with p.d.f.

    $f(x, \theta) = \theta e^{-\theta x}; \theta > 0, 0 \leq x < \infty$

    the critical region for the hypothesis is $y \geq \frac{2}{\theta_0}$. Then type-I error and type -II error respectivley will be

    (a) e^{-6} and e^{-4} (b) e^{-4} and e^{-2}

    (c) e^{-2} and e^{-4} (d) e^{-4} and e^{-6}

51. Let $x_1, x_2, x_3, ..., x_n$ be a random sample from the population with p.d.f.

    $f(x, \theta) = \theta e^{\theta-1}; 0 \leq x < \infty, \theta > 0$

    Which one of the following is correct?

    (a) $t_1 = \prod_{i=1}^{n} x_i$ is sufficient estimator for θ

    (b) $t_1 = \prod_{i=1}^{n} x_i$ is sufficient estimator for θ

    (c) $t_1 = \prod_{i=1}^{n} x_i$ is sufficient estimator for θ

    (d) There does not exist any sufficient estimator for θ

52. Let $X_1, X_2, X_3, ..., X_n$ be i.i.d. $U(0, \theta)$ variates. Let
$Y = \max(X_1, X_2, X_3, ..., X_n)$
Then the unbiased estimator of $(3\theta^3 + 5\theta^5)$ is given by

(a) $(n+3)\, Y^3 + (n+5)\, Y^5$

(b) $\left(\dfrac{n+3}{n}\right)Y^3 + \left(\dfrac{n+5}{n}\right)Y^5$

(c) $3(n+3)\, Y^3 + 5(n+5)\, Y^5$

(d) $3\left(\dfrac{n+3}{n}\right)Y^3 + 5\left(\dfrac{n+5}{n}\right)Y^5$

53. Let X be a random variable following binomial distribution with parameters n = 10 and p. Suppose x is a sample value of size 1. The test is that if $x \le 3$, then reject H_0: $P = \frac{1}{2}$ and accept H_1: $p = \frac{1}{4}$. The size of the critical region is

(a) $\frac{1}{8}$

(b) $\frac{9}{64}$

(c) $\frac{5}{32}$

(d) $\frac{11}{64}$

54. Let X have a p.d.f. of the form $f(x, \theta) = \theta x^{\theta-1}, 0 < x < 1$. To test H_0: $\theta = 1$ against the alternative H_1: $\theta = 2$, we use a random sample X_1, X_2 of size n = 2 and define the critical region

$$\omega = \left\{(x_1, x_2); \frac{3}{4x_1} \le x_2\right\}$$

The size of the type-I error is
[Given, ln (0.75) = – 0.3]

(a) 0.01

(b) 0.025

(c) 0.05

(d) 0.1

55. A random variable takes the values 1, 2 and 3 with probabilities θ^2, $2\theta(1-\theta)$ and $(1-\theta)^2$ respectively with $0 < \theta < 1$. However the observed frequencies of 1, 2 and 3 are n_1, n_2 and n_3 respectively. The maximum likelihood estimator of θ is given by

(a) $\dfrac{2n_1 - n_2}{2(n_1 + n_2 + n_3)}$

(b) $\dfrac{2n_1 + n_2}{2(n_1 + n_2 + n_3)}$

(c) $\dfrac{n_1 - 2n_2}{2(n_1 + n_2 + n_3)}$

(d) $\dfrac{n_1 + 2n_2}{2(n_1 + n_2 + n_3)}$

56. Let $X_1, X_2, X_3, ..., X_n$ be i.i.d. random variables from $N(\mu, \sigma^2)$. Then the value of k for which
$t_{2n}(X) = k[(X_1 - X_2)^2 + (X_3 - X_4)^2 + ... + (X_{2n-1} - X_{2n})^2)$
is an unbiased estimator of σ^2 is given by

(a) $\frac{1}{n}$ (b) $\frac{1}{2n}$

(c) $\frac{1}{3n}$ (d) $\frac{1}{4n}$

57. Let T be MVU estimator of $g(\theta)$. Let T_1 and T_2 be unbiased estimators of $g(\theta)$ with efficiencies e_1 = 0.4 band e_2 = 0.9 respectivley. Let ρ be the correlation coefficient between T_1 and T_2 whose values lie in the interval

(a) $0.335 \le \rho \le 0.825$ (b) $0.345 \le \rho \le 0.835$

(c) $0.335 \le \rho \le 0.845$ (d) $0.365 \le \rho \le 0.855$

58. If T_1 and T_2 be unbiased estimators of $g(\theta)$ with variances $\sigma_1^2 = 1$ and $\sigma_2^2 = 4$ and $Corr(T_1, T_2) = \frac{1}{4}$, then the values of W_1 and W_2 for which $T = W_1T_1 + W_2T_2$ is BLUE for $g(\theta)$ are respectively

(a) $\frac{7}{8}$ and $\frac{1}{8}$ (b) $\frac{5}{8}$ and $\frac{3}{8}$

(c) $\frac{1}{2}$ and $\frac{1}{2}$ (d) $\frac{1}{8}$ and $\frac{7}{8}$

59. Which of the following statements is/are correct?

1. Cramer-Rao inequality gives an upper bound for the variance of an unbiased statistic.
2. Rao-Blackwellization means conditioning on a sufficient statistic to reduce variance.

Select the correct answer using the code given below.

(a) 1 only (b) 2 only

(c) Both 1 and 2 (d) Neither 1 nor 2

60. Consider the following statments:

1. If T_n is consistent for θ, then for any function f, $f(T_n)$ is consistent for $f(\theta)$.
2. Method of moments gives consistnet estimators.

Which of the above statements is/are correct?

(a) 1 only (b) 2 only

(c) Both 1 and 2 (d) Neither 1 nor 2

61. Consider the testing problem for $N(\theta, 1)$:

P_1: H_0: $\theta = \theta_0$ vs. H_1: $\theta > \theta_0$

P_2: H_1: $\theta = \theta_0$ vs. H_1: $\theta \neq \theta_0$

The UMP level α test exists

(a) for P_1 but not for P_2 (b) for P_2 but not for P_1

(c) for both P_1 and P_2 (d) neither for P_1 nor for P_2

62. Let $\frac{X}{\sigma_1^2}$ and $\frac{Y}{\sigma_2^2}$ be two independent chi-square variates with 2 and 6 degrees of freedom respectively. An unbiased estimator of $\frac{\sigma_1^2}{\sigma_2^2}$ is given by

(a) $\frac{X}{Y}$ (b) $\frac{2X}{Y}$

(c) $\frac{3X}{Y}$ (d) $\frac{4X}{Y}$

63. Let X be a binomial random variable with parameters n and θ. Let

$$tn(X) = \frac{x - \frac{\sqrt{n}}{2}}{n - \sqrt{n}}$$

Then consider the following statements:

1. $t_n(X)$ is biased estimator of θ.
2. $t_n(X)$ is consistent estimator of θ.

Which of the above statements is/are correct?

(a) 1 only (b) 2 only

(c) Both 1 and 2 (d) Neither 1 nor 2

64. A sample is drawn from the population

$$f(x; \alpha, \beta) = \frac{\beta^\alpha}{\Gamma\alpha} x^{\alpha-1} e^{-\beta x}, x \geq 0$$

and the values of first and second order sample moments about origin are 10 and 150 respectivley. THen the estimators of α and β obtained by method of moments are

(a) $\hat{\alpha} = 2$ and $\hat{\beta} = \frac{1}{5}$ (b) $\hat{\alpha} = \frac{1}{2}$ and $\hat{\beta} = 5$

(c) $\hat{\alpha} = 2$ and $\hat{\beta} = 5$ (d) $\hat{\alpha} = \frac{1}{2}$ and $\hat{\beta} = \frac{1}{5}$

65. Consider the following statements:

Statement I: SPRT sometimes provides a decision.

Statement II: Probability of terminating SPRT is one.

Which one of the following is correct in respect of the above statements?

(a) Both Statement I and Statement II are true and Statement II is the correct explanation of Statement I

(b) Both Statement I and Statement II are ture but Statement II is not the correct explanation of Statement I

(c) Statement I is true but Statement II is false

(d) Statement I is false but Statement II is true

66. Consider the following statements:
    1. Indian Statistical is decentralized by federal structure as also by subjects.
    2. State Statistical System is centralized.
    3. Statistical coordination is done by

    Which of the above statements are correct?

    (a) 1 and 2 only (b) 2 and 3 only
    (c) 1 and 3 only (d) 1, 2 and 3

67. Consider the following statements:
    1. National Statistical Commission has the responsibility of statistical audit.
    2. NSSO collect data by sample surveys.
    3. Censuses are conducted by RGI only/

    Which of the above statements are correct?

    (a) 1 and 2 only (b) 2 and 3 only
    (c) 1 and 3 only (d) 1, 2 and 3

68. Indian Statistical System is supported by which legialative framework?
    1. The Collection of Statistics Act, 2008
    2. The Registration of Births and Deaths Act, 1969
    3. The Census Act, 1948

    Select the correct answer using the code given below.

    (a) 1 and 2 only (b) 2 and 3 only
    (c) 1 and 3 only (d) 1, 2 and 3

69. Consider the following:
    1. National Family Health Survey— Ministry of Health and Family Welfare
    2. Civil Registration System — Registrar General and Census Commissioner of India
    3. Consumer Expenditure Survey — National Sample Survey Office

    Which of the above are correctly matched?

    (a) 1 and 2 only (b) 2 and 3 only
    (c) 1 and 3 only (d) 1, 2 and 3

70. Which of the following is/are the publication/publications of National Accounts Division of CSO in the MOSPI?
    1. National Accounts Statistics
    2. Input-Output Transactions Table
    3. Economic Census

    Select the correct answer using the code given below.

    (a) 1 only (b) 1 and 2
    (c) 1 and 3 (d) 2 and 3

71. Agricultrue Census data is collected in Land Records States through

1. complete enumeration of units
2. Khasra registers retabulation
3. sampling techniques

Which of the above is/are correct?

(a) 1 only (b) 2 only

(c) 1 and 2 (d) 1 and 3

72. Which one of the following is correcct in respect of Gross Enrolment Ratio (GER) in Grade-I?

(a) $GER = \frac{\text{Total Grade} - \text{I enrolment}}{\text{Population of age 6 years}} \times 100$

(b) $GER = \frac{\text{New entrants in Grade} - \text{I}}{\text{Population of age 6 years}} \times 100$

(c) $GER = \frac{\text{New entrants of age 6 years Grade} - \text{I}}{\text{Population of age 6 years}} \times 100$

(d) $GER = \frac{\text{Total Grade} - \text{I enrolment}}{\text{Population of age 6 years}} \times 1000$

73. The reference period in employment/unemployment surveys by NSSO is

1. one year
2. two weeks
3. each day of reference week
4. one week

Which of the above is/are correct?

(a) 1, 2 and 3 (b) 1, 3 and 4

(c) 1 only (d) 3 only

74. Which one of the following equations is valid?

(a) Promotion rate + Repetition rate + Dropout rate = 100

(b) Promotion rate + Repetition rate – Dropout rate = 100

(c) Promotion rate – Repetition rate + Dropout rate = 100

(d) None of the above

75. The Agriculture Census in India is conducted

(a) annual basis (b) quinquennial basis

(c) decadal basis (d) ad hoc basis

76. Consider the following:

1. The Prevention of Food Adulteration Act, 1954
2. The Medical Termination of Pregnancy Act, 1971
3. The Food Safety and Standards Act, 2006

Which of the above comes/come under the jurisdiction of MOHFW?

(a) 2 only (b) 1 and 3 only

(c) 1 and 2 only (d) 1, 2 and 3

77. Sample registration for collecting vital statistics is

(a) a fixed panel survey

(b) a cross-sectional survey

(c) both fixed panel survey and cross-sectional survey

(d) neither fixed panel survey nor cross-sectional survey

78. If the price index for the year 2015 is 110.3 and the price index for the year 2005 is 98.4, then what is the purchasing power of money (in ₹) of 2005 compared of 2015?

(a) 1.12 (b) 1.25

(c) 1.35 (d) 0.89

79. Consumer price index numbers revial the state of

(a) inflation

(b) deflation

(c) both inflation and deflation

(d) neither inflation nor deflation

80. The following table gives the frequency distribution of number of live births born to women in the age group 15-45 years:

Age group	Number of women	Number of live births
15-19	20000	600
20-24	18000	1200
25-29	14000	800
30-45	8000	96

The value of General Ferility Rate (GFR) based on the abovedata is

(a) 44.933 (b) 89.866

(c) 449.33 (d) 898.66

STATISTICS - II
2016

Time Allowed : Two Hours | *Maximum Marks: 200*

INSTRUCTIONS

1. IMMEDIATELY AFTER THE COMMENCEMENT OF THE EXAMINATION, YO SHOULD CHECK THAT THIS TEST BOOKLET *DOES NOT* HAVE ANY UNPRINTED OR TORN OR MISSING PAGES OR ITEMS, ETC. IF SO, GET IT REPLACE BY A COMPLETE TEST BOOKLET.
2. **Please note that it is the candidate'sresponsibility to encode and fill in the Roll Number and Test Booklet Series A, B, C or D carefully and without any omission or discrepancy at the appropriate places in the OMR Answer Sheet. Any omission/discrepancy will render the Answer sheet liable for rejection.**
3. You have to enter your Roll Number on the Test Booklet in the Box provided alongside. *DO NOT* write *anything else* on the Test Booklet.
4. This Test Booklet contains **80** items (questions).Each item comprises four responses (answers). You will select the response which you want to mark on the Answer Sheet. In case you feel that there is more than one correct response, mark the response which you consider the best. In any case, choose *ONLY ONE* response for each item.
5. You have to mark all your responses *ONLY* on the separate Answer Sheet provided. See directions in the Answer Sheet.
6. All items carry equal marks.
7. Before you proceed to mark in the Answer Sheet the response to various in the Test Booklet, you have to fill in some particulars in the Answer Sheet as per intructions sent to you with your Admission Certificate.
8. After you have complited filling in all your responses on the Answer Sheet and the examination has concluded, you should hand over to the Invigilator *only the Answer Sheet*. You are permitted to take away with you the Test Booklet.
9. Sheets for rough work are appended in the Test Booklet at the end.
10. **Penalty for wrong answers:**

    THERE WILL BE PENALTY FOR WRONG ANSWERS MARKED BY A CANDIDATE IN THE OBJECTIVE TYPE QUSTION PAPERS.

    (i) There are four alternatives for the answer to every question. For each question for which a wrong answer has been given by the candidate, **one-third** of the marks assigned to that question will be deducted as penalty.

    (ii) If a candidate gives more than one answer, it will be treated as a **wrong answer** even if one of the given answers happens to be correct and there will be same penalty as above to that question.

    (iii) If a question is left blamk,i.e., no answer is given by the candidate, there will be **no penalty** for that question.

DO NOT OPEN THIS TEST BOOKLET UNTIL YOU ARE TOLD TO DO SO

1. For what value of α, the BLUE of β_1 and β_2 are uncorrelated for the model

   $E(y_1) = 2\beta_1 + \beta_2, E(y_2) = \beta_1 - \beta_2, E(y_3) = \beta_1 + \alpha\beta_2$?

   (a) -1 (b) 0

   (c) 1 (d) 2

2. Let $y_i \sim N(0, 1)$ where I = 1, 2, 3, ... n be n independent standard normal variates, and $y'Ay$ be a quadratic from where A is an idempotent matrix, then what will be the distribution of $y'Ay$?

   (a) Normal distribution

   (b) Chi-square distribution

   (c) Bivariate Normal distribution

   (d) Rectangular distribution

3. A certain task can be accomplished in a factory by four different workers on five different types of machines. A sample study un context of a two-way design without repeated value is being made with tow fold objectives of examining whether the four workers differ with respect to mean productivity and whether it is same for five machines. The researcher involved in this study reports gathered data as under:

   Sum of squares for variance between machines = 53.8

   Sum of squares for variance between workers = 53.8

   Sum of squares for total variance = 174.2

   The F-statistic between machines is equal to:

   (a) 0.95 (b) 1.24

   (c) 1.48 (d) 1.75

4. The following data pertain to a test involving analysis of variance:

   Estimate of population variance based on variance among the sample means = 18.50 Estimate of the population variance based on the variance within the samples = 12.50 The F-ratio for the sample is equal to:

   (a) 0.68 (b) 1.48

   (c) 6.00 (d) 31.00

5. In the Gausss Markov linear model, let $\hat{y}$ denote the vector of fitted values and $\hat{\varepsilon}$ denote the vector of residuals. Consider the following statements:

   1. The components of $\hat{y}$ are pairwise uncorrelated.
   2. The components of $\hat{\varepsilon}$ are pairwise uncorrelated.

   Which of the above statements is/are correct?

   (a) 1 only (b) 2 only

   (c) Both 1 and 2 (d) Neither 1 nor 2

6. Suppose $b_1, b_2, b_3, ..., b_n$ are independent $N(0, \sigma^2)$ random variables and ε_{ij} are independent $N(0, \tau^2)$ random variables for i = 1, 2, 3, ..., k and j = 1, 2, 3, ..., n. Suppose we observe only $X_n = b_i + \varepsilon_{ij}$ for i = 1, 2, 3, ..., k and j = 1, 2, 3, ..., n. Then which of the following assertions are true?

   1. $Var(X_{ij}) = \sigma^2 + \tau^2$ for all i, j
   2. $Cov(X_{ij'}, X_{ij}) = 0$ for all i, j except when i = i′ and j = j′

3. $\frac{(X_{ij} - X_{ij'})^2}{2}$ is an unbiased estimator of σ^2 for $j \neq j'$

Select the correct answer using the code given below:

(a) 1 and 2 only (b) 1 and 3 only

(c) 2 and 3 only (d) 1, 2 nad 3

7. Which of the following statements are correct about generalized inverse of a matrix A?
   1. A generalized inverse of a matrix is defined as $A\bar{A}A = A$.
   2. A generalized inverse is not unique.
   3. A matrix to have generalized inverse must be non-singular.
   4. A martrix to have generalized inverse may be either square matrix or rectangular matrix

   Select the correct answer using the code given below:

   (a) 1, 2 and 3 (b) 1, 2 and 4

   (c) 2, 3 and 4 (d) 1, 3 and 4

8. Which of the following statements are associated with residuals of regression model?
   1. The sum of the residuals in any regression model that contains as intercept is always zero.
   2. The sum of the observed values y_i is not equal to sum of the fitted values $\hat{y}_i$.
   3. The sum of the residuals weighted by the corresponding regressor variable is zero.
   4. The sum of the residuals weighted by the corresponding fitted values is zero.

   Select the correct answer using the code given below:

   (a) 1, 2 and 3 (b) 1, 3 and 4

   (c) 1, 2 and 4 (d) 2, 3 and 4

9. For a simple linear regression model $y = \beta_0 + \beta_1 x + \varepsilon$, consider the following statements where $\hat{\beta}_0$ and $\hat{\beta}_1$ are estimates of β_0 and β_1.
   1. $\text{Cov}\ (y, \hat{\beta}_1) \neq 0$
   2. $\text{Cov}\ (\hat{\beta}_0, \hat{\beta}_1) = -\bar{x}V(\hat{\beta}_1)$
   3. $E(y) = \beta_0 + \beta_1 x$
   4. $\hat{\beta}_0 = \bar{y} - \hat{\beta}_1 x$

   Which of the above are correct?

   (a) 1, 2 and 3 (b) 1, 3 and 4

   (c) 2, 3 and 4 (d) 1, 2 and 4

10. Which of the following statements are correct in order to obtain the hypothesis H_0: $\beta_1 = 0$ for the model $y_i = \beta_0 + \beta_1 x_i + \varepsilon_i$?
    1. y_i is $N(\beta_0 + \beta_1 x_i, \sigma^2)$

2. $\hat{\beta}_1$ is $N\left(\beta_1, \frac{\sigma^2}{\sum_{i=1}^{n}(x_i - x)^2}\right)$

3. $\frac{(n-2)\,\hat{\sigma}^2}{\sigma^2}$ is χ^2_{n-2}

4. $\hat{\beta}_1$ and $\hat{\sigma}^2$ are not independent

Select the correct answer using the code given below:

(a) 1, 2 and 3 (b) 1 and 2 only

(c) 1, 2 and 4 (d) 3 and 4

For the next three (03) items that follow:

A company used three different methods to train its employees. The number of units of output produced by different employees trained by the three training methods is given below:

Method A:	50	45	55	44		
Method B:	64	48	52	56	44	
Method C:	46	42	48	45	57	42

It has to be tested whether the three different methods are satisfactory at 5% level of significance (Given $F_{2,12}$ at 0.05 = 3.89 as the critical value)

11. Which of the following is/are the null and alternate hypothesis for testing whether the mean number of units produced per hour is different for the different training methods?

1. $H_0: \mu_A = \mu_B = \mu_C$
2. $H_0: \mu_A \neq \mu_B \neq \mu_C$
3. $H_1: \mu_A, \mu_B$ and μ_C are not all equal
4. $H_1: \mu_A = \mu_B = \mu_C$

Select the correct answer using the code given below:

(a) 1 and 3 (b) 1 and 4

(c) 1 and 2 (d) 2 and 3

12. The estimate of the population variance on the basis of the variance among the sample means for the above methods is:

(a) 45.25 (b) 48.36

(c) 52.58 (d) 55.65

13. The estimate of the population variance within the samples for the different methods is:

(a) 25.67 (b) 31.07

(c) 38.646 (d) 39.097

14. In the Gausss-Markov linear model, what is the possible number of distinct solutions of the normal equations?

(a) Either 0 or 1 nor infinite (b) 1 only

(c) Infinite (d) Either 1 or infinite

15. If in a linear model $y_i = \beta_0 + \beta_1 x_i + \varepsilon_i$ for $i = 1, 2, 3, \ldots, n$, $E(\varepsilon_i) = 0$, $E(\varepsilon_i, \varepsilon_j) = 0$ for all $i \neq j$, then which of the following statements are correct for the method of estimation by least squares?

    1. The least square estimates of the parameters β_0 and β_1 are determined by minimizing the sum of squares of residuals.
    2. The observations y_i are pairwise uncorrelated.
    3. The observations yi are jointly independent and each y_i is a normal random variable.

    Select the correct answer using the code given below:

    (a) 1 and 2 only (b) 2 and 3 only
    (c) 1 and 3 only (d) 1, 2 and 3

16. If in a linear model $y_i = \beta_0 + \beta_1 x_i + \varepsilon_i$ for $i = 1, 2, 3, \ldots, n$ where ε_i are normal and independently distributed random variables with mean 0 and variance σ^2, the maximum likelihood estimators of β_0, β_1 and σ^2 are denoted by b_0, b_1 and $\hat{\sigma}^2$ respectively, then which of the following are correct for these estimators?

    1. The estimators are jointly complete sufficient statistics.
    2. (b_0, b_1) is independent of $\hat{\sigma}^2$.
    3. $\dfrac{(n-2)\,\hat{\sigma}^2}{\sigma^2}$ is a Chi-square random variable with $(n - 2)$ degrees of freedom.

    Select the correct answer using the code given below:

    (a) 1 and 2 only (b) 2 and 3 only
    (c) 1 and 3 only (d) 1, 2 and 3

17. What is R in linear hypothesis H_0: $R\beta = r$ with two restrictions $\alpha_0 = 2\alpha_1$ and $3\alpha_1 = 4\alpha_3$ in three variable linear model?

    (a) $\begin{bmatrix} 1 & -2 & 0 & 0 \\ 0 & 3 & 0 & -4 \end{bmatrix}$ (b) $\begin{bmatrix} 0 & -2 & 0 & 0 \\ 1 & 3 & 0 & -4 \end{bmatrix}$

    (c) $\begin{bmatrix} 3 & 0 & 1 & 0 \\ 0 & -2 & -4 & 0 \end{bmatrix}$ (d) $\begin{bmatrix} 1 & 0 & -2 & 0 \\ 3 & 0 & -4 & 0 \end{bmatrix}$

18. Mean square error criteria are used for selection of which one of the following?

    (a) Explanatory variables (b) Model
    (c) Estimates (d) Response variables

19. In which one of the following assumptions do the general linear model and generalized linear model differ?

    (a) Linearity (b) Homoscedasticity
    (c) Unbiasedness (d) Nonmulticollinearity

20. Consider the following statements associated with R^2 and $\bar{R}^2$ criteria:

1. R^2 increases with the inclusion of relevant explanatory variable only.
2. R^2 increases whether the included explanatory variable is relevant or irrelevant.
3. $\bar{R}^2$ decreases if the included explanatory variable is irrelevant.

Which of the above statements are correct?

(a) 1 and 2 only (b) 1 and 3 only

(c) 2 and 3 only (d) 1, 2 and 3

21. Let $X_1, X_2, X_3, \ldots, X_n$ be i.i.d. P(λ) variables. Which of the following statements are correct?

1. $T = \sum_{i=1}^{n} X_i$ is a complete sufficient statistic for λ
2. $\bar{X} = \frac{T}{n}$ is the unique UMVUE for λ
3. $E(X_i | T)$ is the unique UMVUE for λ

Select the correct answer using the code given below:

(a) 1 and 2 only (b) 2 and 3 only

(c) 1 and 3 only (d) 1, 2 and 3

22. Consider the following statements:

Statement-I: Where the parent distribution is discrete, the non-randomised tests may not exactly attain a given level of significance α.

Statement-II: α usually has a low value like 0.01 or 0.05. Even inclusion of any single discrete point with positive probability in the critical region often makes the level greater than the prescribed value.

Which one of the following is correct in respect of the above two statements?

(a) Both Statement-I and Statement-II are true and Statement-II is the correct explanation for Statement-I

(b) Both Statement-I and Statement-II are true but Statement-II is not the correct explanation for Statement-I

(c) Statement-I is true but Statement-II is false

(d) Statement-I is false but Statement-II is true

23. Consider the following statements:

Statement-I: Sequential Probability Ratio Test (SPRT) requires, on an average, smaller number of observations than a non-sequential test with identical error controlling properties.

Statement-II: SPRT can be carried out graphically.

Which one of the following is correct in respect of the above two statements?

(a) Both Statement-I and Statement-II are true and Statement-II is the correct explanation for Statement-I

(b) Both Statement-I and Statement-II are true but Statement-II is not the correct explanation for Statement-I

(c) Statement-I true but Statement-II is false

(d) Statement-I is false but Statement-II is true

24. Let $X_1, X_2, X_3, \ldots, X_n$ be independent random variables distributed uniformly on the interval (0, θ). If n is odd, which of the following is/are the unbiased estimator(s) of θ?

1. $X_{(n)}$
2. $2X_{\left(\frac{n+1}{2}\right)}$

Select the correct answer using the code given below:

(a) 1 only (b) 2 only

(c) Both 1 and 2 (d) Neither 1 nor 2

25. If $X_1, X_2, X_3, \ldots, X_n$ be independent random variables distributed as b(1, p), then which of the following statements are cofrrect?

1. $T = \sum_{i=1}^{n} X_i$ is sufficient for p
2. $T = \sum_{i=1}^{n} X_i$ is complete for p
3. T^2 is unbiased for p^2

Select the correct answer using the code given below :

(a) 1 and 2 only (b) 2 and 3 only

(c) 1 and 3 only (d) 1, 2 and 3

26. For testing hypothesis $H_0: \theta = \theta_0$ against the alternative $H_1: \theta = \theta_1$, λ is the likelihood ratio; A and B (B < A) are the constants. Under the SPRT criteria, consider the following statements:

1. If $\lambda \geq A$, we terminate the process with the acceptance of H_0
2. If $\lambda \leq B$, we terminate the process with the rejection of H_0
3. If $B < \lambda < A$, we continue sampling by taking an additional observation

Which of the above statements is/are correct?

(a) 1, 2 and 3 (b) 1 and 3 only

(c) 2 and 3 only (d) 3 only

27. If $X_1, X_2, X_3, \ldots, X_n$ is a random sample of size n from Cauchy distribution with pdf f(x) = $\frac{1}{\pi[1+(x-\mu)^2]}; -\infty < x < \infty$, then which one of the following is true for estimating μ?

(a) Sample mean is a consistent estimator but not sample median

(b) Sample median is a consistent estimator but not sample mean

(c) Both sample mean and sample median are consistent estimators

(d) Neither sample mean nor sample median is a consistent estimator

28. If T_1 and T_2 are independent and unbiased estimators of parameter θ with $V(T_1) = \sigma_1^2$ and $V(T_2) = 2\sigma_1^2$, then the unbiased estimator of θ given by $T = \lambda T_1 + (1 - \lambda) T_2$ has minimum variance if λ equals:

(a) 2/3 (b) 1/2
(c) 1/3 (d) 1/4

29. Consider the following statements pertaining to likelihood ratio tests:

1. The likelihood ratio criterion offers a method of constructing tests of hypotheses which do not fall within the purview of Neyman-Pearson Lemma
2. The likelihood ratio test statistic λ is the ratio of the supremum of the likelihood under H_0 to the supremum of the likelihood in the unrestricted parametric space
3. The critical region of the likelihood ratio test is the left hand tail of the distribution of λ

Which of the above statements are correct?

(a) 1 and 2 only (b) 2 and 3 only
(c) 1 and 3 only (d) 1, 2 and 3

30. Let $X_1, X_2, X_3, \ldots, X_n$ be a random variable with pdf

$$f(x;\alpha,\beta) = \begin{cases} \dfrac{1}{\beta^\alpha \overline{|\alpha}} e^{-\frac{x}{\beta}} x^{\alpha-1}; & x, \alpha, \beta > 0 \\ 0, & \text{otherwise} \end{cases}$$

What is the consistent estimator for β^2?

(a) $\dfrac{\sum_{i=1}^{n} X_i^2}{n\alpha(\alpha+1)^2}$ (b) $\dfrac{\sum_{i=1}^{n} X_i^2}{n\alpha^2(\alpha+1)}$

(c) $\dfrac{\sum_{i=1}^{n} X_i^2}{n\alpha(\alpha+1)}$ (d) $\dfrac{\sum_{i=1}^{n} X_i^2}{n^2\alpha(\alpha+1)}$

31. Which one of the following sampling designs is used in conducting the Consumer Expenditure Survey by the National Sample Survey Office (NSSO)?

(a) Simple Random Sampling
(b) Quota Sampling
(c) Stratified Multi-stage Random Sampling
(d) Judgement Sampling

32. Given a random sample from

$$F(x, \alpha) = \frac{2}{\alpha^2}(\alpha - x), 0 < x < \alpha$$

What is the MLE for α?

(a) x
(b) 2x
(c) $\frac{x}{2}$
(d) None of the above

33. Consider the following statements:
    1. Size of Type-I error is P {rejecting $H_0 | H_0$ is true}
    2. Power of a test is P {rejecting $H_0 | H_1$ is true}
    3. $H_1: \mu \neq \mu_0$ is a right tailed hypothesis

    Which of the statements given above are correct?

    (a) 1 and 2 only
    (b) 2 and 3 only
    (c) 1 and 3 only
    (d) 1, 2 and 3

34. The Manager of a cyber café says that the number of customers visiting on the weekdays followed a Binomial distribution. Which one of the following techniques can be used to test the hypothesis at a given level of significance?
    (a) Test of significance of mean
    (b) Chi-square test as a test of goodness of fit
    (c) Test of significance of difference between two means
    (d) Correlation analysis

35. What is an unbiased estimator of θ for the distribution, $f(x, \theta) = \theta e^{-\theta x}, x \geq 0$?

    (a) $\frac{(n-1)\bar{x}}{n}$
    (b) $\frac{(n-1)}{n\bar{x}}$
    (c) $\frac{\bar{x}}{n-1}$
    (d) $\frac{1}{(n-1)\bar{x}}$

36. Consider the following statements regarding the properties of an estimator:
    1. Every consistent estimator is unbiased.
    2. If an estimator t_n based on n observations is a consistent estimator of θ, then for any $\varepsilon > 0$, Prob $\{|t_n - \theta| < \varepsilon\}$ tends to one as $n \to \infty$
    3. Since consistency is a limiting property, no consistent estimator actually exists as sampling size is finite.

    Which of the above statements are not correct?

    (a) 2 and 3 only
    (b) 1 and 3 only
    (c) 1 and 2 only
    (d) 1, 2 and 3

37. Consider a random sample $X_1, X_2, X_3, \ldots, X_n$ of size n from $N(\theta, \theta^2)$, the statistic

    $T = \left(\sum_{i=1}^{n} X_i, \sum_{i=1}^{n} X_i^2\right)$ for θ is:

    (a) Sufficient and complete
    (b) Sufficient but not complete
    (c) Not sufficient but complete
    (d) Neither sufficient nor complete

38. In usual notations, if a quantity ϕ (T, θ) exists, whose distribution is independent of θ, then which of the following are correct?

1. $\phi(T, \theta)$ is called a confidence interval.
2. $\phi(T, \theta)$ is a pivotal quantity.
3. $\phi(T, \theta)$ can be used to define $(1 - \alpha)$ 100% confidence interval for θ.

Select the correct answer using the code given below:

(a) 1 and 3 only (b) 1 and 2 only

(c) 2 and 3 only (d) 1, 2 and 3

39. Consider the following statements with respect to Neyman-Pearson Lemma if C is a critical region of size α and k is a constant.

1. $\frac{L_0}{L_1} \leq k$ inside C
2. $\frac{L_0}{L_1} \geq k$ outside C
3. C is a most powerful critical region of size α for testing $\theta = \theta_0$ against $\theta = \theta_1$

Which of the above are correct?

(a) 1, 2 and 3 (b) 2 and 3 only

(c) 1 and 3 only (d) 3 only

40. To compare the quality of LED TVs of Brand 'A' and Brand 'B', a statistician collects the following data:

$X_1, X_2, X_3, \ldots, X_n$ are the number of dead pixels in a random sample of n Brand 'A' TVs and $Y_1, Y_2, Y_3, \ldots, Y_m$ are the number of dead pixels in a random sample of m Brand 'B' TVs.

Assuming that the X_is and Y_is are independent Poisson random variables with mean λ_1 and λ_2 for Brand 'A' and Brand 'B' TVs respectively, the statistician decides to test the hypothesis $H_0: \lambda_1 = \lambda_2$ versus $H_1: \lambda_1 \neq \lambda_2$.

Here H_0 and H_1 are respectively:

(a) Simple and simple (b) Simple and composite

(c) Composite and simple (d) Composite and composite

41. If X_i follows $U(\theta, \theta)$ be a random sample for I = 1, 2, 3, ..., n, then what is an unbiased estimator of θ?

(a) $\overline{X}$ (b) $\frac{\overline{X}}{2}$

(c) $2\overline{X}$ (d) $\sqrt{\overline{X}}$

42. X has a Poisson λ distribution. Then $(\overline{X} - S^2)$, where $\overline{X}$ is the sample mean based on a random sample of size n and $S^2 = \dfrac{\sum (X_i - \overline{X})^2}{n}$, is an unbiased estimator of:

(a) 0 (b) $\dfrac{\lambda}{n}$

(c) $\lambda - \lambda^2$ (d) $\left(1 - \dfrac{1}{n}\right)\lambda$

43. An unbiased estimator of $\dfrac{1}{\theta}$ for the distribution $f(x, \theta) = \theta\,(1 - \theta)^{x-1}$, $x = 1, 2, 3, \ldots, \infty$; $0 < \theta < 1$ is:

(a) $\dfrac{1}{x}$ (b) $\dfrac{1}{n\overline{x}}$

(c) $n\overline{x}$ (d) $\overline{x}$

44. If $X_1, X_2, X_3, \ldots, X_n$ is a random sample from b(1, p), then:

(a) Sample mena $\overline{X}$ is unbiased for p but not consistent

(b) Sample mean $\overline{X}$ is consistent for p but not unbiased

(c) Sample mean $\overline{X}$ is unbiased and consistent for p

(d) Sample mean $\overline{X}$ is neither unbiased nor consistent for p

45. Consider the following statements:

1. If T is an unbiased estimator of θ, then T^2 is an unbiased estimator of θ^2
2. If T is a consistent estimator of θ, then T^3 is a consistent estimator of θ^3

Which of the above statements is/are correct?

(a) 1 only (b) 2 only

(c) Both 1 and 2 (d) Neither 1 nor 2

46. What is the MLE of θ based on a random sample of size n drawn from a population with pdf as

$$f(x, \theta) = \begin{cases} \theta e^{-\theta x}, & \theta < x < \infty \\ 0, & \text{otherwise} \end{cases} ?$$

(a) $\overline{x}$ (b) $\dfrac{1}{\overline{x}}$

(c) Largest observation (d) Smallest observation

47. If population variance of an infinite population is σ^2 and a sample of 25 items is selected from this population, then what is the standard error of sample mena?

(a) $\dfrac{\sigma^2}{25}$ (b) $\dfrac{\sigma}{5}$

(c) $\dfrac{\sigma}{25}$ (d) σ

48. Consider the following statements:

Statement-I: An SPRT always provides a decision.

Statement-II: Probability of terminating an SPRT is one.

Which one of the following is correct in respect of the above two statements?

(a) Both Statement-I and Statement-II are true and Statement-II is the correct explanation for Statement-I

(b) Both Statement-I and Statement-II are true but Statement-II is not the correct

(c) Statement-I is true but Statement-II is false

(d) Statement-I is false but Statement-II is true

49. Consider the following statements:

1. The purpose of hypothesis testing is to make a judgement about the difference between the sample statistic and the hypothesized population parameter.
2. When the Null hypothesis is rejected the alternate hypothesis is accepted.
3. The purpose of hypothesis testing is to test the correctness of the computed value of the sample statistic.
4. If the Null hypothesis is not rejected, this does not ensure that the Null hypothesis is true.

Which of the above statements are correct?

(a) 1, 2 and 3 (b) 1, 3 and 4

(c) 1, 2 and 4 (d) 2, 3 and 4

50. Which one of the following statements is correct?

(a) The mean of the sampling distribution of mean is greater than the population mean.

(b) The sampling distribution of mean approaches normality as the sampling size decreases.

(c) As the standard error of mean increases, the value of any sample mean will be closer to the value of the population mean.

(d) As the standard error of mean decreases, the precision of the sample mean as an estimator of the population mean increases.

51. Suppose $X_1, X_2, X_3, \ldots, X_{10}, Y_1, Y_2, Y_3, \ldots, Y_{10}$ are independent random variables where X_is have density $f_x(x) = \frac{1}{\lambda} e^{-\frac{x}{\lambda}}$ $x > 0$ and Y_is have density $f_Y(y) = \frac{1}{2\lambda} e^{-\frac{x}{2\lambda}}$, $y = 0$.

What is MLE of λ based on all X_is and Y_is?

(a) $\frac{\overline{X}+\overline{Y}}{2}$ (b) $\frac{\overline{X}+\overline{Y}}{3}$

(c) $\frac{2\overline{X}+\overline{Y}}{4}$ (d) $\frac{\overline{X}+2\overline{Y}}{5}$

52. In a normal population $N(\mu, \sigma^2)$ with $\sigma^2 = 4$, in order to test the null hypothesis $\mu = \mu_0$ against the alternative $\mu = \mu_1$, where $\mu_1 > \mu_0$ based on a random sample of size n, the value of k such that $\overline{x} > k$ provides a critical region of size $\alpha = 0.05$ is:

(a) $\mu_0 + \frac{1.645}{\sqrt{n}}$

(b) $\mu_0 + \frac{3.290}{\sqrt{n}}$

(c) $\mu_0 + \frac{1.96}{\sqrt{n}}$

(d) $\mu_0 + \frac{3.92}{\sqrt{n}}$

53. For testing the null hypothesis $H_0: \mu = \mu_0$ against the alternative $H_1: \mu \neq \mu_0$ at α% level of significance on the basis of a random sample of size n from a normal population with known variance $\sigma^2 = 1$, consider the following statements with respect to likelihood ratio criteria (λ):

1. The value of λ is $e^{-\frac{n}{2}(\bar{x}-\mu_0)^2}$
2. The null hypothesis is rejected if $\lambda \leq k, 0 \leq k \leq 1$
3. λ is a ratio of the maximum likelihood function for all values of μ in parameter space and maximum likelihood space and maximum likelihood function for all values of μ under H_0

Which of the above statements are correct?

(a) 1 and 2 only
(b) 2 and 3 only
(c) 1 and 3 only
(d) 1, 2 and 3

54. Consider the following statements:

1. If $X_1, X_2, X_3, \ldots, X_n$ is a random sample from normal population, then the sample variance S^2 is consistent estimator of σ^2.
2. If $X_1, X_2, X_3, \ldots, X_n$ is a random sample from normal population with mean 0, then $\frac{\sum X_i^2}{n}$ is unbiased estimator of σ^2.
3. If $X_1, X_2, X_3, \ldots, X_n$ is a random sample from an exponential population with probability density function $f(x, \theta) = \begin{cases} \frac{1}{\theta} e^{-\frac{x}{\theta}}; & x > 0, \\ 0; & \text{otherwise} \end{cases}$, then $\bar{X}$ is consistent estimator for parameter θ.
4. If $X_1, X_2, X_3, \ldots, X_n$ is a random sample from $U(0, \beta)$, then the nth order statistic Y_n is unbiased estimator β.

Which of the above statements are correct?

(a) 2, 3 and 4
(b) 1, 2 and 4
(c) 1, 3 and 4
(d) 1, 2 and 3

55. Cramer Rao Jower bound of variance for the parameter θ of the distribution with pdf

$f(x, \theta) = \frac{1}{\pi} \frac{1}{1+(x-\theta)^2}$ where $-\infty < x < \infty$ is:

(a) $\frac{1}{n}$

(b) $\frac{2}{n}$

(c) $\frac{1}{n^2}$

(d) $\frac{2}{n^2}$

56. An estimator with larger variance is preferred in which one of the following cases?

(a) X follows gamma $(1, \beta)$ (b) X follows $U(0, \theta)$

(c) X follows gamma $\left(1, \frac{1}{\beta}\right)$ (d) X follows gamma $\left(1, \frac{1}{\theta}\right)$

57. Let $X_1, X_2, X_3, \ldots, X_n$ be independently and normally distributed with mean 0 and variance σ^2. What is the minimum variance unbiased estimator of σ^2?

(a) $\frac{1}{n-1}\sum_{i=1}^{n} X_i^2$ (b) $\frac{1}{n}\sum_{i=1}^{n} X_i^2$

(c) $\frac{1}{n}\sum_{i}^{n}(X_i - \bar{X})^2$ (d) $\frac{1}{n-1}\sum_{i}^{n}(X_i - \bar{X})^2$

58. If X_1, X_2 and X_3 is a random sample of size 3 from a population with mean μ and variance σ^2. What is the value of λ for which $T_3 = \frac{1}{3}(\lambda X_1 + X_2 + X_3)$ is an unbiased estimator for μ?

(a) 1/4 (b) 1/3

(c) 1/2 (d) 1

59. If $\bar{X}$ and S^2 are the mean and variance of a random sample of size n from a normal population with mean μ and standard deviation σ, then consider the following statements:

1. $\bar{X}$ is unbiased and consistent estimator of μ.
2. S^2 is consistent estimator of σ^2.
3. The random variable $\frac{(n-1)\,S^2}{\sigma^2}$ has a Chi-square distribution with $(n - 1)$ degrees of freedom.

Which of the above statements are correct?

(a) 1 and 2 only (b) 2 and 3 only

(c) 1 and 3 only (d) 1, 2 and 3

60. If the pdf of a random variable X is $f(x; \theta) = 1 - \theta^2,\ 0 \le x \le \frac{1}{1-\theta^2}$ and if we reject H_0: $\theta = \frac{1}{2}$ against H_1: $\theta = \frac{3}{4}$ whenever $x \ge 1$, then what is the power of the test?

(a) 15.16 (b) 1/2

(c) 7.16 (d) 9/16

61. Consider the following statements:

Statements-I: Fisher's Index number is known as ideal Index number.

Statement-II: Fisher's Index number is the arithmetic mean of Laspeyre's Index number and Paasche's Index number which show upward bias and downward bias respectively.

Which one of the following is correct in resect of the above two statements?

(a) Both Statement-I and Statement-II are true and Statement-II is the correct explanation for Statement-I

(b) Both Statement-I and Statement-II are true but Statement-II is not the correct explanation for Statement-I

(c) Statement-I is true but Statement-II is false

(d) Statement-I is false but Statement-II is true

62. If $X_1, X_2, X_3, \ldots, X_n$ is a random sample from $N(0, \sigma^2)$, then which one of the following statements is correct?

(a) $\sum_{i=1}^{n} X_i^2$ is minimal sufficient statistic for σ^2

(b) $\sum_{i=1}^{n} X_i$ is sufficient statistic for σ^2

(c) $\overline{X}$ is minimal sufficient statistic for σ^2

(d) There is no minimal sufficient statistic for σ^2

63. If $X_1, X_2, X_3, \ldots, X_n$ is a random sample from the uniform distribution on [0, a] where $a \in (0, \infty)$, then which of the following statements are correct?

1. Maximum likelihood estimator of 'a' is same as the moment estimator of 'a'
2. Maximum likelihood estimator of 'a' is $X_{(n)} = \text{Max}\{X_1, X_2, X_3, \ldots, X_n\} = \hat{a}$
3. $\frac{n+1}{n}\hat{a}$ is an unbiased estimator of 'a' where $\hat{a}$ is maximum likelihood estimator of 'a'
4. Method of moments estimator is unbiased estimator of 'a'

Select the correct answer using the code given below:

(a) 2, 3 and 4 (b) 1, 3 and 4

(c) 1, 2 and 4 (d) 1, 2 and 3

64. Randomised test is used for testing parametric hypothesis regarding distribution of a random variable X:

(a) Whenever X has a discrete distribution

(b) Whenever exact size α test is required

(c) When X is a discrete random variable and exact size α test is required

(d) When X is a continuous random variable and exact size α test is required

65. If $X_1, X_2, X_3, \ldots, X_n$ is a random sample from Poisson distribution with parameter λ, then the maximum likelihood estimator of $\log \lambda$ is given by:

(a) $e^{\sum_{i=1}^{n} \frac{X_i}{n}}$ (b) $\log\left(\frac{\sum_{i=1}^{n} X_i}{n}\right)$

(c) $e^{\sum_{i=1}^{n} X_i}$ (d) $\log\left(\sum_{i=1}^{n} X_i\right)$

66. griculture Census in India is conducted at an interval of:

(a) 3 years (b) 5 years

(c) 8 years (d) 10 years

67. Which one of the following sampling designs is used for General Crop Estimation Survey (GCES)?

(a) Simple Random Sampling (SRS)

(b) Judgement Sampling

(c) Stratified Multi-stage Random Sampling

(d) Quota Sampling

68. Which of the following are the components of the schemen 'Im[rovement of Agricultural Statistics'?

1. Timely Reporting Scheme (TRS)
2. Improvement of Crop Statistics (ICS)
3. Establishment of Agency Reporting Agricultural Statics (EARAS)
4. Studying cost of cultivation of principal crops in India

Select the correct answer using the code given below:

(a) 2, 3 and 4 (b) 1, 3 and 4

(c) 1, 2 and 4 (d) 1, 2 and 3

69. Minimum Support Prices (MSP) of major agricultural products are recommended to the Government by:

(a) Directorate of Economics and Statistics

(b) Directorate of Marketing and Inspection

(c) Commission for Agricultural Costs and Prices

(d) Directorate of Rice Development

70. Which one of the following index numbers is used for calculating the Dearness Allowance (DA) of Central Government Employees?

1. Consumer Price Index (Rural, Urban, Combined)
2. Consumer Price Index (Industrial Workers)
3. Wholesale Price Index
4. Index of Industrial Production

Select the correct answer using the code given below:

(a) 2 only (b) 1 and 2 only

(c) 1, 2 and 3 (d) 1, 3 and 4

71. Consider a single observation from the population $f(x, \theta) = \theta e^{-\theta x}, 0 < x < \infty$.

Let $x \geq 1$ be the critical region for testing $H_0: \theta = 2$ against $H_1: \theta = 1$. What are the values of type I and type II errors respectively?

(a) $\frac{e-1}{e}, \frac{1}{e^2}$ (b) $\frac{1}{e}, \frac{e-1}{e^2}$

(c) $\frac{e-1}{e^2}, \frac{1}{e}$ (d) $\frac{1}{e}, \frac{e-1}{e}$

72. Which one of the following organizations of the Government is responsible for collection, compilation and dissemination of Trade Statistics in India?

(a) Central Statistical Office

(b) Directorate General of Commercial

(c) Department of Industrial Policy and Promotion

(d) Tariff Commission

73. What are the major sources of data on Official Statistics?

1. Census and Sample Surveys
2. Administrative Records

Select the correct answer using the code given below:

(a) 1 only (b) 2 only

(c) Both 1 and 2 (d) Neither 1 nor 2

74. Which of the following are the major sources on 'Health Statistics' in India?

1. Sample Registration System (SRS)
2. Civil Registration System (CRS)
3. National Family Healthy Survey (NFHS)

Select the corrects answer using the code given below:

(a) 1 and 2 only (b) 2 and 3 only

(c) 1 and 3 only (d) 1, 2 and 3

75. Which of the following is/are correct for Consumer Price Index (Rural, Urban, Combined)?

1. Base year is 2012
2. Weights have been derived from the Consumer Expenditure Survey conducted by NSSO during 2011-2012

Select the correct answer using the code given below:

(a) 1 only (b) 2 only

(c) Both 1 and 2 (d) Neither 1 nor 2

76. Which of the following are part of mandate of SDRD?

1. Planning of Survey
2. Formulation of Sampling Design

3. Conducting of Sample Survey
4. Preparation of Survey Reports

Select the correct answer using the code given below:

(a) 1, 2 and 4 (b) 1, 2 and 3
(c) 1, 3 and 4 (d) 2, 3 and 4

77. Which of the following equations are correct in respect of National Accounts?

1. NDP = GDP + CFC
2. GNI = GDP + net factor income from abroad
3. NNI = GNI – CFC

Select the correct answer using the code given below:

(a) 1 and 2 only (b) 2 and 3 only
(c) 1 and 3 only (d) 1, 2 and 3

78. The first phase of Population Census is associated with which of the following?

1. House listing
2. Housing Census
3. Population Enumeration

Select the correct answer using the code given below:

(a) 1 and 2 only (b) 2 and 3 only
(c) 1 and 3 only (d) 1, 2 and 3

79. Which of the following is/are correctly matched?

1. Population Census – Office of Registrar General and Census Commissioner
2. Economic Census – Central Statistics Office

Select the correct answer using the code given below:

(a) 1 only (b) 2 only
(c) Both 1 and 2 (d) Neither 1 nor 2

80. The Unified District Information System for Education (U-DISE), which is an important source of school education data, has been developed by which one of the following?

(a) National Council of Educational Research and Training
(b) National University of Educational Planning and Administration
(c) University Grants Commission
(d) National Sample Survey Office

STATISTICS
Paper II 2015

Time Allowed : Three Hours | Maximum Marks: 200

INSTRUCTIONS

Please read each of the following instructions carefully before attempting questions. There are EIGHT questions divided under TWO sections. Candidate has to attept SIX questions in all. Question No. 1 and 5 are compulsory and out of the remaining. FOUR are to be attempted choosing at least TWO from each Section. The number of marks carried by a question/part is indicated aginst it. Unless otherwise mentioned, symbols and notations have their usual standard meanings. Assume suitable data, if necessary and indicate the same clearly. Candidate should attempt questions/parts as per the instructions given in the Section. All parts and sub-parts of a question are to be attempted together in the answer book. Atempts of questions shall be counted even if attempted partly. Any page or portion of the page left blank in the answer book mst be clearly struck off. Answers must be writtn in ENGLISH only.

Section A

1. Answer all of the following: **5×8=40**

(a) Let X be a random variable havig probability density function

$$f_X(x, \theta) = \frac{1}{\theta}, \; 4 < x < 4 + \theta$$
$$= 0, \quad \text{otherwise.}$$

Find an unbiased estimator of θ^2 based on a sample of size 1.

(b) Consider the matrix

$$X' = \begin{pmatrix} 1 & 1 & 1 & 1 & 1 & 1 & 1 & 1 \\ 1 & 1 & 1 & 1 & 0 & 0 & 0 & 0 \\ 0 & 0 & 0 & 0 & 1 & 1 & 1 & 1 \\ 1 & 2 & 3 & 4 & 1 & 2 & 3 & 4 \end{pmatrix}$$

Find a basis of the column space (X) and obtain a g-inverse of $X'X$.

(c) Consider the Gauss-Markov model

$E(y_1) = 2\beta_1 + \beta_2$

$E(y_2) = \beta_1 - \beta_2$

$E(y_3) = \beta_1 + \alpha\beta_2,$

with usual assumptions. Determine α so that the best linear unbiased estimators (BLUEs) of β_1 and β_2 are uncorrelated.

(d) Let $y_1, y_2, ..., y_n$ be a random sample from $N(\mu, \sigma^2)$ where μ and σ^2 are both unknown. Obtain a confidence interval for μ with confidence coefficient $(1 - \alpha)$.

(e) Show that, if T is a sufficient statistic for θ, any solution of the likelihood equatio will be the function of this statistic. State true or false. A minimal sufficient statistic is always sufficient.

(f) Stating the regularity conditions, give the Cramer-Rao lower bound for the variance of an unbiased estimator of a parameter. Give an example, each, of a situation where the regularity conditions (i) does not hold (ii) holds.

(g) Show, in the context of Gauss Markov model $(Y, X\beta, \sigma^2 I)$, that the projection of an unbiased estimator of an estimable linear parametric function $\lambda'\beta$ is also an unbiased estimator of $\lambda'\beta$.

(h) Consider an unbalanced one way fixed effects model

$y_{ij} = \mu + \alpha_i + e_{ij}, i = 1, ... k, j = 1 ... n_i$

where $E(e_{ij}) = 0$ for all i, j. Obtain the constraint needed for estimability of the parameters. Discuss the analysis of variance in a situation where the model is applied.

2. **Answer all of the following:** **10×3=30**

(a) Consider the linear model $\underset{\sim}{y} = X\beta + \underset{\sim}{e}, E(\underset{\sim}{e}) = 0$, disp $(\underset{\sim}{e}) = \sigma^2 V$, V known and positive definite and σ^2 is unknown. Show that the estimator $l'\underset{\sim}{y}$ is the BLUE for $E(l'\underset{\sim}{y})$ iff $l'\underset{\sim}{y}$ is uncorrelated with all unbiased estimators of zero.

(b) Let $X_1, X_2, ... X_n$ be a random sample from the probability distribution with density

$$f_X(x, \theta) = \frac{1}{\theta} e^{\frac{x}{\theta}}, \quad 0 < x < \infty$$

$$= 0, \quad \text{otherwise}$$

where $0 < \theta < \infty$. Show that $\overline{X} = \frac{1}{n}\sum_{i=1}^{n} X_i$ is a minimum variance bound estimator and has variance $\frac{\sigma^2}{n}$.

(c) Write Tukey's non-additive model for a set of two-way classified data with one observation per cell. Suggest an estimator of the non-additivity parameter and find the distribution under additivity. Derive a test for additivity for such a model.

3. Answer all of the following: **10×3=30**

(a) The observations

3.9, 2.4, 1.8, 3.5, 2.4, 2.7, 2.5, 2.1, 3.0, 3.6, 3.6, 1.8, 2.0, 4.0, 1.5

are a random sample from a rectangular population with pdf

$$f(x; a, b) = \frac{1}{b-a}, \quad a \le x \le b$$

$$0, \quad \text{otherwise}$$

Estimate the parameters by the method of moments.

(b) Explain how the Rao-Blackwell theorem helps one to find a uniformly minimum variance unbaiased estimator (UMVUE) of an unknown parameter. What is the relevance of the Lehman-Scheffe theorem in this scenario? Is $X_1, X_2, \ldots X_n$ are Bin (1, p) varites, find the UMVUE of p.

(c) For a completely balanced two-way random effects model, find unbiased estimators of different variance components. Explain how to obtain the variance of an unbiased estimator of any one variance component corresponding to a main effect. Find an approximte 100(1 – α)% confidence INterval to any arbitrary linear function of variance components.

4. Answer all of the following: **10×3=30**

(a) Consider the following cross classified model without replication.

$y_{ij} = \mu + \beta_j + e_{ij}, \ E(e_{ij}) = 0, i = 1, 2. j = 1, 2, 3.$

Where $\underset{\sim}{y} = (y_{11}\ y_{12}\ y_{13}\ y_{21}\ y_{22}\ y_{23})'$

$\beta = (\mu_1, \alpha_1, \alpha_2, \beta_1, \beta_2, \beta_3)$ and

$$X = \begin{pmatrix} 1 & 1 & 0 & 1 & 0 & 0 \\ 1 & 1 & 0 & 0 & 1 & 0 \\ 1 & 1 & 0 & 0 & 0 & 1 \\ 1 & 0 & 1 & 1 & 0 & 0 \\ 1 & 0 & 1 & 0 & 1 & 0 \\ 1 & 0 & 1 & 0 & 0 & 1 \end{pmatrix}$$

Write down the normal equations and find all solutions. Show that $\alpha_1 - \alpha_2$ and $\beta_1 - 2\beta_2 + \beta_3$ are estimable and give their least squares estimators.

(b) Obtain the sufficient statistics for the following distributions:

(i) $f(x, \theta) = e^{-\frac{x}{\theta}}, 0 < x < \infty; \theta > 0.$

(ii) $f(x, \theta) = (1-\theta)^x\ \theta, x = 0, 1, 2 \ldots ; 0 < \theta < 1.$

(c) Let $X_1, X_2 \ldots X_n$ be a random sample from the binomial distribution with probability mass function.

$$f(x, \theta) = \theta^x(1-\theta)^{1-x} \qquad x = 0, 1; 0 < \theta < 1$$

$$= 0 \qquad \text{otherwise}$$

Examine whether the statistic $T = \sum_{1}^{n} X_i$ is omplete for this distribution.

Section B

5. Anser all of the following: **5×8=40**

(a) Let $X = (X_1, X_2, X_3)$ be distributed as $N_3(\mu, \Sigma)$ where $\mu' = (2, -3, 1)$ and

$$\Sigma = \begin{pmatrix} 1 & 1 & 1 \\ 1 & 3 & 2 \\ 1 & 2 & 2 \end{pmatrix}$$

(i) Find the distributio of $3X_1 - 2X_2 + X_3$.

(ii) Find a 2 × 1 vector $\underset{\sim}{a}$ such that X_2 and $X_2 - a'\begin{pmatrix} X_1 \\ X_2 \end{pmatrix}$ are independent.

(b) Find the maximum likelihood estimators of the 2 × 1 mean vector $\underset{\sim}{\mu}$ and the 2 × 2 covariance matrix Σ based on the random sample

$$X = \begin{bmatrix} 3 & 4 & 5 & 4 \\ 6 & 4 & 7 & 7 \end{bmatrix}$$

from a bivariate normal population.

(c) Explain the notaion of unbiassedness with regard to a test of a hypothesis. Examine the validity of the statement. A Most Powerful (MP) test is invariably unbiased.

(d) To test the hypothesis $H_0: \theta = \theta_0$ against $H_1: \theta = \theta_1$ for the distribution

$$f(x, \theta) = \theta^x (1-\theta)^{1-x}, \quad x = 0, 1; 0 < \theta < 1$$
$$= 0 \qquad \text{otherwise,}$$

develop the sequential probability ratio test.

(e) Distinguish between the single sampling plan and double sampling plan. Discuss how the O.C curves can be used for comparing two sampling plans.

(f) Let $\underset{\sim}{X} = (X_1, X_2, X_3)'$ be distributed as $N_3(\mu, \Sigma)$ where $\underset{\sim}{\mu} = (10, -7, 2)'$ and

$$\Sigma = \begin{pmatrix} 2 & -1 & 3 \\ -1 & 5 & -3 \\ 3 & -3 & 5 \end{pmatrix}$$

Find the partial correlation between X_1 and X_2 given X_3.

(g) Show that T^2 statistic is invariant under changes in the units of measurements for a p × 1 random vector X of the form $\underset{\sim}{Y} = C\underset{\sim}{X} + \underset{\sim}{d}$ where C is a p × p nonsingular matrix, $\underset{\sim}{d}$ is a p × 1 vector.

(h) Distinguish between control chart for variables and control chart for attributes. Give an example for each. When will you say that a process is in control? Suppose that all the points in a control chart falls above the central line. What will be your conclusion?

6. **Answer all of the following:** **10×3=30**

(a) Derive the likelihod ratio test for comparing the means of k independent homoscedastic normal populations.

(b) Let $\underset{\sim}{X}_1, \underset{\sim}{X}_2, ..., \underset{\sim}{X}_n$ be a random sample from an $N_p(\mu, \Sigma)$ population with Σ, a positive definite matrix. Derive $100(1 - \alpha)\%$ simultaneous confidence intervals for $\underline{l}'\underline{\mu}$ for all $\underline{l}' \in \mathbb{R}^p\{0\}$.

(c) Sample of size n = 5 are taken from a manufacturing process every hour. A qulity characteristic is mesured, and $\overline{X}$ and R are computed for each sample. After 25 samples have been analysid, we have $\sum_{j=1}^{25} \overline{x}_j = 662.50$ and $\sum_{j=1}^{25} R_i = 9.00$. Assume that the quality characteristic is normally distributed.

(i) Find the control limts for the $\overline{X}$ and R charts.

(ii) Assume that both charts exhibit control, if specifications are 26.40 ± 0.50, estimate the fraction nonconforming. Express your answer in terms of CDF of N(0, 1) random variable.

[For $n = 5$, $A_2 = 0.577$, $A = 1.342$, $A_3 = 1.427$, $D_1 = 0$, $D_2 = 4.918$, $D_3 = 0$, $D_4 = 2.115$ and $d_2 = 2.326$

7. **Answer all of the following:** **10×3=30**

(a) Find a Most Powerful (MP) test for testing the simple hypohesis $H_0: \sigma^2 = \sigma_0^2$ against the simple alernative $H_1: \sigma^2 = \sigma_1^2$ based on random observations from $N(\mu, \sigma^2)$ where μ is known. Show that this MP test is UMP (uniformly most powerful).

(b) (i) Let A_i be distributed as Wishart $W_m(A \mid \Sigma)$, $i = 1, 2$ and A_1, A_2 be independent. Show that $A_1 + A_2$ is distributed as $W_{m_1+w_2}(A_1 + A_2 \mid \Sigma)$.

(ii) If A is disributed nas $W_m(A \mid \Sigma)$, then CAC′ is distributed as $W_m(CAC' \mid C\Sigma C')$ where C is a nonsingular matrix of order m.

(c) (i) Explain the terms average outgoing quality (AOQ) and average total inspection (ATI).

(ii) Let N = 10,000, n = 89 and C = 2. Determine Pa, the probability of acceptance and use it to determine AOQ and ATI.

8. **Answer all of the following:** **10×3=30**

(a) For a sequential probability ratio test of strength (α, β) and stopping bounds A and B (B < A), show that

$$A \le \frac{1-\beta}{\alpha} \text{ and } B \ge \frac{\beta}{1-\alpha}.$$

(b) Let

$$\Sigma = \begin{pmatrix} 3 & 1 & 1 \\ 1 & 3 & 1 \\ 1 & 1 & 5 \end{pmatrix}$$

Determine

(i) the principal components y_1, y_2 and y_3.

(ii) the proportion of variance explained by each one of them.

(iii) correlation between the first principal component y_1 and the third original random variable.

(c) What is meant by acceptance sampling by attributes? Outlining the criteria for the goodness of sampling inspection plan, give briefly the steps in the Dodge inspection plan.

GENERAL STATISTICS
Paper II 2014

Time Allowed : Three Hours

Maximum Marks: 200

INSTRUCTIONS

Please read each of the following instructions carefully before attempting questions. There are EIGHT questions divided under TWO sections. Candidate has to attept SIX questions in all Question No. 1 and 5 are compulsory and out of the remaining. FOUR are to be attempted choosing at least TWO from each Section. The number of marks carried by a question/part is indicated aginst it. Unless otherwise mentioned, symbols and notations have their usual standard meanings. Assume suitable data, if necessary and indicate the same clearly. Candidate shold attempt questions/parts as per the instructions given in the Section. All parts and sub-parts of a question are to be attempted together in the answer book. Atempts of questions shall be counted even if attempted partly. Any page or portion of the page left blank in the answer book mst be clearly struck off. Answers must be writtn in ENGLISH only.

Section A

1. Answer all of the following: **5×8=40**

(a) $x_1, x_2, ..., x_n$ be a random sample from U(0, θ) obtain te moment estimator of **. Also find its variance.

(b) Obtain a g-inverse (A^-) of A given below nad verify that $AA^-A = A$

$$A = \begin{bmatrix} 1 & 2 & 3 \\ 4 & 5 & 6 \end{bmatrix}.$$

(c) Define compltencess. Verify whether Bin (1, p) is complete.

(d) Find the sum of squares due to

$$\left(\sum_{i=1}^{p}\sum_{j=1}^{q} a_i b_j y_{ij}\right) \Big/ \left(\sum_{i=1}^{p} a_i^2\right)\left(\sum_{j\neq 1}^{q} b_j^2\right)$$

under suitable assumptions on y_{ij}'s where a_i and b_j's are consants. State its usse in Analysis of variance.

(e) Let X_1, X_2, X_3 and X_4 be four random variables such that

$E(X_1) = \theta_1 - \theta_3$, $E(X_2) = \theta_1 + \theta_2 - \theta_3$.

$E(X_3) = \theta_1 - \theta_3$, $E(X_4) = \theta_1 - \theta_2 + \theta_3$.

where θ_1, θ_2, θ_3 are unknown parameters. Assume var $(X_i) = \sigma^2$, i = 1, 2, 3, 4.Check if σ_2 is estimable. If so obain its BLUE.

(f) $x_1, x_2, ..., x_n$ is a andom sample from the following distribution

$$f(x, \alpha) = e^{-(x-\alpha)}, \quad x \geq \alpha;$$
$$= 0 \quad \text{otherwise}$$

Find MLE of α.

(g) Let $x_1, x_2, ..., x_n$ be a random sample from U[0, θ]. Let $T = \left(\prod_{i=1}^{n} x_i\right)^{1/n}$. Is T an unbiased of θ?

If not suggest an unbiased estimator of θ which is a function of T.

(h) Let X be exponentially distributed with parameter θ. Obtain MLE of θ based on a sample of size n, from the above distribution.

2. Answer all of the following: 10×3=30

(a) Define estimability of a linear parametric function in a Gauss Markoff model. State and prove a necessary and sufficient condition for estimability.

(b) For the Pareto distribution with pdf

$$f(x, \lambda) = \frac{\lambda}{x^{\lambda+1}} x \geq 1, \lambda > 0$$

Show that method of moments fails if $0 < \lambda < 1$. State the method of moments estimator when $\lambda > 1$. Is it consistent? Justify your answer.

(c) Consider the model with normal assumptio on error variables.

$$E(y_1) = \theta_1 - \theta_2 + \varepsilon_1$$
$$E(y_2) = \theta_2 - \theta_3 + \varepsilon_2$$
$$\vdots \quad \vdots \quad \vdots$$
$$E(y_n) = \theta_n - \theta_1 + \varepsilon_n$$

Find the error function(s) and the BLUE of $\theta_1 - \theta_2$.

3. Answer all of the following: 10×3=30

(a) A manufacturer of television sets is interested in the ffect of tube conductivity of five differet types of coating for colour picture tubes. Sample means are

$$\bar{y}_1 = 49, \bar{y}_2 = 51, \bar{y}_3 = 53, \bar{y}_4 = 57, \bar{y}_5 = 58.$$

Error Mean sum of squares = 54.0

(i) Is there a difference in coating for colour picture tubes? F value = 3.09.

(ii) Determine which pairs differ significantly using Bonferroni t-interval. Comment on the same.

$$\left[t_{15}\left(\frac{0.05}{20}\right) = 3.286\right]$$

(b) $X_1, X_2, ..., X_n$ are i.i.d. random variables from $N(\theta, 1)$ where θ is an integer. Obtain MLE of θ.

(c) Suppose

$E(Y_{ij}) = \alpha_i + \beta_i X_{ij}, \qquad 1 \le j \le n_i, 1 \le i \le K$

where Y_{ij} are independent homoscedastic normal variables, X_{ij}'s are non stochastic and α_i and β_i are unkonw parameters.

(i) Find a suitable test of $H_{01}: \beta_1 = \beta_2 = .. = \beta_K$

(ii) Assuming $\beta_1 = \beta_2 = .. = \beta_K$, derive a test for $H_{02}: \alpha_1 = \alpha_2 = .. = \alpha_K$.

4. Answer all of the following: **10×3=30**

(a) Obtain unbiased estimators of the variance components in two way classification model with interaction, with r observations per cell when there are S_1 levels of factor A and S_2 levels of factor B.

(b) $x_1, x_2, ..., x_n$ be a random sample from a population having pmf

$$P_N(x) = \begin{cases} \frac{1}{N} & \text{if } x = 1, 2 \ldots N \\ 0 & \text{otherwise} \end{cases}$$

Derive UMVUE of N.

(c) Show that $Z = \frac{1}{6}(X_1 + 2X_2 + 3X_3)$ is not a sufficient estimator of the Bernaulli parameter θ.

Section B

5. Answer all of the following: **5×8=40**

(a) Let X be r.v. with pmf under H_0 and H_1 given below. Find M.P. test with $\alpha = .03$

x	1	2	3	4	5	6
$f_0(x)$	0.01	0.01	0.01	0.01	0.01	0.95
$f_1(x)$	0.05	0.04	0.03	0.02	0.01	0.85

(b) A single observation of a r.v. having a geometric distribution with pmf

$f(x, \theta) = \theta(1-\theta)^{x-1}, \qquad x = 1, 2, 3, ...$

$\qquad = 0 \qquad$ otherwise.

The null hypothesis $H_0: \theta = 0.5$ against the alternative hypothesis $H_1: \theta = 0.6$ is rejected if the observed value of the r.v. is greater than or equal to 5. Find probabilitiesof type I error and type II eror.

(c) The pdf of 5 variate normal distribution is given by:

$$\frac{1}{(2\pi)^{5/2} - 30} \exp\left\{-\frac{1}{2}\left[(x_1 - 5)^2 + \frac{(x_2 - 2)^2}{9} + \frac{x_3^2}{5} + \frac{(x_4 + 1)^2}{4} + \frac{x_5^2}{5}\right]\right\}$$

Obtain mean vector and variance covariance matrix of the distribution.

(d) Let $X \sim N_3(0, \Sigma)$ $\Sigma = \begin{bmatrix} 1 & \rho & 0 \\ \rho & 1 & \rho \\ 0 & \rho & 1 \end{bmatrix}$

Find ρ such that $X_1 + X_2 + X_3$ and $X_1 - X_2 - X_3$ are independent.

(e) Find 3-sigma contol limits for a

(i) C chart with process averageequal to 4 nonconformities.

(ii) U chart with process average $c = 4$ and $n = 4$.

(f) Justify the statement:

P chart is equivalent to Chi-square test of homogenity.

(g) A sample of size n from normal distribution $N(\theta, \sigma^2)$ with $\sigma^2 = 4$ wasobserved. 95% confidence interval for θ was computed from the above sample. Find the value o n if the confidence interval is (0.02, 10.98).

(h) Bring out the difference between a randomized test and a nonrandomized test. Eplain how the decesion based on a randomized test can be taken in the discreteset up.

6. Aswer all of the following: **10×3=30**

(a) Consider the Hypothesis H_0: $p = \frac{1}{2}$ against H_1: $p = 1$ for a binomial X for which $n = 2$. List all possible critical regions for which $\alpha \le \frac{1}{2}$. Which of htese regions minimizes $\alpha + \beta$.

(b) Consider an i.i.d sample of size $n = 5$ from bivarite normal distribution.

$$X \sim N_2\left(\mu, \begin{bmatrix} 3 & a \\ a & 1 \end{bmatrix}\right). \bar{X}' = [0, 0.5]$$

For what values of a would the hypothesis H_0: $\mu = (0, 0)'$ be rejected in favour of H_1: $\mu \ne (0, 0)'$ at 5% level of significance. (Chi-square table value = 5.99).

(c) Obtain expressions for OC and ASN function under (i) Single sampling plan (ii) Double sampling plan.

7. Answer all of the following: **10×3=30**

(a) Let $X \sim N_3(\mu, \Sigma)$. $\Sigma = \begin{bmatrix} 1 & 2 & -1 \\ 2 & 6 & 0 \\ -1 & 0 & 4 \end{bmatrix}$

Set

$Y_1 = X_1 + X_3$, $Y_2 = 2X_1 - X_2$ and $Y_3 = 2X_3 - X_2$. Find the conditional distribution of Y_3 given $Y_2 = 0$, $Y_2 = 1$.

(b) $x_1, x_2, ..., x_n$ is a random sample from $N(0, \sigma^2)$ (σ^2 not specified). Derive likelihood ratio test of testing $H_0: \theta = \theta_0$ against $H_1: \theta \neq \theta_0$.

8. Answer alll of the following: **10×3=30**

(a) Let X be a r.v. following exponential distribution

$$f(x, \theta) = \theta^{e-\theta x} \qquad x > 0$$
$$= 0 \qquad \text{otherwise}$$

Obtain SPRT of strength α, β for testing $H_0: \theta = 8$ against $H_1: \theta > 8$

(b) $$(X_1, X_2, X_3) \sim N_3\left(\underline{0}, \begin{bmatrix} 1 & \rho_{12} & \rho_{13} \\ & 1 & \rho_{23} \\ & & 1 \end{bmatrix}\right)$$

Show that $1 + 2\rho_{12}\rho_{13}\rho_{23} \geq \rho_{12}^2 + \rho_{13}^2 + \rho_{23}^2$

(c) A proposed triple sampling plan is as follows:

Tale a forst sample of 2 articles. If both good accept, if both bad reject. If 1 good and 1 bad reject, take a second sample of 2. If both good accept. If both bad reject. If 1 good and 1 bad reject. If 1 good and 1 bad take a third sample of 2. If both articles in the third sample are good, accept; otherwise reject. Find the OC of this plan assuming that a large lot of p% defective is submitted for inspection.

GENERAL STATISTICS
Paper II 2013

Time Allowed : Three Hours | *Maximum Marks: 200*

INSTRUCTIONS

Candidates should attempt FIVE questions in ALL including Questions No. 1 and 5 which are compulsory. THe remaining THREE questions should be answered by choosing at least ONE question each from Section A and Section N. The number of marks carried by each question is indicated against each. All parts and sub-parts of a question are to be attempted together in the answer book. Attempts of a part/question shall be counted even if attempted partly. Any page or portion of the page left blank in the answer book must be clearly struck off. Answers must be written only in ENGLISH. (Symbols and abbreviations are as usual.) Any essential data assumed by candidates for answering questions must be clearly stated.

Section A

1.Attempt any five of the following: **8×5=40**

(a) Assume a full rank model $Y = X\beta + \in$, where $\in \sim N_n(0.\ \sigma^2 I_n)$. $X(n \times p)$ is the design matrix and $\beta(p \times 1)$ is the parameter vector. Construct a test for H_0: $\beta = 0$ against H_1: $\beta \neq 0$.

(b) Consider the linear model $Y = X\beta + \in$, where X is $(n \times p)$ and $\in \sim N_n(0, \sigma^2 I_n)$. State and prove a necessary and sufficient condition for any linear parametric function $l'\beta(l \neq 0)$ to be estimable.

(c) Define Fisher Informaion. Illustrate its application in estimation theory. Derive Fisher Information about the parameter θ in a random sample of size n from an exponential distribution with parameter θ.

(d) Let g(θ) be a real valued estimable function of an unknown parameter θ and T be a complete suffcient statistic. Prove that an unbaised estimator of g(θ) based on T is enough for finding the UMVUE of g(θ).

(e) Show that the S.S. due to be a testable hypthesis in a linear model, can be expressed as the difference between conditional and unconditional S.S. due to error.

(f) State and prove Rao-Blackwell theored.

2. (a) In a general linear model setup $(Y, X\beta, V)$, derive the covariance between the BLUEs of two estimable linear parametric functions $p'\beta$ and $q'\beta$.

(b) Consider a two way fixed effects model with m observations per cell:

$y_{ijk} = \mu_{ij} + e_{ijk}; i = 1 \ldots p; j = 1 \ldots q; k = 1 \ldots m$

with

$\mu_{ij} = \mu + \alpha_i + \beta j + \gamma_{ij}$

where the parameters are defined with respect to a system of weights; $\{e_{ijk}\}$ are random errors. Show that the above representation of μ_{ij} in terms of μ, α, β_j and γ_{ij} is unique for a given system of weights. 10

(c) Define (i) Efficiency and (ii) UMVUE. Let T_0 and T_1 be two unbiased estimators for θ with efficiency e_θ. Then prove that no linear combinations of T_0 and T_1 can be a MVUE. 10

(d) Distinguish between confidence interval and tolerance limits.

Based on a random sample of size n from a Gamma (α, β), obtain the moment estimators of α and β. Suggest a large sample confidence interval for α when $\beta = 1$. 10

3. (a) Consider the linear model

$E(Y_i) = \mu_i - \mu_{i+1}, i = 1 \ldots n-1$

$E(Y_n) = \mu_n - \mu_1$

$E(Y_i - E(Y_i))(Y_j - E(Y_j)) = \sigma^2$ if $i = j$

$= 0 \quad i \neq j$

(i) Show that $\overline{Y} = \frac{1}{n}(Y_1 + \ldots + Y_n)$ is the only error function.

(ii) Find the BLUE of $\mu_j - \mu_{j+1}$ for $j = 1, 2, \ldots, n$ with $\mu_{n+1} = \mu_1$.

(iii) Find the BLUE of $\sum_{j=1}^{n} t_j \mu_j$ with $\sum_{j=1}^{n} t_j = 0$

(iv) Find an estimate of σ^2. 10

(b) Write Tukey's non-additive model for a set of two-way classified data with one observation per cell. Suggest an estimator of the non-additivity parameter and find its distribution under additivity. Construct a test for additivity for such a model. 10

(c) State and Prove Cramer-Rao inequality with usual notations. 10

(d) State the properties of a maximum likelihood estimator (MLE). Based on a random sample of size n from the distribution with pdf

$$f(x; \alpha, \beta) = \frac{1}{\beta - \alpha} \qquad \alpha \leq x \leq \beta$$

obtain a MLE of α and β. 10′

4. (a) Discuss the following statements:

(i) A statistic can be minimal sufficient without being complete

(ii) A maximum likelihood estimate is not necessarily unique 10

(b) For a two-way ANOVA with K treatments and n blocks, show that

$$E\left[\frac{K\sum_{j=1}^{n}(\bar{X}_j - \bar{X}..)^2}{n-1}\right] = \sigma^2 + \frac{K\sum_{j=1}^{n}\beta_j^2}{n-1}$$

where β_j is the jth block effect. 10

(c) If $X_1, X_2, ..., X_n$ constitute a random sample from uniform $(0, \theta)$, then show that $\left(\frac{n+1}{n}\right)X_{(n)}$ is an unbiased estimator of θ where $X_{(n)}$ denotes the largest observation. Also show that

(i) $2\bar{X}$ is unbiased for θ

(ii) Compare the efficiency of these two estimators. 10

(d) Define a family of uniformly most accurate confidence sets for an unknown parameter θ, with confidence level $(1 - \alpha)$ where $0 < \alpha < 1$. Give an example to show that $(1 - \alpha)$ confidence interval is not unique. 10

Section B

5. Attempt any five of the following: **8×5=40**

(a) Define a similar test. Obtain a similar test for $H_0: \sigma^2 = \sigma_0^2$ against $H_1: \sigma^2 < \sigma_0^2$ when the samples are drawn from $N(\sigma, \sigma^2)$, where μ is unknown.

(b) State monotone likelihood ratio property of a family of distributions. Use the property to test $H_0: \theta = \theta_0$ against $H_1: \theta > \theta_0$ for a random variable having a distribution function $F(x; \theta)$, $\theta \varepsilon \Omega$.

(c) Define:

(i) randomized decision rules

(ii) admissibility of a decesion rule

(iii) Complete class of decision rules

(iv) Minimax decision rules

(d) Let X be a p-dimensional random vector with mean μ and dispersion Σ of rank $r(\leq p)$. Show that with probability 1, $X = \mu + LY$, where $L(p \times r)$ is of rank r. Hence discuss the possibility when $r = 1$.

(e) Distriguish between defects and defectives. Discuss the control charts for defects and defectives clearly mentioning their importance and specify their control limits (no proof is required).

(f) Let $X(p \times 1)$ be a random vector with dispersion $\Sigma(> 0)$. Find the principal components of X and their variances when

(i) $\Sigma = \sigma^2 I_p$ and

(ii) $\Sigma = \sigma^2\left[(1-\rho) I_p + \rho \underline{I}_p \underline{I}_p'\right]$

where $\underline{I}_p$ is a $p \times 1$ vector with unit elements and σ^2, $\rho(> 0)$ are known constants.

6. (a) Define a simple and a composite hypothesis. State and prove (nessary part only) Neyman Pearson Fundamental lemma for testing a simple hypothesis against one sided alternatives. 10

(b) In estimating the parameter p of a Binomial (2, p), random variable Y, find, under squared error loss, the risk when (i) $d_1(y) = \frac{y}{2}$ and (ii) $d_2(y) = \frac{y+1}{y}$ where $d_1(y)$ and $d_2(y)$ are the estimators (decision rules) based on $Y = y$.

(c) In an examination each student had to answer p questions carrying equal marks which were examined independently by two examiners. The problem is to test the hypothesis that there is no significant difference between the average marks awarded by the two examiners on each question on the basis of marks obtained by a random sample o N students, $2(N - 1) \geq p$. A ssuming that the marks distrubution for the two examiner are multivariate normal with a common unknown positive definite dispersion matrix, suggest and justify a sized unbiased test for the problem, $0 < \alpha < 1$. 10

(d) Obtain the control limits for the following data providing the number of cloured threads (considered as defects) in 15 pieces of cloth and comment: 10

7, 12, 3, 20, 5, 4, 3, 10, 8, 9, 6, 21, 7, 20.

7. (a) Define size of a test. Show that the power of a Neyman-Pearson test exceeds its size.

The specifications for a certain kind of wire has mean strength of 185 pounds. If five pieces randomly selected from different rolls have breaking strength of 171.6, 191.8, 178.3, 184.9 and 189.1 pounds, test the null hypothesis $H_0: \mu = 185$ against $H_1: \mu < 185$ at 5% level of significance.

[Given $t_{05,4} = 2.132$] 10

(b) Discuss Fisher-Behren's problem for testing two multivariate population means. 10

(c) Consider the problem of classifying a random vector into one of the two populations $N_p(\mu_1, \Sigma)$ and $N_p(\mu_2, \Sigma)$ where μ_1, μ_2, Σ (positive definite) are means and dispersion matrix and all the parameters are known. Assuming a simple loss function, derive the Bayes rule for the problem and show that the rule is admissible. 10

(d) What is Statistical Quality Control and what is Statistical Process Control? Discuss various types of variations encontered in a process and their methods of eliminations. 10

8. (a) Let $X_1, X_2, ..., X_n$ be inpendent and identically distributed random variables having pmf

$$f(x; p) = p^x(1 - p)^{1-x}, x = 0, 1$$
$$= 0 \qquad \text{otherwise}$$

Propose a SPRT for testing $H_0: p = p_0$ against $H_1: p = p_1$. Also find the ASN functions of the test. 10

(b) Discuss the general idea of classifications problem. Also discuss the procedure for classifying intwo one of two populations with known probability distribution. 10

(c) For the problem of estimating μ on the basis of a random sample from $N(\mu, 1)$ with absolute error loss $(-1 \leq \mu \leq 1)$, show that the sample mean is an inadmissible estimator. 10

(d) Write short notes on:

(i) Canonical Correlation Analysis

(iii) Bootstrapping the standard error of a trimmed mean. 10

GENERAL STATISTICS
Paper II 2012

Time Allowed : Three Hours | *Maximum Marks: 200*

INSTRUCTIONS

Candidate should attempt FIVE questions in ALL including Questions No. 1 and 5 which are compulsory. The remaining THREE questions should be answered by choosing at least ONE question each from Section A and Section B. The number of marks carried by each question is indicated against each. Answers must be written only in ENGLISH. (Symbols and abbreviations are as usual.) Any essential data assumed by candidates for answering questions must be clearly stated. Two graph sheets are attached to this question paper for answering graph-related questions. Candidate is expected to carefully detach these and attach them securely to the answer book

Section A

1. (a) If $l_1'\bar{\underline{\beta}}$ and $l_2'\bar{\underline{\beta}}$ are least squares estimators of two estimable functions $l_1'\underline{\beta}$ and $l_2'\underline{\beta}$ respectively, then show that —

(i) $V(\underline{l}_2'\bar{\underline{\beta}}) = \sigma^2 \underline{l}_1' \bar{S} l_1$

(ii) $\text{cov}(\underline{l}_1'\bar{\underline{\beta}}, \underline{l}_2'\bar{\underline{\beta}}) = \sigma^2 l_1' \bar{S} l_2$

where $\bar{S}$ is the generalised inverse of $S = X'X$

(b) Consider the following balanced one-way classification random effects model:

$Y_{ij} = \mu + a_i + e_{ij}, \; i = 1, 2, ..., n$

where a_i's and e_{ij}'s are independent; and $a_i \sim N(0, \sigma_a^2)$ and $e_{ij} \sim N(0, \sigma_e^2)$. How would you test H_0: $(\sigma_a^2 > 0)$? 8

(c) Explain the purpose of the Gauss-Markoff theorem, and prove it. 8

(d) Let $X_1, X_2, ..., X_n$ be a random sample from the uniform distribution

$$f(x, \theta) = \begin{cases} \dfrac{1}{\theta}, & 0 \le x \le \theta \\ 0, & \text{otherwise} \end{cases}$$

Examine the consistency of the estimators $T_1 = X_{(n)}$, $T_2 = X_{(1)} + X_{(n)}$ and $T_3 = 2\overline{X}$ for estimating θ. 8

(e) Give an example of sufficient statistic which is not complete. Define bounded completeness. 8

2. (a) Consider the function of observations $y = C'Y$, $y_1 = C_1'Y$, $y_2 = C_2'Y$, ..., $y_k = C_k'Y$

Show that the necessary and sufficient condition that the function y is dependant on $y_1, y_2, ..., y_k$ is that the coefficient vector of y is dependant on the coefficient vectors of $y_1, y_2, ..., y_k$. 10

(b) Under what condition the Cramer-Rao inequaluty reduces to the equality? Illustrate through an example how it helps in obtaining a UMVU estimate. 10

(c) Let T_0 be an MVUE, while T_1 is any other unbiased estimator with efficiency e_θ. If r_θ be the correlation coefficient between T_0 and T_1, then show that

$r_\theta = \sqrt{e_\theta}$ 10

(d) Explain the tests for regression coefficients in short. 10

3. (a) Let X_1, X_2, X_3 are three uncorrelated random variables having common variance σ^2, If

$E(X_1) = \theta_1 + \theta_2$, $E(X_2) = 2\theta_1 + \theta_2$, $E(X_3) = \theta_1 + 2\theta_2$

obtain the unbiased estimates of θ_2. Also obtain their variances and the covariances. 10

(b) In a genetical experiment, the observed frequencies in four possible classes (AB, Ab, aB, ab) are reported as 125, 18, 20 and 34. The corresponding probabilities of each group are

$$\frac{1}{4}(3 - 2\theta + \theta^2), \frac{1}{4}(2\theta - \theta^2), \frac{1}{4}(2\theta - \theta^2) \text{ and } \frac{1}{4}(1 - 2\theta + \theta^2)$$

respectively. Obtain the MLE of θ and its variance. 10

(c) Let

$X \sim BD(x, p)$ and $L(p, d(x)) = (p - d(x))^2$

If p is assumed to have a uniform prior distribution $(0 < p < 1)$, then obtain the Bayes estimate of p and the corresponding Bayes risk. 10

(d) Let T_1 be unbiased for $g(\theta)$ with $E(T_1^2) < \infty$ and sufficient. Let $h(T) = E(T_1 | T)$, then show that—

(i) $E[h(T)] = g(\theta)$

(ii) $V\{h(T)\} \leq V(T_1)$

equality holding iff $P\{|T_1 - h(T)| = 0\} = 1$. 10

4. (a) Show that the maximum likelihood estimate is a BAN estimator. 10

(b) Let $\{X_1, X_2, ..., X_n)$be a random sample from $N(\mu, \sigma^2)$ when both (μ, σ^2) are unknown. Obtain $100(1 - \alpha)\%$ confidence interval for σ^2. 10

(c) If $X_1, X_2, ..., X_n$ are i.i.d. Poisson (λ), obtain a UMVUE of $g(\lambda) = e^{-\lambda}(1 + \lambda)$. 10

(d) Explain shortly Bootstrap and Jackknife methods. 10

Section B

5. (a) An urn contains 10 marbles out of which M are white and 10 – M are black. To test H_0: (M = 5) against H_1: (M = 6), one draws three marbles from the urn without replacement. The hypothesis is rejected if the sample contains 2 or 3 white marbles otherwise it is acceptabed. Find the values of α and β. 8

(b) In usual notion, prove that

$$E\{e^{Z_n t}[\theta(t)]^{-n}\} = 1$$

for any point t in the set D. 8

(c) Let X be $N_p(\mu, \Sigma)$. Obtain the characteriistic function and show that Y(= CX) is also normal N_p. 8

(d) For a single sampling plan for attributes, obtain the probability of acceptance, (L(p)) of the lot for known values of C. 8

(e) If

$$D_n = \sup_x |F_n(x) - F_x(x)|$$

show that it is distribtion free, where $F_n(x)$ is the empirical distribution function ad $F_X(x)$ is the cummulative distribution function. 8

6. (a) Develop a test for $H_0: \theta = \theta_0$ against $H_1: \theta \neq \theta_0$ based on a random sample of size n from an exponential distribution with mean $\frac{1}{\theta}$. 10

(b) Discuss the problem of symmetry associated with the testing of several multivariate population mean vectors. 10

(c) Develop a sequential test for H_0: $p = p_0$ agianst H_1: $p = p_1$, if the sampling is done from B(1, p). Also obtian the OC function and ASN function. 10

(d) Develop the discriminant function to descriminate between two normal populations $N(\underline{\mu}_{(1)}, \Sigma)$ and $N(\underline{\mu}_{(2)}, \Sigma)$. Determine the probabilities of misclassifications. 10

7. (a) In a decision problem

$$\Omega = \left\{\frac{1}{5}, \frac{1}{2}\right\}, A = \{a_1, a_2\}, P_0(X = 1) = \theta, P_0(X = 0) = 1 - \theta$$

and the loss table is given as

Ω \ A	a_1	a_2
θ_1	0	10
θ_2	10	0

(i) Find all possible decision rules.

(ii) Find risk corresponding to all decision rules.

(iii) Find minimax decision rules.

(iv) Find a set of admissible decision rules. 10

(b) Define an empirical distribution function. For a random variable with emprical distribution functin Fn(x), show that $P\left[F_n(x) = \frac{j}{n}\right] = \binom{n}{j} [F_X(x)]^j \, [1 - F_x(x)]^{n-j}, \quad j = 0, 1,$ 2, ..., n 10

(c) Define the following terms: 10

(i) AOQ

(ii) AOQL

(iii) LTPD

(iv) ASN and OC function

(v) ATI

(d) Develop a test for independence of sets of variates in a p-variate normal distribution. 10

8. (a) Consider a q-normal population

$N(\mu^{(i)}, \Sigma_i), i = 1, 2, ..., q$

Develop a test for

$H_0: \Sigma_1 = \Sigma_2 = ... = \Sigma_q = \Sigma$ 10

(b) Define a single-parameter exponential family of distributions. State the tests for-

(i) $H_0: \theta \leq \theta_0$ versus $H_1: 0 > \theta_0$

(ii) $H_0: \theta_1 \leq \theta \leq \theta_2$ versus $H_1: \theta < \theta_1$ or $0 > 0_2$

Are these tests UMP and unbiased? 10

(c) A coin is tested 8 times and the total number of heads were observed. A test procedure rejects the null hypothesis that the coin is unbiased. If the number of heads is less than 2 or more than 6, obtain α and power of the test for $p = 0.2$. 10

(d) Explain a two-person zero-sum game. State the fundamental theorem of game theory. 10

GENERAL STATISTICS
Paper II 2011

Time Allowed : Three Hours | *Maximum Marks: 200*

INSTRUCTIONS

Candidate should attempt FIVE questions in ALL including Questions No. 1 and 5 which are compulsory. The remaining THREE questions should be answered by choosing at least ONE question each from Section A and Section B. The number of marks carried by each question is indicated against each. Answers must be written only in ENGLISH. (Symbols and abbreviations are as usual.) Any essential data assumed by candidates for answering questions must be clearly stated. Two graph sheets are attached to this question paper for answering graph-related questions. Candidate is expected to carefully detach these and attach them securely to the answer book

Section A

1. **Attempt any *five* parts of the following:** **8×5=40**

   (a) Obtain the least square estimates of the parameters in a simple linear regression model, where the errors are i.i.d normal variates. Check whether they are unbasised.

   (b) Show that $l'\hat{\beta}$ has minimum variance in the class of linear unbiased estimators of $l'\beta$, if $l'\beta$ is estimable, for the model $(Y, X\beta, \sigma^2 I)$.

   (c) For the linear model of one way analysis of variance, derive the test for testing equality of the parameters.

   (d) Show that, a statistic T_n for θ is consistent, if $E(T_n) \to 0$ and Var $(T_n) \to 0$, as $n \to \infty$

   (e) Find the MLE for the parameter θ based on samples from a uniform distribution over $[\theta - Y_2, \theta + Y_2]$.

   (f) Obtain the MVB estimator for the parameter θ for the population

   $$f(x) = \frac{1}{\theta^p \, \Gamma(\rho)} e^{-x/\theta} x^{p-1}; 0 \le x < \infty; \text{given } p > 0$$

2. (a) Show that the best fitting linear function for the points $(x_1, y_1), \ldots, (x_n, y_n)$ satisfy the equation

$$\begin{vmatrix} x & y & 1 \\ \sum_i x_i & \sum_i y_i & n \\ \sum_i x_i^2 & \sum_i x_i y_i & \sum_i x_i \end{vmatrix} = 0, i = 1, ..., n.$$

(b) Considering the sum of the angles is 180°, find the best estimates of the three angles A, B, C for the following data by method of least squares:

A: 35° 40 45°

B: 60° 62° 58°

C: 83° 80° 77° 10

(c) Obtain an unbiased estimator of $\frac{1}{\theta}$ for

$f(x) = \theta (1 - \theta)^{x-1}; x = 1, 2, ...; 0 < \theta < 1.$

Also, what is its distribution? 10

(d) If T_1 is the most efficient estimator and T_2 is any other estimator of θ with efficiency 'e', show that

$$\text{Var}(T_1 - T_2) = \left(\frac{1}{e} - 1\right) \text{Var}(T_1)$$ 10

3. (a) For the linear model $Y = X\beta + \varepsilon$ and A and B matrix of constants, show that,

$X'XA = X'XB$, iff $XA = XB$. 10

(b) For the one-way model

$y_{ij} = \mu + \alpha_i + l_{ij}; i = 1, 2, 3; j = 1, 2, ..., n_i;$

$E(l_{ij}) = 0$, check whether $\mu + \alpha_1$ and $\alpha_1 - \alpha_3$ are estimable, when $n_i = 4 - i$. 10

(c) Show that the mean square deviation $E(\hat{\theta} - \theta)^2$ of an estimator $\hat{\theta}$ of θ can never fall below a positive limit, when the range is independent of θ and the second derivative of the likelihood function exists. 10

(d) Find the MLE for N for the hypergeometric distribution

$$f(x) = \begin{cases} \dfrac{\binom{M}{x}\binom{N-M}{n-x}}{\binom{N}{n}}, & \max(0, n - N + M) \le x \le \min(n, M) \\ 0, & \text{otherwise.} \end{cases}$$

4. (a) For the simple linear model

$y_i = \beta_0 + \beta_1 x_i + l_i, i = 1, ..., N$

obtain the variance of $\hat{\beta}_1$. 10

(b) Write a note on Bhattacharya's bounds. Explain how it is a generalization of the Cramer – Rao inequality. 10

(c) If two most efficient estimators is distributed in the bivariate normal form (in the limit), show that the correlation between them tends to unity. 10

(d) Let $X_1, ..., X_n$ denote a sample from b(1, θ), $0 < \theta < 1$ where

$$h(\theta) = \frac{\Gamma(\alpha+\beta)}{\Gamma(\alpha)\,\Gamma(\beta)}\theta^{\alpha-1}(1-\theta)^{\theta-1}, 0<\theta<1.$$

Show that, the Bayes decision rule for the quadratic loss function, is a weighted average of the MLE of θ and the mean $\alpha/(\alpha+\beta)$ og yhr prior distribution. 10

Section B

5. **Attempt any *five* parts of the following:** **8×5=40**

(a) Distinguish between randomized and non-randomized tests. Given an example.

(b) Obtain the MP size α test for testing H_0: $p = p_0$ against H_1: $p = p_1$; $p_1 > p_0$ based on a sample of size n from b(1, p).

(c) Explain the uses of control charts in qualify control.

(d) What is double sampling insepction plan? Suggest the general method of plotting the OC function of such a plan.

(e) Let $X \sim N_p(\mu, \Sigma)$. Find the marginal distribution of any sub vector of X.

(f) What is the Neyman — Pearson fundamental lemma? Explain its usefulness in Testing of Statistical Hypotheses.

6. (a) Obtain the BCR for testing H_0: $\sigma = \sigma_0$ against H_1: $\sigma = \sigma_1$ based on samples from $N(0, \sigma^2)$. 10

(b) What is an unbiased test? Give an example. 10

(c) What do you understand by producer's risk and consumer's risk in single sampling inspection plans? Explain their importance. 10

(d) Find the MLE's for σ and Σ for the population $N_p(\sigma, \Sigma)$ 10

7. (a) Obtain the OC for the normal distribution with unit variance while testing H_0: $\theta = \theta_0$ against H_1: $\theta = \theta_1$. 10

(b) What are AOQ and AOQL? Explain their uses. 10

(c) Derive the null distribtion of sample correlation coefficient based on samples from a bivariate normal population? 10

8. (a) Test the hypothesis H_0: $\theta = \theta_0$ against H_1: $\theta \neq \theta_0$ based on a sample of size n from a uniform distribution in the interval $0 \le x \le \theta$. 10

(b) What are sequantial sampling plans? Explain one of them. 10

(c) Obtain the distribution of the sample variance and covariance matrix in samples from a p-variate normal population. 10

(d) What is dimension reduction technique? (Use principal components to explain the technique.) 10

GENERAL STATISTICS
Paper II 2010

Time Allowed : Three Hours | *Maximum Marks: 200*

INSTRUCTIONS

*Candidates should attempt **FIVE** questions in **ALL** including Questions No. 1 and 5 which are compulsory. The remaining **THREE** questions should be anwered by choosing at least ONE question each from Section A and Section B. The number of marks carried by each question is indicated against each. Answers must be written only in ENGLISH. (Symbols and abbreviations are as usual) Any essential data assumed by candidates for answering questions must be clearly stated.*

Section A

1. Attempt any 5 parts of the following:

(a) Samples of sizes n_1 and n_2 are drawn from two population having means μ_1 and μ_2 respectively with a common variance σ^2. Find the BLUE of $I_1\mu_1 + I_2\mu_2$ and obtain its variance. 8

(b) State and prove Gauss-Markoff theorem stating all basic assumptions and model requirements. 8

(c) Consider four independent random variables with $E(y_1) = E(y_2) = \theta_1 + \theta_2$; $E(y_4) = \theta_1 + \theta_3$; $V(y_i) = \sigma^2$, $i = 1, 2, 3, 4$.

Determine the condition for estimability of a linear parametric function $l'\theta = \sum_{i=1}^{4} l_i \theta_i$. Also obtain a solution of the normal equations and the sum of squares due to error. 8

(d) If $X_1, X_2, ..., X_n$ are iid from N(0, 1). Investigate the behaviour of the following estimators in terms of unbiasedness, consistency, efficiency and sufficiency:

(i) $T_1 = \frac{X_1 + 2X_2}{3}$, (ii) $T_2 = \frac{\sum_{i=1}^{n} X_i}{n}$, (iii) $T_3 = \frac{\sum_{i=1}^{n} X_i}{n+1}$. 8

(e) If

$$f(x/\theta) = \exp\left[\frac{1}{x}\{\theta A'(\theta) - A(\theta)\} - A'(\theta) + S(x)\right]$$

is a distribution indexed by parameter θ, then obtain the Maximum likelihood estimator of θ. 8

(f) Discuss the following estimation procedures:

(i) Pivotal method of constructing confidence interval.

(ii) Bootstrap method of finding revised estimates. 8

2. (a) Let X_1, X_2, X_3 be three uncorrelated random variables having common variance σ^2. If $E(X_1) = \theta_1 + \theta_2$, $E(X_2) = 2\theta_1 + \theta_2$, $E(X_3) = \theta_1 + 2\theta_2$. Show that the least squares estimates $\hat{\theta}_1, \hat{\theta}_2$ satisfy the equations:

$$6\hat{\theta}_1 + 5\hat{\theta}_2 = x_1 + 2x_2 + x_3$$

$$5\hat{\theta}_1 + 6\hat{\theta}_2 = x_1 + x_2 + 2x_3$$

Obtain:

(i) $V(\hat{\theta}_1)$, $V(\hat{\theta}_2)$ and $\text{Cov}(\hat{\theta}_1, \hat{\theta}_2)$

(ii) the Error sum of squares. 10

(b) Let $X_1, X_2, ..., X_n$ denote a random sample from a population with mean μ and variance $\sigma^2(< \infty)$.

Find the BLUE of μ. Using appropriate examples show that this estimator may attain Cramer-Rao lower bound for some distribution, while for some other distribution, there exists an unbiased estimator which is better than the BLUE. 10

(c) State and prove factorization theorem for sufficiency. Hence or otherwise investigate the sufficiency of the estimator, $T = \frac{1}{6}(X_1 + 2X_2 + 3X_3)$ for θ in Bernoulli distribution. 10

(d) Give the statement of Bhattracharya bounds. Investigate the existence of Bhattacharya bound for θ if:

$f(x; \theta) = \theta(1 - \theta)^x$, $x = 0, 1, 2, ..$

Further verify whether there exists any MVB estimator or not? Compare the estimates. 10

3. (a) For a model $E(y) = A\theta$, $D(y) = \sigma^2 1$, describe the estimation space and error space and find the least squares estimator for θ. Show that the columns A and $Y - A\hat{\theta}$ are orthogonal. 10

(b) Define a one-way analysis of variance model, stating all its asumptions. Prepare the complete ANOVA table with the corresponding Expected SS for error and total. 10

(c) Let $(X_1, X_2, ..., X_m)$ and $(Y_1, Y_2, ..., Y_n)$ be two independent samples from $N(\mu_1, \sigma^2)$, $N(\mu_2, \sigma^2)$ respectively where μ_1, μ_2 and σ^2 are all unknown. Obtain a $100(1 - \alpha)\%$ confidence interval for $\mu_1 - \mu_2$.

(d) Show that a consistent solution of a likelihood equation is asymptotically normal under certain conditions to be stated. 10

4. (a) Let y_i, $i = 1, 2, ... n$ be independent random variables with $E(y_i) = \alpha + \beta x_i$; $V(y_i) = \sigma^2$, where $x_1, x_2, ..., x_n$ are given. Obtain the estimators of α, β and the variances of the estimators. 10

(b) Let $(X_1, X_2, ..., X_n)$ be a random sample from $N(\mu, \sigma^2)$, σ^2 is unknown. Use pivotal method to find a $100(1 - \alpha)\%$ confidence interval for μ. 10

(c) Distinguish between Uniformly minimum variance unbaised (UMVU) and Minimum variance bound (MVB) estimator. Show that UMVU estimator is always unique, it it exists. 10

(d) If $\overline{X}_1$ is the mean of a random sample of size n from $N(\mu, \sigma_1^2)$ and $\overline{X}_2$ is the mean of another random sample of size n from $N(\mu, \sigma_2^2)$, and the two samples are independent then show that:

(i) $p\overline{X}_1 + (1-p)\overline{X}_2, 0 \le p \le 1$ is unbiased for μ, and

(ii) the variance of the estimator is minimum when $p = \dfrac{\sigma_2^2}{\sigma_1^2 + \sigma_2^2}$. 10

Section B

5. **Attempt an 5**

(a) Distinguish between:

(i) Simple and composite hypothesis

(ii) Randomized and non-randomized tests

(iii) Null and alternative hypothesis

(iv) Prior and posterior distribution. 8

(b) Given a radom sample from $N(\mu, 1)$, propose a test for $H_0: \mu = 10$ against $H_1: \mu = 11$. Obtain the critical region of the test and power of the test. 8

(c) Dicuss the steps involved in setting the control limits for R-charts when the population range R is unknown. 8

(d) Obtain the moment generating function of a multivariate normal distribution $N_p(\mu, \Sigma)$. 8

(e) If X ~ Poisson (λ) and if λ assumes a prior distribution gamma (α, β), obtain a Bayes estimate for λ. 8

(f) Explain sequential probability ratio test procedure. Obtain OC and ASN functions for testing $H_0: \theta = \theta_0$ versus $H_1: \theta = \theta_1$, if X follows a Bernoulli distribution with parameter θ. 8

6. (a) Define:

(i) Exponential family of distributions

(ii) Uniformly most powerful test

(iii) Unbiased test

(iv) Similar test. 10

(b) If two samples of size n_1 and n_2 are drawn from two normal populations with different variances, develop a test for:

$H_0: \sigma_1^2 = \sigma_2^2$ versus $H_1: \sigma_1^2 \neq \sigma_2^2$. 10

(c) Find the distribution of sample correlation coefficients r_{ij}'s$(i < j = 1, 2 \ldots \rho)$ when the corresponding population correlation coefficients, $\rho_{ij} \neq 0$ $(i \neq j = 1, 2 \ldots \rho)$ in sampling from a p-variate normal distribution. 10

(d) Distinguish between LTPD and AOQL. Design sampling plan for inspecting large batches (N large) which has a 95% chance of accepting batches with 0.5% defective and a 5% chance of accepting batches with 5% defective. 10

7. (a) A coin is tossed for which probability θ of getting head is either $\frac{1}{3}$ or $\frac{2}{3}$. We are asked to decide which value of θ is true. The coin is tossed once and the loss function is $L(\theta, d)^2 = (\theta - d)^2$. Find:

(i) All possible decision rules

(ii) Risk for all decision rules

(iii) Minimax decision rules

(b) Define Mahalanobis D^2-Statistic Establish a suitable relationship with T^2-Statistics. Hence or otherwise obtain the null distribution of D^2-Statistics. 10

(c) If $X \sim N_p(\mu_1, \Sigma)$ and $X = \begin{pmatrix} X^{(1)} \\ X^{(2)} \end{pmatrix}$, where

$$X^{(1)} = \begin{pmatrix} x_1 \\ x_2 \\ \vdots \\ x_q \end{pmatrix} \text{ and } X^{(2)} = \begin{pmatrix} x_{q+1} \\ \vdots \\ x_p \end{pmatrix}$$

Obtain $E[X^{(1)} \mid X^{(2)}]$. 10

(d) Let X be a single observation from a probability function p(x) which is positive as the non-negative integers and zero elsewhere. For testing H_0: $p(x) = \frac{e^{-1}}{x!}$ versus H_1: $p(x) = \frac{1}{2^{x+1}}$, obtain the critical region and show that the test is unbaised. 10

8. (a) Let $X_{(1)} < X_{(n)}$ be the extreme Statistics in a random sample of size n from a rectangular distribution over (θ, θ + 1). To test H_0: θ = 0 against H_1: θ > 0, the test is rejected if $X_{(1)} < 1$ or $X_{(n)}$ c, where c is a constant. Determine c so that the test has size α and show that the test is unbiased. 10

(b) Show that SPRT terminates with probability one. 10

(c) Large batches of screws are subject to a single sampling plan with n = 60, c = 2. If the process average P = 0.01, does this lot accept batches of high quality $(p \le \bar{p})$ with high probability? If the proportion of defective in a batch is 0.05, what is the chance of accepting the batch? 10

(d) Define a Wishart distribution. State and prove its reproductive property. 10

GENERAL STATISTICS
Paper II 2010

Time Allowed : Three Hours | *Maximum Marks: 200*

INSTRUCTIONS

Candidates should attempt FIVE questions in ALL including Questions No. 1 and 5 which are compulsory. The remaining THREE questions should be answered by choosing at least ONE question each from Section A and Section B. The number of marks carried by each question is indicated against each. Answers must be written only in ENGLISH. (Symbols and abbreviations are as usual) Any essential data assumed by candidates for answering questions must be clearly stated.

Section A

1. Attempt any five sub-parts.

(a) Let a be any $n \times m$ matix and K be any $m \times m$ non-singular matrix and let $B = AK$. Show that

$BB^{-} = AA^{-}$

where A^{-} denotes g-inverse of matrix A. 8

(b) Let $l_1' \hat{\beta}$ and $l_2' \hat{\beta}$ be the least squares estimators of two estimable linear functions $l_1' \hat{\beta}$ and $l_2' \hat{\beta}$ respectively. Prove that

$\text{Var } (l_1' \hat{\beta}) = \sigma^2 \, l_1' \, C^{-} l_1,$

$\text{Var } (l_2' \hat{\beta}) = \sigma^2 \, l_2' \, C^{-} l_2,$

$\text{Cov } (l_1' \hat{\beta}, l_2' \hat{\beta}) = \sigma^2 \, l_1' \, C^{-} l_2,$

where C^{-} denotes a g-inverse of $C = A'A$. 8

(c) Consider three independent random variables y_1, y_2, y_3 having a common variance σ^2 and expectations $E(y_1) = \beta_1 + \beta_2$, $E(y_2) = \beta_1 + \beta_3$, $E(y_3) = \beta_3 - \beta_2$. Find the BLUE of the function $\beta_1 - \beta_2 + 2\beta_3$. 8

(d) Let $x_1, x_2, \ldots, x_n$ be independent observations from a rectangular population in the range 0 to θ. Obtain the best estimate of θ, in the sense of its important properties. 8

(e) Let $x_1, x_2, \ldots, x_n$ be random sample drawn from the population

$$f_\theta(x) = \begin{cases} \theta, & \text{if } x = 1 \\ \dfrac{(1-\theta)}{(\lambda-1)}, & \text{if } x = 2, 3, ..., \lambda \\ 0, & \text{otherwise,} \end{cases}$$

where θ and λ are unknown.

Find maximum likehihood estmators of θ and λ. 8

(f) Explain the concept of completeness of a statistic. Show that

$$T = \sum_i X_i$$

is a complete sufficient statistic for the parameter θ in a random sample $X_1, X_2, ..., X_n$ drawn from the population

$f_\theta(x) = \theta^x(1-\theta)^{1-x}, x = 0, 1.$ 8

2. (a) Prove that a generalized inverse of any matrix always exists, but not unique. 10

(b) Let S_L denote the sum of squares with r degrees of freedom due to the set L_y of linear functions $l'y$, where $y = A\beta + \varepsilon$, $E(\varepsilon) = 0$, $D(\varepsilon) = \sigma^2 I$.

Show that S_L/σ^2 is distributed as non-central chi-square with r degrees of freedom and non-centrality parameter $\delta = S_L, \eta/\sigma^2$, where

$$S_{L,\eta} = \sum_{i=1}^{r} (l_i' \eta)^2$$ 10

(c) Define Minimum Variance Bound (MVB) estimator.

Let $x_1, x_2, ..., x_n$ be a random sample from a population with pdf

$$f(x, \theta) = \begin{cases} \theta(1+x)^{-(1+\theta)}, & x > 0, \theta > 0 \\ 0, & \text{otherwise} \end{cases}$$

Obtain MVB estimator of $1/\theta$ and e^θ. 10

(d) When would you use minimum chi-square method of estimation? Describe the methods of minimum chi-squar and modified minimum chi-square and compare them with the maximum lielihood method. 10

3. (a) Define Estimation Space and Error Space. When is a linear function $l'Y = \sum_i l_i Y_i$ said to belong to error?

If $Y = C'Y$ be any liear function of observations $Y_1, Y_2, ..., Y_n$ and if C_o be a resolved part of C along the estimation space, show that

$E(Y) = E(C_o' Y)$. 10

(b) Consider the model

$Y_1 = \alpha_1 + \varepsilon_1,$

$Y_2 = 2\alpha_1 - \alpha_2 + \varepsilon_2,$

$Y_3 = \alpha_1 + 2\alpha_2 + \varepsilon_3,$

where $\varepsilon \sim (0, 1)$.

Derive an appropriate test to test the hypothesis

$H_0: \alpha_1 = \alpha_2$. 10

(c) Find the MLF of θ for the exponential family of distributions

$f_\theta(x) = \exp\{C(\theta) + Q(\theta)\, T(x) + H(x)], \theta \in \Theta \subset R^1$ and prove that there exists a solution of the likelihood function, if and only if $T(x)$ and $-C'(\theta)/Q(\theta)$ have the same range of values. 10

(d) Let $x_1, x_2, \ldots, x_n$ be a random sample from the uniform distribution $U(0, \theta)$. Obtain $100(1 - \alpha)\%$ confidence interval for θ and explain how the length of the interval be made shortest. 10

4. (a) For the linear model

$Y = A\beta = \varepsilon$

with $E(\varepsilon) = 0$

$D(\varepsilon) = \sigma^2 I$,

show that F-test can be applied to test the hypothesis $H_0: \beta = 0$. 10

(b) Let T_1 and T_2 be MVU etimators of a parameter θ. Show that no unbiased linear combination of T_1 and T_2 can be an MVU estimator of θ. 10

(c) Discuss in detail, under appropriate assumptions, the analysis of a balanced two-way cross classification under random effects model. 10

(d) Define uniformly most accurate (UMA) and uniformly most accurate unbiased (UMAU) confidence sets.

Using the relationship between confidence intervals and hypothesis testing, find UMAU confidence set of level $1 - \alpha$ for σ^2 in random sampling from $N(\theta, \sigma^2)$ population, θ being assumed known. 10

Section B

5. **Attempt any *five* sub-parts.**

(a) Which of the two types of error is considered to be more serious in testing statistical hypotheses? Explain with appropriate examples. How is the problem tackled? State the major steps involved in testing statistical hypotheses. 8

(b) Define unbaisedness of a test and explain why such a test is most desirable.

Let the power function of every test ϕ of $H_0: \theta \in \Theta_0$ against $H_1: \theta \in \Theta_1$ be continuous in θ. Then prove that a UMP α-similar test is UMP unbiased. 8

(c) Explain the terms: stopping rule, decision rule, stopping region, stopping variable with examples in sequential test procedure. 8

(d) Explain chance causes and assignable causes of variation in quality manufactured product. Assuming that the characteristic variable follows normal distribution with unknown mean and unknown s.d., give the central line and the control limits for $\overline{X}$ and R-charts. 8

(e) Let $X \sim N_p(\mu, \Sigma)$ and suppose that X, μ and Σ are paritioned as

$$X = \begin{bmatrix} X^{(1)} \\ X^{(2)} \end{bmatrix}, \mu = \begin{bmatrix} \mu^{(1)} \\ \mu^{(2)} \end{bmatrix} \text{ and } \Sigma = \begin{bmatrix} \Sigma_{11} & \Sigma_{12} \\ \Sigma_{21} & \Sigma_{22} \end{bmatrix}$$

where $X^{(1)}$ has l elements, $l < p$.

Under what condition are $X^{(1)}$ and $X^{(2)}$ stochastically independent? 8

(f) Let $A \sim W(p, n, \Sigma)$ and let A and Σ be partitioned into q and (p – q) rows and columns

$$A = \begin{bmatrix} A_{11} & A_{12} \\ A_{21} & A_{22} \end{bmatrix}, \Sigma = \begin{bmatrix} \Sigma_{11} & \Sigma_{12} \\ \Sigma_{21} & \Sigma_{22} \end{bmatrix}$$

where A_{11} and Σ_{11} are each $q \times q$ and W(o) denotes Wishart statistic.

Prove that $A_{11} \sim W(q, n, \Sigma_{11})$. 8

6. (a) Let $X_1, X_2, ..., X_n$ be independent random variables each distributed as exponential distribution with pdf

$$f(x, \theta) = \frac{1}{\lambda} e^{-(x-\theta)}, x > \theta,$$

λ being known. Apply likelihood ratio method to test $H_0: \theta = \theta_0$ against $H_1: \theta > \theta_0$. 10

(b) Define O.C ASN functions. Derive formulae for these functions of Wald's sequential probability ratio test. 10

(c) What do you mean by ASN and ATI in acceptance sampling plans? Show their relationship, if any. Obtain ASN and ATI functions of Double Sampling plan by attribute. 10

(d) Explain Discriminant function and state its uses. Describe how discrimination between two multivariate normal populations can be tested. 10

7. (a) Let $x_1, x_2, ..., x_n$ be a random sample from the population

$$f(x, \theta) = \frac{1}{\theta} e^{-x/\theta}, 0 \le x \le \infty, \theta > 0.$$

Find α-size UMP critical region to test $H_0: \theta \le \theta_0$ against $H_1: \theta > \theta_0$. 10

(b) Define Bayes decision rule.

Let $X \sim N(\mu, 1)$ and let a priori distribution of μ be N(0, 1). Assuming quadratic loss function

$L(\mu, \delta) = [\mu - \delta(X)]^2$,

find Bayes estimate of μ and the corresponding Bayes risk. 10

(c) What is a sequential sampling plan? When would you advocate the use of such a plan? Determine the acceptance and rejection lines of a sequential plan for fraction defectives. 10

(d) State the reproduction property of Wishart distribution.

Let $A \sim W(p, n, \Sigma)$. Consider the transformation $A = CBC'$, where C is a non-singular $p \times q$ matrix. Show that B is distributed as $W(p, n, \Lambda)$, where $\Lambda = C^{-1} \Sigma C'^{-1}$. 10

8. (a) Let $X \sim N(0, 1)$ under H_0 and $X \sim C(1, 0)$ under H_1, where C(.) denotes Cauchy variate. Find α-size MP test for testing H_0 against H_1. 10

(b) Let $X_1, X_2, ..., X_n$ be independent and identically distributed random variables each having pdf

$$f_\theta(x) = \begin{cases} \theta^x (1-\theta)^{1-x}, & x = 0, 1 \\ 0, & \text{otherwise} \end{cases}$$

Test $H_0: \theta = 0$ against $H_1: \theta = \theta_1$ by SPRT. Also find the OC function of the test. 10

(c) Explain how principal components can be extracted from a covariance matrix.

Let $X' = [X_1, X_2, ..., X_k]$ have a covariance matrix Σ, with eigenvalue-eigenvector pairs (λ_i, e_i), $i = 1, 2, ..., k$,

where $\lambda_1 \geq \lambda_2 \geq ... \geq \lambda_k \geq 0$.

Let $Y_i = e_i' X$, $i = 1, 2, ..., k$, be the principal components. Show that

$$\sigma_{11} + \sigma_{22} + ... + \sigma_{kk} = \sum_{i=1}^{k} \lambda_i = \sum_{i=1}^{k} \text{var}(Y_i)$$

10

(d) Define canonical variables and conomical correlations. Show that the canonical correlation is invariant under scale transformation. 10

STATISTICS-III

STATISTICS
Paper- III 2023

Time Allowed : Three Hours | *Maximum Marks: 200*

QUESTIONS PAPER SPECIFIC INSTRUCTIONS

Please read each of the following instructions carefully before attempting questions.

*There are **EIGHT** questions divided under **TWO** Sections. Candidate has to attempt **FIVE** questions in all. Both the questions in Section **'A'** are compulsory. Out of the **SIX** questions in Section **'B'**, any **THREE** questions are to be attempted. The number of marks carried by a question/part is indicated against it. Unless otherwise mentioned, symbols and notations have their usual standard meanings. Assume suitable data, if necessary, and indicate the same clearly. Attempts of questions shall be counted in sequential order. Unless struck off, attempt of a question shall be counted even if attempted partly. Any page or portion of the page left blank in the Question-cum-Answer (QCA) Booklet must be clearly struck off. Answers. must be written in ENGLISH only.*

SECTION A

1. (a) From the following data, calculate price index numbers for the current year by (i) Laspeyres' method, (ii) Paasche's method, (iii) Marshall-Edgeworth method and (iv) Fisher's ideal method :

Items	Base year		Current year	
	Quantity	Price	Quantity	Price
A	15	4	10	6
B	20	3	25	4
C	10	6	20	5
D	30	5	25	5

10

(b) Consider a simple linear regression model

$y_i = \beta_0 + \beta_1 x_i + \varepsilon_i, E(\varepsilon_i) = 0, V(\varepsilon_i) = \sigma_i^2, i = 1, 2, ..., n$

Obtain the variance of ordinary least squares estimate (OLSE) and generalized least squares estimate (GLSE). Show that var (GLSE) var (OLSE).

Also, show that the efficiency of OLSE and GLSE depends on the correlation between $\sigma_i(x_i - \bar{x})$ and $\frac{x_i - \bar{x}}{\sigma_i}$

Discuss briefly the estimation procedure in the two cases when-

(i) σ_i^2, i = 1, ..., n are known;

(ii) σ_i^2, i = 1, ..., n are partially unknown (viz., $\sigma_i^2 \propto \sigma^2 X_i^{2\lambda}$). 15

(c) With two strata, a sampler would like to have $n_1 = n_2$ for administrative convenience, instead of using values given by Neyman allocation. If $V(\bar{y}_{st})$, $V_N(\bar{y}_{st})$ denote the variances given by $n_1 = n_2$ and Neyman allocation respectively ignoring fpc, show that the fractional increase in variance

$$\frac{V(\bar{y}_{st}) - V_N(\bar{y}_{st})}{V_N(\bar{y}_{st})} = \left(\frac{r-1}{r+1}\right)^2$$

where $r = \frac{n_1}{n_2}$ as given by Neyman allocation. Samples of size n_1 and n_2 have been drawn by simple random sampling without replacement (SRSWOR) from two strata. 15

2. (a) How can one overcome the difficulty of changing expectation with each draw in sampling with varying probability and without replacement? Explain with examples. 10

(b) Consider AR(2) given by $X_t = X_{t-1} - 0.5X_{t-2} + w_t$, where w_t is white noise $(0, \sigma^2)$.

(i) Is the process weak (covariance) stationary? Give reasons for your answer.

(ii) Calculate corr (X_1, X_2) and corr (X_5, X_7).

If the coefficient of X_{t-1} is 1.1 and that of X_{t-2} is — 0.18, is the AR(2) process still covariance stationary? 15

(c) What are autoregressive and distributed lag models? Explain Koyck's approach of estimating distributed lag models. 15

SECTION—B

3. (a) In case of ratio estimator, when does the concept of two ratios arise? Explain with the help of an example. Derive the expression for covariance between two estimates of these ratios which are correlated and have different denominators. Also, write down the estimate of this covariance. 10

(b) Define product and regression estimators of the population mean. Derive their mean squared errors to the first order of approximation and compare their efficiencies. 15

(c) In a village, there are 8 orchards serially numbered from 1 to 8 with 350, 440, 200, 400, 500, 250, 300, 260 trees respectively. Their yields (in 10 kg) are respectively 400, 500, 220, 440, 600, 300, 350, 300. A sample of 2 orchards with PPSWOR was drawn. The orchards bearing serial numbers 8 and 3 were selected in the sample. Calculate Des Raj ordered estimator of population total and estimate its standard error. 15

4. (a) Explain the Durbin-Watson (D-W) test for autocorrelation and give the conclusions. Also, mention the basic assumptions underlying the D-W d-statistic. 10

(b) Following is the data relating to the regression model

$Y_i = \beta_1 + \beta_2 X_{2i} + \beta_3 X_{3i} + e_i$

where Y = per capita consumption expenditure, X_2 = per capita disposable income and X_3 = time.

$N = 15,\ \bar{Y} = 1942.333,\ \bar{X}_2 = 2126.333,\ \bar{X}_3 = 8.0$

$\Sigma(Y_i - \bar{Y})^2 = 830121\text{- }333,\ \Sigma(X_{2i} - \bar{X}_2)^2 = 1103111.\ 333,\ \Sigma(X_{3i} - \bar{X}_3)^2 = 280$

$$(X'X)^{-1} = \begin{bmatrix} 37.237491 & -0.0225079 & 1.3366965 \\ -0.0225079 & 0.0000137 & -0.008319 \\ 1.336965 & -0.0008319 & 0.054034 \end{bmatrix}$$

$$X'Y = \begin{bmatrix} 29135 \\ 62905821 \\ 247934 \end{bmatrix}$$

Find the least square estimate of β say $\hat{\beta}$, variance-covariance matrix of $\hat{\beta}$, R^2 and adjusted R^2 ($\bar{R}^2$). 15

(c) Discuss the identifiability of each of the following simultaneous equations models with the structural equations :

(i) $y_1 = \beta_{13} y_3 + \gamma_{11} x_1 + \gamma_{13} x_3 + \varepsilon_1$

(ii) $y_1 = \gamma_{21} x_1 + \gamma_{23} x_3 + \varepsilon_2$

(iii) $y_2 = \beta_{33} y_3 + \gamma_{31} x_1 + \gamma_{32} x_2 + \varepsilon_3$ 15

5. (a) Calculate the Fisher's ideal price index from the following data and show that it satisfies both time reversal test and factor reversal test :

Commodity	Base year		Current year	
	Price	Total value	Price	Total value
A	6	300	10	560
B	2	200	2	240
C	4	240	6	360
D	10	300	12	288
E	8	320	12	432 .

10

(b) Explain price elasticity of demand. Give reasons for the negative values of price elasticity of demand in most situations.

Suppose the price elasticity of demand for a commodity is – 0.3. If there is a 5% increase in the price of the commodity, by what percentage will the demand for the commodity go down?

(c) Show that the two MA(1) processes

$X_t = \varepsilon_t + \theta\varepsilon_{t-i}$

$Y_t = \eta_t + \frac{1}{\theta}\eta_{t-1}$

have the same autocorrelation function. Here $\varepsilon_t \sim WN(O, \sigma_\varepsilon^2)$, $\eta_t \sim WN(0, \sigma_\eta^2)$, ε_t and η_t are independent. 15

6. (a) Explain briefly the objectives of forming NSSO and its current functions. 10

(b) In two-stage sampling with first stage units of equal size M, if n first stage units out of N and then m subunits from each of the first stage units are selected by simple random sampling without replacement, show that sample mean is an unbiased estimator of population mean. Find the variance of sample mean and its unbiased estimate. 15

(c) Explain cumulative total method for the selection of a PPS sample. Obtain a BLUE of population total in a PPS sample of size n. 15

7. (a) Briefly mention about limited-information maximum likehood method for simulateous equations models. Write down some important relationships between limited-information maximum likelihood method and two-stage least squres method. 10

(b) Consider the follwing regession model:

$$y = X\beta + u,\ u \sim N(0, \sigma^2 I_n)$$

where $y(n \times 1)$, $X(n \times p)$, $\beta(p \times 1)$ and $u(n \times 1)$. Furthor $cov(X, u) \neq 0$.

(i) Show that OLSE is inconsistent.

(ii) Suppose that $Z(n \times p, n > p)$ is an instrumental variable (IV) matrix, Z is independent of u but is highly correlated with X. Using Z, derive an appropriate estimator β, so that the estimator of β, and asymptotically $(n \to \infty)$ normal. 15

(c) (i) In a simple regresion model justify whether the OLS estimator in the presence of perfect multicollinearity are BLUE or not. 5

(ii) In a simple regression model does a high value of R^2 indicate a definite evidence of high collinearity? Explain. 5

(iii) Explain any two remedial measures of multicollinearity in a simple regression mode. 5

8. (a) If the ratio between Laspeyres' and Paasche's index number is 28/27, find the missing figure (x) inn the following table:

Commodity	Base year		Current year	
	Price	Quantity	Price	Quantity
A	1	10	2	5
B	1	5	x	2

10

(b) Consider ARIMA (1, 1) process given by

$$X_t = 0.5X_{t-1} + W_t - 0.3W_{t-1}$$

where W_t is the white noise $(0, \sigma^2)$. Since the process is weakly stationary, it has the World representation (in terms of usual notations $\psi_0, \psi_1, \psi_2, ...$). Calculate the first four coefficients in the representation. 15

(c) Explain briefly:

(i) Engel curves

(ii) Lorenz curves

(iii) Gini coefficient

STATISTICS
Paper- III 2022

Time Allowed : Three Hours | *Maximum Marks: 200*

QUESTIONS PAPER SPECIFIC INSTRUCTIONS

Please read each of the following instructions carefully before attempting questions.

*There are **EIGHT** questions divided under **TWO** Sections. Candidate has to attempt **FIVE** questions in all. Both the questions in Section 'A' are compulsory. Out of the **SIX** questions in Section **'B'**, any **THREE** questions are to be attempted. The number of marks carried by a question/part is indicated against it. Unless otherwise mentioned, symbols and notations have their usual standard meanings. Assume suitable data, if necessary, and indicate the same clearly. Attempts of questions shall be counted in sequential order. Unless struck off, attempt of a question shall be counted even if attempted partly. Any page or portion of the page left blank in the Question-cum-Answer (QCA) Booklet must be clearly struck off. Answers. must be written in **ENGLISH** only.*

SECTION 'A'

1. (a) Consider a population of size N. Let S_1 be a simple random sample of size n_1 drawn without replacement. Another simple random sample S_2 of size n_2 was also drawn without replacement from the remaining population.

(i) Find the probability of obtaining the combined sample $S_1 \cup S_2$ from the population.

(ii) Define $\hat{\bar{Y}}_\alpha = \alpha\hat{\bar{Y}}_1 + (1-\alpha)\hat{\bar{Y}}_2, 0 < \alpha < 1$. Show that $\hat{\bar{Y}}_\alpha$ is an unbiased estimator for the population mean. Here $\hat{\bar{Y}}_i$ is the mean of sample S_i, i = 1, 2. (7 + 8)

1. (b) Consider the multiple regression model with a set of linear equality restrictions binding the regression coefficients.

(i) Derive the restricted regression estimator by minimizing the residual sum of squares under the set of restrictions.

(ii) Obtain the bias of the restricted regression estimator when the restrictions may not be true. Show that the estimator is unbiased and satisfies linear restrictions provided the restrictions are true. (6+4)

1. (c) (i) Explain the steps in constructing a consumer price index and discuss a method of its construction.

(ii) Indicate the precautions required while using the consumer price index numbers.

(10+5)

2. (a) (i) Describe a ratio estimator. Obtain the bias of a ratio estimator.

(ii) Under standard notations it is given

$N = 10{,}000, n = 100, \bar{X} = 50, \hat{\bar{Y}} = 4500, \hat{\bar{X}} = 45, s_y^2 = 25, s_x^2 = 16$ and the sample correlation coefficient between x and y, $\hat{\rho} = 0.8$.

Estimate the population mean using ratio estimator and its variance. (4+6)

2. (b) Consider the multiple linear regression model $y = X\beta + u$ where y: n × 1, X: n × k, β: k × 1, u: n × 1.

(i) How are the properties of ordinary least squares estimator affected when X and u are correlated and plim $\left(\frac{1}{n}X'u\right)$ is also not equal to zero?

(ii) Derive the instrumental variables (IV) estimator of β when the number of instrumental variables is greater than the number of explanatory variables. Give its interpretation as a two-stage least squares estimator. (5 + 10)

SECTION 'B'

3. (a) (i) Distinguish between sampling and non-sampling errors.

(ii) Describe the effect of non-response on the bias of the sample estimate of the population mean under simple random sampling. (5+5)

3. (b) (i) We are interested in the average age of a large population of employees in a particular service sector. The population is stratified based on the information of their age. A simple random sample was then taken from each strata with a total size 100. Under standard notations, using the information given in the table and ignoring fpc

Stratum age	$\frac{N_h}{N}$	$\bar{Y}_h$	S_h^2	n_h
<40	50%	25	16	40
40 – 50	30%	45	10	20
> 50	20%	58	20	40

(i) Give the stratified estimator of the population mean. Is this estimator different from simple mean calculated over all the sample ?

(ii) Give the variance of the estimator in (i). ·

(iii) What would have been the gain in precision had you resorted to proportional allocation ? Obtain the strata sample size using proportional allocation. (3+4+8)

3. (c) For estimating mean of the population, show that systematic sampling is more effective in removing the effect of a suspected linear trend in the population than simple random sampling. 15

4. (a) Consider the following two variables linear model with observations taken as deviation from mean:

$y_t = \beta x_t + u_t;\ t = 1, 2, \ldots, n$

where u_t's follow AR(1) process

$u_t = \rho x_{t-1} + \epsilon_t;\ |\rho| < 1,$

ϵ_t's are iid with mean O and variance σ_ϵ^2.

(i) Obtain the OLS and GLS estimators of β, say b and $\hat{\beta}$ respectively.

(ii) If r_1 is the sample autocorrelation of $\{x_t, t = 1, \ldots, n\}$ of order one and terms of order $O(\rho^k r_1)$ are ignored for all $(k + 1) \geq 3$, then obtain $\frac{\text{Variance }(\hat{\beta})}{\text{Variance (b)}}$. Comment on the relative efficiency of GLS estimator over OLS estimator. (7+8)

4. (b) (i) Define finite and infinite distributed lag models.

(ii) How can we estimate parameters and lag length of finite distributed lag models.

(iii) Consider geometric distributed lag model as a special case of infinite distributed lag model and obtain its mean lag and median lag. (3+4+8)

4. (c) (i) Explain the method of principal component regression for handling the multicollinearity problem.

(ii) How can we select the number of principal components to be omitted using the scree plot and variance explained criterion? (6+4)

5. (a) Explain the technique of 'concentration curves' assuming Pareto's form of income distribution. 15

5. (b) Define price elasticity of demand. Given that demand function is p = 7 – 8 × 2, then for what value of x, the elasticity of demand will be unity ? [Here x is the quantity demanded and p is the price]. 10

5. (c) (i) Describe the role of CSO in Indian Statistical System.

(ii) Distinguish between 'Income Method' and 'Expenditure Method' of estimating the national income in India. (8+7)

6. (a) (i) Define a Horvitz-Thompson estimator.

(ii) For simple random sampling without replacement, show that the HT estimator is unbiased for the population mean and hence deduce its variance. (4+6)

6. (b) (i) Describe the purpose of double sampling in ratio method of estimation.

(ii) A simple random sample of 15 orchards was selected from 200 orchards in the region to estimate the average yield of apples in the region. In each of the selected 15 orchards, the average yield during the previous session was obtained. For a subsample of 8 orchards from this 15 orchards, the average yield of apples in this season was recorded. Estimate the average yield of apples from all 200 orchards using all the information given in the table below:

Orchard No.	1	2	3	4	5	6	7	8
Yield : previous session	140	119	109	139	127	145	146	188
Yield : present session	128	108	101	125	118	135	133	175
Orchard No.	9	10	11	12	13	14	15	
Yield : previous session	121	144	105	155	115	142	171	

(5+10)

6. (c) (i) Describe cluster sampling. State the sampling variance of the unbiased estimator of population mean in terms of the intra cluster correlation.

(ii) A survey is carried out from a simple random sample of 90 clusters each of 40 households. The clusters are selected using simple random sampling at the rate f = 1/300. To improve accuracy of results, a statistician proposes to reduce by half the size of the clusters by selecting twice as many of them. Show that the relative efficiency is

$$\frac{1+19\rho}{1+39\,\rho}$$

assuming that the inter cluster correlation ρ and other quantities do not change. (7+8)

7. (a) (i) Define endogeneous variables, exogeneous variables and predetermined variables.

(ii) Consider the general structural form of simultaneous equations model and explain the problem of identification using its likelihood function.

(iii) Determine the rank and order conditions for the identification of a particular equation. (2+6+7)

7. (b) Consider the following system of equations :

(i) $Y_{1t} = \beta_{10} + \beta_{11}\, y_{2t} + \gamma_{11}\, x_{1t} + \gamma_{12}\, x_{2t} + u_{1t}$

(ii) $Y_{2t} = \beta_{20} + \beta_{21}\, y_{1t} + u_{2t}$

where y's are endogeneous and x's are predetermined variables. Check the identifiability of both the equations. If any of these two equations is identifiable, explain the method of two-stage least squares for estimating the parameters of that equation. 10

7. (c) (i) For estimating the parameters of a general structural model, describe the methods of indirect least squares (ILS) and two stage least squares (2-SLS).

(ii) Show that for a just identified equation, the two estimators are identical. (10+5)

8. (a) (i) Define a moving average process of order q(MA(q) process) and derive its autocorrelation function.

(ii) Stating the underlying conditions, write an MA(l) process as an autoregressive process of infinite order.

(iii) How can we identify and select the order of autoregressive and moving average processes. (8+3+4)

8. (b) (i) Define spectral density function and normalized form of spectral density function of a stationary process. Prove that the normalized spectral density function is a Fourier transform of autocorrelation function (ACF).

(ii) Derive the spectral density function of an AR(l) process. (10+5)

8. (c) (i) Establish the relationship between periodogram and sample autocovariance function (ACF).

(ii) Show that the periodogram provides an estimate of the spectral density function. What kind of preprocessing of data is required before performing the periodogram analysis? (5+5)

STATISTICS - III
2021

Time Allowed : Three Hours | *Maximum Marks: 200*

Question Paper Specific Instructions

Please read each of the following instructions carefully before attempting questions.

There are EIGHT questions divided under TWO Section. Candidate has to attempt FIVE questions in all. Both the questions in Section -A are compolusory. Out of the SIX questions in Section - B, any THREE questions are to be attempted. The number of marks carried by a question/part is indicated against it. Unless otherwise mentioned, symbols and notations have thier usual standard meanings. Assume suitable data, if necessary, and indicate the same clearly. Attempts of questions shall be counted in sequential order. Unless struck off, attempt of a question shall be counted even if attempted partly. Any page or portion of the page left blank in the Question-cum-Answer Booklet must be clearly struck off. Answers must be written in ENGLISH only.

SECTION A

Both the questions are compulsory.

1. (a) Compare Simple Random Sampling Without Replacement (SRSWOR) and Simple Random Sampling With Replacement (SRSWR) and find the value of n such that variance of the sample mean in SRSWOR is exactly half of the variance of the sample mean in SRSWR of the same size. 10

(b) Consider the simple linear regression model:

$y_i = \beta_0 + \beta_1 x_i + \varepsilon_i,\ i = 1, 2, ..., n;$

$\varepsilon_1, \varepsilon_2, ..., \varepsilon_n$ are independent and identically distributed with mean zero and constant variance σ^2. Show that least square estimates $\hat{\beta}_0$ and $\hat{\beta}_1$ are linear functions of $y_1, y_2, ..., y_n$ and also compute variance-covariance matrix of $\begin{pmatrix} \hat{\beta}_0 \\ \hat{\beta}_1 \end{pmatrix}$ and its determinant. 15

(c) Let $Y_t = Z_t + \theta Z_{t-1}$, where $[Z_t]$ be a sequence of iid random variables with mean zero and variance σ_Z^2. Show that a real valued function of Z, defined as:

$$\gamma(h) = \begin{cases} 1 & h = 0 \\ \rho & h = \pm 1, \\ 0 & \text{otherwise} \end{cases}$$

is an autocovariance function if $|\rho| < \frac{1}{2}$. 15

2. (a) Find the spectral density function f(t) of a continuous parameter process, having correltion function $\rho(t) = e^{-t^2}, -\infty < t < \infty$. Also find the value of $f\left(\sqrt{\log 16}\right)$. 10

(b) From bivariate population of N units, a simple random sample (x_i, y_i); = 1, 2, ..., n is drawn without replacement with corresponding means $(\bar{x}_n, \bar{y}_n)$. Show that $\text{Cov}(\bar{x}_n, \bar{y}_n) = \left(\frac{1}{n} - \frac{1}{N}\right)S_{xy}$. 15

(c) Explain the term exponential smothing. When is exponential smoothing most useful? Interpret the smoothing constatn α, what is its range? How is α related to degree of smoothing? 15

SECTION B

Answer any three question out of the six questions given below.

3. (a) A simple random sample of n clusters, each containing M elements, is drawn from the N clusters in the population. Then show that the smaple mean per element $\bar{\bar{y}}$ is an unbiased estimte of $\bar{\bar{Y}}$ with variance

$$V(\bar{\bar{y}}) = \frac{1-f}{nM} S^2[1 + (M-1)\rho l,$$

where f = sampling fraction and ρ is the intracluster correlation coefficient. 10

(b) Using first approximation to variance of ratio estimator R_n, show that

$$\frac{|\text{Bias in } R_n|}{\sqrt{\text{Var}(R_n)}} \leq \frac{\sqrt{V(x_n)}}{\bar{x}_N}.$$ 15

(c) A village has five orchards, containing 15, 30, 25, 10 and 20 trees respectively. If the yields (in 10 kg) of these 5 orchards are 18, 35, 29, 12, and 24 respevtively and selecting sample of two units at 2nd and 4th position, estimate the total production of five orchards along with standard error using Horvitz-Thompson estimator. 15

4. (a) Let (X, Y) have the joint pdf given bt

$$f(x, y) = \begin{cases} 1 & \text{if } |y| < x, 0 < x < 1, \\ 0 & \text{otherwise.} \end{cases}$$

Show that the regression of Y on X is linear but regression of X on Y is not linear. 15

(b) Given $X'X = \begin{pmatrix} 10 & 0 & 0 \\ 0 & 5 & 0 \\ 0 & 0 & 10 \end{pmatrix}$ and $X'Y = \begin{pmatrix} 10 & 20 \\ 20 & 10 \\ 30 & 20 \end{pmatrix}$, estimate the model

$$y_{1t} = \beta_{12}y_{2t} + \gamma_{11}x_t + \gamma_{12}x_{2t} + u_{1t}$$
$$y_{2t} = \beta_{21}y_{1t} + \gamma_{23}x_{3t} + u_{2t}$$

using 2SLS method. 15

(c) State the methods of detecting presence of Heteroscedasticity. Discuss any one of them. 10

5. (a) Define Laspeyres' index number ad Paasche's index number. If L(p) and P(q) respectively respresents Laspeyrees' index number or price and Paache's index number for quantity, then show that

$$L(p)/L(q) = P(p)/P(q).$$ 15

(b) Define autoregression series of order k. Consider the autoregression process $U_t = a\xi + \varepsilon_t$, where $-\infty < t < \infty$ ε_t, ε_{t+1} and ξ be independent variables with zero mean and unit variance.

Show that the process is stationary with correlation $\rho_1 = \rho_2 = ... = \frac{a^2}{1+a^2}$. 15

(c) Explain Time Series model and its components. 10

6. (a) Explain Stratified Random Sampling method and the problem associated with stratification. Also write down the advantages of Stratified Random Sampling. 15

(b) Explain double sampling plan for attributes and derive the expression of OC-curve in double sampling plan. 15

(c) What is multicollinearity? Discuss the effect of multicollinearity using 3-variate linear regression model. 10

7. (a) For a Markov process

$u_t = \rho u_{t-1} + v_t$ with $|\rho| < 1$

and random variable v_t are such that $E(v_t) = 0$, var $(v_t) = \sigma_V^2$ and Cov $(v_t, v_s) = 0$ for $t \neq s$.

(i) $u_t = \sum_{r=0}^{\infty} \rho^r v_{t-r}$

(ii) $\text{Var}(u_t) = \frac{\sigma_V^2}{1-\rho^2}$

(iii) $\text{Cov}(u_t, u_{t-s}) = \frac{\rho^5}{(1-\rho^2)}\sigma_V^2$

(b) Discuss Durbin-Wastson test for Autocorrelation. The data of the following table are the OLS residuals of a consumption function:

$$\hat{C}_t = -3.02 + 0.93\, Y_t$$

Calculate Durbin-Watson d-statistic. Write your conclusion. 10

Year	e_t
1994	0.6
1995	1.9
1996	– 1.8
1997	– 2.7
1998	– 2.9
1999	1.4
2000	3.3

2001	0.3
2002	0.8
2003	2.3
2004	– 1.4
2005	– 1.1

(Table for d-statistic significance points is attached)

For Q.No. 7(b)

The Durbin-Watson d-Statistic Significance Points of d_L and d_v 5%

n	d_L	d_v	d_L	d_v	d_L	d_v	d_L	d_v	d_L	d_v
15	1.09	1.36	0.95	1354	0.82	1.75	0.69	1.97	0.56	2.21
16	1.10	1.37	0.98	1.54	0.86	1.73	0.74	1.93	0.62	2.15
17	1.13	1.38	1.02	1.54	0.90	1.71	0.78	1.90	0.67	2.10
18	1.16	1.39	1.05	1.53	0.93	1.69	0.82	1.87	0.71	2.06
19	1.18	1.40	1.08	1.53	0.97	1.68	0.86	1.85	0.75	2.02
20	1.20	1.41	1.10	1.54	1.00	1.68	0.90	1.83	0.79	1.99
21	1.22	1.42	1.13	1.54	1.03	1.67	0.93	1.81	0.93	1.96
22	1.24	1.43	1.15	1.54	1.05	1.66	0.96	1.80	0.86	1.94
23	1.26	1.44	1.17	1.54	1.08	1.66	0.99	1.79	0.90	1.92
24	1.27	1.45	1.19	1.55	1.10	1.66	1.01	1.78	0.93	1.90
25	1.29	1.45	1.21	1.55	1.12	1.66	1.04	1.77	0.95	1.89
26	1.30	1.46	1.22	1.55	1.14	1.65	1.06	1.76	1.01	1.86
27	1.32	1.47	1.24	1.56	1.16	1.65	1.08	1.76	1.01	1.86
28	1.33	1.48	1.26	1.56	1.18	1.65	1.10	1.75	1.03	1.85
29	1.34	1.48	1.27	1.56	1.20	1.65	1.12	1.74	1.05	1.84
30	1.35	1.49	1.28	1.57	1.23	1.65	1.14	1.74	1.07	1.83
31	1.36	1.50	1.30	1.57	1.24	1.65	1.16	1.74	1.09	1.82
32	1.37	1.50	1.31	1.57	1.26	1.65	1.18	1.73	1.11	1.81
33	1.38	1.51	1.32	1.58	1.27	1.65	1.19	1.73	1.13	1.81
34	1.39	1.51	1.33	1.58	1.28	1.65	1.21	1.73	1.15	1.80
35	1.40	1.52	1.34	1.58	1.29	1.65	1.22	1.73	1.16	1.80
36	1.41	1.52	1.35	1.59	1.29	1.65	1.24	1.73	1.18	1.80
37	1.42	1.53	1.36	1.59	1.31	1.66	1.25	1.72	1.19	1.79
38	1.43	1.54	1.37	1.59	1.32	1.66	1.26	1.72	1.21	1.79
39	1.43	1.54	1.38	1.60	1.33	1.66	1.27	1.72	1.22	1.79
40	1.44	1.54	1.39	1.60	1.34	1.66	1.29	1.72	1.23	1.78
45	1.47	1.57	1.43	1.62	1.38	1.67	1.34	1.72	1.29	1.77

50	1.50	1.59	1.46	1.63	1.42	1.67	1.38	1.72	1.34	1.77
55	1.53	1.60	1.49	1.64	1.45	1.68	1.41	1.72	1.38	1.77
60	1.55	1.62	1.51	1.65	1.48	1.69	1.44	1.73	1.41	1.77
65	1.57	1.63	1.54	1.66	1.50	1.70	1.47	1.73	1.44	1.77
70	1.58	1.64	1.55	1.67	1.52	1.70	1.49	1.74	1.46	1.77
75	1.60	1.65	1.57	1.68	1.54	1.71	1.51	1.74	1.49	1.77
80	1.61	1.66	1.59	1.69	1.56	1.72	1.53	1.74	1.51	1.77
85	1.62	1.67	1.60	1.70	1.57	1.72	1.55	1.75	1.52	1.77
90	1.63	1.68	1.61	1.70	1.59	1.73	1.57	1.75	1.54	1.78
95	1.64	1.69	1.62	1.71	1.60	1.73	1.58	1.75	1.56	1.78
100	1.65	1.69	1.63	1.72	1.61	1.74	1.59	1.76	1.57	1.78

Note: k′ = Number of explanatory variables excluding the constant term.

n = Number of observations.

(c) State the conditions of identification for structural form of the system of simultaneous equations.

Discuss the identification of the following model, assuming Y's as endogenous and X's as predetermined variables: 15

$$Y_1 = \alpha_{10} + \alpha_{12}Y_2 + \alpha_{13}Y_3 + \beta_{11}X_1 + u_1$$
$$Y_2 = \alpha_{20} + \alpha_{23}Y_3 + \beta_{21}X_1 + \beta_{22}X_2 + u_2$$
$$Y_3 = \alpha_{30} + \alpha_{31}Y_1 + \beta_{31}X_1 + \beta_{32}X_2 + u_3$$
$$Y_4 = \alpha_{40} + \alpha_{41}Y_1 + \alpha_{42}Y_2 + \beta_{42}X_3 + u_4$$

8. (a) Explain AR(p), MA(q), ARMA(p, q) and ARIMA(p, d, q) processes. How would you find out the appropriate values of p, d and q while modelling the given time series? State the procedure to estimate the parameters of the ARIMA model. 15

(b) Define Dickey-Fuller (DF) test. How would you use DF test to find out if the given time series contains a unit root? If a unit root exists, how would you characterize such a time series? 15

(c) Explian autocovariance and autocorrelation functions. If $y_1, y_2, ..., y_n$ are n are n observations made at n successive time points of a stationary process, then in usual notations define autocovariance and autocorrelation matrix of order n. For n = 3, show that

$$-1 \le \frac{\rho_2 - \rho_1^2}{1 - \rho_1^2} \le 1.$$ 10

GENERAL STATISTICS
Paper III 2019

Time Allowed : Three Hours

Maximum Marks: 200

INSTRUCTIONS

Please read each of the following instructions carefully before attempting questions:

There are ***EIGHT*** *questions divided under* ***TWO*** *Sections. Candidate no. 1 and 5 are compulsory choosing and on: of the remaining.* ***THREE*** *are to be attempted choosing at least* ***ONE*** *from each Section. The number of marks carried by a question/part is irdicated against it. Unless other-wise mentioned, symbols and notations have their usual standard meanings. Assume suitable data, if necessary and indicate the same clearly. Candidates should attempt question/parts as per the instructions given in the Section. All parts and sub-parts of a question are to be attempted together in the answer book. Attempts of questions shall be counted in chronological order. Unless struck off, attempt of a question shall be counted even if attempted partly. Any page or portion of the page left blank in the answer book must be clearly struck off. Answers must be written in* ***ENGLISH*** *only.*

Section A

1. (a) Describe cumulative total and Lahiri's methods of selecting a sample. Show that both the methods provide probability proportional to sample size. 10

   (b) For a multiple linear regression model satisfying all the basic assumptios, show that ordinary least squares (OLS) estimator of regression coeffient vector β and estimator of error variance σ^2 based on OLSE of β are unbiased, jointly sufficient and efficient estimators of β and σ^2. 15

   (c) Given $X_t = \beta_1 + \beta_2 t + w_t$, $w_t \sim iid(0, \sigma^2)$ where β_1 and β_2 are constants.

   (i) Determine whether X_t is stationary.

   (ii) Show that $Y_t = X_t - X_{t-1}$ is stationary.

   (iii) Show that the mean of moving average $v_t = \frac{1}{2q+1}\sum_{i=-q}^{q} X_{t-i}$ is $\beta_1 + \beta_2 t$. 15

2. (a) Distinguish clearly between sampling and non-sampling errors. In this context, describe why non-response errors arise. Explain the steps of Hansen-Hurwitz technique of sub-sampling of non-respondents for estimating the population mean. Obtain the variance of the suggested estimator. 15

(b) Define beast linear unbiased predictor (BLUP). Obtain the expression for BLUP in case of a simple linear regression model satisfying all the basic assumptions. Show that BLUP can be written in terms of BLUE of the suggested estimator. 15

(c) The demand and supply function for three commodities are given below:

$d_A = 64 - 9p_A - 3p_B - 3p_C; S_A = 10 + 6p_A$

$d_B = 12 + 3p_A - 6p_B + 3p_C; S_B = 15 + 6p_B$

$d_C = 21 - 3p_A + 3p_B - 5p_C; S_C = 3 + p_C$

Find the equilibrium values for prices and supplies for all the three commodities. 10

Section B

3. (a) Differentiate between PPS and xPS sampling schemes. What is Midzuno-Sen sampling scheme? Obtain the probability of selecting a sample of n from a population of size N under this scheme. Hence prove that the usual ratio estimator becomes unbiased under this scheme. 10

(b) In what sense does cluster sampling differ from simple random sampling? A sample of n clusters in drawn at random without replacement from a population consisting of N clusters each of size M. Obtain the best linear unbiased estimator of the mean per unit in the population and show that its approximate variance is

$$\frac{N-n}{Nn} \cdot \frac{S^2}{M} \{1 + (M-1)\rho\}$$

where N is large enough, and ρ and S^2 respectivley denote the intra-class correlation coefficiennt and population mean square. 15

(c) What is Horvitz-Thompson estimator of population total? Give the Yates-Grundy expression of its variance and obtain a unbiased estimator of this varianace will never be negative under Midzuno-Sen sampling scheme. 15

4. (a) Explain multicollinearity problem in a regression model. What are its consequences? State different indicators of multicollinearity and explain. 10

(b) Define ridge estimator. Obtain its mean squared error. Derive the region for the ridge parameter such ridge estiamtor domiantes OLSE under mean squared error criterion. 15

(c) Describe a heteroscedastic regression model. Explain how to estimate the parameters fo heteroscedastic regression model with $D(\varepsilon) = \sigma^2 V$, when (i) V is competely known and (ii) V is partially known. 15

5. (a) (i) Let the price index numbers computed by Laspeyreas' and Paasche's methods be denoted respectively by L(p) and P(p). Let similar quantities for quantity indices be defined and denoted as L(q) and P(q). Prove that if the values of any three of the above are known, the remaining one can be calculated.

(ii) If Bowley's and Fisher's price indices are denoted by x and y respectively, then show that Laspeyres' index (L) and Paashe's index (P) are given by

either $L = x + \sqrt{x^2 - y^2}$ and $P = x - \sqrt{x^2 - y^2}$

or $L = x - \sqrt{x^2 - y^2}$ and $P = x + \sqrt{x^2 - y^2}$ 10

(b) (i) What are the advantage and disadvantages of fixed-based and chain-base indicea?

(ii) What are the points to be considered in selecting a base period for the purpose of calculating an index number? 15

(c) Show that the real-valuled function

$$r(h) = \begin{cases} 1, & \text{if } h = 0 \\ \rho, & \text{if } h = \pm 1 \\ 0, & \text{otherwise} \end{cases}$$

is an auto-covariance function, if $|\rho| < \frac{1}{2}$.. 15

6. (a) (i) Show how you would find the sample size $n_i (i = 1, 2, ..., k)$ to be selected from the ith stratrum under optimum allocation if the total cost of the survey is a fixed quantity.

(ii) The ratio of the sizes and the standard deviations of two strata are 11 and 9 respectivley. The ratio of the sample sizes for a general allocation is n_1/n_2 and that for the Neyman allocation is n_1'/n_2' and the ratio of the two ratios is 2. If the objective is to estimate the population mean by taking with replacement random samples from within strata, compare the precision of the two allocations. 15

(b) Define procisely the simple random sampling with and without replacement. If as SRSWOR sample of size n is selected from a population of size N, then show that inclusion probabilities π_i and $\pi_{ij} (i \neq j)$ are respectively given by n/N and n(n – 1)/N(N – 1).

A random sample of 150 boys from 6505 boys in an area showed that 31 had some kind of deficiency. Estimate the proportion of deficient boys in the population and find the standard error of your estimate. 10

(c) Why is the method of systematic sampling widely used in practice? Illustrate your answer with some practical situations. Show that the systematic sampling is more precise than simple is larger than the population variance as a whole. What happen if the units in the same systematic sample have a positive correlation among them? 15

7. (a) Define instrumental variable estimtor. Using instrumental variable method, obtain the estimate of the regression coefficient in a first-order auto-correlated regression model containing lagged endogenous varibel Y_{t-1}. 15

(b) Derive rank condition for identification of a structural equation when there are zero restrictions on the structural parameters. 10

(c) Describe 2-stage least squares (2SLS) method of estiamtion. Show that 2SLS estimators are identical to indirect least squares (ILS) estimtors if the equation is exactly identified. 15

8. (a) For a moving average process with weights $\{a_1, a_2, ..., a_m\}$ of random components $\{e_i, i = 1, 2, ...\}$, where e_i's are iid $N(0, \sigma^2)$, obtain the correlogram function. Find its form, when all the weights are equal annd their sum is 1. 15

(b) Show that if X(t) is a real process, then its spectrum h(ω) can be put in the form

$$h(\omega) = \frac{\sigma_X^2}{2\pi} + \frac{1}{\pi}\sum_{t=1}^{\infty} k(t)\cos(\omega t)$$

where $k(\cdot)$ is the auto-covariance function and $\sigma_X^2 = k(0) = var(X(t))$. 100

(c) A sequence of price indices was cosntructed with 2001 as base year and from 2004, the base year was changed to 2003. Using the data given below, splice the first series (with base 2001) to second series (with base 2003) and then calculate new indices by shifting the base to 2004: 15

Year	2001	2002	2003	2004	2005	2006
IN_{2001}	100	125	118.75	–	–	–
IN_{2003}	–	–	100	115	124.2	130.41

GENERAL STATISTICS
Paper III 2017

Time Allowed : Three Hours | *Maximum Marks: 200*

INSTRUCTIONS

Please read each of the following instructions carefully before attempting questions:

*There are **EIGHT** questions divided under **TWO** Sections. Candidate no. 1 and 5 are compulsory choosing and on: of the remaining. **THREE** are to be attempted choosing at least **ONE** from each Section. The number of marks carried by a question/part is irdicated against it. Unless other-wise mentioned, symbols and notations have their usual standard meanings. Assume suitable data, if necessary and indicate the same clearly. Candidates should attempt question/parts as per the instructions given in the Section. All parts and sub-parts of a question are to be attempted together in the answer book. Attempts of questions shall be counted in chronological order. Unless struck off, attempt of a question shall be counted even if attempted partly. Any page or portion of the page left blank in the answer book must be clearly struck off. Answers must be written in ENGLISH only.*

Section A

All questions of this section are compulsory.

1. (a) Explain sampling and non-sampling errors. State the sources of non-sampling errors. 10

(b) Consider the three-variable regression model

$Y_i = \beta_0 + \beta_1 X_{i1} + \beta_2 X_{i2} + \varepsilon_i, i = 1, 2, ..., n$

where X_1 and X_2 are two independent varibles, Y is the dependent variable, β's are the co-efficients and ε is the random component, $\varepsilon \sim N(0, \sigma^2)$. Obtain the estimates of parameters using OLS method of estimation. 15

(c) The following figures give the production of a commodity of a country from 2001 to 2007:

Year	Production (in thousand metric tonnes)
2001	4.7
2002	5.9
2003	7.2
2004	7.9

2005	7.6
2006	7.0
2007	7.9

Obtain the trend values by a four-year moving average method. 15

2. (a) The following data show the cost of living indices for different groups along with their weights (% of expenditure), for middle-class people of some city in 2010. Obtain the general cost of living index number. Mr. X was getting a salary of ₹ 25,000 in 2010 and ₹ 82,900 in 2016. Calculate how much he ought to have recived as extra allowance in 2016 to maintain his same standard of living. 10

Group	Base year group index	Weight
Food	396	71.3
Clothing	550	2.7
Fuel and Light	360	9.3
House rent	110	6.7
Miscellaneous	290	10

(b) A simple random sample of 25 households was drawn from a city area containing 1345 households. The number of persons per houssehold in the smaple were as follows:

5, 6, 3, 4, 2, 3, 3, 3, 4, 4, 3, 2, 7, 4, 7, 6, 4, 4, 1, 4, 3, 4, 5, 6, 3.

Estimate the total number of people in the area and also compute the variance of the estimate. 15

(c) Discuss the concept of heterscedasticity. Explain this by graphical representation. Show that OLS estimators are unbiased even under the condition of heteroscedasticity. Obtain its variance. 15

Section B

Answer any three questions out of the six questions given below.

3. (a) A finite population of size 98 is divided into three strata. It is given that $N_1 = 2N_2 = 4N_3$ and $S_1 = 2S_2 = 4S_3$. If a sample of 21 is to be selected from the population, obtain the number of units to be selected from each stratum under Neyman allocation. 10

(b) Define linear systematic sampling scheme with N =NK. Obtain the expression for the variance of the sample mean in this case. When will this be more advantageous than SRSWOR scheme? 15

(c) Define Horvitz-Thompson unordered estimator $\hat{Y}_{HT}$ for the population total Y. Obtain an expression for $V(\hat{Y}_{HT})$. Comment on the estimator. 15

4. (a) Explain generalized least squares method of estimation. Write its model along with assumptions. Obtain the estimates of parameters and their variances. 15

(b) Discuss the meaning of Autocorrelation. Give a comparison between autocorrelation adn serial correlation with an example. Give example of variance-covariance matrix of size 3 to show

(i) heterosedasticity with no autocorrelation

(ii) homoscedasticity wioth autocorrelation

(iii) heteroscedasticity with autocorrelation.

Prove that mean of autocorrelated U's turns out to be zero. 15

(c) For general linear model, show that least sqauares estimator $\hat{\beta}$ is the test linear unbiased estimate of β. 10

5. (a) Two stationary time series u_t and u_t' are added together and a new series is formed by $v_t = ut + u_t'$. If u_t and u_t' are independent, show that the autocorrelation of lag κ of v_t is given by

$$\frac{\rho_\kappa \, Var(u_t) + \rho'_\kappa \, Var(u'_t)}{Var\,(u_t) + Var\,(u'_t)}$$

where ρ_κ and ρ'_κ refer to the autocorelation of u_t and u_t' respectively. 15

(b) State the law of demand.

Consider the following econometric model:

q_i (quantity demanded) $= a_0 + b_0 p_i + u_i \; (b_0 < 0)$

q_i (quantity demanded) $= a_1 + b_1 p_i + v_i \; (b_1 < 0)$

the errors u_i and v_i being uncorrelated.

Find the slope of the regression line q_i and p_i. 15

(c) What is peridodogram?

A time series u_t is comp osed of one periodic with period λ and amplitude a and the other term an irregular component (b_t)

$$u_t = a \sin \frac{2\pi t}{\lambda} + b_t$$

Describe a method for finding the true cylical period λ.

Indicate how you will modify the method if the cyclial component is composed of several periodic terms $\lambda_1, \lambda_2, ..., \lambda_k$. 10

6. (a) Explain double sampling scheme. Give an example. Obtain the ratio estimator for the population mean of the study variate when the mean of the auxiliary variate is unknown. 10

(b) In a two-stage sampling, the first and the second stage units are drawn by adopting SR-SWOR. Suggest an unbiased estimator for the population mean. Derive an expression for its variance. 15

(c) State the linear regression estimate for population mean. Obtain the estimate of the regression coefficient by least square method. Show that this estimate is unbiased. Under what condition is the estiamte unbiased? 15

7. (a) What is the need of simultaneuos equation system in economy theory? Discuss Keynesian model as a structural equation model of a national economy. Obtain its reduced form equations and hence reduced form disturbance term. 15

(b) Let Y_1 and Y_2 be two endogenous variables. Let further X_1, X_2 and X_3 be three predetermined variables. A simultaneous equation is expressed as

$$Y_1 = \gamma_{21} Y_2 + \beta_{11} X_1 + \varepsilon_1$$

$$Y_1 = \gamma_{22} Y_2 + \beta_{22} X_2 + \beta_{32} X_3 + \varepsilon_2$$

Discuss a method to identify the model. 15

(c) Discuss full information maximum likelihood method of estimation. Discuss only how to find the normal equtions. 10

8. (a) Define a stationary time series.

For the stationary AR(2) process

$$X_t = \frac{5}{6}X_{t-1} - \frac{1}{6}X_{t-2} + e_t$$

where $e_t \sim N(0, \sigma_e^2)$ denotes the noise.

Find the autorcorrelation function of lags 1 and 2. 10

(b) Describe the different schemes for explaining the oscillations in a stationary time series. Explain the use of correlograms for discriminating between the above schemes. 15

(c) Define Gini coefficient.

The following table presents data on distribution of personal income by decile group separately for both rural and urban sectors of a country for the year 2010.

On a graph paper, draw the Lorenz curve for each sector.

Also, compute the Gini coefficient for each sector.

Hence compare the income inequeality of two sectors. 15

Household	Percentage share in total income	
	Rural	Urban
0 – 10	3.0	2.3
10 – 20	4.4	3.3
20 – 30	5.4	4.1
30 – 40	6.4	4.8
40 – 50	7.4	5.8
50 – 60	8.3	7.0
60 – 70	9.6	8.7
70 – 80	10.9	10.0
80 – 90	13.8	14.0
90 – 100	30.8	40.0

GENERAL STATISTICS
Paper III 2017

Time Allowed : Three Hours | *Maximum Marks: 200*

INSTRUCTIONS

Please read each of the following instructions carefully before attempting questions:

*There are **EIGHT** questions divided under **TWO** Sections. Candidate no. 1 and 5 are compulsory choosing and on: of the remaining. **THREE** are to be attempted choosing at least **ONE** from each Section. The number of marks carried by a question/part is irdicated against it. Unless other-wise mentioned, symbols and notations have their usual standard meanings. Assume suitable data, if necessary and indicate the same clearly. Candidates should attempt question/parts as per the instructions given in the Section. All parts and sub-parts of a question are to be attempted together in the answer book. Attempts of questions shall be counted in chronological order. Unless struck off, attempt of a question shall be counted even if attempted partly. Any page or portion of the page left blank in the answer book must be clearly struck off. Answers must be written in **ENGLISH** only.*

Section A

Both the questions are compulsory/

1. (a) For SESWOR (N, n). show that the sam ple proprotion p is unbiased for the population proportion P. Also derive the sampling variance of this estimator. 10

   (b) What is the problem in estimating a linear regression model in presence of multicollinearity? How is multicollinearity detected? Explain how ridge estimation tackles this issue. 15

   (c) Consider the MA(1) process $X_n = e_n + \beta e_{n-1}$, where $e_n \sim N(0, 1)$. For a data set it is noted that autocovariances are $\hat{\gamma}_0 = 1$ and $\hat{\gamma}_1 = -0.25$.

   (i) Estimate β. Which value of the estimate do you think we should choose and why?

   (ii) What problem do we have if $\hat{\gamma}_1 = -0.5$? How would the variance of the error have affected the change? 10

2. (a) Given below are the figures on production (in thousand matric tons) of a cooperative sugar factory:

Year:	2010	2011	2012	2013	2014	2015	2016
Production:	77	88	84	91	98	90	

(i) Fit a linear trend by least squares method. Tabulate the trend values.

(ii) Compute the monthly estiamted increase in production during the period. 10

(b) If, in every stratum, the simple estimator $\overline{y}_h$ is unbiased, then show that

$$\overline{y}_{st} = \sum_{h=1}^{1} W_h \overline{y}_h$$

is unbiased for population mean $\overline{y}$, where W_h is the proprotion of population units in the strata and L denotes the total number of strata in the population.

Derive the sampling variance of $\overline{y}_{st}$ and state how you woudl unbiasedly estimate the same. 15

(c) In the contex of a finitely distributed lag model, discuss the problem of OLS estimation and suggest how to obtain good (consistent) estimates of the parameters in such a model by bringing in some restrictions on lag weights. 15

Section B

Answer any three questions of the six questions given below.

3. (a) Explain and illustrate the following:

(i) Two-stage sampling

(ii) Two-phase sampling

Pinpoint the difference between the two types of sampling schemes. 10

(b) Write briefly on

(i) Sampling size determination in surveys;

(ii) Cumulative total method for PPSWR sampling.

(iii) Rao-Hartley-Cochran Scheme. 15

(c) Discuss the following allocations of the sample size in stratified random sampling:

(i) Proportional allocation

(ii) Neyman allocation

(iii) Optimum allocation with a linear coast function

Explain the practical implication of these methods. 15

4. (a) Discuss Koyck approach to an inifinitely distributed lag model and obtain the mean lag fro Koyck's model. What are the basic features of Koyck's transofrmed model? 10

(b) For the following linear regression model

$Y_i = \beta_1 + \beta_2 X_i + u_i \quad i = 1, ..., n$

$E(u_i) = 0, \ Cov(u_i, u_j) = 0 \ \ i \neq j, \ E(u_i^2) = \sigma_i^2,$

obtain the OLS estimates of β_1 and β_2 when σ_i^2, i = 1, ..., n are known. Discuss what steps could be taken when σ_1^2, i = 1, ..., n are unknown. Revise the least squates estimates of β_1 and β_2 when $\sigma_1^2 = \sigma^2 E^2(Y_i)$ where σ^2 is unknown. 15

(c) Discuss the problem of estimating parameters by OLS in the presence of serial correlation in the following model:

$Y_t = \beta_1 + \beta_2 X_t + u_t$

$u_t = \rho u_{t-1} + \varepsilon_t, -1 < \rho < 1$, ρ is known

$E(\varepsilon_t) = 0, V(\varepsilon_t) = \sigma^2, Cov(\varepsilon_t, \varepsilon_{t+s}) = 0 \; s \neq 0$

Propose suitable estimates of β_1 and β_2. Also calucalate the variance of the estimate of β_2. How can this estiamte be modified when ρ is unknown? 15

5. (a) Demand and supply functions of a certain commodity are respectively

$$x_d = 240 + 10\frac{dp}{dt} - 4p \text{ kg per month;}$$

$$x_s = 100\frac{dp}{dt} + 6p - 60 \text{ kg per month;}$$

where p is price of the commodity at time t.

Find the time path of p for dynamic equilibrium if the initial price is to be ₹ 72 per kg.

10

(b) Explain briefly the methods of computing price index numbers

(i) by simple average of price relatives;

(ii) by simple aggregate of pricesl; and

(iii) by weighted aggregate of prices. 15

(c) Discuss the different forms of the Engel curve that are usually employed for fitting to family-budget data. In such fitting, how would you tackle the following complications?

(i) Household expennditure on a particular item depends, besides depending on income, on the number of persons per family.

(ii) Consumption of families of the same size differs because of varying age and sex consumption. 15

6. (a) Give an illustration for linear systematic smapling. Show that, under this method, a positive correlationn between units in the same sample inflates the sampling variance of the estimator of population total. 10

(b) Consider a population of N = 6 units wioth values 1, 2, 3, 4, 5 and 6.

(i) Write down all possible samples of size 2 drawn by SRSWOR scheme. Verify that the sample mean is unbiased for the population mean.

(ii) Also compute the sampling variance of the sample mean. 15

(c) Explain the ratio method of estimation for estimating a population total. Show that it is generally biased. Evaluate the mean squared error of the estimator to the first order of approximation. Assume SRSWOR of n units from the population.

7. (a) Using standard notations, briefly explain the instrumental variable technique in the context of estiamting the coefficient in a linear regression model. State the situations when this technique is applicable. 10

(b) State the rank and order conditions for identifiability of parameters in a system of structural equations. Which one of those two conditions is sufficient for identifiability? Establish this condition mathematically. 15

(c) Discuss the estimation of prameters of an equation apperaing in a simultaneouos equation system by Limited Information Maximum Likelihood method. State whether the estimator (if it exists) is unique. (An outline of the apprpach is adequate) 15

8. (a) Show that the relationship $X_t = 0.7X_{t-1} + 0.3X_{t-2} + \varepsilon_t + 0.7\varepsilon_{t-1}$ (where ε_t denotes white nosie) deflnes ARIMA (1, 1, 1) model. 10

(b) What do you understand by the seasonal variations in a time series? Give example.

(c) Definen correlogram.

For an infinite series generated by the average of a random component with equal weights, show that the correlogram is

$$\rho_k = \begin{cases} 1 - \dfrac{k}{m} & \text{for } k \leq m \\ 0 & \text{for } k > m \end{cases}$$

15

GENERAL STATISTICS
Paper III 2015

Time Allowed : Three Hours | Maximum Marks: 200

INSTRUCTIONS

Please read each of the following instructions carefully before attempting questions:

*There are **SIX** questions divided under **TWO** Sections. Candidate has to attempt FIVE questions in all. All the THREE questions in Section A are compulsory. Out of the THREE questions in Section B, TWO questions are to be attempted. Attempts of questions shall be counted in sequential order. Unless struck off, attepmt of a question shall be counted even if attempted partly. The number of marks carried by a question/part is indicated against it. Unless otherwise mentioned, symbols and notations have their usual standard meanings. Assume suitable data, if necessary and indicate the same clearly. All parts and sub-parts of a question are to be attempted together inn the answer book. Any page or portion of the page left blank in the answer book in the answer book must be clearly struck off. Answers must be written in ENGLISH only.*

Section A

All the three questions are compulsory.

1. (a) Define Des Raj;s orderd estimator for population mean on the basis of a sample of size 2 and show that it is unbiased. 10

(b) Let π_i and $\pi_{ij}(j \neq i)$ be the inclusion probabilities of first and second order respectively in a simple random sample of size n, selected from a finite population of size N. Then show that

(i) $\sum_{i=1}^{N} \pi_i = n$ and

(ii) $\sum_{(j \neq i)=1}^{N} \pi_{ij} = n(n-1)$. 10

(c) Give a practical example where two-stage sampling scheme may be adopted. For equal size first-stage units, obtain an estimator for population mean in two-stage sampling and its variance. Discuss the problem of allocation of first and second-stage sample sizes for a fixed cost. 20

2. (a) Describe the problem of multicollinearity in general linear model and explain how will you detect it. 10

(b) In usual notation consider the standard linear model: $Y = X\beta + U; U \sim N(0, \sigma^2 I)$. Show that the MLE $\hat{\beta}$ of β have the distribution $N(\beta, \sigma^2(X'X)^{-1})$ assuming $X'X$ to be an invertible matrix. 10

(c) (i) Explain the identification problem in a system of simultaneous. State, without proof, the rank and order conditions for identifiability of an equation. 10

(ii) Identify the following system:

$$y_1 = 3y_2 - 2x_1 + x_2 + U_1$$
$$y_2 = y_3 - x_3 + U_2$$
$$y_3 = y_1 - y_2 - 2x_3 + U_3$$ 10

3. (a) Construct the price index number for 2010 with 2005 as base year form the following data by using

(i) Laspeyre's

(ii) Paasche's and

(iii) Fisher' s method

Item	Price (in Rs.)		Quality	
	2010	2005	2010	2005
A	10.50	8.25	6	4
B	6.40	6.00	10	6
C	15.20	10.80	6	5
D	6.25	4.00	8	5

Verify whether the Time Reversal Test is satisfied by the abovementioned index numbers. 10

(b) Define price elasticity of demand (η_p) and interpret when η_p is

(i) < 1

(ii) > 1 and

(iii) $= 1$

If the demand function is $p = 10 - 5x^2$, for what value of x elasticity of demand will be unity? (x is the quantity demanded and p is the price). 10

(c) Define autocorrelation of lag K of a statinary process. Consider the time series model defined by

$X_t = \alpha_1 X_{t-1} + \alpha_2 X_{t-2} + \alpha_3 X_{t-3} + \epsilon_t$

where (ϵ_t) is white noise.

(i) Show that the autocorrelation coefficient with lag 1 for the process is:

$$\rho_1 = \frac{\alpha_1 + \alpha_2\alpha_3}{1 - \alpha_2 - \alpha_1\alpha_3 - \alpha_3^2}$$

(ii) Consider the case where

$\alpha_1 = \alpha_2 = \alpha_3 = 0.2$.

Comment on the stationarity of this model.

You may use $5 - x - x^2 - x^3 \simeq (1.278 - x)(3.912 + 2.278x + x^2)$.

Calculate ρ_1 and ρ_2. 20

Section B

Attempt any two quetions

4. (a) A finite population of size 100 is divided into two strata. In the usual notaitons, it is given that $N_1 = 60, N_2 = 40, S_1 = 2S_2$. If a sample of size 24 is to be selected from the population, obtain the number of units to be selected from each of the stratum under Neymann allocation. 10

   (b) For the model $y = X\beta + u$ if X and u are correlated show that the OLS estimator for β is not consistent. Discuss the use of instrumental variable technique to obtain a consistent estimator of β. 10

   (c) Consider a time series $y_t = T_t + C_t + I_t$ where T_t a trend, C_t a cyclical component and I_t a random component. Discuss the effect of moving averages on cyclical and random components assuming $C_t = a \sin \frac{2\pi t}{\lambda}$. 20

5. (a) Explain Koyck's approach to distributed geometric lag model. 10

   (b) What is a chain index number? Discuss its advantages and disadvantages over fixed-bbase index number. 10

   (c) In what sense cluster sampling is different from simple random sampling? Define an unbiased estimator for population mean in case of cluster sampling with equal cluster size. Compare the efficiency of cluster sampling in terms of intra-class correlation coefficient with respect to simple random sampling without replacement. 20

6. (a) You believe that a set of data is the realization of an MA(1) process $X_n = e_n + \beta e_{n-1}$, where the errors e_n are standard normal. You have calculated the sample auto-covariane function and found that $\hat{\gamma}_0 = 1$ and $\hat{\gamma}_1 = -0.25$. Estimate the parameter β. Which value of β do you think you should choose and why? 10

   (b) Describe the Lahiri's method of selecting a probability proportional to size sample froma finite population of size N. 10

   (c) Describe lag model and distributed lag model What are the differennt lag schemes? How would you estimate lags by applying ordinary least square? 20

GENERAL STATISTICS
Paper III 2015

Time Allowed : Three Hours | *Maximum Marks: 200*

INSTRUCTIONS

Please read each of the following instructions carefully before attempting questions:

*There are **EIGHT** questions divided under **TWO** Sections. Candidate no. 1 and 5 are compulsory choosing and on: of the remaining. **THREE** are to be attempted choosing at least **ONE** from each Section. The number of marks carried by a question/part is irdicated against it. Unless other-wise mentioned, symbols and notations have their usual standard meanings. Assume suitable data, if necessary and indicate the same clearly. Candidates should attempt question/parts as per the instructions given in the Section. All parts and sub-parts of a question are to be attempted together in the answer book. Attempts of questions shall be counted in chronological order. Unless struck off, attempt of a question shall be counted even if attempted partly. Any page or portion of the page left blank in the answer book must be clearly struck off. Answers must be written in **ENGLISH** only.*

Section A

1. Answer any five parts of the following: $8 \times 5 = 40$

(a) Show that for SRSWOR, the sample proportion is an unbiased estimator of the population propotion of members possesing a certian character. Hence obtain the variance of the estimator. 8

(b) Explain the principal of forming strata and clusters. What are the differences between stratified sampling and cluster sampling? 8

(c) (i) Explain why the variance of the estimate of population mean based on a single systematic sample is not unbiasedly estarrable. 8

(ii) If two independent systemmatic samples of size four each from a population cf 36 units have y-value of a characteristic y as

24, 26, 22, 28

and 27, 25, 23, 29

respectively, calculate an unbiased estiamte of principles of design of experiments and their analogy in smaple surveys with the corresponding concepts. 8

(d) Explain briefly the main principle of design of experiments and their analogy in smaple surveys with the corresponding concepts. 8

(e) Discuss how you would proceed with the nalysis if data on one plot is missing in a Latin Square Design. 8

(f) Suppose an experimenter wants to conduct a 3^3 experiment in blocks of size 9 plots. Write down the treatments to 3 blocks with AB^2 as the confounding contrast. 8

2. (a) Consider a population $U = \{u_1, u_2, u_3, u_4\}$. The value of the study variable are $y(u_i) = i$, $i = 1(1)$ 4.

(i) A sample of size 2 is drawn from the population with (i) SRSWOR (ii) SRSWR. Calculate V_1 = Var $(\bar{y} | \text{SRSWOR})$ and V_2 = Var $(\bar{y} | \text{SRSWOR})$ where $\bar{y}$ denotes the sample mean.

(ii) A linear systematic sample of size 2 is drawn when the units of the population are arranged as follows:

Arangme 1 : u_1, u_4, u_2, u_3

Arangme 2 : u_1, u_4, u_4, u_3

Caculate Var $(\bar{y} | \text{arrangement 1})$ v_3 = and Var$(\bar{y} | \text{arrangment 2}) = v_4$.

(iii) Show that $v_4 < v_1 < v_2 < v_3$. 10

(b) (i) For any sampling design, describe the ratio method of estimating the populationt total Y of a study variate y, when auxilliary information on a related variable x is av table with a known population total X. Denote the estimator by $\hat{Y}_R$ abd derive its approximate bias.

(ii) Consider two ratio estimtor r_1 and r_2 for a parameter θ based on a sample of size n with biases $B(r_1) = b_1$ and $B(r_2) = b_2 = nb_1$. Using this information, obtain an unbiased estimator of θ and its variance expression. 10

(c) Consider a population U = {1, 2, 3, 4, 5}. For a sampling design, probabilities of samples drawn are $P_r\{(1, 2)\} = 0.2$, $P_r\{(2, 3, 4)\} = 0.1$, $P_r\{(1, 4, 5)\} = 0.3$, $P_r\{(2, 4, 5)\} = 0.2$, $P_r\{(1, 2, 3, 4)\} = 0.2$. Calculated the first-order inclusion probabilities. Obtain estimates $\sum_{i \in S} \frac{l_i y_i}{\pi}$ of the parametric function $\sum_{i=1}^{N} l_i y_i$ where l_i's are known real numbers, not all zero. 10

(d) For a two-stage sampling design, let n village be selected with probabiliteis proportional to a given size and with replacement from a population of N villages. From the ith selected village consisting of M_i household (hh), m_i households olds are selected by simple random sampling without replacement. Write down an unbiased estimator of $Y = \sum_{i=1}^{N} \sum_{j=1}^{M_i} Y_{ij}$, where Y_{ij} is the value of a study variate for the jth hh of the ith village. Also write down an unbiased estimator of $\text{Var}(\hat{Y})$. 10

3. (a) Describe how uniformity trials in experimental designs and pilot studies in sample surveys are conducted, mentioning their uses. 10

(b) Find the C-matrix for the following design and obtain independent estimatable treatment contrasts:

$B_1 = (1, 2, 2), B_2 = (2, 4, 4), B_3 = (1, 1, 2), B_4 = (3, 4, 4)$. 10

(c) Explain what is menat by a split-plot design. Suppose that factor A has p levels which are arranged in a Randomized Block Design having r replicates. Let factor B have q levels whch are applied to plots of a block after subdividing each plot into q sub plots. Write down the model, clearly explaining the notations and assumptions and presennt a blank ANOVA table with sources of variation and degrees of freedom. 10

(d) State the condotopms tp ne satisfied by a Partially Balanced Incomplete Block (PBIB) design.

Prove the following restrictions of a PBIBD:

(i) $\sum_{j=1}^{m} n_j = v - 1;$

(ii) $r(K-1) = \sum_{j=1}^{m} n_j \lambda_j$ 10

4. (a) What are the advantage of stratified sampling? Consider the alloccation of sample size n_i to strata given by $n_i \propto N_i \sigma_i^{\alpha}$, where N_i is the stratum size, σ_i is the within stratum standard deviation of the ith statum, (i = 1, 2, ..., k) and δ is real. Write down an expression for the $(\hat{\hat{Y}}_{St.})$ where $\hat{\hat{Y}}_{St.}$ stands for the unbiased estimator of the population mean $\bar{Y}$ of the study variate y based on Simple Random Sampling without replacement in each stratum. 10

(b) Consider a populationn $U = \{u_1, u_2, ..., u_N\}$ Observations of study variable (y) and auxiliary variable (x) are y_i, $x(u_i = x_i$, i = 1, 2, ..., N.

Let $P_i = \frac{X_i}{X}$ where $X = \sum_{i=1}^{N} X_i$. A sample of size n is drawn with PPSWR. Show that for population total $T = \sum_{1}^{N} y_i$, the estimator $\hat{Y}_{pps} = \frac{1}{n}\sum_{i=1}^{n}\frac{y_i}{P_i}$ is an unbiased estimator. Obtain the variance of the estimator of the population total. 10

(c) Verify whether the following arrangement is a symmetrical BIB desgin. Consider each set a block:

(12, 0, 2, 8), (6, 7, 9, 2), (4, 5, 7, 0), (5, 6, 8, 1), (11, 12, 1, 7), (3, 4, 6, 12), (10, 11, 0, 6), (9, 10, 12, 5), (2, 3, 5, 11), (1, 2, 4, 10), (8, 9, 11, 4), (7, 8, 10, 3), (0, 1, 3, 9).

Is it a connected BIBD? 10

(d) 32 plots are arranged in the form of a 4 = 8 rectangle. Give a design for 2^5 factorial experiment with factors A, B, C, D and E in these plots confounding the effects ABC, CDE, ABDE with the rows and AB, CD, ABCD, BDE, ADE, BCE, ACE with the columns. 10

SECTION B

5. Answer any five parts of the following: 5×8=40

(a) List the main components of a time series. Explain the method of link relative for measurement of seasonal fluctuations of a time series. 8

(b) Discuss tge considerations in the choice of (i) base period and (ii) the formula (method), for constructing price index numbers. 8

(c) Decribe exact and near multicollinearity in a regression model. Discuss, along with justification, the effect of these situations on (i) sampling variance and (ii) prediction. 8

(d) Describe the problem of heteroscedascedasticity in linear regression models. Outline any one method for overcoming this problem. 8

(e) Explain the use of Pareto curve in the study of income distribution. 8

(f) Describe in detail Indirect Least Squares method for estimating structural paremeters. Is the estimator unbiased and/or consistent? 8

6. (a) State the problem of autocorrelation in a general linear model (GLM). Why does this problem arise? Demonstrate its effect on ordinary least squares estimator (OLSE). 10

(b) What do you mean by forecasting in economic models? Define best linear unbiased predictor and obtain the same in simple linear regression model satisfying al the basic assumptions. 10

(c) Explain variate-differnece method for trend analysis. How is the appropriate order of differencing determined? 10

(d) In the construction of price index numbers, explain the terms 'time reversal test' and 'factor reversal test'. Show that both these tests are satified by the Fisher index. 10

7. (a) Explain the identification problem in a system of simultaneous equation. State, without proof, the rank and order conditions for identifiability of an equation.

Examine for identifiability of the following model:

Demand: $M_t = \beta_0 + \beta_1 Y_t - \beta_2 R_1 + \beta_3 P_t + U_{1t}$

Supply: $M_t = \alpha_0 + \alpha_1 Y_1 + U_{2t}$

where M = money, Y = income,

R = rate of interest, P = price.

Assume that R and P are predetermined. 10

(b) Describe the two-stage least squares (2SLS) procedure for structural estimation in *** simultaneous equations model. Show that in coincides with indirect least squares method wher the equation is exactly idenified. 10

(c) Discuss how the Engel curve is constructed on the basis of family budget data. Explain and interpret the Engel law in this context. How are variations in household size and composition handled? 10

(d) Write down th auto correlation function of order k, for an AR(1) model $X_t = 0.7X_{t-1} + \epsilon_1$. where $\{\epsilon_t\}$ is a white noise process. Show that this model can be expressed as a moving average process of infinite order. Check the model for statiionarity. 19

8. (a) The following information concerns changes in price and consumption (quantity) of certain major components of the consumption-basket of the labour class:

Sl. No.	Item	Unit	Year 2000		Year 2014	
			Price (Rs.)	Consumption	Price (Rs.)	Consumption
1	Rice	Quintal	500	16	640	20
2	Wheat	Quintal	240	12	320	10
3	Cloth	Metre	16	50	20	35

Compute price index using:

(i) Fisher's method;

(ii) Marshall-Edgeworth method.

Also interpret the results. 10

(b) Discuss the main aspects of the sampling design used by the NSSO for collection of data on household consumer expencitures. If you were to improve upon this design, explain what modifications you would suggest, with a clear justification. 10

(c) Define periodogram. Stage the connection between the periodogram and the autocovariance function of a time series. Show that h(w) defined by

$$h(w) = \left(\frac{1}{2\pi}\right) \sum_{t=-\infty}^{\infty} K(\tau) \exp(-iw\tau)$$

is of period 2π where K(.) is the auto covariance function. 10

(d) Define parital auto correlation function (PACF). Determine this function for the model:

$X_t = 0.7 X_{t-1} + 0.3 X_{t-2} + \epsilon_1$

where $\{\epsilon_t\}$ is a sequence of uncorrelated random variables with mean zero and variance σ^2_ϵ. 10

GENERAL STATISTICS
Paper III 2014

Time Allowed : Three Hours | *Maximum Marks: 200*

INSTRUCTIONS

Candidates should attempt FIVE questions in ALL including Questions No. 1 and 5 which are compulsory. The remaining THREE questions should be answered by choosing at least ONE question each from Section A and Section B. The number of marks carried by each question is indicated against each. Answers must be written only in ENGLISH. (Symbols and abbreviations are as usual) Any essential data assumed by candidates for answering questions must be clearly stated.

Section A

1. Answer any five parts of the following: 8×5=40

(a) You are asked to plan sample survey to find out the incident of educated unemployment in your State. Give details of your plan including an outline of a suitable questionaire for this purpose. 8

(b) In statisfied population with two strata, the values of W_h, S_h and C_h are given. If the cost function is of the form $C = c_1n_1 + c_2n_2$, obtain expression for $\frac{n_h}{n}$, h = 1, 2; that minimize C for gives value of $V(\bar{y}_{st})$; where the symbols have their usual meanings. 8

(c) A random sample of 150 boys from 6505 boys in an area showed that 31 had some kind of deficiency. Estimate the proportion of deficient boys and the standard error of youresti-mate. 8

(d) What is meant by the design of experiment? Describe the situations in which the three basic designs, namely CRD, RBD and LSF are appropriate, and state the rule or rules by which treatments are allocated to units in these designs. 8

(e) What do you understand by a split-plot design? When will such a design be adopted? Distinguish it from a usual confounded factorial experiment. 8

(f) Obtain necessary conditions for a symmetric BIBD with an even number of treatments to exist. 8

2. (a) From the following analysis of variance table of a cluster sample estimate its efficiency relative to simple random sampling. Assume that the clusters are of equal size and the numberof clusters in the population is very large:

Source	S.S.	d.f.
Between clusters	40	5
Within clusters	96	24

10

(b) What are the situations in which ratio estimte is used? Obtain an unbiased ratio type estimator for the popultion mean 10

(c) Suppose a simple random sample of size 2 is drawn from a finite population (y_1, y_2, y_3). Corresponding to the three possible samples $S_1 = (y_1, y_2)$, $S_2 = (y_2, y_3)$ and $S_3 = (y_1, y_3)$ a linear estimator l(S) for estimating the population mean is defined as follows:

$l(S_1) = 2/3\, y_1 + 1/2\, y_2$, $l(S_2) = 1/2\, y_2 + 1/2\, y_3$, $l(S_3) = 1/3\, y_1 + 1/2\, y_3$.

(i) Show that the estimator l(S) is unbiased estimator of population mean and obtain its variance.

(ii) If $y_1 = 1$, $y_2 = 2$ and $y_3 = 3$ show that $V(l(S) < V(\overline{y})$; where $\overline{y}$ is the mean of sample of size 2. 10

(d) A population consists of 6 units with sizes of the auxiliary variable as 12, 33, 45, 84, 16, 10. Select a PPS sample of size 2, given that the two selected random random numbers from 1 to 200 are 27 and 186. Also state unbiased estimator of the selected random smaple. 10

3. (a) What is meant by analysis of covariance (ANCOVA)? Discuss the test procedure to test the necissity of the use of ANCOVA in one way and two-way classifications. 10

(b) Let N be the incident matrix of a BIBD with parameters v, b, r, k, λ.

(i) Show tht NN′ is non inveritble matrix if k = v.

(ii) Show that the characteristic roots of NN′ are rk and r – λ of multiplicative 1 and v – 1 respectively. 10

(c) Construct balanced group of sets for 2^4 factrial, blocks of 4 units in which CD, ABC, ABD are confounded. 10

(d) Explain clearly the purposes of replications, randomizations and local control in design of experiments. 10

4. (a) Define linear systematic. Does it give equal probility of selection to all the population units? State the advantages and limitations of systematic sampling. Can a systematic sample be drawn without a physical list of population unitsd? Justify your claim. 10

(b) Consider a population U = {1, 2, 3} with the following design P({1, 2}) = 1/2, P({1, 3}) = 1/4 = P({2, 3}). Give the first order inclusive probability. Hence check whether the design is fixed size design. Give the variance-covariance matrix of indicator variables for inclusion in the sample. 10

(c) What is an incomplete block design? When is it said to be balanced? Explain how inter-block information can be recovered in a balanced incompete block design. 10

(d) Define a Latin square design. Show how you split up the total sum of squares into components for this design. Give the analysis of variance table. 10

SECTION B

5. Answer any five parts of the following: 8×5=40

(a) Define price elasticity of demand and income elasticity of demand. Point out their uses in economic analysis. 8

(b) Let d_1 and d_2 represent the demand of a commodity for two strata of a population. If η_1 and η_2 be the elasticities of demand with respect to national income for the two strata. Show that the corresponding elasticity η for the two strata combined would be given by:

$\eta = (\eta_1 d_1 + \eta_2 d_2)/(d_1 + d_2)$. 8

(c) Define Laspeyres' and Paasche's index numbers. It is sometimes stated that Laspeyres' price index number tends to overstimate price changes while Paasche's price index number temds to underestimate them. Justify or refute the above statement giving reasons. 8

(d) Describe General Linear Model in K independent variables. Justify the inclusion of a random error in this model. 8

(e) Explain the type of multicollinearity that arise in econometric investiagations. What are the implications of this problem (i) for prediction of dependent variable and (ii) for the estimation of regression coefficients? 8

(f) Discuss how by pooling the time series and cross section data, multicollinearity can be resolved. 8

6. (a) What are the two mathematical model employed for time series analysis? Can one model be considered as a partticular type of the other one? Which one of the two models is considered t o be more useful and why? Discuss each of the above aspects. 10

(b) Define oscillatory times series. State the difference between cyclical time series and oscillarory time series. State the reasons which are responsible to produce oscillatory time series. Can oscillatory time-series be said to be stationary time series? 10

(c) Discuss how you will proceed for constructing a cost of living index number for a given expenditure group in a city. 10

(d) What is periodigram? Discuss how the periodogram becomes helpful to determine the periodicity hidden in the time series. 10

7. (a) In usual notaiton, consider the standard linear model: $Y = X\beta + U, U \sim N(0, \sigma^2)$. Show that the MLE $\hat{\beta}$ of β have the distribution $N(\beta, \sigma^2(X'X)^{-1})$, assuming $X'X$ to be an inveritble matirx. 10

(b) Discuss +the problem of hetroscadasticity in GLM. Discribe Glejser test for detectinng hetroscadasticity. What are the difficuliteis in using Glejser test? How do you overcome these difficulties? 10

(c) Explain the term 'autocorrelation'. What are the consequences of autocorrelation? Explain how the Durbin-Watson d statistic is used to detect the presence of autocorrelation. 10

(d) Describe the problem of 'multicollinearity' in econometrics and explain how will you detect it. 19

8. (a) Define Fisher index number. Show why Fisher index number is said to be ideal index number. Also show why Laspeyres' and Paasche's index number are not ideal one. 10

(b) For an infinite series generated by the moving average of a random component with equal weights, the correlogram is given by:

$$r_k = \begin{cases} 1 - \dfrac{k}{m}, & \text{for} \le m \\ 0, & \text{for } k > m. \end{cases}$$ 10

(c) What is Ridge regression? Show that Ridge regression estimator can not only resolve the deadlock of multicollinearity but it can also give an efficient estimator even though it is a biased estimator. 10

(d) After listing the underlying conditions, show that the indirect least squares method of estimation and the 2-SLS method of estimation are equivalent. 10

GENERAL STATISTICS
Paper III 2013

Time Allowed : Three Hours | *Maximum Marks: 200*

INSTRUCTIONS

Candidates should attempt FIVE questions in ALL including Questions No. 1 and 5 which are compulsory. The remaining THREE questions should be answered by choosing at least ONE question each from Section A and Section B. The number of marks carried by each question is indicated against each. Answers must be written only in ENGLISH. (Symbols and abbreviations are as usual) Any essential data assumed by candidates for answering questions must be clearly stated.

Section A

1. Answer any five parts of the following: $8\times5=40$

   (a) In simple random sampling without replacement (SRSWOR), the sample mean $\bar{y}$ is an unbiased estimator of population mean $\bar{Y}$. Obtain the variance of the estimator of the population total Y. 8

   (b) Describe the priciples of stratification. Explain how the allocation of sample size in different strata is made. 8

   (c) Discuss a procedure, using Sen-Midzuno scheme, to obtain the inclusion probability of n units. 8

   (d) Identify the design given below, whose blocks are: (1, 2, 3, 4), (2, 3, 4) and (4, 1, 2, 3).

   Write its parameters. Suppose a treatment '3' belonging to 3rd row and 4th column is missing. How can you estimate that missing treatment?? Estimate that value. Write degrees of freedom for error and total variation. 8

   (e) Construct a key of 25 confounded factorial experiment conducted into a block of size 8. Discuss how to construct other blocks. Write its confounded interactions. 8

   (f) Discuss the concept of Balanced incomplete block design (BIBD). How does this design differ from randomised block design? For a BIBD with parameters v, b, r, k and λ, show that $b \geq v$. 8

2. (a) Give the names of various procedure for selecting a sample using probability proportional to size (PPS) scheme. Obtain an unbiased estimator of the populationn mean under PPS. 10

(b) Show that ratio estimator is unbiased if the line of regression of Y on X is a straight line and passingg through origin. 10

(c) Discuss two-stage samplinng. Let n first stage units be selected from a population of N units and m second stage units from each chosen first stage unit be selected using simple random sampling without replacement. Obtain the variance of sample neab $\bar{y}$. 10

(d) Explain circular system sampling. Show that minimum value of ρ is $\frac{-1}{(n-1)}$, when $V_{sy}(\bar{y}) = 0$, where ρ is instraclass correlation and $\bar{y}$ is the sample mean. 10

3. (a) Explain the need of Factorial experiments. Develop a method to estimate all main effects and interaction effects of 2^3-factorial experiment. Give its ANOVA table. 10

(b) In a two-way classified data, the incidence matrix of the design is given below. Analyze the data.

Block

		1	2	3	4	5	6	7
Treatment	1	1	0	0	0	1	0	1
	2	1	1	0	0	0	1	0
	3	0	1	1	0	0	0	1
N =	4	1	0	1	1	0	0	0
	5	0	1	0	1	1	0	0
	6	0	0	1	0	1	1	0
	7	0	0	0	1	0	1	1

Show that the variance of the estimates of all treatmetn constrasts $(\hat{t}_i - \hat{t}_j)$ is constant for all $i \neq j = 1, 2, ..., v$. 10

(c) What is a symmetrical BIBD? If N is the incidence matrix of SBIBD and λ is the number of treatments common in any two blocks, then establish a relation between N and λ. 10

(d) For a PBIB design with parameters v, b, r, k, λ_i, n_j, show that $\sum_{i=1}^{m} n_i \lambda_i = r(k-1)$. 10

4. (a) In simple random sampling without replacement, obtainn the sampling variance of the regression estimator $\bar{y}_t$. Show that the estimator is superior to SRSWOR. 10

(b) Describe a procedure for systematic sampling under linear trend in the population. Obtain the expressions of population mean and population variance. 10

(c) Explain split-plot design. Considering main plot treatment α, sub-plot treatment β and the number of replications in the RBD for main plot treatments be r, write the ANOVA table of main plot totals. 10

(d) For the following experiment:

Replication – 1

Block – 1	Block – 2	Block – 3
0 2 2	1 1 1	0 2 1
0 0 0	0 0 1	0 0 2
0 1 1	2 0 2	1 1 2
2 2 0	0 2 0	2 2 2
1 2 1	2 2 1	2 0 0
2 1 2	1 0 0	1 2 0
1 0 2	0 1 2	1 0 1
2 0 1	1 2 2	2 1 1
1 1 0	2 1 0	0 1 0

Replication – 2

Block – 4	Block – 5	Block – 6
0 2 2	0 2 1	0 2 0
1 0 1	1 0 0	1 0 2
2 0 2	2 0 1	2 0 0
0 1 1	0 1 0	0 1 2
1 1 2	1 2 2	1 2 1
2 2 1	2 1 2	1 1 0
0 0 0	1 1 1	2 1 1
2 1 0	2 2 0	0 0 1
1 2 0	0 0 2	2 2 2

identify the experiment. Find the confounded experiment. Write the type of confounded interactions. Further write its generalized confounded interaction, if available. Give your comments. 10

SECTION B

5. Answer any five parts of the following: 8×5=40

(a) Discuss various steps of finding adjusted monthly indices of seasonal variations using link relative method. 8

(b) Obtain the complementary function and particular integral of first order regressive model. Show that U_t is a moving averge of random elements with weights 1, a, a^2, ... a^{k-1}. 8

(c) Discuss simple aggregate method of Index number. Why is weighted average of price relative index preferred over simple aggreage mthod? Show that weighted average of price relativge index number is same as that of Paasche's index number. 8

(d) Let under usual linear model set-up, $\hat{\beta}$ is OLS estimator given by $\underline{\hat{\beta}} = (X'X)^{-1} X'Y$. Let $\hat{\hat{\beta}}$ be a new linear estimator obtained by augmentinng p'y in the coefficient of Y. Under what conditions, $\hat{\hat{\beta}}$ is unbiased estimatro fo β? Further obtain its variance. Mention under what condition $V(\hat{\beta})$ and $V(\hat{\hat{\beta}})$ will be same. 8

(e) Consider a hypothetical data

$X_1 = (10, 15, 18, 24, 30)$; $X_2 = (50, 75, 90, 120, 150)$ and $X_3 = (52, 75, 97, 129, 152)$.

Find the type of multicollinearity between X_1 and X_2 and X_2 and X_3. Discuss how to tackle the multicollinearity problem using a prior estimator. 8

(f) Explain heteroscedasticity. Show that under heteroscedastic model, OLS estimator is less efficient than the weighted least square estimator. 8

6. (a) Why do the errors occur in the measurement of price and quantity index number? Give the name of those errors. 10

(b) Discuss the relevance fo variate difference method in time series analysis data. Show that $V(\Delta^k U_t) = E[\Delta^k \varepsilon_t]^2$. 10

(c) Explaining Pareto's law of income distribution, show that the elasticity decreases in the number of persons while passing to a higher income class. 10

(d) Show that for a series generated by an m-points simple moving average of random components, the correlogram consists of a straignt line joining the points (m, 0) and (0, 1) together with k-axis from the point (m, 0) onwards. 10

7. (a) For a model $Y = X\beta + e$, if $e \sim N(0, \sigma^2 \Omega)$, where Ω is a positive semi-define matrix, can we use OLD method of estimation? If not, why? Using which method of estimation, can $\hat{\beta}$ be estimated? Obtain its variance. 10

(b) Consider a simple regression model $y_t = \beta X_t + U_t$. Let $U_t = \rho U_{t-1} + e_t$, with $E[e_t] = 0$, $E[e_t, e_{t-1}] = 0$, $V(e_t) = \sigma^2$. If U_t are AR(1) errors, show that $\rho_j = \rho^j$, where ρ is autocorrelation coefficient. 10

(c) What is the rank condition of identification problem? For the simultaneous equation model:

$$Y_1 = \Gamma_{21} Y_2 + \beta_{11} X_1 + e_1 \quad (1)$$

$$Y_1 = \Gamma_{22} Y_2 + \beta_{22} X_2 + \beta_{32} X_3 + e_2 \quad (1)$$

discuss a method to identify the equation (1) only. 10

(d) Consider measurement errprs in one variable are in the limit uncorrelated with measurement erros in other variable. Again measurement errors in both variables are uncorrelated with their true values, then show that under such situations, the OLS estimator $\hat{\beta}$ is inconsistent for β. 10

8. (a) Discuss Engel's curve. Explain Engel's curve for constant price of a demand function $d = f(\mu, p)$, where μ is national income and p is price. 10

(b) Explain the following: 10

(i) Weighted Aggregates method

(ii) Criteria of a good index number

(c) Explain the effect of Ridge estimator in multicollinearity. Show that Ridge estimator is biased. Obtain its bias and variance. 10

(d) Explain Keysian income determination simultaneous equation model. Show that simultaneous equation model violates the assumptions of OLS estimtor. 10

GENERAL STATISTICS
Paper III 2012

Time Allowed : Three Hours

Maximum Marks: 200

INSTRUCTIONS

Candidates should attempt FIVE questions in ALL including Questions No. 1 and 5 which are compulsory. The remaining THREE questions should be answered by choosing at least ONE question each from Section A and Section B. The number of marks carried by each question is indicated against each. Answers must be written only in ENGLISH. (Symbols and abbreviations are as usual) Any essential data assumed by candidates for answering questions must be clearly stated.

Section A

1. (a) Show that for a simple random sample

$$s^2 = \sum_{i=1}^{n}(y_i - \bar{y})^2 / (n-1)$$

is an unbbiased estimate of s^2.

(b) Let y_i be the y-value of the ith unit and P_i be corresponding selection probability, i = 1, 2, ..., N. Then, based on a sample of size n drawn with replacement, show that an unbiased estimator for population total is

$$\hat{Y}_{PPS} = \frac{1}{n}\sum_{i=1}^{n}\frac{y_i}{P_i}$$

(c) Let the blocks of a BIBD be (1, 2), (1, 3) and (2, 3). Obtain the non-zero eigen value of C-matrix of BIBD and hence estimates of treatments.

(d) What is a 2^3 factorial experiment? Discuss a method to estimate all main effects and interaction effects considering replication size r. Also write ots ANOVA table.

(e) A factorial experiment 2^6 is conducted into a block of size 8 by confounding the interaction effects ABC, ACDE and BCD. Write th total number of blocks per replication, number of blocks per replication, number of generalized confounded interactions. Write all generalized interactions. Is it possible to save 2-factor interactions from being confounded in the experiment?

8×5=40

2. (a) Obtain an unbiased estimator of the gain due to PPSWR sampling as compared to SRSWR.

(b) Show that the ratio estimator is better than the one based on SPRSWOR if $\rho > \frac{1}{2}$ when $C_X = C_Y$.

(c) Show that the biase of the usual regression estimator is $-\text{cov}(\bar{x}, b)$.

(d) Show that mean of a systematic sample is more precise than the mean of a simple random sample of size n under a certain condition to be obtained by you. 10×4=40

3. (a) Discuss the construction of a BIBD with parameters $v = 9, b = 12, r = 4, k = 3$ and $\lambda = 1$ using EG (N, S) method.

(b) Let four treatments be arranged in three blocks. The arrangement is given below:

Block 1: $[t_1\ t_2\ t_3\ t_4]$

Block 2: $[t_2\ t_3\ t_4\ t_1]$

Block 3: $[t_3\ t_4\ t_1\ t_2]$

Identify the block design. Write its parameters. If the treatment t_4 in Block 3 is missing, estimate the missing value. Write its ANOVA table.

(c) Discuss symmetrical BIBD. For an SBIBD under usual notations, show that

$$|N| = r(r-\lambda)^{\frac{v-1}{2}}$$

(d) Discuss the layout of a Latin square design. Give its example. Write its model (one observation per experimental unit). Give its ANOVA table. Write null hypothesis. Give comments on acceptance and rejection of null hypothesis. 10×4=40

4. (a) Discuss the allocation of a sample to different strata in stratified sampling. Explain proportional allocation and hence obbtain the variance of mean of a stratified sample under proportional allocation.

(b) Explain error of measurement. Write its model. For the given model $Y_{ij} = x_i + a_j + e_{ij}$, obtain its sample mean and then show that $\bar{Y}...$ is not an unbiased estimator provided $n_j = \frac{n}{m} = \bar{n}$ and $n_i = \frac{n}{h} = p$.

(c) Construct a group divisible design with parameters $v = 8 = b, r = 3 = k, \lambda_1 = 0, \lambda_2 = 1, m = 4, n = 2$. Further identify the type of GD design.

(d) Estimate the treatment effect of BIB design under intrablock analysis using C-matrix of the block design. 10×4=40

SECTION B

5. (a) What are the different methods for measurement of trend? Discuss the method of fitting a straight line using least squares method.

(b) Discuss link relative method to estimate seasonal fluctuations, with appropriate illustrations.

(c) Consider a model

$$Y = \beta_0 + \beta_1 X_1 + \beta_2 X_2 + (\varepsilon - \bar{\varepsilon})$$

with $\Sigma X_1 = \Sigma X_2 = 0$, where

$X_2 = 2\theta X_1 + V$, $\Sigma X_1^2 = \Sigma X_2^2 = 1$,

$\Sigma V = 0$, $\Sigma X_1 V = 0$

Does the model contain multicollinearity? If yes/no, explain. Also obtain $V(\hat{\beta}_i)$, $i = 1, 2$ and $V(\hat{\beta}_i)$.

(d) Let the deamand function be expressed as $P = 4 - 5X^2$. For what value of X, the elsticity of demand will be unirary?

(e) Let true X be related as $X = X^* + \varepsilon_X$, where ε_X is the measurement error in X. Now for the given regression relation $Y = X^*\beta + \varepsilon_Y$, show that measurement errors in one variable are in the limit uncorrelated with the measurement errors in the other variable and measurement errors in both variables are uncorrelared with true values. 8×5=40

6. (a) Wrtie various types of identification problem. Identify only the first simultaneous equation:

$$Y_1 = \Gamma_{21} Y_2 + \beta_{11} X_1 + \varepsilon_1$$
$$Y_2 = \Gamma_{22} Y_2 + \beta_{22} X_2 + \beta_{32} X_3 + \varepsilon_2$$

(b) Discuss forecasting accuracy and Theil's U coefficient.

(c) Let $Y = X\beta + \varepsilon$, where $\varepsilon \sim N(0, \sigma^2 Q)$. Obtain the estimate of β and its variance, where Ω is known symmetric and positive definite of order n.

(d) Under heteroscedasticity, show that OLS estimator is less efficient than the weightage least squares estimator even though OLS is an unbiased estimator. 10×4=40

7. (a) Obtain the general solution of first-order autoregression model.

(b) Obtain the correlogram for the series $U_{t+1} = aU_t + \varepsilon_{t+1}$, $|a| < 1$ with $E(\varepsilon) = 0$, provided $\varepsilon_{t+1} = b\varepsilon_t + \eta_{t+1}$, $|b| < 1$, and successive values of η are independent.

(e) Describe Pareto's law of income distribution and its graph. What type of data is required for determining it?

(d) Using curves of concentration, discuss the formulation of the problem of distribution of income. 10×4=40

8. (a) Discuss Engel's law and Engel's curve. Explain Engel's curve for constant price.

(b) If the demand curve is of the form $p = ae^{-kx}$, where p is the price and x is the demand, prove that the elasticity of demand is $\frac{1}{kx}$. Hence deduce the elasticity of demand of $p = 10e^{-\frac{x}{2}}$.

(c) Show that sum of squares due to sample residual is an unbiased estimtor.

(d) Discuss the practical consequences of autocorrelation. Show that

$$V(U_t) = \frac{\sigma^2}{1 - \rho^2}$$

10×4=40

GENERAL STATISTICS
Paper III 2011

Time Allowed : Three Hours | *Maximum Marks: 200*

INSTRUCTIONS

Candidates should attempt FIVE questions in ALL including Questions No. 1 and 5 which are compulsory. The remaining THREE questions should be answered by choosing at least ONE question each from Section A and Section B. The number of marks carried by each question is indicated against each. Answers must be written only in ENGLISH. (Symbols and abbreviations are as usual) Any essential data assumed by candidates for answering questions must be clearly stated.

Section A

1. Attempt any five parts: 8×5=40

(a) Discuss Lahiri's method of selecting samples for PPS scheme. Give a suitabled example to select. 4 units when N = 10, M = 60, by taking your choice of sample number and its corresponding size.

(b) Explain the concept of simple random/sampling with and without replacement. In a simple random sampling, show that s^2 is an unbiased estimator of S^2.

(c) For the ratio estimator of the population mean $\overline{Y}$, obtain the biase of $\overline{y}_r$ in terms of covariance. Further show that if the coefficient of variation of $\overline{x}$ is suifficiently small, the basis compared to standard error of $\overline{y}_r$ may be considered to be negligible.

(d) For symmetric BIBD, show that

$|N| = \sqrt{r(r-\lambda)^{v-1}}$, where N is the incidence matrix of SBIBD.

(e) Discuss 3^2 factorial experiments. Explain a method to estimate all the main effects and interaction effects at single degree of freedom for 3^2 factorial experiment. Write its ANOVA table considering replication size 2.

(f) Construct a key block of a 3^4 confounded factorial into a block of size 9 by confounding the interactions ABC and AB^2D. Write all its generalized confounded interactions. Construct its one more block.

2. (a) Let for a stratified random sampling

$$n_i = \frac{W_i S_j}{\sqrt{\mu_o c_j}}$$

where μ_0 is constant e_i is the cost per unit in i^{th} stratum, $W_i = \frac{N_i}{N}$, S_i^2 is the mean square based on N_i units. Estimate the sample size n under optimum allocation for fixed cost e_0.

(b) In two stage sampling with equal first stage units, obtain the variance of the sample mean $\bar{\bar{y}}_2$.

(c) Discuss cluster sampling. Let $\bar{\bar{y}}$ be the sample mean based of M elements. $\bar{y}$ is the sample mean based on a sample of nM elements drawn for SRS without replacement from NM elements in the population. Obtain Relative efficiency of $\bar{\bar{y}}$ with respect to $\bar{y}$ (without getting the derivation of $V(\bar{y})$ and $V(\bar{\bar{y}})$). Write its ANOVA table.

(d) Explain aligned sample and unaligned systematic sampling method. Give an example of each with m = 3, l = 3, n = 3 and k = 4, where nm units of population are arranged in the form of ml rows each containing nk units. 10×4=40

3. (a) Discuss a method of construction of BIBD with parameters v – b = 11, r = k = 6 and λ = 3.

(b) Explain Randomized block design. Obtain non-zero eigen value of C matrix of RBD. Estimate $t_i(i = 1, 2, .., v)$ using non-zero eigen value of C matrix.

(c) Discuss missing plot techniques in a RBD. Suppose one observation, say, t_i is missing in one block of RBD, derive a method to estimate that missing value.

(d) Discuss symmetrical BIBD For a SBIBD, show that any two blocks have exactly λ treatments in common. 10×4=40

4. (a) Explain diffference estimator of population mean. Obtain its mean and variance. Hence obtain the linear regression estimator of $\bar{Y}$.

(b) In a PPSWOR scheme, let $z_i = \frac{y_i}{NP_i}$. Obtain $E(\bar{z})$ and $V(\bar{z})$.

(c) Discuss group divisible PBIB design of two associate classes. Construct a PBIB design with parameters v = 8 = b, r = 3 = k, λ_1 = 0 and λ_2 = 1. Further obtain the value of m and n.

(d) Explain the layout of split plan designs. Write its model and assumptionns, Give ANOVA table of sub-plot observations (only df and sum of squares). 10×4=40

Section B

5. Answer any five parts: 8×5=40

(a) Explain moving average [m, p]. Let $U_t = a_0 + a_1 t$, with p = 1 and m = 2k + 1, obtain the coefficient. e_i of U_t and [m, p].

(b) Let $U_t = a\xi + e_t$, $-\infty < t < \infty$, where e_t's are i.i.d. with $E(e_t) = 0$ and $V(e_t) = 1$. Show that the process is stationary with correlation.

(c) For the following table:

Commodity

	A	B
p_0	1	1
q_0	10	5
p_1	2	X
q_1	5	2

where p and q stand for price and quantity for 0 and 1 time periods respectively. Find the value of X if the ratio between Laspeyres' (L) andn Paasche's (P) index number is

L : P : : 28 : 27

(d) For the general linear model $Y = X\beta + e$, following observations

$\Sigma x_1^2 = 50,\ \Sigma x_2^2 = 960,\ \Sigma x_1 x_2 = -60,$

$\Sigma x_1 y_1 = 30,\ \Sigma x_2 y = 40,\ \bar{X}_1 = 5,\ \bar{X}_2 = 6$ and

$\bar{Y} = 5$

are given, where lower case letters $y_j\ x_j$ $(j = 1, 2)$ are given as $y = Y - \bar{Y}$ and $x_j = X_j - \bar{X}_j$. Obtain OLS estimator.

(e) Discuss the effect of imperfect multicollinearity on test and errors. Consider a model

$y = \beta_0 + \beta_1 x_1 + \beta_2 x_2 + (e - \bar{e})$ with

$\Sigma x_1 = \Sigma x_2 = 0$ and $x_2 = \theta x_1 + v$ with

$\Sigma x_1^2 = \Sigma x_2^2 = 1,\ \Sigma x_1 x_2 = \theta,\ \Sigma v = 0$ and

$\Sigma x_1 y = 0.$

Do you think multicollinearity is present in the model? If yes, give reasons. Further show that as θ increases, $V(\hat{\beta}_i)$ also increases.

(f) Explain demand function. Discuss Pigou's method of deriving demand curves from time series data. Inndicate the assumptions made. Give a criticism of the method.

6. (a) Give the various steps for finding the variance of the random component using variate differnece method. In F-test used for testing the significance of homogeneity of two successive estimates of variane? If yes, ok, otherwise which test can be used? Discuss.

(b) Explain the errors in the measurement of price and quanity index number.

(c) Discuss second order autoregressive series. For this series, obtain complementary function (CF) only.

(d) Explain curve of concentration. Obtain income concentration for Pareto's law of income distribution. 10×4=40

7. (a) For generalized least square linear model $\underline{Y} = X\underline{\beta} + \underline{e}$, write assumptions. Obtain $V(\hat{\beta})$ and estimate $\hat{\sigma}^2$. provided given another linear model is $Y^* = X^*\beta + e^*$, where $X^* = T^{-1}X$, $Y^* = T^{-1}Y$, $e^* = T^{-1} e$, $\Omega = TT'$ and $e^* \sim N(0, \sigma^2)$.

(b) If $U = cx^{\alpha}y^{\beta}$ is an individual's utility functions of two goods, show that the demand for the goods is

$$x = \frac{\alpha}{\alpha+\beta}\frac{\mu}{p_x} \quad \text{and} \quad y = \frac{\beta}{\alpha+\beta}\frac{\mu}{p_y}$$

where p_x and p_y are the fixed price and μ be the individual fixed income.

(e) For which simultaneous equation, is indirect least square method of estimation used? Discuss a method to estimate parameters using indirect least square estimtor.

(d) Discuss economic forecasting of one single future observation on Y_T. 10×4=40

8. (a) For the auto-regressive scheme

$$U_{t+2} = aU_{t+1} + bU_t = e_{t+2},$$

show that if e is a random variable and the series is long, then

$$\frac{\text{Var (U)}}{\text{Var (e)}} = \frac{(1+b)}{(1-b)[(1+b)^2 - a^2]}$$

and hence show that, variance of the generated series may be much greater than that of e itself.

(b) Explain the formulation of the problem of distribution of income. Further discuss its mathematical formulation in order to find number of person with income x or more.

(c) Discuss the method of estimating the parameters of simultaneous equation model using two stage least sqauare method.

(d) Explain rank condition of identification problem of simultaneous equation model. 10×4=40

GENERAL STATISTICS
Paper III 2010

Time Allowed : Three Hours	Maximum Marks: 200

INSTRUCTIONS

Candidates should attempt FIVE questions in ALL including Questions No. 1 and 5 which are compulsory. The remaining THREE questions should be answered by choosing at least ONE question each from Section A and Section B. The number of marks carried by each question is indicated against each. Answers must be written only in ENGLISH. (Symbols and abbreviations are as usual) Any essential data assumed by candidates for answering questions must be clearly stated.

Section A

1. Attempt any five parts: $8\times5=40$

   (a) What procautions would you take in planning for a simple survey?

   (b) Explain the concepts of linear and circular systematic sampling giving suitable illustrations. Further show that for linear systematic sampling. Further show that for linear systematic sampling, sample mean is an unbiased estimator for population mean.

   (c) What is cluster sampling? In the case of cluster sampling for proportions, obtain an unbiased estimator of population proportion. Also compute variance of your estimator.

   (d) Define SBIBD. Show that for SBIBD, if the number of treatments is even then $(r-\lambda)$ is a perfect square.

   (e) Discuss the procedure for carrying out the analysis and testing procedure by means of ANOVA table for two way classification.

   (f) 4 treatments N, F, K and S are administered in 4 blocks through 4 columns. The layout of design is as shown below:

Columns

Blocks				
	N	P	K	S
	P	K	S	N
	K	S	N	P*
	S	N	P	K

Idenfity the above design.

If the observation (*) in third row and fourth column is missing, how would you estimate the missing yield?

2. (a) Explain thhe concept of statification in strafied Random samplinng. What is proportional and optimum allocation in stratified simple Random sampling?

With usual notations show that:

$$V(\bar{y}_{st})_{opt} < V(\bar{y}_{st})_{prop} < v(\bar{y})_{ran.}$$

(b) How would you determinne the sample size in the case of SRSWR and SRSWOR when RSE is fixed?

(c) What is PPS Sampling? Explain why such type of sampling is needed? Describe Lahiri's method for PPS selection of sample.

(d) What are ratio and regression estimates?

How would you obtain bias of these estimators? 4×10=40

3. (a) Write a critical note on the method of Double Sampling.

(b) A hypothetical population has the population units in linear trend given by $Y_i = a + b_i (i = 1, 2, .., N)$.

Show that

$$V(\bar{y}_{WR}) = \frac{b^2}{12^n}(N+1)(N-1)$$

$$V(\bar{y}_{WOR}) = \frac{b^2}{12}(k-1)(N+1) \text{ where } N = nk$$

and $V(\bar{y}_{SY}) = \frac{b^2}{12}(k^2 - 1)$.

Hence deduce that:

$$V(\bar{y}_{SY}) : V(\bar{y}_{WOR}) : V(\bar{y}_{WR}) = \frac{1}{n} : 1 : 1.$$

(c) What is intrablock and interblock analysis?

Discuss how would you carry out interblock analysis for BIBD.

(d) Show that for BIBD:

(i) $bk = rv$

(ii) $r(k-1) = \lambda(v-1)$.

Further show that for resolvable BIBD:

$b \geq v + r - 1$.

Name the design when equality holds good. 10×4=40

4. (a) Discuss the layout for 2^3 factorial experiment with suitable illustration. How would you carry out the analysis of such a design?

(b) Describe under which situations a Latin square design can be preferred to completely randomised design and randomised block design. What are the merits and demerits of LSD?

(c) What is confoundling in a factorial experiment? Explain why it is necessary.

(d) What do you understand by PBIBD? What restrictions are imposed upon the parameter of first type of PIBIBF? 4×10=40

SECTION B

5. Answer any five parts: 8×5=40

(a) What are the three tests of index number? Verify whether the following index number satisfies any of these tests:

$$r = \frac{1}{2}(L + P)$$

where L = Lasperaye's Price Index Number

P = Paasche's Price Index Number.

(b) Discuss in detail the variate difference method to obtain trend component in a time series.

(c) Examine whether the following semi-log function represents a demand function or not?

$\log_e P = A - BX \ (P > 0, X > 0, A > 0, B > 0, A > B)$

where P = Price, X = Demand.

If yes, compute the elasticity of demand when A = 30 and B = 0.4.

(d) State clearly the basic assumption underlying classical general model. Explain briefly the situation when the basic assumption about the rank of datamatrix is violated.

(e) What is the problem of identification in simultancous linear equations system model?

(f) Discuss the ratio to trend method for separating the seasonal compoment in a time series.

6. (a) What is the problem of heteroscedasticity in linear models?

(b) What is multiple coefficient of determination R^2 for K variate general linear model?

How would you make a choice for a suitable linear model on the basis of R^2?

(c) Discuss briefly the steps involved in the construction of cost of living index number.

(d) What is C.S.O.?

Describe briefly the role and importance of C.S.O. for execution of Indian statistical data. 4×10=40

7. (a) For Leontief's static input-output open system model, explain the following terms:

(i) Transaction Matrix

(ii) Technology Matrix

(iii) Input-Output Coefficients

(iv) Gross Output Vector

(v) Bill of Goods.

(b) Write a critical note on the methods of estimating national income of India.

(c) Discuss Slustsky-Yule effect when moving average procedure ios carried out on the random component of a given time series.

(d) What are the errors of measurement in the case of linear models?

What are the consequences for these errors and briefly explain how would you deal with such situation. 10×4=40

8. (a) What is the problem of Autocorrelation in linear models?

   Discuss about its effect and state briefly how would you tackle the problem of autocorrelation.

   (b) What are order and rank conditions for identification in simultaneous linear equations system model?

   (c) Write a critical note on Pareto's income distribution with specific reference to Indian data.

   (d) Explain clearly about the following:

   (i) Generalised least squares method

   (ii) Weighted least squares method

   (iii) Eigenvalue approach for dealing with multicollinearity in linear models. $10 \times 4 = 40$

GENERAL STATISTICS
Paper III 2009

Time Allowed : Three Hours | *Maximum Marks: 200*

INSTRUCTIONS

Candidates should attempt FIVE questions in ALL including Questions No. 1 and 5 which are compulsory. The remaining THREE questions should be answered by choosing at least ONE question each from Section A and Section B. The number of marks carried by each question is indicated against each. Answers must be written only in ENGLISH. (Symbols and abbreviations are as usual) Any essential data assumed by candidates for answering questions must be clearly stated.

Section A

1. Answer any five parts: 5×8=40

   (a) What do you mean by sampling frame? Why do you need it? Give reasons for for preferring the sampling to complete enumeration.

   (b) Describe the procedure for drawing a simple random sample of size n without replacement from a finite population of size N. Obtain the probabilities of drawing a specified sample random sampling with and without replacement.

   (c) Distringush between two-stage and two-phase sampling schemes. Give suitable examples.

   (d) Give the layout and analysis of a completely randomized design. Which of the basic principles are statisfied in this design and how?

   (e) Explain the rerm 'connected' in the context of block designs Show that a balanced incomplete block (BIB) desogm with usual parameters v, b, r, ** and **, is always connected

   (f) What do you mean by confounding in a factorial experiment? Explain how you will obtain the confounded interactions from a key block.

2. (a) Obtain an unbiased estimator of population variance in case of simple random sampling without replacement.

   (b) Obtain $y_1, y_2, .., y_n$ be the measurements with respect to a characteristic Y on the units of a simple random sample drawn without replacement from a population of size N.

   $$\text{covariance } (y_i, y_j) = -\frac{\sigma^2}{N-1}$$

where

$$\sigma^2 = \frac{1}{N}\sum_{i=1}^{N}(Y_i - \bar{Y})^2$$

(c) Explain the principle of stratification. How would you determine the best mode of stratification?

Without two strata a sampler would like to have $n_1 = n_2$ for administrative convenience instead of using the values given by the Neyman allocation. If $V(\bar{y}_{st})$ and $V_{opt}(\bar{y}_{st})$ denote the variances given by the $n_1 = n_2$ and the Neyman allocations respectively show that

$$\frac{V(\bar{y}_{st}) - V_{opt}(\bar{y}_{st})}{V_{opt}(\bar{y}_{st})} = \left(\frac{r-1}{r+1}\right)^2$$

where $r = \frac{n_1}{n_2}$ as given by Neyman allocation.

(d) Explain cluster sampling. Show that the efficiency of cluster sampling relative to simple random sampling is approximately equal to

$$\frac{1}{1+(M-1)\rho}$$

where the symbols have their usual meaning. Interpret this result. 4×10=40

3. (a) Obtain an estimator of a missing observation in a Latin square design. How does the subsequent an alysis differ from the usual case?

(b) Explain the unifromly trials. Discuss their role in picking up a proper design.

(c) Describe the analysis of a BIB desgin with the recovery of interblock infromation.

(d) Following are the block contents of one of the blocks of a replicate of a 2^5 experiment in factors A, B, C, D and E:

a, bc, cd, be, de, abd, ace, abcde.

Identify the confounded effects. Write down the remaining blocks of the replicate. 4×10=40

4. (a) In a two-stage sampling schedme, the population consists of N first-stage units andn each first stage unit has M second stage units. A sample of n first stage units and m second stage units from each selected first stage unit is drawn with equal probability at each stage. Obtain the expression for the variance of the unbiased estimator of the population mean.

(b) Explain the ratio method of estimation of the mean of a population on the basis of a simle random sample without replacement. Obtain the standard error of this estimator when the sample size is large.

(c) What is the use of analysis of covariance? Give the general procedure of analysisof covariance for a RBD, stating the necessary assumptions.

(d) What is a split plot desgin? Give an example of a situation where this is a natural choice. Outline the analysis of data from a split-plot experiment where the main plots form the randomized block. 4×10=40

SECTION B

5. Answer any five parts: 5×8=40

   (a) Distinguish between fixed base and chain base method for the construction of index numbers. Discuss their relative merits.

   (b) Explain ratio to moving average method for calculating seasonal indices.

   (c) Describe the Yule-Slustsky effect of moving average operation on the random component of a time series.

   (d) Discuss the problems involved in the statistical estimaationn of market demand function.

   (e) If the demand curve is of the form

   $p = ae^{-kx}$

   where p is the price and x is the demand, prove that the elasticity of demand is $\frac{1}{kx}$. Hence deduce the elasticity of demand for $p = 10\ e^{-x/2}$.

   (f) State the problem of measurement errors in the explanatory variables of a linear regression model and explain its consequences.

6. (a) What is a peridogram? Describe the method of periodogram analysis for determining the hidden-periodicites in a time-series.

   (b) Explain the time-reversai and factor-reversal tests for an ideal index number. Give an example of index number which satisfies both of these tests.

   (c) Descreibe, briefly, the Engel's law and Engel's curve. What are the different forms of Engel's curve usually emloyed for fitting to the family budget data?

   (d) State the porbability density function of the Pareto distribution and give its cumulative form Interpret the constants involved. 4×10=40

7. (a) What are the assumtions in the classical linear model? Show that the least squares estimator for the vector of coefficients is the best linear unbiased estimator.

   (b) Discuss the possibility of consistent estimation of parameters in an equation whose distribances are serially correlated.

   (c) Describe the two-stage least squares method of estimation for the simultaneous equations model. Show that two--stage least squares estimators are consistent.

   (d) State the problem of identification in the simultaneous equations model. State the order annd rank conditions for identifiability. Illustrate your answer with an example. 4×10=10

8. (a) Describe different schemes for explanining the oscillations in a stationary time series. Explain the use of correlagram for discriminating among the above schemes.

   (b) Define Marshall – Edgeworth index number and examine whether it satisfies Fisher's tests for index numberes. Also show that this index number will lie between the Lasperyres' and Paashe's index numbers.

   (c) Discuss Goldfeld – Quandt. What are the causes of multicollinearity? How will you detect the same and solve it? 4×10=10

STATISTICS-IV

STATISTICS
Paper- IV 2023

Time Allowed : Three Hours | *Maximum Marks: 200*

QUESTIONS PAPER SPECIFIC INSTRUCTIONS

Please read each of the following instructions carefully before attempting questions.

*There are **FOURTEEN** questions divided under **SEVEN** Sections. Candidate has to choose any **TWO** Sections and attempt the questions therein. All the Sections carry equal marks. The number of marks carried by a question/part is indicated against it. Wherever any assumptions are made for answering a question, they must be clearly indicated. Diagrams/Figures, wherever required, shall be drawn in the space provided for answering the question itself. F-table and Graph paper can be found at the end of both sections in the booklet. Unless otherwise mentioned, symbols and notations have their usual standard meanings. Attempts of questions shall be counted in sequential order. Unless struck off, attempt of a question shall be counted even if attempted partly. ' Any page or portion of the page left blank in the Question-cum-Answer (QCA) Booklet must be clearly struck off. Answers must be written in **ENGLISH** only.*

SECTION 'A'

(Operations Research and Reliability)

1. (a) (i) A company produces two type of sausces – A and B. Both these sauces are made by blending two ingredients – X and Y. A certain level of flexibility is permitted in the formulae of these products. Indeed, the restrictions are that (i) B must contain no more than 75 percent of X, and (ii) A must contain no less than 25 percent of X, and no less than 50 percent of Y. Up to 400 kg of X and 300 kg of Y could be purchased. The company can sell as much of these sauces as it produces at a price of ₹ 18 for A and ₹17 for B. The ingredients X and Y cost ₹1.60 and ₹2.05 per kg respectively.

The company wishes to maximize its net revenue from the sale of these sauces. Formulate this problem as LP model.

(ii) The production department of a company requires 3600 kg of raw material for manufacturing a particular item per year. It has been estimated that the cost of placing an order is ₹36 and cost of carrying inventory is 25 percent of the investment in the inventories. The price is ₹10 per kg. Help the Purchase Manager to determine and ordering policy for raw material.

(b) Show that necessary and sufficient condition for the existence of a feasible soulution to the transportation problem is

$$\sum_{i}^{m} a_i = \sum_{j}^{n} b_j .$$

The is, the total capacity (or supply) must equal requirement (or demand). 10

(c) Solve the following game after reducing it to a 2 × 2 game. 10

		Player B		
		B_1	B_2	B_3
	A_1	1	7	2
Player A	A_2	6	2	7
	A_3	5	1	6

(d) Five elements (a, b, c, d and e) of a system are connected as shows below, which also indicates the reliability of each element. Calculate the system reliaility. 10

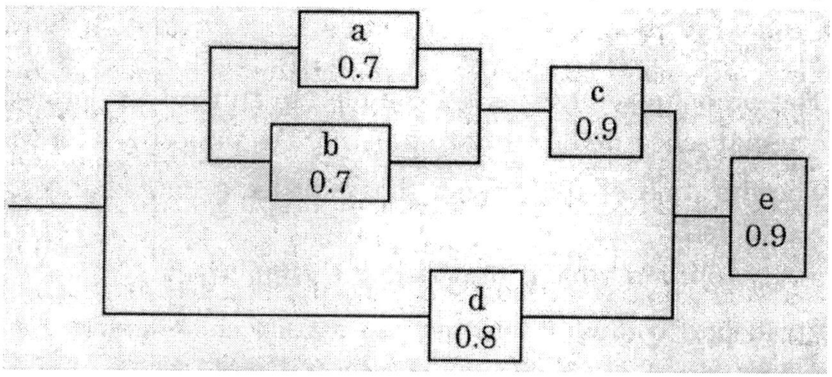

(e) If x* and y* be feasible solution to the primal and dual LP problem, respectively, then a necessary and sufficient condition for x* and y* to be optimal solutions to their respective problems is

$y_i \cdot x_{n+j} = 0, i = 1, 2, ..., m$

and $x_j \cdot y_{m+j} = 0, j = 1, 2, ..., n$

where x_{n+i} is the ith slack variable in the primal LP model and y_{m+j} the jth surplus variable for the dual problem. 10

2. Answer any two questions of the following:

(a) The following network diagram represents activities associated with a project:

Activities:	A	B	C	D	E	F	G	H	I
Optimistic time:	5	18	26	16	15	6	7	7	3
Pessimistic time:	10	22	40	20	25	12	12	9	5

Most likely time:	8	20	33	18	20	9	10	8	4

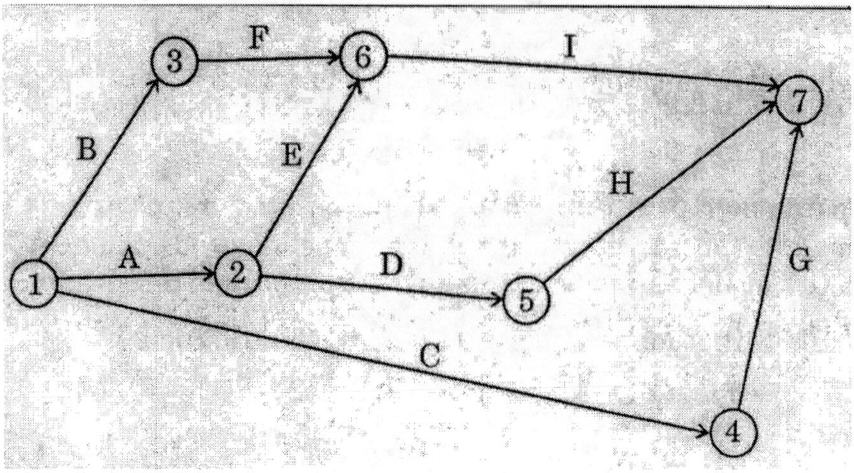

Determine the following: 25

(i) Expected activity time and variance.

(ii) The earliest and latest expected completion time of each event.

(iii) The critcal path.

(iv) The probability of expected completion time of the project if the original scheduled time of completing the project in 4.15 weeks.

(v) The duration of the project that will have 95% chance of being completed.

(Normal distribution table is provided at the end (page 17)).

(b) A road transport company has one reservation clerk on duty at a time. He handles information of bus schedules and makes reservations. Customers arrive at a rate of 8 per hour and the clerk can, on an average, service 12 customers per hour. After stating your assumptions, answer the following:

(i) What is the average number of customers waiting for the service of the clerk?

(ii) What is the average time a customer has to wait before being served?

(iii) The maagement is contemplating to install a computer system for handling information and reservatiuons. This is expected to reduce to service time from 5 to 3 minutes. The additional cost of having the new system works out to ₹50 per day. If the cost of goodwill of having to wait is estimated to be 12 paise per minute spent wiating before being served, should the company install the computer system? 25

Assume an 8-hour working day.

(c) The Weibull probability function for failure is stated as

$$f(t) = \begin{cases} \alpha\beta t^{\beta} e^{-\alpha t^{\beta}} & \text{when } t \geq 0 \\ 0 & \text{when } t < 0 \end{cases}$$

The parameter β is referred as shape parameter and α as the scale parameter. Calculate the reliability function and comment on the reliability model for shape parameter. Also calculate hazard function. 25

(d) (i) Show that for a negative exponential distribution

$f(t) = \lambda e^{-\lambda t}; 0 < \lambda < \infty$

$0 \leq t < \infty$

Intensity function i(t) and hazard rate function h(t) are same. 10

(ii) A city corprotion has decided to carry out road repairs on four main arteries of the city. The government has agreed to make a special grant ₹ 50 lakh towards the cost with a condition that the repairs be done at the lowest cost and quickest time. If the conditios warrant, a supplementary token grant will also be considered fabourably. The corporation has floated tenders and five contractors have sent in their bids. In order to expedite work, one road will be awarded to only one contractor.

Cost of repair (₹ in lakh)

	Road →	R_1	R_2	R_3	R_4
	C_1	9	14	19	15
	C_2	7	17	20	19
Contractor	C_3	9	18	21	18
	C_4	10	12	18	19
	C_5	10	15	21	16

(I) Find the best way assigning the repair work to the contractors and the costs.

(II) If it necessary to seek supplementary grants, what should be the amount sought?

(III) Which of the five contractors will be unsuccessful in his bid?

SECTIONB

(Demography and Vital Statistics)

3. (a) In the usual notations, prove that 10

(i) $\dfrac{dL(x)}{dx} = -d(x)$

(ii) $\dfrac{d\overset{o}{e}(x)}{dx} = \mu(x)\overset{o}{e}(x) - 1$

where $\mu(x) = \dfrac{d}{dx}\log_e [l(x)]$

(b) The population of a town in two census years is as follows:

Year	Population
1971	54,892
2001 1,08,431	

Calculate the following : 10

(i) The rate of increase in population per thousand per annum,

(ii) The estimate of the population in 1995.

(c) Show that 10

(i) $nP_X = Px \cdot P_{X+1} \text{.......} P_{X+n-1}$

(ii) $nq_x = \frac{d_{x+n-1}}{l_x}$

where the notations have their usual meanings.

(d) Fill in the blanks of the following skeleton table which are marked with question marks. 10

Age x	l_x	d_x	p_x	q_x	L_x T_x	$\overset{o}{e}_x$	
20	693435	2762	?	?	?	35081126	?
21	620673	–	–	–	–	?	?

(e) (i) Find an expression for μ(x) assummg l(x) as a fourth degree polynomial. 5

(ii) Find the differential coefficient of p(x, t) with respect to t and x. 5

4. Answer any two of the following :

(a) Define vital statistics and write in detail the methods for collecting data for vital statistics. 25

(b) Compute the crude and standardised death rates of the two populations A and B, regarding A as standard population from the following data : 25

Age Group (years)	**A**		**B**	
	Population	**Death**	**Population**	**Death**
Under 10	20,000	600	12,000	372
10-20	12,000	240	30,000	660
20-40	50,000	1250	62,000	1612
40-60	30,000	1050	15,000	525
Above 60	10,000	500	3,000	180

(c) Calculate the general fertility rate, total fertility rate and the gross reproduction rate from the following data, assuming that for every 100 girls, 106 boys are hom. 25

Age of Women	Number of Women	Age-SFR (per 1000)
15-19	212,619	98·0
20-24	198,732	169·6
25-29	162,800	158·2
30-34	145,362	139·7

35-39	128,109	98·6
40-44	106,211	42·8
45-49	86,753	16·9

(d) What is logistic curve? Explain the method of three selected points for fitting the logistic curve to a population data. 25

SECTION C

(Survival Analysis and Clinical Trials)

5. (a) Obtain the hazard function of Weibull distribution and show that exponential distribution is a particular case of it. 10

(b) Explain the standard life table method for estimating the distribution of life times. Derive the maximum likelihood estimates of, in the usual notation, q_j s, j = 1, 2, ..., k and find the information matrix. 10

(c) Construct a test to test the significance of exponential parameter for the case of Type 2 censoring and construct a (1 - a) confidence interval for the parameter. 10

(d) Discuss the primary and secondary response variables in clinical trials and rules to measure them. 10

(e) Explain data collection methods and steps to optimize collecting high quality data in clinical trials. 10

6. Answer any two of the following :

(a) (i) Suppose that a sample of n units is put on test and the test is to be terminated at a preassigned time T or earlier if all units fail before T. Suppose that each unit on test consists of two independent exponential components with means λ_1, λ_2 respectively. Obtain the maximum likelihood estimates of λ_1 and λ_2. 10

(ii) Obtain approximate maximum likelihood estimates when the number of failures due to either cause is recorded for K specified time intervals. 15

(b) Estimate the survival probabilities by using an actuarial estimator and find the variances of the estimators from the following data : 25

Time Interval	Number of Survivors at the beginning of the interval	Observed number of Deaths	Number of Withdrawals
0-50	68	16	3
50-100	49	11	0
100-200	38	4	2
200-400	32	5	4
400-700	23	2	6
700-1000	15	4	3
1000-1300	8	1	2
1300-1600	5	1	3
1600 +	1	0	1

(c) Compare the empirical distributions of survival times for the groups of patients with dementia at ages of diagnosis 73 and 74 by using log rank test from the following data and comment. 25

Age at Diagnosis	No. of Cases	Length of Survival Time in Years						
73	17	0·58	1·08	1.25	1.67	2.00	2.08	2.17
		3.75	4.25	4.58	4.92	5.25	6.75	7.83
		7.84	9.17	11.50				
74	25	0.50	1.00	1.25	1.41	1.42	1.58	1.66
		1.67	2.25	2.33	2.92	3.08	3.75	3.92
		4.17	4.67	5.00	5.25	5.83	7.25	8.50
		9.33	10.33	11.25	12.50			

(Given χ^2_1 (0.05) = 3.841)

(d) Discuss various designs/approaches used in Phase to Phase IV studies and their applications. 25

SECTIOND

(Quality Control)

7. (a) Distinguish between Specification limits and Tolerance limits. 10

(b) How is the choice between p and np charts made ? Give their applications (three each). 10

(c) Obtain the factors A_2, D_3 and D_4 used in connection with the computation of control limits for mean and range. 10

(d) (i) Distinguish between AQL and AOQL.

(ii) Obtain AOQL, if the number of defectives conform to a Poisson distribution with parameter np. 5+5=10

(e) Discuss Sampling Inspection Plans with reference to statistical quality control. Compare sampling inspection by attributes with inspection by variables. 10

8. Answer any two of the following :

(a) Write an explanatory note on four important curves which tell the behaviour of a given sampling plan. 25

(b) (i) Suppose that a process quality characteristic that is normally and independently distributed is plotted in a Shewhart $\bar{X}$ control chart with three sigma control limits $\mu_0 \pm 3\sigma_{\bar{X}}$. Suppose that the process mean llo experiences an upward shift of 1.4σ. Determine how long, on an average, will it take to detect this shift if samples of size four are taken every hour. 10

(Note: Normal distribution table is provided at the end (page 17))

(ii) Explain single sampling plan and obtain its OC and ASN functions. 15

(c) Derive the ASN for testing $\theta_0 = 0$ against $\theta_1 = 1$ where θ is the normal mean with unit variance keeping $\alpha = 0.01$ and $\beta = 0.01$ (i.e. keeping both producer's risk and consumer's risk at par at 1% level). 25

(d) Derive OC function to test $H_0 : \theta = \theta_0$ against $H_1 : \theta = \theta_1$ where θ is a Bernoulli parameter and write the OC function when $\theta_0 = 0{\cdot}05$, $\theta_1 = 0{\cdot}10$, $\alpha = 0{\cdot}08$ and $\beta = 0{\cdot}03$. 25

SECTION E
(Multivariate Analysis)

9. (a) Let $X = (X_1, X_2, X_3, X_4)N' \sim N_4(\mu, \Sigma)$ with
$\mu = (1, 2, 3, 4)'$ and

$$\Sigma = \begin{pmatrix} 4 & 3 & 2 & 1 \\ 3 & 3 & 2 & 1 \\ 2 & 2 & 2 & 1 \\ 1 & 1 & 1 & 1 \end{pmatrix}$$

Then obtain the distribution of

$$\begin{pmatrix} X_1 - X_2 - X_3 + X_4 \\ X_1 + X_2 + X_3 + X_4 \end{pmatrix}$$ 10

(b) Let $X_1, X_2, \ldots, X_N$ be N independent observations from $N_p(\mu_0, \Sigma)$, where μ_0 is a given vector. Derive the maximum likelihood estimator of L. 10

(c) Let $V = \begin{pmatrix} X & Y \\ Y & Z \end{pmatrix}$ follow Wishart distribution $W_2(n, I)$. Obtain the distribution of $U = \frac{1}{5}X + \frac{4}{5}$ $(Y + Z)$. 10

(d) Define Hotelling's T^2-statistic and show that it is invariant under a non-singular linear transformation. 10

(e) Let X be a 3-dimensional random vector with variance-covariance matrix

$$\Sigma = \begin{pmatrix} 9 & 3 & 3 \\ 3 & 9 & 3 \\ 3 & 3 & 9 \end{pmatrix}.$$

Determine the first principal component and the proportion of the total variability that it explains. 10

10. Answer any two of the following:

(a) (i) Let

$$X \sim N_3\left(\begin{pmatrix} 1 \\ 2 \\ 3 \end{pmatrix}, \begin{pmatrix} 11 & -6 & 2 \\ -6 & 10 & -4 \\ 2 & -4 & 6 \end{pmatrix}\right),$$

$Z_1 = X_2 - X_3$

$Z_2 = X_2 + X_3$

$Z_3 \mid Z_1, Z_2 \sim N(Z_1 + Z_2, 10)$.

Derive: 15

I. The joint distribution of Z_1, Z_2 and Z_3

II. The conditional mean of X_3 given X_1 and X_2

III. $\rho^2_{3.12}$

(ii) Let $X = (X_1, X_2, X_3)'$ have trivariate normal distribution $N_3(\mu, \Sigma)$, where $\mu = (1, 1, 1)\mu$ and

$$\Sigma = \begin{pmatrix} 1 & 1 & 1 \\ 1 & 2 & 2 \\ 1 & 2 & 3 \end{pmatrix}.$$

Show that $(X_2 - X_1)^2 + (X_3 - X_2)^2$ has a chi-square distribution. State the degrees of freedom. 10

(b) (i) Two psychological tests were given to 32 men and 32 women. The variables taken were y_1 : tool recognition, y_2 : vocabulary.
Mean vectors and pooled sample covariance matrix of two samples are

$$\bar{y} = \begin{pmatrix} 15.97 \\ 15.91 \end{pmatrix}, \bar{y}_2 = \begin{pmatrix} 12.34 \\ 13.91 \end{pmatrix}$$

and $S = \begin{pmatrix} 7.164 & 6.047 \\ 6.047 & 15.89 \end{pmatrix}$

Use Hotelling's T^2-statistic to test $H_0 : \mu_1 = \mu_2$ at 5% level of significance. 15
[You are given: $F_{0.05}(2, 61) = 3{\cdot}14$, $F_{0.05}(61, 2) = 19.49$]

(ii) Let $\begin{pmatrix} y \\ x \end{pmatrix}$ be a partitioned random vector with mean vector $\begin{pmatrix} \mu_y \\ \mu_x \end{pmatrix}$ and covananc matnx $\begin{pmatrix} \Sigma_{yy} & \Sigma_{yx} \\ \Sigma_{xy} & \Sigma_{xx} \end{pmatrix}$. Show that for any matrix A of suitable dimensions

$E(x' A y) = \text{trace}(A \Sigma_{yx}) + \mu_x' A \mu y.$ 10

(c) (i) Suppose $n_1 = 11$ and $n_2 = 12$ observations are made on two random vectors X_1 and X_2 which are assumed to have bivariate normal distribution with a common covariance matrix Σ, but possibly different mean vectors μ_1 and μ_2. The sample mean vectors and pooled covariance matrix are

$$\bar{X}_1 = \begin{pmatrix} -1 \\ 1 \end{pmatrix}, \bar{X}_2 = \begin{pmatrix} 2 \\ 1 \end{pmatrix}, S_{pooled} = \begin{pmatrix} 7 & -1 \\ -1 & 5 \end{pmatrix}.$$

Obtain Mahalanobis sample distance D^2 and Fisher's linear discriminant function. Assign the observation $X_0 = \begin{pmatrix} 0 \\ 1 \end{pmatrix}$ to either population π_1 or π_2. 15

(ii) If $A_1 \sim W_P(n_1, \Sigma)$ and $A_2 \sim W_P(n_2, \Sigma)$ which is independent of A_1, then derive the distribution of $A_1 + A_2$. 10

(d) (i) Define canonical correlations and canonical variates. Prove that canonical correlations are invariant under a non-singular linear transformation. 10

(ii) For a random sample of size n from
$N_4(\mu, \Sigma)$, we obtain
$\hat{\mu} = (18, 15, 18, 14)$ and

$$\hat{\Sigma} = \begin{pmatrix} 9.5 & 5.2 & 6.9 & 4.6 \\ 5.2 & 5.4 & 5.1 & 3.5 \\ 6.9 & 5.1 & 10.0 & 5.6 \\ 4.6 & 3.5 & 5.6 & 4.5 \end{pmatrix}$$

I. Find the estimates of the parameters of the conditional distribution of(X_3, X_4) given (X_1, X_2).

II. Find the partial correlation $r_{34\cdot12}$. 15

SECTION F
(Design and Analysis of Experiments)

11. (a) (i) What are the main sources of experimental error ?

(ii) How is the efficiency of an experiment increased by increased replications and local control? 5+5=10

(b) How is the efficiency of a design measured ? Derive the expressions to measure the efficiency of a Latin Square Design over Randomised Block Design, when: 10

(i) rows are used as blocks

(ii) columns are used as blocks

(c) Prove that for a 2^n factorial experiment in blocks of 2^k plots, if any two effects are confounded, then their generalised interaction is also confounded. 10

(d) What do you understand by "Analysis of Covariance" ? Illustrate by giving suitable example. How does the use of concomitant variables help to control the error of an experiment? 10

(e) A factorial experiment with seven factors, each at two levels, is to be conducted in blocks of size 8. Write the complete set of interactions to be confounded such that no main effect and two-factor inter ctions get confounded. 10

12. Answer any two of the following :

(a) (i) Write down the Yates' algorithm for analysing 3^2 factorial experiments. 10

(ii) In a 3^3 factorial experiment conducted in two replications in blocks of 3^2 plots, the following information is given :

Treatment Combinations in one of the Blocks

Replication 1	Replication 2
100	001
201	102
112	012
210	110
222	121
002	200
121	222
020	211
011	

Identify the confounded interaction in each replicate. 15

(b) (i) State the restrictions imposed on number of treatments along with their replications as we pass from a CRD to an RBD and then to an LSD. 10

(ii) Consider an RBD with one missing value. Perform the appropriate analysis estimating the missing value. 15

(c) (i) "Split-Plot Designs are sometimes referred to factorial designs with main effects confounded." Discuss. 10

(ii) In Split-Plot Designs, if e_1 and e_2 are the main plot and sub-plot errors, both estimated in units of single sub-plot, explain why e_1 is expected to be larger than e_2. 5

(iii) Complete the following ANOVA table given for a Split-Plot Design: 10

Source ofVariation	d.f.	S.S.	M.S.S.	F
Blocks	3	27	–	3
Varieties	–	–	–	4
Error I	6	–	–	
Manure	–	–	–	4
Variety × Manure	–	–	18	–
Error II	27	243	9	

(d) (i) How do you compare the differences in a set of paired treatment means usmg: 10

I. Least significant difference.

II. Duncan's multiple range test.

(ii) Explain the statistical analysis of 'Analysis of Covariance' for a one-way layout with one concomitant variable. 15

SECTION G

(Computing with C and R)

13. (a) Write a C-program to compute the roots of a quadratic equation using switch statement. 10

(b) Write a C-program to test whether a given string is palindrome defining a function. 10

(c) Write a C-program to find the median of a given vector of elements. 10

(d) Write R code for correlation coefficient and correlation test. 10

(e) Write R code to perform two-sample t-test writing your own function. 10

14. Answer any *two* of the following:

(a) Given student records containing name, register number, and average marks, write a C-program using structures to assign grades A, B, C and D.

(i) Arrange student records according to merit.

(ii) Give number of students in each grade and display the results. 25

(b) Write an interactive C-program to fit a Poisson distribution for a given observed frequency distribution and test for its goodness of fit and store the results in a file. 25

(c) Given a two-way ANOVA table with 5 treatments, 8 blocks and 3 observations per cell, write R code to (i) test the normality of the observations (ii) perform two-way ANOVA and post hoc test, and (iii) display the results. 25

(d) In a study sample, males of various ages were tested for blindness and the results recorded as given below :

Age:	25	35	45	55	75
Number tested :	60	60	60	60	60
Number blind :	4	15	25	29	34

Write a R code to fit a logistic model and display the result. 25

STATISTICS
Paper- IV 2022

Time Allowed : Three Hours | *Maximum Marks: 200*

QUESTIONS PAPER SPECIFIC INSTRUCTIONS

Please read each of the following instructions carefully before attempting questions.

*There are **FOURTEEN** questions divided under **SEVEN** Sections. Candidate has to choose any **TWO** Sections and attempt the questions therein. All the Sections carry equal marks. The number of marks carried by a question/part is indicated against it. Wherever any assumptions are made for answering a question, they must be clearly indicated. Diagrams/Figures, wherever required, shall be drawn in the space provided for answering the question itself. F-table and Graph paper can be found at the end of both sections in the booklet. Unless otherwise mentioned, symbols and notations have their usual standard meanings. Attempts of questions shall be counted in sequential order. Unless struck off, attempt of a question shall be counted even if attempted partly. ' Any page or portion of the page left blank in the Question-cum-Answer (QCA) Booklet must be clearly struck off. Answers must be written in **ENGLISH** only.*

SECTION 'A'

(Operations Research and Reliability)

1. (a) Given the following information related to a project, draw thearrow diagram and find the critical path and total duration of the project :

Activity (i - j)	Duration .(in days)
0 – 1	2
1 – 2	8
1 – 3	10
2 – 4	6
2 – 5	3
3 – 4	3
3 – 6	7
4 – 7	5
5 – 7	2
6 – 7	8

(b) What do you mean by an assignment problem ? How do you interpret it as a linear programming problem (LPP) ?

If the completion times (in hours) of different jobs by different workers are as given in the following table, determine the optimal assignment schedule of jobs to the workers:

Jobs

Workers		A	B	C	D	E	F
	I	16	47	14	27	0	26
	II	0	7	27	43	49	28
	III	0	12	33	24	5	5
	IV	8	13	11	15	0	6
	V	3	14	13	0	4	7
	VI	52	10	10	30	21	0

10

(c) The failure law of a component has the following probability density function :

$f(t) = (r + 1)A^{r+1}/(A + t)^{r+2}, t > 0;$

where A and r are two non-negative constants.

Derive the expressions of the reliability function and the hazard function. Also show that the hazard function is decreasing in t. 10

(d) State the Bellman's principle of optimality in dynamic programming. State how an LPP can be formulated as a dynamic programming problem. ·

Obtain the solution of the following LPP using dynamic programming :

Maximize $Z = 2x_1 + 5x_2$

subject to $2x_1 + x_2 \leq 430$

$2x_2 \leq 460$

$x_1, x_2 \geq 0.$ 10

(e) Let two components operate independently in parallel. Let failure times of both the components have exponential distribution with parameters α_1 and α_2 respectively.

Show that

(i) the pdf of the failure time of the system, say T, is not exponentially distributed, and

(ii) the expected value of T is given by .

$$E(T) = \frac{1}{\alpha_1} + \frac{1}{\alpha_2} - \frac{1}{\alpha_1 + \alpha_2}.$$ 10

2. Answer any two questions of the following :

(a) (i) Find an expression for the optimum order quantity, Q*, in a single period inventory model without set-up cost when the demand rate is instantaneous and units are continuous.

A company sells a variety of cooked fishes by weight. It makes a profit of ₹35 per kg if the fishes are sold on the day of the catch. If the company fails to sell the fishes. on the same day of catch, it disposes them on the next day at the loss of ₹30. If the demand is known to be rectangular between 2000 and 3000 kg, determine the optimum daily amount of inventory of cooked fishes, assuming that the demand is instantaneous. 15

(ii) Three independently functioning components are connected into a single system as shown below :

**

Suppose that the reliability for each of the components for an operational period of t hours is given by

$R(t) = e^{-0.03t}$.

(a) If Tis the time to failure of the entire system (in hours), what is the pdf of T?

(b) What is the reliability of the system ?

(c) How does the reliability of the system compare with R(t)? 10

(b) (i) What are the issues which could be answered using sensitivity analysis in linear programming problems ?

For the following LPP

Maximize $Z = 3x_1 + 2x_2$

subject to $x_1 + 2x_2 \leq 6$

$2x_1 + x_2 \leq 8$

$-x_1 + x_2 \leq 1$

$x_2 \leq 2$

$x_1, x_2 \geq 0$

The optimal table' is obtained as

i	Basis	Cost	Solution	3	2	0	0	0	0
				x_1	x_2	s_1	s_2	s_3	s_4
1	x_2	2	4/3	0	1	2/3	– 1/3	0	0
2	x_1	3	10/3	1	0	– 1/3	2/3	0	0
3	x_3	0	3	0	0	– 1	1	1	0
4	x_4	0	2/3	0	0	– 2/3	1/3	0	1
		Z	38/3	0	0	1/3	4/3	0	0

(a) Find the status and worth of each resource.

(b) Find the possible range of the cost coefficient associated with variable x_1 for which the optimum solution remains unchanged. 15

(ii) Suppose that each of the three electronic devices has a failure law given by an exponential distribution with parameters β_1, β_2 and β_3. Suppose that these three devices function independently and are connected in parallel to form a single system.

(a) Obtain an expression for R(t), the reliability of the system.

(b) Obtain an expression for the pdf of T, the time to failure of the system.

(c) Find the mean time to failure of the system. 10

(c) (i) Develop hazard functions when the life pattern of a system was described by

(a) exponential and

(b) gamma distribution

In each case, find E(T), the mean time to failure. 15

(ii) Distinguish between ' pure' and 'mixed' strategies of players in a two-person zero-sum game. In order to get mixed strategies of the players A and B in the following rectangular game, solve the game graphically :

	Plyayer B			
Player A	1	3	–3	7
	2	5	4	–6

10

(d) (i) What do you mean by sequencing problem? In this context, explain the terms

(a) total elapsed time,

(b) idle time on a machine and

(c) no passing rule.

Find the sequence that minimizes the total time required in performing the following jobs on three machines in the order ABC :

Processing time (in hours) on	Jobs					
	1	2	3	4	5	6
Machine A	8	3	7	2	5	1
Machine B	3	4	5	2	1	6
Machine C	8	7	6	9	10	9

(ii) Give the concept and definition of censoring. What are Type-I, Type-II and random censoring ?

Considering that each patient in a hospital has the same exponential density of survival and has the same point of entry into the study and the study is terminated after the survival time of the dth patient ($n \geq d$), find the maximum likelihood estimator of the parameter λ of the exponential density. 10

SECTION 'B'

(Demography and Vital Statistics)

3. (a) Differentiate between Total Fertility Rate (TFR), Gross Reproduction Rate (GRR) and Net Reproduction Rate (NRR). How does the NRR indicate the growth of the population ? 10

(b) The following part of a life table contains four typographical errors, each of a single digit. Find the errors and correct them.

x	l_x	${}_sd_x$	${}_sq_x$	${}_sL_x$	T_x	e^0_x
20	95772	857	0.008953	476495	4922814	51.533
25	94265	699	0.007368	472566	4456319	47.975
30	94166	800	0.008496	468895	3983754	42.306

10

(c) Explain the meaning of vital statistics. Name some of the important vital statistics and give their usefulness and shortcomings. 10

(d) What do you understand by

(i) True infant mortality rate,

(ii) Neo-natal infant mortality rate,

(iii) Modified infant mortality rate ?

Distinguish between them in terms of their utility in measuring the infant mortality as accurately as possible. 10

(e) Explain the reason for preparing model life tables. In this context, mention what are United Nations Model Life Tables. 10

4. Answer any **two** of the following :

(a) Describe the logistic curve, generally used for the projectipn of a human population at a time t. Describe some of its properties. Illustrate how would you fit a logistic ·curve to the given set of data using Pearl and Reed method. 25

(b) What is a life table and what are its uses ? Explain various columns of a life table and mention their relationships.

Fill out the several columns of the following abridged life table by employing the usual definitions:

x	$_5q_x$	l_x	$_5d_x$	$_5L_x$	$_5m_x$	T_x	e_x^0
20	0.006338	94864	—	—	—	5024927	—
25	0.006650	—	—	—	—	—	—
30	0.008087	—	—	—	—	—	—
35	—	92879	—	—	—	—	—

25

(c) Why the standardization of death rates is sometimes necessary ? Explain the direct and indirect methods of standardization. Calculate

(i) crude death rate and

(ii) standardization death rate using direct method for the following data :

Age group (in years)	Population	Deaths	Standard population
0 – 5	2000	100	10000
5 – 10	1600	48	8000
10 – 25	2400	24	15000
25 – 45	6000	30	25000
45 and above	8000	104	40000

25

(d) (i) What is stable population theory ? Define a stable population. How does it differ from the stationary population ? 10

(ii) Define crude birth rate, age-specific birth rates, general fertility rate and total fertility rate. State the utility of total fertility rate. 15

SECTION 'C'

(Survival Analysis and Clinical Trials)

5. (a) If lifetime distribution of a device follows Weibull distribution with pdf

$f(t) = \lambda\alpha t^{\alpha-1} e^{-\lambda t^{\alpha}}$, $t > 0$; $\lambda > 0$ and $\alpha > 0$.

Find hazard rate function. 10

(b) What are the principles of ethical clinical trials ? 10

(c) Establish the relationship between Life Table parameters q_x and μ_x. 10

(d) What is Cox proportional hazards model ? Show tliat ratio of hazard functions for any two subjects is constant. 10

(e) How survival function of Wei bull distribution will take form of survival function for Cox proportional hazard model ? 10

6. Answer any two of the following :

(a) The joint distribution of deaths due to various risks $R_\delta(\delta = 1, 2, \ldots, k)$ as well as survivors in age group (t_i, t_{i+1}) is :

	Death due to various Risks				Survivors	Total
	R_1	R_2	....	R_k		
Frequency	d_{i1}	d_{i2}	...	d_{ik}	l_{i+1}	l_i
Probability	Q_{i1}	Q_{i2}	...	Q_{ik}	p_i	1

Find the maximum likelihood estimators for p_i and $Q_{i\delta}$. 25

(b) Suppose the data from a clinical trial consist of deaths at 2·1, 2·9, 3·6, 4·5, 5·6 and 6·9 months and censored observations at 3·0, 3·6, 6·9 and 9·1 months. Compute the Kaplan-Meier estimator of the survival function. 25

(c) Researchers would like to test a new therapy. They are planning to conduct a randomized clinical trial in which group A receives the · tested therapy and group B receives a therapy that is currently in use. Our purpose is to test :

H_0: $\mu_A = \mu_B$ against H_1: $\mu_A > \mu_B$ with $\mu_A - \mu_B = \delta$ is minimum detectable difference. If α and β are size of type-I and type-II errors respectively, show that sample size (n) required for testing H_0 satisfies equations :

$$K = \Phi^{-1}\left(1 - \frac{\alpha}{2}\right) \text{ and}$$

$$\Phi\left(K + \frac{\delta}{2\sqrt{\frac{\sigma}{n}}}\right) - \Phi\left(-K + \frac{\delta}{2\sqrt{\frac{\sigma}{n}}}\right) = \beta,$$

where σ is population standard deviation and

$$\Phi(x) = \int_{-\infty}^{x} \frac{1}{2\pi} e^{-\frac{1}{2}y^2} \, dy.$$

(d) Discuss various phases involved in a clinical trial. Also discuss the pros and cons of each phase. 25

SECTION 'D'

(Quality Control)

7. (a) (i) What is the need for quality control ?

(ii) What are the advantages of Statistical Quality Control ? 10

(b) Derive the control limits for $\bar{X}$-chart. 10

(c) Determine the control limits for number of defectives when

(i) the standards are given

(ii) the standards are not given 10

(d) What do you mean by process capability ? Explain the different measures of process capability and write their interpretations. 10

(e) What is a CUSUM (cumulative sum) control chart? State its advantages and disadvantages. 10

8. Answer any two of the following :

(a) (i) Explain how would you interpret Shewhart control charts to decide whether the process is in control or not. 10

(ii) When should the control ch~rts for fraction defectives be prepared ?

How will you prepare the control charts for fraction defectives when

(a) the standards are given

(b) the standards· are not given 15

(b) (i) Write a note on operating characteristic (OC) curve for control charts. 10

(ii) State the situation for use of Exponentially · Weighted Moving Average (EWMA) control charts and also determine its control limits. 15

(c) (i) Mention the situations where Acceptance Sampling is most likely to be useful.

(ii) State the advantages and disadvantages of Acceptance Sampling.

(iii) Explain the operating procedure of single sampling plan. Also determine the effect of n and C on the OC curve. 25

(d) Explain the operating procedure of a Double Sampling Inspection plan. Derive its OC curve, Average Sample Number (ASN) and Average Total Inspection (ATI). 25

SECTION 'E'

(Multivariate Analysis)

9. (a) Let (X_1, X_2) have a bivariate normal density with mean vector $\underline{\mu} = (\mu_1, \mu_2)'$, variance-covariance matrix $\sum = \begin{pmatrix} \sigma_{11} & \sigma_{12} \\ \sigma_{21} & \sigma_{22} \end{pmatrix}$ and correlation coefficient $\rho_{12} = \text{corr}(X_1, X_2)$. Show that X_1, X_2 are stochastically independent if and only if $\rho_{12} = 0$. 10

(b) Let $\underset{\sim}{X} \sim N_3(\underset{\sim}{\mu}, \Sigma)$ with $\underset{\sim}{\mu}' = (2, -3, 1)$ and $\sum = \begin{pmatrix} 1 & 1 & 1 \\ 1 & 3 & 2 \\ 1 & 2 & 2 \end{pmatrix}$

(i) Find the distribution of $3X_1 - 2X_2 + X_3$.

(ii) Relabel the variables if necessary, and find a 2×1 vector $\underset{\sim}{a}$ such that X_2 and $X_2 - \underset{\sim}{a}' \begin{bmatrix} X_1 \\ X_3 \end{bmatrix}$ are stochastically independent. 10

(c) Find the maximum likelihood estimates of the 2×1 mean vector $\underset{\sim}{\mu}$ and the 2×2 variance-covariance matrix L based on the random sample

$$\underset{\sim}{X} = \begin{pmatrix} 3 & 6 \\ 4 & 4 \\ 5 & 7 \\ 4 & 7 \end{pmatrix}$$

from a bivariate normal population. 10

(d) Let $\underset{\sim}{X}_1, \underset{\sim}{X}_2, \ldots, \underset{\sim}{X}_n$ be a random sample of size n from a p-variate normal distribution with mean vector $\underset{\sim}{\mu}$ and variance-covariance matrix Σ. Then show that

(i) $\bar{\underset{\sim}{X}} \sim N_p\left(\underset{\sim}{\mu}, \left(\frac{1}{n}\right)\Sigma\right)$.

(ii) $(n-1)$ S is distributed as a Wishart distribution with $(n-1)$ degrees of freedom where $S = \frac{1}{(n-1)} \sum_{i=1}^{n} (\underset{\sim}{X}_j - \bar{\underset{\sim}{X}})(\underset{\sim}{X}_j - \bar{\underset{\sim}{X}})'$. 10

(e) Give formal mathematical definition of the ith pair of canonical variables and corresponding canonical correlation, for i = 1, 2, ... , k, in terms of the standard notations involving variance-covariance matrix Σ. Provide the necessary details, without proofs, for obtaining the c'anonical variables and their correlations. 10

10. Answer any **two** of the following :

(a) Let $\underset{\sim}{X}_1, \underset{\sim}{X}_2, \underset{\sim}{X}_3$ and $\underset{\sim}{X}_4$ be independent $N_p(\underset{\sim}{\mu}, \Sigma)$ random vectors.

(i) Find the marginal distributions for each of the random vectors

$$\underset{\sim}{V}_1 = \frac{1}{4}\underset{\sim}{X}_1 - \frac{1}{4}\underset{\sim}{X}_2 + \frac{1}{4}\underset{\sim}{X}_3 - \frac{1}{4}\underset{\sim}{X}_4$$

and $\underset{\sim}{V}_2 = \frac{1}{4}\underset{\sim}{X}_1 + \frac{1}{4}\underset{\sim}{X}_2 - \frac{1}{4}\underset{\sim}{X}_3 - \frac{1}{4}\underset{\sim}{X}_4$. 10

(ii) Find the joint distribution of the random vectors $\underset{\sim}{V}_1$ and $\underset{\sim}{V}_2$ defined in (i). 15

(b) (i) Let $\underset{\sim}{X}_1, \underset{\sim}{X}_2, \ldots, \underset{\sim}{X}_n$ be a random sample from an $N_p(\underset{\sim}{\mu}, \Sigma)$ population. Show that the Hotelling's T^2 statistic for testing H_0: $\underset{\sim}{\mu} = \underset{\sim}{\mu}_0$ vs H_1: $\underset{\sim}{\mu} \neq \underset{\sim}{\mu}_0$ is a generalization of the square of the t-statistic for testing H_0: $\underset{\sim}{\mu} = \underset{\sim}{\mu}_0$ vs H_1: = $\underset{\sim}{\mu} \neq \underset{\sim}{\mu}_0$ in the univariate case: · · 10

(ii) Evaluate T^2, for testing H_0: $\underline{\mu}'$ (7, 11), using the data

$$X = \begin{pmatrix} 2 & 12 \\ 8 & 9 \\ 6 & 9 \\ 8 & 10 \end{pmatrix}$$

Specify the distribution of T^2.

Test H_0 at the $\alpha = 0{\cdot}05$ leveL What concluion do you reach ? 15

(c) (i) Let $Y_1 = \underline{e}_1' \underline{X}, Y_2 = \underline{e}_2' \underline{X}, ..., Y_p = \underline{e}_p' \underline{X}$ be the principal components obtained from the variance-covariance matrix L. Obtain the correlation coefficient between Y_i and X_k where i, k = 1, 2, ..., p. Here $(\lambda_1, \underline{e}_1), (\lambda_2, \underline{e}_2), ..., (\lambda_p, \underline{e}_p)$ are the eigenvalue-eigenvector pairs for Σ. 15

(ii) Let $\Sigma = \begin{pmatrix} 2 & 0 & 0 \\ 0 & 4 & 0 \\ 0 & 0 & 4 \end{pmatrix}$.

Determine the principal components Y_1, Y_2 and Y_3. What can you say about the eigenvectors (and principal components) associated with eigenvalue that are not distinct. 10

(d) (i) Consider the linear function Y = $\underline{a}'\underline{X}$. Let $E(\underline{X}) = \underline{\mu}_1$ and cov$(\underline{X})$ if $\underline{X}$ belongs to population π_1. Let $E(\underline{X}) = \underline{\mu}_2$ and cov$(\underline{X}) = \sum$ if $\underline{X}$. belongs to population π_2. Let m = $\frac{1}{2}(\underline{a}'\underline{\mu}_1 + \underline{a}'\underline{\mu}_2)$. Given that $\underline{a}' = (\underline{\mu}_1 - \underline{\mu}_2)' \Sigma^{-1}$ show that

(a) $E(\underline{a}'\underline{X} \mid \pi_1) - m = \underline{a}'\underline{\mu}_1 - m > 0$

(b) $E(\underline{a}'\underline{X} \mid \pi_2) - m = \underline{a}'\underline{\mu}_1 - m < 0$ 15

(ii) Show that $-\frac{1}{2}(\underline{x} - \underline{\mu}_1)' \Sigma^{-1} (\underline{x} - \underline{\mu}_1) + \frac{1}{2}(\underline{x} - \underline{\mu}_2)' \Sigma^{-1}$ is equal to

$(\underline{\mu}_1 - \underline{\mu}_2)' \Sigma^{-1} \underline{x} - \frac{1}{2}(\underline{\mu}_1 - \underline{\mu}_2)' \Sigma^{-1} (\underline{\mu}_1 + \underline{\mu}_2)$. 10

SECTION 'F'

(Design and Analysis of Experiment)

11. (a) Characterize a Completely Randomized Design (CRD). State its merits and demerits. 10

(b) Discuss the Statistical Analysis of m x m Latin Square Design for one observation per experimental unit. 10

(c) Give the Yates' method of computing effect totals in 2^3 factorial experiment. 10

(d) State the advantages and disadvantages of confounding. 10

(e) Explain the Factorial Experiment with an example. 10

12. Answer any two of the following :

(a) For the two-way classification (with one observation per cell) model

$X_{ij} = \mu + \beta_j + \varepsilon_{ij}$ (i = 1, 2, ... k
j = 1, 2, ... h)

where e_{ij} is the error effect due to chance and $\sum_{i=1}^{k} \alpha_i = 0 = \sum_{j=1}^{h} \beta_j$

(i) Obtain the least square estimates of μ, α_i and β_j.

(ii) Obtain the expectation of various sum of squares.

(iii) Also give the ANOVA Table. 25

(b) (i) The Table below gives the yield of wheat (kgs/plot) as observed in an experiment carried out in a 4 × 4 Latin Square. The Four manurial treatments are indicated by A, B, C and D. Analyse the data and write a brief report on your findings. (Given that $F_{0.05}(3, 5) = 5{\cdot}41$)

A 12	C 19	B 10	D 8
C 18	B 12	D 6	–
B 22	D 10	A 5	C 21
D 12	A 7	C 27	B 17

15

(ii) Write down the special features of a Split-Plot Design. Give Statistical model and appropriate analysis of variance table for Split-Plot Design. 10

(c) (i) Define mam effects and interactions with reference to a 23 factorial experiment. 15

(ii) Explain a confm,mding scheme to run a 3^3 experiment using blocks of 9 plots each by consider'ing to confound the AB^2C^2 component and write the ANOVA for completely confounding AB^2C in replicates. 10

(d) (i) Explain Strip-plot Design with layout for 3 replications and state its significance.

(ii) Illustrate the Strip-Plot Design as a randomization and layout with

(a) 3 varieties of wheat (Horizontal Treatments)

(b) 3 levels of nitrogen (vertical treatment)

(c) 6 Replicates

Also, outline the ANOVA Table. 25

SECTION 'G'

(Computing with C and R)

13. (a) The Fibonacci numbers are defined recursively as follows:

$x_1 = x_2 = 1,$

$x_n = x_{n-1} + x_{n-2}, n > 2.$

Write a function that will generate and print the first n Fibonacci numbers. 10

(b) Given bivariate data (x_i, y_i), i = 1, 2, ... , n. Write a C-program to compute variancecovariance matrix (Σ) of the data. 10

(c) Write a C-program that returns 1 if its argument is a prime number and returns 0 otherwise. 10

(d) Write R-eade for fitting binomial distribution with parameters n, p of data (i,.fi); i = 0, 1, 2, ... , k. 10

(e) Write R-eade to find highest common factor of two positive numbers. 10

14. Answer any two of the following:

(a) Write a C-program for counting characters, words and lines in the input text. 25

(b) Write a C-program to construct linear linked list. Add functions to carry out the following operations on linear linked list.

(i) Count the number of nodes.

(ii) Write out contents.

(iii) Adding node at the end. 25

(c) Suppose X follows Normal distribution with mean a, standard deviation b and pdi $f_x(x)$, where $-\infty < a < \infty, b > 0$.

Write R-eade to compute:

(i) $P(X > t) = \int_t^{\infty} f_x(x)dx;$

(ii) $MD = \int_{-\infty}^{\infty} |x - mean| f_x(x)\, dx$ 25

(d) In usual notations, consider the following linear model :

$y_1 = \beta_1 - 2\beta_2 + 3\beta_3 + \epsilon_1$

$y_2 = 2\beta_1 + 3\beta_2 - \beta_3 + \epsilon_2$

$y_3 = -\beta_1 + 7\beta_2 + 4\beta_3 + \epsilon_3$

Write an R-program to find .the estimate of parameters and their variances. 25

STATISTICS - IV
2021

Time Allowed : Three Hours | Maximum Marks: 200

Question Paper Specific Instructions

Please read each of the following instructions carefully before attempting questions.

There are FOURTEEN questions divided under SEVEN Section. Candidate has to attempt TWO Sections and attempt the questions therein. All the Sections carry equal marks. The number of marks carried by a question/part is indicated against it. Wherever any assumptions are made for answering a question, they must be clearly indicated. Diagrams/ Figures, wherever required, shall be drawn in the space provided for answering the question itself. Graph paper can be found at the end of the booklet. Unless otherwise mentioned, symbols and notations have their usual standard meanings. Attempts of questions shall be counted in sequental order. Unless struck off, attempt of a question shall be counted even if attempted partly. Any page or portion of the page left blank in the Question-cum-Answer Booklet must be clearly struck off. Answers must be written in ENGLISH only.

Section A
(Operation Reserach and Reliability)

(a) Find the sequence that minimises the total elapsed time required to ecomplete the following taks: 10

Tasks	A	B	C	D	E	F	G
Time on Machine I	3	8	7	4	9	8	7
Time on Machine II	4	3	2	5	1	4	3
Time on Machine III	6	7	5	11	5	6	12

(b) For the following pay-off table, transform the zero-sum game into an equivalent Linear Programming Problem and solve the game by Simplex Method: 10

Player B

		B_1	B_2	B_3
	A_1	1	–1	3
Player A	A_2	3	5	–3
	A_3	6	2	–2

(c) A suspermarket has two girls ringing up sales at the counters. The service time for each counter is exponential with 4 minutes, and people arrive in a Poisson fashion at the rate of 10 an hour.

Calculatea:

(i) Probability of having to wait for service.

(ii) Expected percentage of idle time for each girl.

(iii) If the customer has to wait, what is the expected length of his waiting time? 10

(d) A manufacturing company purchases 9000 parts of a machine for its annual requirements, ordering one month's requirement at a time. Each part cost ₹20. The ordering cost per order is ₹15 and the carrying charges are 15 percent of the average inventory per year. You have been assigned to suggest a more economical purchasing policy for the company. What advice would you offer and how much would it save the company per year? 10

(e) Describe Project Evaluation and Review Technique (PERT) and its procedure stepwise.

A small project is composed of activities whose time estimates are listed in the following table. Activities are identified by their begining (i) and ending (j) node numbers.

Activity	Estimated Duration (in weeks)		
i – j	Optimistic	Most Likely	Pessimistic
1 – 2	1	1	7
1 – 3	1	4	7
1 – 4	2	2	8
2 – 5	1	1	1
3 – 5	2	5	14
4 – 6	2	5	8
5 – 6	3	6	15

(i) Draw the Project Network.

(ii) Find the expected duration and variance of each activity.

(iii) What is the excepted projected length?

(iv) Calculation the Variance and Standard deviation of the project length. 10

2. Answer any two questions of the following:

(a) (i) A marketing manager has 5 salesmen and 5 sales districts. Considering the capabilities of the salesmen and the nature of the districts, the marketing manager estimates that sales per month (in hundred rupees) for each salesman in each district would be as follows:

		Salesmen				
		A	B	C	D	E
	1	32	38	40	28	40
Districts	2	40	24	28	21	36
	3	41	27	33	30	37
	4	22	38	41	36	36
	5	29	41	40	35	39

Find the assignment of salesmen to districts that will result in maximum sales. 10

(ii) Describe Algorithm for solving n-jobs through 2-machines. The following table gives machine processing times for the five jobs on the two machines A and B:

Jobs	Processing times (in hours)	
	Machine A	Machine B
1	3	4
2	8	10
3	5	6
4	7	5
5	6	8

Determine the optimal sequence of jobs that minimizes the total elapsed time. Also find the idle time of Machine A and Machine B. 15

(b) Find the Basic Feasible Solution of the following Transportation Problem by Vogel's Approximation Method:

		D_1	D_2	D_3	D_4	D_5	Available ↓
Origins	O_1	4	3	1	2	6	80
	O_2	5	2	3	4	5	60
	O_3	3	5	6	3	2	40
	O_4	2	4	4	5	3	20
Demand →		60	60	30	40	10	

Using MODI Method, also find the optimum transportation plan. 25

(c) (i) A commodity is to be supplied at a constant rate of 200 units per day. Supplies of any amounts can be had at any required time, but each ordering costs ₹ 50. Cost of holding in inventory is ₹ 2 per unit per day while delay in the supply of the items induces a penalty of ₹ 10 per unit per delay of 1 day. Find the optimal policy (q, t) where 't' is the reorder cycle period and 'q' is the inventory level after reorder. What would be the best policy if the penalty cost becomes infinite? 10

(ii) For (M|M|1): (∞|FIFO) queue system, derive the steady state distribution of the queue of the queue length. Also obtain the probability density function of waiting time excluding service time distribution. 15

(d) (i) A recorded lifetime (in hours) for identical items are as follows:

10.2, 89.6, 54.0, 96.0, 23.3, 30.5, 41.2, 0.8, 3.6, 28.0, 73.2, 31.6

Assuming lifetime has Gama Distribution with parameters λ and ν, find the estimate for the failure rate λ. 10

(ii) Consider an item with failure rate function given by

$h(t) = \alpha\lambda(\lambda t)^{\alpha-1}; > 0.$

Obtain the Reliability Function, Conditional Survial Function $P[T > x + t \mid T > t]$, Mean Time To Failure (MTTF) and Mean Residual Lifetime. 15

SECTION B

(Demography and Vital Statistics)

3. (a) Discuss on hospital records and ad hoc surveys in relation to vital statistics information. 10

(b) Discuss internal migrations, rural-urban migrations and international migrations. 10

(c) Distinguish between the terms fecundity and fertility. Mention the variouos measures of fertility. Also discuss their relative merits and demerits. 10

(d) Given that the complete expections of life at ages 25 and 26 for a specific group are 22.08 and 21.93 years respectively. THe number of people living at age 25 is 45324. Find the number that attains age 26. 10

(e) Describe intercensal and post-censal estimates of population growth assuming linear growth and exponential growth in mathematical method. 10

4. Answer any two of the following:

(a) Write a critical note on the salient features of Indian Censuses 1991 and 2001.

(b) Explain Pearl and Reed method of fitting logistic curve for population projection.

(c) Calculate

(i) General Fertility Rate (GFR),

(ii) Specific Fertility Rate (SFR),

(iii) Total Fertility Rate (TFR), and

(iv) Gross Reproduction Rate (GRR)

from the data given below: 25

Age group of child bearing females	Number of Women ('000)	Total Births
15 – 19	16.0	260
20 – 24	16.4	2244
25 – 29	15.8	1894
30 – 39	14.8	916
40 – 44	15.0	280
45 – 49	14.5	145

Assume that the proportion of female births is 46.2 percent.

(d) Fill in the blanks of the following table which are marked with question marks (?): 25

Age x	l_x	d_x	q_x	p_x	L_x	e_x^0
20	693435	?	?	?	?	35081126
21	690673	–	–	–	?	

SECTION C
(Survival Analysis and Clinical Trial)

5. (a) Define the survival function and the hazard function. Derive these function for the Weibull distribution. 10

(b) Define Kaplan-Meier estimaor of the survival function using standard notation. 10

(c) Define the proportional hazards model in terms of the survival function. Explain why it is called a semi-parametric model. Derive the estimator of its baseline hazard function. 10

(d) Make a critical comparison between cross-sectional and longitudinal designs. Describe their relative advantages and disadvantages. 10

(e) Discuss the need of clinical trials and explain the ethical consideration involved in clinical trials. 10

6. Answer any two of the following:

(a) Consider a survival distribution with constant hazard $\lambda = 0.07$ on (0, 5] and $\lambda = 0.14$ on (5, ∞). Plot this hazard function and the corresponding survival function on (0, 10).

What is the median survival time? 25

(b) Define time and order censoring. If the lifetime distribution is exponential with parameter λ, derive the maximum likelihood estimator of λ under these two censoring schemes.

Also, derive Fisher information in the two cases. 25

(c) Describe the four phases of clinical trials explaining their respective objectives in detail. 25

(d) Explain the difference between censoring and truncation. Also, explain right-censoring and left-censoring with the help of two examples each. Suppose X is a non-negative random variable and t, t_1, t_2 are positive real constants, identify the probability distributions of X conditional on

(i) $X > t$,

(ii) $X < t$, and

(iii) $t_1 < X < t_2$

respectively. 25

SECTION D
(Quality Control)

7. (a) (i) What do you mean by Statistical Quality Control (SQC)? Discuss its need and utility.

(ii) Distringuish between process control and product control. Discus the sistuations where they are used. 5+5=10

(b) Discuss various sources of assignable causes and random causes of variations. Also, state how they are detected in manufacturing process. 10

(c) What is control chart? Explain the basic principles underlying the control charts. Discuss the role of control charts in manufacturing process. 10

(d) Explain the construction of control chart for $\overline{X}$ and R. Also, mention the criterion for detecting 'Lack of Contol' in $\overline{X}$ and R charts. 10

(e) What is an acceptance sampling plan? Discuss a single sampling plan (n, c), where the sampling is carried out using a binomial model. Find P_a if $n = 10$, $c = 3$ and $p = 0.05$. 10

8. Answer any two of the following:

(a) Evaluate the ARL to detect a shift in the process average (no change in process variation) by one unit of standard deviation in the higher side. Assume the use of $\overline{X}$-chart with subgroup size 5 and probability of not detecting the shift is at most 0.05. 25

(b) What is Average Sample Number (ASN)? Explain the method of calculation for single sampling and double sampling plan and also discuss the relative merits and demerits. Why is ASN calculated? 25

(c) An improvement in the process has resulted in increase of Cpk from 0.06 to 0.09. Estimate the reduction in % of non-conforming products. Assume the following: Process average has not changed, Cp = Cpk and process is in statistical control. 25

(d) (i) Describe the construction of p-chart (control chart for fraction defective). Discuss the cases when standards are specified and standards are not specified. 10

(ii) The following are the figures of defectives in 22 lots each containing 2000 rubber belts:

425, 430, 216, 341, 225, 322, 280, 306, 337, 305, 356, 402, 216, 264, 126, 409, 193, 326, 280, 389, 451, 420

Find control limits. 15

SECTION E
(Multivariate Analysis)

9. (a) Define bivariate normal distribution and obtain its

(i) Characteristic function, and

(ii) Marginal distribution of X_1. 10

(b) Let $X \sim N_3(\mu, \Sigma)$ with $\mu' = (2, 3, -1)$ and $\Sigma = \begin{bmatrix} 7 & 3 & 2 \\ 3 & 4 & 1 \\ 2 & 1 & 2 \end{bmatrix}$.

(i) Obtain the conditional distribution of X_1 and X_2 given $X_3 = 2$.

(ii) Find the partial correlation coefficient between X_1 and X_2 given X_3.

(c) Define Hotelling's T^2 and mention its applications. Show that

$$T^2(p, m) = \frac{mp}{m-p+1} F_{F-\alpha-F+1}$$ 10

(d) Let $X \sim N_3(\mu, \Sigma)$ with $\mu' = (-3, 1, 4)$ and $\Sigma = \begin{bmatrix} 1 & -2 & 0 \\ 2 & 5 & 0 \\ 0 & 0 & 2 \end{bmatrix}$.

Which of the following random variables are independent? Explain. 10

(i) X_1 and X_2

(ii) X_2 and X_3

(iii) (X_1, X_2) and X_3

(e) Define Wishart distribution and obtain its characteristic function. Also establish its additive property. 10

10. Answer any two of the following:

(a) Discuss the procedure for testing the null hypothesis H_0: $\mu = \mu_0$ against H_1: $\mu \neq \mu_0$ regarding the specified mean vector of the multivariate normal distribution $N_p(\mu, \Sigma)$.

Let the data matrix for a random sample of size n = 3 from a bivariate normal distribution be

$$X = \sum = \begin{bmatrix} 6 & 10 & 8 \\ 9 & 6 & 3 \end{bmatrix}$$

Evaluate the observed value of T^2 for $\mu_0' = (9, 5)$. What is the sampling distribution of T^2 in this case? 25

(b) Define canomical correlation coefficient and canoical variates. In the usual notations, show that the canonical correlations are the solution of

$$\begin{vmatrix} -\lambda\Sigma_{11} & \Sigma_{12} \\ \Sigma_{21} & -\lambda\Sigma_{22} \end{vmatrix} = 0.$$

(c) Define Wishart matrix D and its distribution. Also, point out the applications of this distribution. If $D \sim W_p(D; n; \Sigma)$, then show that $\frac{|D|}{|\Sigma|}$ is distributed as the product of p independent chi-square variates with d.f.n, n – 1, n – 2, ..., n – p + 1, respectively. Also, obtained $E(|D|^h)$ for h = 1, 2, 3, ... If X_1 X_2 X_3 are independently and indentically distributed as $N_2(\mu, \Sigma)$, with $\mu = 0$ and $\sum = \begin{bmatrix} 1 & 2 \\ 2 & 4 \end{bmatrix}$, obtain $E[X_1, X_1' + X_2, X_2' + X_3, X_3']$. 25

(d) A researcher wants to determine a procedure for discriminating between two multivariate populations. The researcher has enough data available to estimate the density functions $f_1(X)$and $f_2(X)$ associated with population π_1 and π_2 respectively, where C(2|1) = 50 and C(1|2) = 100. In addition, it is known that about 20% of all possible items (for which the measurements X can be recorded) belong to π_2.

(i) Give the minimum ECM rule (in general form) for assigning a new item to one of the two populations.

(ii) Measurements recorded on a new item yield the density values $f_1(X) = 0.3$ and $f_2(X) = 0.5$. Given the preceding information, assign this item to population π_1 or population π_2. 25

SECTION F

(Design and Analysis of Experiments)

11. (a) For the one-way classified fixed effect model:

$Y_{ij} = \mu + \alpha_i + \varepsilon_{ij}$; (i = 1, 2, ..., k, j = 1, 2, ..., n_j),

where $\varepsilon_{ij} \sim N(0, \sigma_e^2)$.

(i) Obtain the Least Square Estimates of μ & α_i's.

(ii) Obtain E(SST) and E(SSE),

where

SST = Sum of Squares due to treatment.

SSE = Sum of Squares due to error.

(iii) Also give ANOVA table. 10

(b) Distinguish between 'total confounding' and 'partial confounding' in a 2^3-factorial experiment.

The following are three replicates each consisting of a complete block o a 2^3-factorial experiments in blocks of 4 plots involving three fertilizers N, P and K each at two levels.

Replicate I

Block 1	np	npk	(1)	k
Block 2	p	n	pk	nk

Replicate II

Block 3	(1)	npk	nk	p
Block 4	n	pk	np	k

Replicate III

Block 5	pk	nk	(1)	np
Block 6	np	npk	p	k

Identify the treatment effects confounded in each replicates and outline its ANOVA. 10

(c) Explain what you understand by 'Missing plot technique'. Suppose one observation is missing in an m^2-Latin Square design. Let the missing observation be x. Obtain the estimate of missing observation x in a Latin Square design and analyse the data. 10

(d) (i) In a 2^5-factorial experiment, the key block is given by

(1), ad, bc, abcd, abe, ace, cde and bde.

Identify the Confounding Effects. 5

(ii) Given the principal block of 2^4-design as

(1), ab, cd, abcd.

Identify the Confounding Effect. 5

(e) Explain a Split-plot Experiment. How does it differ from Randomised Block Design (RBD)? Discuss the advantages and disadvantages relative to RBD. Also, give compartive study of the Split-plot design and Factorial design. 10

12. Answer any two of the following:

(a) Let Y_1, Y2 and Y_3 be independent random variables with common variance σ^2 and Expectation given by:

$E(Y_1) = \theta_1 + \theta_3$

$E(Y_2) = \theta_2 + \theta_3$

$E(Y_3) = \theta_3 + \theta_3$

(i) Prove that $b_1 + b_2\theta_3 + b_3\theta_3$ is estimable if and only if $b_3 = b_1 + b_2$.

(ii) If $b_1\theta_1 + b_2\theta_2 + b_3\theta_3$ is estimable, find its Best Linear Unbiased Estimator (BLUE) and its variance.

(iii) In a Randomised Block Design (RBD) with r-blocks and v-treatments, the yield of treatment 1 and 2 in the first block are mixed up and only thier total yield is known. Estimate the mixed up yields and show that the bias in the estimated treatment sum of squares is given by

$$\text{bias} = \frac{(T_1 - T_2)^2}{2(r-1)^2}$$

and that the loss of efficiency due to mixing of the yield is

$[1 + (v - 1)(r - 1)]^{-1}$. 25

(c) Let Y_{ij} (i = 1, 2 ..., s, j = 1, 2, .., r) be independent Normal observations with common variance σ^2 and expectation given by

$E(Y_{ij}) = \mu + \alpha_i + t_j + \beta x_{ij}$; (i = 1, 2, ..., r, j = 1, 2, ..., s),

where μ, α_i's, t_j's and β are unknown parameters.

Derive the statistics for testing (i) $\beta = 0$, and (ii) $t_1 = t_2 = \ldots = t_r = 0$. 25

(d) (i) Explain basic priciples of design of experiments pointing out the role each one plays in the valid and accurate interpretation of the data. Explain how these principles are used in Randomised Block Design (RBD). Explain the situtations in which RBD is considered as an improvement over CRD. 10

(ii) Explain the Analysis of Variance of two-way classification data with one observation per cell. Show that Mean Square Error is an unbiased estimate of population variance. 15

SECTION G

(Computing with C and R)

13. (a) Express $A = \dfrac{B + C}{D}$ in prefix and postix forms. 10

(b) Write a C program to check if the given matrix is idempotent. 10

(c) Write a C program to find the product of the digits of a 7-digits of a positive integer, where none of the digits is zero. 10

(d) Given n positive integers, with R code to arrange these numbers in descending order. 10

(e) Given bivariate data (x_i, y_i), i = 1, 2, ..., n, write R code to compute the rank correlation coefficient between X and Y. 10

14. (a) Suppose X follows the gamma distribution with parameters a and b, where a, b > 1. Write a C program to compute

$$P[X > t] = \int_t^{\infty} (\text{density function of X})\, dx.$$ 25

(b) State the relative advantages and disadvantages of call by value and call by reference in C programming. Write a C programming to evaluate the series

$$\exp[x] = 1 + x + \frac{x^2}{2!} + \frac{x^3}{3!} + \ldots,$$

wihout using any built-in function. 25

STATISTICS-IV
2019

Time Allowed : Three Hours | *Maximum Marks: 200*

INSTRUCTIONS

Please read each· of the following instructions carefully before attempting questions.

There are FOURTEEN questions divided under SEVEN sections. Candidate has to choose any TWO Sections and attempt the questions therein. All the Sections carry equal marks. The number of marks carried by a question/part is indicated against it. Wherever any assumptions are made for answering a question, they must be clearly indicated. Diagrams / Figures, wherever required, shall be drawn in the space provided for answering the question itself. Unless otherwise mentioned, symbols and notations have their usual standard meanings. Chi-Square Distribution Table is given with Q. 10(b). Attempts of questions shall be counted in sequential order. Unless struck off, attempt of a question shall be counted even if attempted partly. Any page or portion of the page left blank in the Question-cum-Answer Booklet must be clearly struck off Answers must be written in ENGUSH only.

Section A

(Operations Research and Reliability)

1. (a) A department head has four subordinates and four tasks to be performed. The subordinates differ in efficiency and the tasks differ in their intrinsic difficulty. His estimate of the time each man would take to perform each task is given in the matrix below :

Task	**Men**			
	E	F	G	H
A	18	26	17	11
B	13	28	14	26
C	38	19	18	15
D	19	26	24	10

How should the tasks be allocated to a man so as to minimize the total man hours? 10

(b) There are four villages V_1, V_2, V_3 and V_4 which are affected due to_floods. Food items are to be dropped in these villages by aircrafts A_1, A_2 and A_3. Details of trips are given in the following table :

	V_1	V_2	V_3	V_4	Total Number of Trips from A_i
A_1	2	5	9	10	50
A_2	10	8	6	3	60
A_3	8	10	5	3	40
Total Number of Trips from V_j	30	50	60	40	

Solve the transportation problem to drop maximum food. 10

(c) Solve the following zero-sum game for two persons. Obtain the optimum strategies for both players and value of the game. 10

Player A

$$\text{Player B}\begin{bmatrix} 2 & 4 & 1 \\ 3 & -1 & 2 \\ -1 & 2 & 3 \end{bmatrix}$$

(d) An aircraft uses rivets at a constant rate of 5000 kg per year. The rivets cost ₹ 20 per kg and the company personnel estimate that it costs ₹ 200 to place an order and the carrying cost of inventory is 10% per year.

(i) How frequently should orders for rivets be placed and what quantities should be ordered for?

(ii) If the actual costs are ₹ 500 to place an order and 15% for carrying cost, the optimum policy would change. How much will the company be losing per year because of imperfect cost information? 10

(e) Consider a system of n independent components with failure rates $\lambda_1, \lambda_2, \dots, \lambda_n$ respectively. If we assume that the lifetime of the components follow exponential distribution, what is the probability that the component j is the first component to fail ? 10

2. Answer any two of the following :

(a) Find the optimal solution to the LP problem:

Maximize $z = -x_1 + 3x_2 - 3x_3$

subject to the constraints

$3x_1 - x_2 + x_3 = 7$

$-x_1 + 2x_2$ *** 0

$-4x_1 + 3x_2 + 8x_3 \leq 10$

and $x_1, x_2, x_3 \geq 0$.

(i) Within what range does the cost of x_1 vary so that the optimality remains unaffected ?

(ii) Within what range does the cost of x_3 vary so that the optimality remains unaffected ?

25

(b) (i) Describe the problem of replacement of items whose maintenance cost increases with time and value of money also changes with time.

(ii) A machine costs ₹ 5000. Operating costs are ₹ 800 per year for the first five years and increasing by ₹ 200 per year in the sixth and subsequent years. Assuming a 10% discount rate of money per year, find the optimum length of time to hold the machine before it is replaced. (Assume that the machine will be eventually sold for scrap at a negligible price). 25

(c) (i) For MIMIC : (∞ | FIFO) queue system, derive the steady state distribution of the queue length.

(ii) A tax consulting centre has four service counters to receive their customers. There is an average arrival rate of ten persons per hour to this centre and each tax advisor spends an irregular amount of time, which have been found to follow exponential distribution. The average service time is 20 minutes. Calculate the average number of customers in the system, average queue length and average waiting time for a customer. 25

(d) (i) Consider an item with failure rate function

$$h(t) = \frac{t}{1+t}.$$

Obtain reliability function, MTTF, conditional survival function:

$P(T > x + t \mid T > t)$ and mean residual life function.

(ii) Suppose 100 electronic components are subjected to life testing until all of them failed. The results are given in the following table. Estimate the reliability at the end of each interval and failure rate at the start of each interval.

Time interval in hours		Number of good components	
Start	**End**	**Start**	**End**
0	10	100	76
10	20	76	56
20	30	56	38
30	40	38	26
40	50	26	15
50	60	15	7
60	70	7	3
70	80	3	1
80	90	1	0

Section B
(Demography and Vital Statistics)

3. (a) Explain the meaning of Vital Statistics. Give its usefulness and shortcomings. 10

(b) What is Sample Registration System (SRS) ? What factors are studied under SRS ? Give its shortcomings. 10

(c) Derive an algebraic expression relating the probability of a person dying between the age of x and (x + 1), q_x to the force of mortality, μ_x. 10

(d) Describe how the Abridged life table will be constructed by Greville's method. 10

(e) Complete the following Life Table (with usual notation) : 10

Age in Years	l_x	d_x	q_x	p_x	L_x	T_x	e_x^0
11	12000	?	?	?	?	?	?
12	8000	?	?	?	?	?	?
13	6000	?	?	?	?	?	?
14	4000	-	-	-	3000	?	?

4. Answer any two of the following :

(a) (i) Explain any one method offitting Gompertz growth curve. 15

(ii) What is Chandrasekaran- Deming formula? Explain it. 10

(b) With usual notation, in a life table, e_1 is equal to e_0 and $l_x = (l_1/l_0)^x\, l_0$, for $0 \leq x < 1$, then show that Po= exp $(-1/e_1)$. 25

(c) Explain different net migration rates as proposed by Hamilton. 25

(d) Given the life table of three men A, B and C aged 90, 91 and 92 years respectively as follows:

Age x	90	91	92	93	94	95	96	97	98	99	100
l_x	16090	11490	8012	5448	3607	2320	1447	873	590	98	0

where l_x = Number living at age x. Complete the life table and find the probability that

(i) A, B and C will be alive in two years time (i.e. at the end of two years)

(ii) All will be dead within two years, and

(iii) C will be alive for 6 years' time. 25

Section C

(Survival Analysis and Clinical Trials)

5. (a) Consider the survival model characterized by the following piecewise-constant hazard function :

$$\lambda(t) = \begin{cases} \lambda_1, & 0 \leq t < \pi_1 \\ \lambda_2, & \pi_1 \leq t < \pi_2 \\ \lambda_3, & \pi_2 \leq t \end{cases}$$

where π_1 and π_2 are known constants. Based on right censored data (x_j, δ_i), i = 1, ... n, derive the MLEs of λ_1, λ_2 and λ_3 and their standard errors. 10

(b) The survival times of 11 patients with Acute Myelogenous Leukemia are given below :

9, 13, 13^+, 18, 23, 28^+, 31, 34, 45^+, 48, 161^+,

where censored data are marked by"+" in the superscript.

Calculate the Kaplan-Meier estimate of S(20) and obtain the standard of log of that estimate. Compare the estimate under the assumption of an exponential distribution. 10

(c) Consider a family of lifetime distributions which has a hazard function $\lambda(t) = 2t/\beta^2$. Write down the "survival function S(t) for this family of models and obtain the MLE $\hat{\beta}$ of β. Also write the expression for the standard error. 10

(d) A clinical trial studies the survival of lung cancer patients, where the patients were randomly assigned to an experimental treatment or to a placebo. The survival times of patients were recorded.

Based on the data set, a researcher fits the model below :

coxph(formula = surv(time, obs) ~ trt, data= X, method= "exact")

	coef	exp(coef)	se(coef)
trt	- 0·8188	0·4410	0·7376

State the model and the assumptions. Test whether the treatment is effective. State the null and the alternative hypotheses and your conclusions at the confidence level of 95%.

(Given that $z_{\cdot 975} = 1{\cdot}96$)

(e) Define a competing risk model. Explain a non-parametric inference procedure for such a model. 10

6. Answer any two of the following :

(a) Assume the hazard rate is at time 0 and linearly increases $\lambda(\lambda > 0)$ as time increases 2 units. Derive the survival function, the probability density function and the median of survival time. Discuss the shape of hazard function and the probability density function. 5+5+5+10=25

(b) Suppose that the time to death X has an exponential distribution with hazard rate λ and the right censoring time C is exponential with hazard rate θ. Let

$T = \min(X, C)$ and $\delta = 1$ if $X \leq C$; 0 if $X > C$.

Assume that X and C are independent.

(i) Find $P_r(\delta = 1)$.

(ii) Derive the survival function of T.

Let $(T_1, \delta_1), \ldots (T_5, \delta_5)$ be 5 randomly taken observations. Assume they follow the above model and it can be shown that δ and T are independent. Construct the likelihood function and the MLE of λ. 5+5+15=25

(c) The survival time of two treatment groups are recorded as follows :

Treatment A: 3, 5^+, 8, 10^+

Treatment B : 2, 2, 6

(i) Compare the survival function of two treatment groups using two sample log rank tests. First, write out the null and alternative hypotheses. Then calculate the test statistic and the variance of test statistics. Describe the distribution of the test statistic under the null hypothesis. Do not calculate p-value, but simply interpret the conclusions in different situations.

(ii) Assume the two treatments have no difference and so we can combine all observations in one group. Find the MLEs of the parameters when the survival time is assumed to follow the Weibull distribution with shape parameter $\alpha = 2$ i.e. $f(t) = 2\lambda t\, e^{-\lambda t^2}$ $t > 0$. 13+12=25

(d) Justify the use of Phase III in clinical trials. Discuss briefly the analysis in Phase I- III trials when the outcomes are ordinal. 10+15=25

Section D

(Quality Control)

7. (a) Explain the concept of Statistical Quality Control. Give its advantages and limitations. 10

(b) Distinguish between Charts for Variables and Charts for Attributes. 10

(c) Explain the following: 10

(i) 3- σ limits

(ii) Natural control limits

(iii) Specification limits

(iv) Modified control limits

(d) A sub-group of 5-items each is taken from a manufacturing process at a regular interval. A certain quality characteristic is measured and $\overline{X}$ and R values computed. After 25 sub-groups it is found that $\Sigma\overline{X} = 357{\cdot}50$ and $\Sigma R = 8{\cdot}8$. If the specification limits are $M{\cdot}4 \neq 0{\cdot}40$; and if the process is in statistical control, what conclusion can you draw about the ability of the process to produce items within specifications ?

(For sub-group of 5-items, $d_2 = 2{\cdot}326$) 10

(e) Explain the situations in which Moving Average Charts and Exponentially Weighted Moving Average Charts are useful. Give limits of these two charts. 10

8. Answer any two of the following :

(a) A food company puts mango juice into cans and advertise as containing 200 mL of the juice. After filling, 20 samples of 4 cans each were collected by a random method at an interval of 60 minutes and quantity of juice in those cans were measured. The excess of 200 mL in each can was presented below. Construct X -chart to control the volume of mango juice and comment on whether the production is under control or not. (Given $A_2 = 0{\cdot}73$ for $n = 4$) 25

Can	**Sample**																			
	1	**2**	**3**	**4**	**5**	**6**	**7**	**8**	**9**	**10**	**11**	**12**	**13**	**14**	**15**	**16**	**17**	**18**	**19**	**20**
1	5	10	8	12	18	20	15	13	9	6	5	3	6	12	15	18	13	10	5	6
2	12	8	15	17	13	16	19	23	8	10	12	15	18	9	15	17	16	20	15	14
3	13	8	17	11	15	14	23	14	18	24	20	18	12	15	6	8	5	8	10	12
4	20	14	10	12	4	20	17	16	5	20	15	18	10	18	16	15	4	10	12	14

(b) The following data is on defective electronic machine parts from a standard brand of manufacturer. Sample sizes and number of defectives in each sample of 12 independent samples are given below. Using suitable control limits, test whether the process is statistically controlled or not.

Sample No.	1	2	3	4	5	6	7	8	9	10	11	12
Sample Size	115	220	210	220	220	255	440	365	255	300	280	330
No. of Defectives	15	18	23	22	18	15	44	47	13	33	42	46

(c) (i) What is control chart ? Explain the basic principles underlying the control charts. 10

(ii) Give the criterion for detecting lack of control m Shewhart's control chart for mean and range. 5

(iii) What are the advantages and limitations of Sampling Inspection technique? 10

(d) (i) Explain the three different important control charts for Attributes. 15

(ii) Explain (a) ASN curve, (b) AOQ curve, (c) ATI curve, and (d) OC curve. 10

Section E
(Multivariate Analysis)

9. Let $X = (X_1\ X_2\ X_3)' \sim N_3(\mu, I)$ with $\mu = (2 - 3\ 1)'$. Then obtain the distribution of (i) $3X_1 - 2X_2 + 5X_3$ and (ii) $(X_1 - X_2 - X_3)'$. 10

(b) Let $X \sim N_p(0, \Sigma)$ with

$$\Sigma = \begin{pmatrix} 1 & 2 & 1 \\ 2 & 5 & 3 \\ 1 & 3 & 4 \end{pmatrix}.$$

(i) Derive the condition under which $X'AX$ and $X'BX$ are independent, where A and Bare any real symmetric matrices of order $p \times p$.

(ii) Are $Y_1 = 2X_1^2 + X_2^2 + 2X_3^2 + 2X_1X_3 + 2X_2X_3$
and $Y_2 = X_1^2 + 2X_1^2 + 3X_3^2 + 2X_1X_2 + 5X_1X_3 - 2X_2X_3$
independent? Justify your answer. 10

(c) If X is a p-variate normal distribution with mean vector μ and dispersion matrix Σ, derive an expression for the expected value of $X'AX$, for any non-zero real symmetric matrix A of real numbers. 10

(d) Define Hotelling's T^2 statistic. Show that it is invariant under linear transformation. 10

(e) Briefly describe the classification problem. Obtain Bayes' classification rule. 10

10. Answer any two of the following:

(a) Let $Z = \begin{pmatrix} X \\ Y \end{pmatrix} \sim N_4(\mu, \Sigma)$, in which X andY are sub-vectors, each of order 2×1, with

$$\mu == \begin{pmatrix} 3 \\ 1 \\ 2 \\ -1 \end{pmatrix} \text{ and } \Sigma = \begin{pmatrix} 3 & 0 & 5 & -2 \\ 0 & 3 & -1 & 4 \\ 5 & -1 & 1 & 2 \\ -2 & 4 & 2 & 1 \end{pmatrix}$$

Find (i) E (X I Y), and (ii) Dispersion matrix of X given Y = y. 25

(b) Explain how you will test $H_0 : \mu = \mu^{(0)}$ in $N_p(\mu, \Sigma)$ when Σ is known. Height and weight of five male college students are given. Assuming the sample is from a bivariate normal with covariance matrix $\Sigma = \begin{pmatrix} 60 & 110 \\ 110 & 265 \end{pmatrix}$, test whether the population mean vector is (166 68)'.

25

Height:	170	172	168	159	169
Weight:	73	65	62	63	70

(c) What are principal components ? Obtain their relation with eigenvalues and eigenvectors of the dispersion matrix. The following are measurements on the test scores (X, Y) of 6 candidates for two subject examinations :

(50, 55), (62, 92), (80, 97), (65, 83), (64, 95), (73, 93)

Determine the first principal components for the test scores, by using Hotelling's iterative procedure. 25

STATISTICS-IV
2018

Time Allowed : Three Hours | *Maximum Marks: 200*

INSTRUCTIONS

Please read each· of the following instructions carefully before attempting questions.

There are EIGHT questions divided under TWO sections. Candidate has to attempt FIVE questions in all. Both the TWO questions in S ection A are compulsory. Out of the SIX questions in S ection B, any THREE questions are to be attempted. Attempts of questions shall be counted in sequential order. Unless struck off, attempt of a question shall be counted even if attempted partly. The number of marks carried by a question I part is indicated against it. Unless otherwise mentioned, symbols and notations have their usual standard meanings. Assume suitable data, if necessary and indicate the same clearly. Any page or portion of the page left blank in the Question-cum-Answer Booklet must be clearly struck off. Answers must be written in ENGLISH only.

Section A

All questions of this section are compulsory.

1. (a) Explain sampling and non-sampling errors. State the sources of non-sampling errors. 10

(b) Consider the three-variable regression model

$Y_i = \beta_0 + \beta_1 X_1 + \beta_2 X_{12} + \varepsilon_i, \ i = 1, 2, \ldots, n$

where X_1 and X_2 are two independent variables, Y is the dependent variable, β's are the co-efficients and ε is the random component, $\varepsilon \sim N(0, \sigma^2)$. Obtain the estimates of parameters using OLS method of estimation. 15

(c) The following figures give the production of a commodity of a country from 2001 to 2007:

Year	Production (in thousand metric tonnes)
2001	4·7
2002	5·9
2003	7·2
2004	7·9
2005	7·6

2006	7·0
2007	7·9

Obtain the trend values by a four-year moving average method. 15

2. (a) The following data show the cost of living indices for different groups along with their weights (% of expenditure), for middle-class people of some getting a salary of ₹ 25,000 in 2010 and ₹ 82,900 in 2016. Calculate how much he ought to have received as extra followance in 2016 to maintain his same standard of living. 10

Group	Base year grosp index	Weight
Food	3**	71.3
Clothing	550	2.7
Fuel and Light	360	9.3
House rent	110	6.7
Miscellaneout	290	10

(b) A simple rendom sample of 25 households was drawn from a city area containing 3745 households. The number of persons per household in the sample were as follows:

5, 6, 3, 4, 2, 3, 3, 3, 4, 4, 3, 2, 7, 4, 7, 6, 4, 4, 1, 4, 3, 4, 5, 6, 3.

Estimate the total number of people in the area and also compute the variance of the estimate. 15

(c) Discuss the concept of heteroscedasticity. Explain this by graphical representation. Show that OLS estimators are unbiased even under the condition of heteroscedasticity. Obtain its variance. 15

Section B

Answer any three questions out of the six questions given below.

3. (a) A finite population of size 98 is divided into three strata. It is given that $N_1 = 2N_2 = 4N_3$ and $S_1 = 2S_2 = 4S_3$. If a sample of 21 is to be selected from the population, obtain the number of units to be selected from each stratum under Neyman allocation. 10

(b) Define linear systematic sampling scheme with N = nk. Obtain the expression for the variance of the sample mean in this case. When will this be more advantageous than SRSWOR scheme ? 15

(c) Define Horvitz-Thompson unordered estimator $\hat{Y}_{HT}$ for the population total Y. Obtain an expression for $V(\hat{Y}_{HT})$. Comment on the estimator. 15

4. (a) Explain generalized least squares method of estimation. Write its model along with assumptions. Obtain the estimates of parameters and their variances. 15

(b) Discuss the meaning of Autocorrelation. Give a comparison between autocorrelation and serial correlation with an example. Give example of variance-covariance matrix of size 3 to show

(i) heteroscedasticity with no autocorrelation

(ii) homoscedasticity with autocorrelation

(iii) heteroscedasticity with autocorrelation.

Prove that mean of autocorrelated U's turns out to be zero. 15

(c) For general linear model, show that least squares estimator $\hat{\beta}$ is the best linear unbiased estimate of β. 10

5. (a) Two stationary time series u_t and u'_t are added together and a new series is formed by $v_t = u_t + u'_t$. If u_t and u'_t are independent, show that the autocorrelation of lag κ of v_t is given by

$$\frac{\rho_\kappa \operatorname{Var}(u_t) + \rho'_\kappa \operatorname{Var}(u'_t)}{\operatorname{Var}(u_t) + \operatorname{Var}(u'_t)}$$

where ρ_κ and ρ'_κ refer to the autocorrelation of u_t and u'_t respectively. 15

(b) State the law of demand.

Consider the following econometric model :

q_i (quantity demanded) $= a_0 + b_0 p_i + u_i$ $(b_0 < 0)$

q_i (quantity supplied) $= a_1 + b_1 p_i + v_i$ $(b_1 > 0)$

the errors u_i and v_i being uncorrelated.

Find the slope of the regression line q_i on p_i. 15

(c) What is periodogram ?

A time series u_t is composed of one periodic with period λ and amplitude α and the other term an irregular component (b_t)

$$u_t = a \sin \frac{2\pi t}{\lambda} + b_t$$

Describe a method for finding the true cyclical period λ.

Indicate how you will modify the method if the cyclical component is composed of several periodic terms $\lambda_1, \lambda_2, ..., \lambda_K$. 10

6. (a) Explain double sampling scheme. Give an example. Obtain the ratio estimator for the population mean of the study variate when the mean of the auxiliary variate is unknown. 10

(b) In a two-stage sampling, the first and the second stage units are drawn by adopting SRSWOR. Suggest an unbiased estimator for the population mean. Derive an expression for its variance.

(You may assume variance of sample mean under SRSWOR). 15

(c) State the linear regression estimate for population mean. Obtain the estimate of the regression coeflicient by least square method. Show that this estimate is unbiased. Under what condition is the estimate unbiased ? 15

7. (a) What is the need of simultaneous equation system in economic theory ? Discuss Keynesian model as a structural equation model of a national economy. Obtain its reduced form equations and hence reduced form disturbance term. 15

(b) Let Y_1 and Y_2 be two endogenous variables. Let further X_1, X_2 and X_3 be three predetermined variables. A simultaneous equation is expressed as

$$Y_1 = \gamma_{21} Y_2 + \beta_{11} X_1 + \varepsilon_1$$

$$Y_1 = \gamma_{22} Y_2 + \beta_{22} X_2 + \beta_{32} X_3 + \varepsilon_2$$

Discuss a method to identify the model.

(c) Discuss full information maximum likelihood method of estimation. Discuss only how to find the normal equations. 10

8. (a) Define a stationary time series.

For the stationary AR(2) process

$$X_t = \frac{5}{6} X_{t-1} - \frac{1}{6} X_{2-2} + e_t$$

where $e_i \sim N(0, + \sigma_e^2)$ denotes the noise.

Find the autocorrelation function of lags 1 and 2. 10

(b) Describe the different schemes for explaining the oscillations in a stationary time series. Explain the use of correlograms for discriminating between the above schemes. 15

(c) Define Gini coefficient.

The following table presents data on distribution of personal income by decile groups of households for each group separately for both rural and urban sectors of a country for the year 2010.

On a graph paper, draw the Lorenz curve for each sector. Also, compute the Gini coefficient for each sector.

Hence compare the income inequality of two sectors. 15

Household	Percentage shore in total income	
	Rural	Urban
0-10	3-0	2 3
10—20	4-4	3-3
20—30	54	4-1
30-40	6-4	48
40—50	7-4	5-8
50-60	83	7-0
60—70	96	87
T0-80	10 9	10 0
80- 90	13 8	14-0
90-100	30-8	40-0

STATISTICS-IV
2017

Time Allowed : Three Hours

Maximum Marks: 200

INSTRUCTIONS

Please read each· of the following instructions carefully before attempting questions. There are FOURTEEN questions divided under SEVEN Sections. Candidate has to choose any TWO· Sections and attempt all the questions therein. All the Sections carry equal marks. The number of marks carried by a question/ part is indicated against it; Unless otherwise mentioned, symbols and notations have their usual standard meanings. Assume suitable data, if necessary and indicate the same clearly. All parts and sub·parts of a question are to be attempted together in the answer book. Attempts of questions shall be counted in sequential order. Unless struck off, attempt of a question shall be counted even if attempted partly. Any page or portion of the page left blank in the answer book must be ·clearly struck off. Answers must be written in ENGLISH only. Normal Distribution, t, F, Gamma and cv of Weibull Tables are attached with the question paper. A graph paper sheet is attached to this question paper which may be carefully detached for answering graph-related question and then must be securely attached with the answer book.

Section A
(Operations Research and Reliability)

1. (a) A newopaper boy has the following proba.bilitleo or selling a magazine

No. of oopies sold	:	10	11	12	13	14
Probobililles	:	0.10	0.15	0.20	0.25	0.30

Coat of a copy is 30 paise and aale price ia 50 paiae. He cannot return unsold copieo. How many copies ohould he order? Solve by EOL criterion. 10

(b) Find an optimum solution to the following transportation problem: 10

		Store				Supply
		1	2	3	4	
Factory	A	4	6	8	13	50
	B	13	11	10	8	70
	C	14	4	10	13	30
	D	9	11	13	8	50
	Demand	25	35	105	20	

(c) A supermarket has two salesgirls at the sales counters. lf the aervlce time for each customer is exponential with a mean of 4 minutes, and if the people arrive in a Poisson fashion at the rate of 10 an hour, then ealculate (i) the probability that a customer has to wait for beina served and (ii) the expected percentage of idle time for each salesgirl (iii) If a customer has to wait, what is the expeeted length or hit waiting time? 10

(d) Let h be the reliability function or a coherent system. Then prove that (i) $h(pup') \geq h(p)$ $uh(p')$ and (ii) $h(p \cdot p) \leq h(p)\, h(p')$ for all $0 \leq p \leq 1$, $0 \leq p' \leq 1$. 10

(e) Obtain the reliability function and tho hazard function for the Weibull distribution. 10

2. Answer any two of the following :

(a) An electronic device consists or four components, each of which must function for the system to function. The system reliability can be improved by installing parallel units in one or more of the components. The reliability (R) of a component with one two or three parallel units and the corresponding cost (C) are as given below. The maximum amount available for this device is 100. The problem is to determine the number of parallel units in each component. Use dynamic programming to solve the problem: 25

No. of units	Components							
	1		2		3		4	
	R	C	R	C	R	C	R	C
1	0.7	10	0.5	20	0.7	10	0.6	20
2	0.8	20	0.7	40	0.9	30	0.7	30
3	0.9	30	0.8	50	0.95	40	0.9	40

(b) The following network diagram represents activities- associated with a p rQject :

Activity :	1-2	1-3	1-4	2-5	2-6	3-6	4-7	5-7	6-7
Optimistic time :	5	18	26	16	15	6	7	7	3
Pessimistic time :	10	22	40	20	25	12	12	9	5
Most likely time :	8	20	33	18	20	9	10	8	4

Determine the (i) critical path, (ii) total and free foats and (iii) duration of the project that will have 95 percent chance of being completed. 25

(c) 25 items were placed on test and the test was terminated after a pre-assigned time $t_0 = 20$ hours ftom the starting time 10 items failed before time t_0 at 3.8, 5.9, 6.3, 6.5, 7.5, 7.7, 10.5, 13.2, 13.5 and 14.0 hours. If the underlying distribution is Weibull with shape parameter equal to 2, then compute m.l.e. of the scale para.meter and estimated standard error of it. 25

(d) (i) Develop an exact test statistic for testing the s hape parameter of the gamma distribution p when the scale parameter a is known, based on moment estimator of the shape parameter and against right-sided alternative.

(ii) For a prototype test vehicle electrical failures for the engine operation occurred at the following kilometers : 28820, 36707, 46128 and 68345 . The total test schedule was 72000 kilometers. Estimate the reliability function assuming exponential electrical failures. Also estimate the kilometers at which 10% of the vehicles will have failed. 13+12

Section-B

(Demography and Vital Statistics)

3. (a) Discuss on hospital records and ad hoc surveys in relation to vital statistics infornnation.1 0

(b) Discuss intemal migrations, rural-urban migrations and international migrations. 10

(c) Define crude and specific death rates. Explain clearly the purpose of standardizing death rates. 10

(d) Given that the complete expectation of life at ages 25 and 26 for a specific group are 22.08 and 21.93 years, respectively. The number of people living at age 25 is 45324. Find the number that attains age 26. 10

(e) Deacribc intercensal and poetoenaal euimates of population growth assuming linear growth and exponential growth in mathematical method. 10

4. Answer any ttvo of the following :

(a) Write a critical note on the salient features of Indian Censuses 1991 and 2001. 25

(b) Explain Pearl and Reed method of fitting logistic curve for population projection. 25

(c) Find the missing values (—) in the following table : 25

x	I_x	d_x	p_x	L_x	T_x	e_x^0	m_x
30	762227	—	—	—	27296732	—	—
31	758580						

(d) What is meant by fe rtility? f<low is it measured? Describe the various fertility rates commonly used. Discuss their relative merits. 25

Section-C

(Survival Analysis and Clinical Trials)

5. (a) A random variable T(≥ 0) has hazard rate at time 1 which is given by

$h(t) = \alpha\lambda t^{\alpha-1}; t \geq 0$

Derive the distribution function F(t) and survival function S(t). Calculate S(t) at t = 5, if α = 2, λ = 1. 10

(b) Define gamma distribution as a failure time model. Discuss the monotonicity property of its hazard rate. 10

(c) Explain the log-rank test in a two-sample problem. 10

(d) Which quality control processes are to be used by the data a nalysis centre to assess the data quality and to handle problems that are observed relating to data and data analysis? 10

(e) Describe the general principles to be observed in preparation or Case-Report Form and the organization of the form. 10

6. Answer any two of the rouowing :

(a) The survival times (in months) or 12 patients, who have undergone a treatment are given below :

10 20 15^+ 60 18 16 17 28^+ 2 30 35^+

where + denotes right censored observations.

Assuming that the survival times follow exponential dia-tribu tion with mean $1/\lambda$, obtain the maximum lik elihood estimate for the mean.

Obtain the maximum likelihood estimate for S(t).

Compute S{t) act t = 10 months. 15+5+5

(b) The fo1lowing data represents the survival times of extremely ill AIDS patients observed in days :

2 72 51^+ 60 33^+ 27 14 24

Compute Kaplan-Meier estimate of the survival function S(t}.

Sketch the graph of S(t) against t.

Compute S(10) and S(25), and compare. 15+5+5

(c) Explain briefly the key categories of clinical trials data that are to be collected. 25

(d) Explain Phase I and Phase II clinical trials. What are MTD and DLT' related to Phase 1 trials? Explain the traditional design approach used in Phase I trials. 25

Section- D
(Quality Control)

7. (a) Explain the basic differences among the chance and special causes of variation that affect process results. 10

(b) State your agreement or disagreement to the statement given below, with brief justification: 10

"A statistically controlled process will always produce 100% results within tolerance limits."

(c) Derive the control limits for the control chart for defects in a constant and varying number of sample unita. 10

(d) Explain the chart which describes the sensitivity or the sampling plan to detect the lot quality level for acceptance. 10

(e) What is Cusum chart? Explain the methodology of using it for process control. 10

8. Answer any two of the following :

(a) Evaluate the ARL to detect a shirt in the process average (no change in process variation) by one unit of standard deviation in the higher side. Assaume use of $\overline{X}$-chart with subgroup size 5 and probability of not detecting the shift is at most 0.05. 25

(b) Explain the expone n tially weighted mo,ing average chart with at least one example of ite potential application. 25

(c) Describe the variable sampling scheme and compare it with the attribute sampling scheme. 25

(d) An improvement in the process has resulted in increase of C_{PK} ftom 0·6 to 0·95. Estimate the reduction in % of nonconforming products. Assume the following: Process average has not changed, $C_p = C_{PK}$ and process is in statistical control. 25

Section-E

(Multivariate Analyala)

9. (a) In the ISS exarnination of a certain year, the distribution of scores in Statistics Papers I, II, III and IV is found to fo1low a 4 -voriate normal distribution with known parameters. Indicate how you would estimate the percentage of candidates in that examination faring better (i) in Papers I and II compared to Papers III and IV, both in the aggregate, and (ii) in Paper I compared to Paper IV. 5+5

(b) In multivariate analysis, often the issue of handling too many variables poses a big probltm. How would you propose to solve the problem? Indicate the procedure. 10

(c) Assuming the form of the conditional distribution of a tnubset $(X_1, X_2, \ldots, X_q)$ of random variables $(X_1, X_2, \cdots, X_p)$, $q < p$, following multivariate normal law for fixed values of $(X_{q+1}, \ldots, X_p)$, derive the expression for the conditional mean of X_1 when $X_2 = x_2, \ldots, 1\, X_p = Xp = x_p$. 10

(d) Define Fisher's linear discriminant function. Give a classifier rule for classifying an individual based on his or her measurements on p identified variables, into one of two mutually exclusive and exhaustive classes, clearly stating the underlying assumptions and explaining the notation you have used. 10

(e) Show that in random sampling from a p-variate normal distribution, the sample variances and covariances follow Wishart distribution. Identify the parameters. 10

10. Answer any two of the following :

(a) (i) Show that if $\underset{\sim}{X}_{p\times1}$ follows $N_p(\underset{\sim}{\mu}_{p\times1}, \Sigma_{p\times p})$, then $Q = (\underset{\sim}{X} - \underset{\sim}{\mu})' \Sigma^{-1} (\underset{\sim}{X} - \underset{\sim}{\mu})$ follows central chi-square distribution with p degrees of freedom.

(ii) Suppose $\underset{\sim}{X}_{p\times1}$ follows $N_p(\underset{\sim}{\mu}_{p\times1}, \Sigma_{p\times p})$ with $E(X_i) = \mu\ \forall\ i$, $V(X_i) = \sigma^2\ \forall\ i$ and $Cov(X_i, X_j) = \rho\sigma^2\ \forall\ i \neq j$. Show that

follows chi-square distibution with p degrees of freedom, where $\bar{X} = \sum_{i=1}^{p} X_i / p$. 10+15

(b) (i) Define multiple correlation coefficient $r_{1.23 \ldots p}$ of X_1 on $X_2, X_3, \ldots, X_p$ taken together, based on the observed set of data x_{ij}, $i = 1(1)\, n$, and write down its expression.

(ii) Derive the simplified form of $r_{1.23 \ldots p}$ for the special case $r_{ij} = r\ \forall\ i \neq j = 1(1)\, p$. 10+15

(c) Derive the maximum likelihood estimators for the parameters of a multivariate normal distribution. 25

(d) Discuss the procedure for testing the null hypothesis

$$H_0: \underset{\sim}{\mu}^{(1)} = \underset{\sim}{\mu}^{(2)}$$

regarding the mean vector of two multivariate normal distributions having identical dispersion matrix. 25

Section- F

(Design and Analysis of Experiment)

11. (a) Discuss the usefulness of the principle of randomization in the context of design of experiments. Use the following set of r·andom numbers to obtain the layout of a randomized block design with 5 blocks of size 4 each for testing the treatments A, B, C and D : 10

518 275 950 305 490 333 068 088 389 933 548 275

950 305 490 334 069 736 545 774 864 062 951 005

(b) A 2^4 experiment has been laid out in 4 replicates, in each replicate con found ing one of the 3 factor interactions. Give the compositions of the 4 key blocks, and write down the ANOVA table. 10

(c) What is a Latin Square Design? What are the main disadvantages of using such a design in field experimertts? Indicate the procedure for obtaining the layout or a 5×5 Latin Square Design. 10

(d) A 3^2 experiment with fa.ctors A and Beach at levels 0, 1 and 2 is to be designed in 2r replicates of 3 incomplete blocks each, such that in r replicates AB is confounded, while in the remaining r, AB^2 is confounded, the other factorial effects remaining unconfounded in the entire design.

Give the layout of the 3 incomplete blocks of each of the two types of replicates, and write down the ANOVA table. 10

(e) The factor A has p levels which require relatively large experimental units. Another factor B has q levels requiring relatively small experimental units. Suggest a suitable design for accommodating both the factors in a single experiment. Discuss the procedure for testing the main effects A and B, as also the interaction eifect AB. 10

12. Answer any two of the following :

(a) It is desired to use a randomized block design with 4 blocks of size 6 each for testing the effects of 5 treatments A, B, C, .D and E. In each block, treatments B, C, D and E aie replicated once each, while treatment A is replicated twice to ensure more precise estimation and testing for A.

Using a suitable model, give the expressions for different sums of squares, and writ.e down the ANOVA table.

Discuss the procedures for testing equality of all treatmernt effects, as also for equality of effects of A and B, if the hypothesis or eqaality of all treatment effects is rejected. 13+12

(b) A 3^3 faetoria1 e¥periment with factors A, B and C each at levels 0, 1 and 2 is to be laid ou t in 9 incomplete blocks or size 3 each, totally sacrificing information on the factorial effects ABC^2, AC^2 and AB^2C^2.

Give the layout of the design.

If this basic pattern is repllcaced r limes, discu~s the procedure for analyzing the experiment. 10+15

(c) Discuss in detail, the procedure for analysis of covariance in a completely randomized design for testing the effects of 1 treatments with r_1, r_2, r_t, replications respectively in the presence of just one concomitant variable. 25

(d) A 2^3 experiment is proposed to be carried out in 2 incomplete blocks of size 4 each pet replicate, retaining flll1 information on all main effects, and sacrificing equal amount of information on the remaining four factorial effects each.

Suggest a scheme of partial confounding ensuring the above, and give the intrablock subgroup in each replicate.

Discuss the method of analysis for the data. 10+15

Section-G

(Computing with C and R)

13. (a) Write a C-prograrn that will generate every nth integer, beginning with n start (i.e., i = n start, n start + n, n start + 2n, etc.), ending wiith n stop. Calculate the sum of those integers that are evenly divisible by some positive integer k. 10

(b) Write a C-program to find whether a given matrix is a symmetric matrix and print the comment. 10

(c) Write a C-program to calculate

$$y = 1 - x + \frac{x^2}{2} - \frac{x^3}{6} + \frac{x^4}{24} - \ldots + (-1)^n \frac{x^n}{n!}$$

defming a recursive function and print it. 10

(d) Write an R-program to fit a lineer relationship of y on x, to get the summary of the relatons hip and to predict y for a given value of x. 10

(e) Write an R-pogram to calculate the median of a set of observations. 10

14. Answer any two of the following :

(a) Write a C-program that will examine each character in a line of text and determine how many of the characters are letters, how many are digits, how many are white space characters, and how many are other kinds or characters (e.g., punctuation characters) and print them. 25

(b) Write a C-program to create a linear linked list, delete an existing component from the list defining suitable functions. 25

(c) Write a C-program to evaluate $y = x^n$, where x and y are floating-point values and n can be an integer or floating point and print it. 25

(d) Write a C·progam to fit a normal distribution to a given observed frequency distribution and test for its goodness of fit and print the result. 25

STATISTICS-IV
2016

Time Allowed : Three Hours | *Maximum Marks: 200*

INSTRUCTIONS

Please read each· of the following instructions carefully before attempting questions. There are FOURTEEN questions divided under SEVEN Sections. Candidate has to choose any TWO· Sections and attempt all the questions therein. All the Sections carry equal marks. The number of marks carried by a question/ part is indicated against it; Unless otherwise mentioned, symbols and notations have their usual standard meanings. Assume suitable data, if necessary and indicate the same clearly. All parts and sub-parts of a question are to be attempted together in the answer book. Attempts of questions shall be counted in sequential order. Unless struck off, attempt of a question shall be counted even if attempted partly. Any page or portion of the page left blank in the answer book must be ·clearly struck off. Answers must be written in ENGLISH only. Normal Distribution, t, F, Gamma and cv of Weibull Tables are attached with the question paper. A graph paper sheet is attached to this question paper which may be carefully detached for answering graph-related question and then must be securely attached with the answer book.

Section A
(Operations Research and Reliability)

1. (a) Solve the following two-person zero-sum game using graphical procedure : 10

$$\begin{bmatrix} 1 & -3 \\ 3 & 5 \\ -1 & 6 \\ 4 & 1 \\ 2 & 2 \\ -5 & 0 \end{bmatrix}$$

(b) If the demand for a certain product has a rectangular distribution between 4000 and 5000, then find the optimal order quantity if the storage cost is ₹ 1 per unit and the shortage cost is ₹ 7 per unit. 10

(c) A supermarket has two salesgirls at the counter. If the service time for each customer is exponential with mean 4 minutes and if people arrive in a Poisson fashion at 10 per hour, then find the expected percentage of idle time for each salesgirl. 10

(d) Find out ML estimators of the parameters in the density

$$\frac{c}{b}x^{c-1}e^{-\frac{x^c}{b}}, x>0, b\,c>0$$

based on the following censored scheme :

$X_{(1)}, X_{(2)}, \dots, X_{(n-r)}$

where n and r are respectively the sample size and number of censored observations. 10

(e) Defining a location-scale family, outline the procedure for obtaining the coefficient of BLUE's. 10

2. (a) A computer contains 10000 resistors. When any resistor fails, it is replaced. The cost of replacing a resistor individually is ₹ 1 only. If all the resistors are replaced at the same time, the cost per resistor comes down to 35 paise. The percent of surviving, S(t), at the end of t-th month is

t :	0	1	2	3	4	5	6
S(t) :	100	97	90	70	32	15	0

Derive the optimum replacement plan. 25

(b) A random sample of 25 observations drawn from Weibull model (with shape parameter= 2 and scale parameter = 4) is given. Obtain the moment estimates of the parameters : 25

1.8487	0.3761	0.7500	3.0530	1.3545
1.8802	1.5700	1.7708	1.3592	3.0466
1.7961	1.5319	0.5903	0.6288	0.6461
1.6560	1.7 172	1.9310	1.0509	1.6173
1.3162	0.7705	1.8889	1.8889	4.1505

Section-B
(Demography and Vital Statistics)

3. (a) Discuss the sources of demographic data in India and also point out the uses and limitations of these data. 10

(b) Explain the stationary and stable population models. Discuss the situation when stationary and stable populations are identical. 10

(c) Explain briefly the uses of life table. In usual notation, prove that .

$$\frac{dL_x}{dx} = -d_x; \quad \frac{dT_x}{dx} = -l_x$$ 10

(d) Define crude death rate, specific death rate and standardized death rate. Interpret these rates:

(e) State the general procedure and steps for the construction of life tables. 10

4. (a) Explain an abridged life table and discuss its different columns. Discuss the King's method for its construction. 25

(b) What do you mean by fertility? Define crude birthrate, general fertility rate, specific fertility rate and age-specific fertility rate. How are these rates computed in practice? 25

Section-C

(Survival Analysis and Clinical Trials)

5. (a) Define hazard function and survival function. Obtain the same for an exponential distribution. 10

(b) If f(t), F(t) and .h(t) are the density, distribution and hazard functions of a random variable T, then show that

$$h(t) = \frac{f(t)}{\bar{F}(t)}, \bar{F}(t) = 1 - F(t)$$

Also establish a suitable relationship between h(t) and reliability function. 10

(c) If p_x is the probability that a person aged x will survive to .age x + 1, then show that $_np_x + {}_nq_x = 1$, where

$$_n p_x = \frac{l_{x+n}}{l_x}$$ 10

(d) Discuss some specific situations in which it would be difficult or inefficient to perform clinical trials. 10

(e) What are the principles for ethical clinical trials? 10

6. (a) Define Type-1 and Type- II censoring schemes. Obtain the maximum likelihood estimator of parameter 9 in exponential distribution under the above censoring schemes. Also obtain the Fisher information for the parameter.

(b) Discuss various phases involved in a clinical trial. Also discuss the pros and cons of each phase. 25

Section-D

(Quality Control)

7. (a) Distinguish between process control and product control. Discuss the situations where they are used. 10

(b) Discuss various sources of assignable causes and random causes of variations. Also state how they are detected in a manufacturing process. 10

(c) Defme the terms ASN, AOQ, ATI and ARL for an acceptance sampling plan. 10

(d) What is an acceptance sampling plan? Discuss a single sampling plan (n, c), where the sampling is carried out using a binomial model. Find P_a, if n = 10, c = 3 and p = 0.05. 10

(e) State the importance of exponentially weighted moving average charts. How are these used in practical situations? 10

8. (a) Dfscuss the importance of control charts for variables. 5

(b) Obtain the control limits for (X, R) and (X, S) charts when standards are known and unknown. 20

(c) In usual notation, show that

$$C_2 = \sqrt{\frac{2}{n}} \frac{\sqrt{(n/2)}}{\sqrt{(n-1)/2}}$$

where C_2 is a constant used for constructing control limits. 5

(d) Discuss in detail the double sampling plan (N, n_1, c), n_2, c_2) stating the assumptions followed in both the stages. Hence or otherwise, obtain the ASN function of this sampling procedu!e.

Section-E

(Multivariate Analysis)

9. (a) Define p-variate normal distribution and obtain its characteristic function. Assume mean vector μ and dispersion matrix Σ. 10

(b) Define Hotelling's T^2 and mention its application. Show that

$$T^2(p, m) = \frac{mp}{m-p+1} F_{p,m-p+1}$$ 10

(c) Explain the importance of principal components and discuss the method for extraction of ·principal components. 10

(d) Define Wishart distribution and obtain its characteristic function. 10

(e) Define canonical variates and canonical correlation. Give your interpretation. 10

10. (a) State the chief properties of Wishart distribution. If

$A_i \sim W_p(\Sigma, n_i)$, i = 1, 2, .. . , k

then show that

$$A = \sum_{i=1}^{k} A_i$$

has the Wishart distribution with parameters Σ and n, where

$$n = \sum_{i=1}^{k} n_i$$

assuming the independence of Ai's. 25

(b) Define multiple correlation coefficient and obtrun its non-null distribution. 25

Section-F

(Design and Analysis of Experiments)

11. (a) What are the basic principles of design of experiments? Explain them and their roles. 10

(b) Define completely randomized design, and mention its merits and demerits. Also give its statistical analysis. 10

(c) Define Latin square design with its applications, advantages and disadvantages. 10

(d) Explain analysis of covariance with its applications. Give an illustration for the use of analysis of covariance in identifying the response variable (y) and concomitant variable (x). 10

(e) Explain split-plot design and give some situations where split-plot design can be suitably adopted. 10

12. (a) What are factorial experiments? The following table gives the layout and the results of 2^3-factorial design laid out in four replicates. The purpose of the experiment is to determine the effect of different kinds of fertilizer, Nitrogen (N), Potash (K) and Phosphate (P) ·on potato crop yield :

Block 1				Block 2			
nk	*kp*	*p*	*np*	*kp*	*p*	*k*	*nk*
291	391	312	373	407	324	272	306
1	*k*	*n*	*nkp*	*n*	*nkp*	*np*	1
101	265	106	450	89	449	338	106

Block 3				Block 4			
p	1	*np*	*kp*	*np*	*nk*	*n*	*p*
323	87	324	423	361	272	103	324
nk	*k*	*n*	*nkp*	*k*	1	*nkp*	*kp*
334	279	128	471	302	131	437	435

Analyze the design and draw conclusions. 25

(b) What is confounding? A 2^3 -factorial experiment is conducted in 2 blocks of size 4 each, in 3 replicates. The arrangements are as follows:

	Replicate 1	Replicate 2	Replicate 3
Key Block	(1), c, ab, abc	(1), a, bc, abc	(1), b, ac, abc

Identify the confounded effect in each replicate. 10

(c) Define a Randomized Block Design (RBD) spedfying the statistical model associated with the design. Carry out a complete analysis of RBD with one missing observation. 15

Section-G

(Computing with C and R)

13. (a) Given a five-digit positive integer, write a C program to find the sum of individual digits. ·

(For example, if the giveri number is 96785, the required sum is 9 + 6 + 7 + a + 5 = 35) 10

(b) Write a C program to pick up the largest tender from a set of tenders assuming that Tender-id and Tender-value for each tender are specified. 10

(c) Express (A -B) * C in inftx and postftx forms. 10

(d) Write a program in R to plot Q-Q plot assuming that the two samples

(X_i = l, 2, ..., 25 and Y_i = l, 2 ..., 250) are drawn from normal population. 10

(e) Given n positive integers, write R code to find their ranks. 10

14. (a) Illustrate call by value and call by reference, and advantages as well as disadvantages of each method. Write a C function to evaluate the series without using a built-in function : 25

$$\sin(x) = x - \frac{x^3}{3!} + \frac{x^5}{5!} - \frac{x^7}{7!} + \ldots \infty$$

(b) Given X – N(μ, σ^2), where μ and σ^2 are specified, write a C program to compute

$$P(X > t) = \int_t^{\infty} \text{Density of } N(\mu, \sigma^2)\, dx$$ 25

STATISTICS-IV
2015

Time Allowed : Three Hours | *Maximum Marks: 200*

INSTRUCTIONS

Candidate should attempt FIVE questions in all including Question Nos 1 and 5 which are compulsory and attempt remaining THREE questions by choosing at least ONE each from Sections-A and B. The number of marks carried by each question is indicated at the end of the question. Answers must be written in ENGLISH. Symbols and abbreviations are as usual. If any data is required to be assumed for answering a question, it may be suitably assumed, indicating this clearly.

Section A

1. (a) Illustrate the following terms with an example : 8

    (i) Irreducible Markov chain

    (ii) Renewal process

    (iii) Wide-sense stationary process

    (iv) Martingale

   (b) If N(t) is a Poisson process, then show that, as $t \to \infty$

   $$P_r\left\{\left|\frac{N(t)}{t} - \lambda\right| > \varepsilon\right\} \to 0$$ 8

   (c) Mention the situation(s) where 'periodic review policy' and 'continuous review policy' in inventory theory are used, and elaborate the ideas of the above policies. 8

   (d) Prove that the number of basic variables in a balanced transportation problem is at most m + n – 1, where m is the number of origins and n is the number of destinations. 8

   (e) Give all basic solutions to the following:

   $12x_1 + 8x_2 + x_3 = 80$

   $x_1 + 4x_2 + x_4 = 48$

   Are these solutions feasible solutions for an LPP setup? 8

2. (a) Define a Galton-Watson branching process. If $\{P_k\}$ is the offspring distribution, then prove the fcllowing identities : 10

(i) $P_n(s) = P_{n-1}[P(s)]$

(ii) $P_n(s) = P[P_{n-1}(s)]$

(b) (i) Discuss a one-dimensional random walk.

(ii) What is Gambler's ruin problem? Obtain the probabilty of ruin, if Gambler plays wish a capital of a rupees. 10

(c) What is a Wiener process? Cbtain the forward diffusion equation of a Wener process. Also discuss any two applications of this process. 10

(d) Show that for M/N/1/∞ queue model

$$P_n = \frac{\lambda_0 \lambda_1 \ldots \lambda_{n-1}}{\mu_1 \mu_2 \ldots \mu_n} P_0$$

where λ_n and μ_n are the rneans of Poisson and exponential cistribution respectively when there are n people in the system. 10

3. (a) Solve the fcllowing prcblen by Simplex method : 10

Maximize $Z = 8x_1 + 6x_2$

subject to

$x_1 + x_2 \leq 10$

$2x_1 + 3x_2 \leq 25$

$x_1 + 5x_2 \leq 35$

$x_1, x_2 \geq 0$

(b) A solicitors' firm employs typists on hourly price-rate basis for their daily work. There are five typists and their charges and speeds are different. According to an earlier understanding, only one job is given to one typist and the typist is paid for a *** hour even if he works for a fraction of an hour. Find the least cost allocation for the followings data : 10

Typist	Rate per hour (**)	No. of pages typed/hour
A	5	12
B	6	14
C	3	8
D	4	10
E	4	11

Job	No. of pages
P	199
Q	175
R	145
S	298
T	178

(c) Derive a formula to simulate a random observation from a Pcisson random variable. 10

(d) What is the basis of classification or inventory in ABC analysis? Illustrate i with a simple example. 10

4. (a) Define a Poisson process. Stating the regularity conditicns, show that $P_n(t) = P\{N(t) = n\}$ is given by the Poisson law

$$P_n(t) = \frac{e^{-\lambda t}(\lambda t)^n}{n!}, n = 0, 1, 2, ...$$ 10

(b) If X_n is a branching process with

$$E(X_t) = m = \sum_{k=0}^{\infty} k_k^2$$

and $\sigma^2 = \text{var}(X_1)$, then show that

(i) $E\{X_n\} = m^n$

(ii) $$\text{var}\{X_n\} = \begin{cases} \frac{m^{n-1}(m^k - 1)}{m-1}\sigma^2, & m \neq 1 \\ r\sigma^2, & m = 1 \end{cases}$$ 10

(c) Trim Sheet Company require rectangular sheets of width 5, 7 and 9 inches to be cut from a roll of width 20 inches. One-dimensional cutting is considered. The requirement:; are 300, 400 and 600 sheets of the three widths respectively. Write a linear programming problem to minimize waste assuming that the excess sheets cut are treated as waste. 10

(d) Given the following basic feasible solution to a transportation problem, obtain four iterations of the optimal solution using stepping stone method : 10

Demands

Sources					
	cost 4, 20	cost 6, 20	cost 8	cost 8	40
	cost 6	cost 8	cost 6, 50	cost 7, 10	60
	cost 5	cost 7, 10	cost 6	cost 8, 40	50
	20	30	50	50	

Section-II

5. Attempt all of the following: 8×5=40

(a) Explain stationanry and stable population. State the situation when the age distribution of two stable populations would be identical. 8

(b) Compute the crude and standardzed death rates of the popuulations A and B, regarding A as standard population, from the follwing data: 8

Age group (years)	A		B	
	Population	Deaths	Population	Deaths
Under 10	20000	600	12000	372
10-20	12000	240	62000	660
20--40	50000	1250	62000	16*2
40-60	30000	1050	15000	525
Above 60	10000	500	3000	180

(c) Explain briefly the uses of life table. 8

(d) Explain stack and queue structures with suitable examples. Write the algorithm to 'add.' and 'delete' into a stack and queue covering all possible cases. 8

(e) Write an algorithm/flowchart for computing product of two matrices A and B of orders $m \times n$ and $n \times p$ respectively. 8

6. (a) Discuss the sources of demographic data in the Indian system. Give your suggestion for the measures to improve the quality of data. 10

(b) Compute GFR, SFR, TFR and GRR from the data given below :

Age group of childbearing females :	15-19	20-24	25-29	39-34
Number of women ('000) :	16.0	16.4	15.8	15.2
Age group of childbearing females :	35-39	40-44	45-49	
Number of women ('000) :	14.8	15.0	14.5	

Assume that the proportion of female births is 46.2 percent. 10

(c) Describe King's method for constructing an abridged life table. 10

(d) Explain the Matrix method of population projection. 10

7. (a) A list of n cistinct inegers is given. Write an algorithm/flowchart, using minimum number of comparsion operations, to find out the second maximum number (i.e., the number less than the maximum number but greater than the others). 10

(b) Describe various types of keys, with appropriate examples, in regard to a database management System. 10

(c) Write down the algorithm to evaluate

$$\int_a^b f(x)\,dx$$

using Weddle's rule. How do you implement it in finding ?(X > 2), where $X \sim N(0, 1)$? 10

(d) Write an algorithm/flowchart to check whether an input non-zero integer n is prime. Prove that the main loop of the algorithm/flowchart for this purposess to be executed up to $\lceil \sqrt{n} \rceil$ times, where $\lceil \sqrt{n} \rceil$ stands for the least integer greater than or equal to $\sqrt{n}$. 10

8. (a) Explain the meaning of the following rates in vital statistics and discuss their importance :

(i) Crude death rate

(ii) Standard birthrate

(iii) General fertility rate

Briefly indicate how these rates can be used in population projection. 10

(b) Describe the procedure and steps for the construction of life table. 10

(c) Describe various types of operating systems. 10

(d) Consider the following four numbers

(1) a = 567 in octal representation

(2) b = ABC in hexadecimal represntation

(3) c = 220 in a hypothetical number system with base 3

(4) d = 786 in another hypothetical number system with base 9

Answer the following questions :

(i) Convert a directly into the corresponding number in hexadecimal representation.

(ii) Convert c directly into the corresponding number in the hypothetical number system with base 9.

(iii) Add a and b to produce the result in hexadecimal number system.

(iv) Add c and d to generate the result in the hypothetical number system with base 9. 10

STATISTICS-IV
2014

Time Allowed : Three Hours

Maximum Marks: 200

INSTRUCTIONS

Candidate should attempt FIVE questions in all including Question Nos 1 and 5 which are compulsory and attempt remaining THREE questions by choosing at least ONE each from Sections-A and B. The number of marks carried by each question is indicated at the end of the question. Answers must be written in ENGLISH. Symbols and abbreviations are as usual. If any data is required to be assumed for answering a question, it may be suitably assumed, indicating this clearly.

Section A

1. Attempt all of the following: 8×5=40

   (a) Deftne (i) persistent, (ii) transient and (iii) ergodic states. Show that if $i \leftrightarrow j$ and if state i is persistent, then state j is also persistent. 8

   (b) Define random walk and explain gambler's ruin problem. 8

   (c) Using graphical method, following problems :

   (i) Maximize $Z = 6x_2 - 4x_2$

   subject to

   $2x_1 - 4x_2 \leq 4$

   $4x_1 - 8x_2 \geq 16$

   $x_1, x_2 \geq 0$ 4

   (ii) Maximize $Z = 10x_1 - 6x_2$

   subject to

   $5x_1 + 3x_2 \leq 30$

   $x_1 + 2x_2 \leq 18$

   $x_1, x_2 \geq 0$ 4

(d) A shop produces three items in lots. The demand rate for each item is constant and can be assumed to be deterministic. No back orders are allowed. The pertinent data for the items is given as follows :

Item	I	II	III
Carrying cost (₹ per unit per year)	20	20	20
Setup cost (₹ per setup)	50	40	60
Cost per unit (₹)	6	7	5
Yearly demand (units)	10000	12000	7500

Determine approximately the economic order quantity for three items subject to the condition that the total value of average inventory levels of these items does not exceed ₹ 1 ,000. 8

(e) Explain the procedure of generating random numbers from $N(\mu, \sigma^2)$, (where μ and σ are specified) using Box-Muller formula. 8

2. (a) Prove that a discrete parameter stochastic process $\{X_n, n \geq 0\}$ is called a martingale if $E\{|X_n|\} < \infty$ and $E\{X_{n+1}/X_n, X_{n-1}, \ldots, X_0\} = X_n$. 10

(b) Define branching process and state the properties of its generating function. 10

(c) Explain the adliitive property of Poisson process and also the difference of two independent Poisson processes. 10

(d) Describe birth and death processes, and show that it is a particular case of Poisson process. 10

3. (a) XYZ Tobacco Company purchases tobacco and stores in warehouses located in the following four cities:

Warehouse Location	Capacity (in tonnes)
City A	90
City B	50
City C	80
City D	60

The warehouse supply tobacco to cigratte companies in three cities that have the following demand:

Cigarette Company	Demand (in tonnes)
Bharat	120
Janata	100
Re Lamp	110

Because of railroad construction, shipments are temporarily prohibited from warehouse at city A to Bharat Cigarette Company.

(i) Find the optimum distribution for XYZ Tobacco Company.

(ii) Are there any multiple optimum solutions? If ·yes, identify them.

(iii) Write the dual of the given transportation problem and use it for checking the optimum solution. 10

(b) Some of the spare parts of a ship cost ₹ 50,000. These parts can only be ordered together with the ship. If not ordered at the time the ship is constructed, these parts are not available as and when needed. Suppose that a loss of ₹ 4, 50,000 is incurred for each spare part that is needed when none is available in the stock and the probability distribution that the spares will be needed for replacement during lifetime is

Spares required	:	0	1	2	3	4	5	≥ 6
Probability	:	0.90	0.04	0.025	0.02	0.01	0.05	0

Find the optimum order quantity. 1

(c) Machine A costs ₹ 45,000 and the operating costs are estimated at ₹ 1,000 for the first year, increasing by ₹ 10,000 per year in the second and subsequent years. Machine B costs ₹ 50,000 and the operating costs are ₹ 2,000 for the first year, increasing by ₹ 4,000 per year in the second and subsequent years. If we now have a machine of type A, should we replace it with B? If so, when? Assume that both machines have no resale value and future costs are not discounted. 10

(d) A bakery keeps stock of a popular brand of cakes. Previous experience shows that the daily demand pattern for the item with associated probabilities is as given below :

Daily demand (in number)	:	0	10	20	30	40	50
Probability	:	0.01	0.20	0.15	0.50	0.12	0.02

Use the following sequence of random numbers to simulate the demand for the next 10 days:

25 39 65 36 12 05 73 89 19 49

Estimate the daily average demand for the ranks on the basis of simulated dao

Can you estimate the daily average demand analytically? If so, find the bias in estimating daily average demand. 10

4. (a) Obtain Chapman-Kolmogorov equation with transition probabilities for a Markow chain. 10

(b) Discuss M/M/1 queuing model with steady-state behaviour. 10

(c) Use simplex method to solve the following problem :

A company makes two kinds of leather belts. Belt A is of high quality and belt B is of low quality. The respective profits are ₹ 4 and ₹ 3 per belt. The production of each of type A requires as much time as belt of type Band if all belts were of type B, the company could make 1000 belts per day. The supply of leather is sufficient for only 800 belts per day (both A and B put together). Belt A requires fancy buckles and only 400 per day are available. There are only 700 buckles a day available for belt B. What should be the daily production of each type of belt to maximize the total profit? 10

(d) Let the value of the money be assumed to be depreciated @ 10% per year and suppose that machine A is replaced after every three years whereas machine B is replaced every six years. The yearly costs (in ₹) of both the machines are given as under :

Year	:	1	2	3	4	5	6
Machine A	:	1,000	200	400	1,000	200	400
Machine B	:	1,700	100	200	300	400	500

Determine which machine should be purchased. 10

Section B

5. Answer all of the following : 8×5=40

   (a) Briefly outline the uses of life tables. 8

   (b) Mention how logistic curve fitting is used for population projection. 8

   (c) Outline and describe the inter-censal and post-censal estimates. 8

   (d) Write short notes on : 8

   (i) Magnetic Ink Character Recognition

   (ii) Plotters

   (e) Use 2's complement to-

   (i) subtract 3 from 5;

   (ii) subtract (-3) from (-5);

   (iii) add (-5) and (-2);

   (iv) add 5 and 4. 8

6. (a) Compute (Q GFR, (ii) SFR, (iii) TFR and (iv) gross production rate from the data given below : 10

Age group of childbearing females	:	15-19	20-24	25-29	30-34
No. of women ('000)	:	16.0	16.4	15.8	15.2
Total births	:	260	2244	1894	1320
Age group of childbearing females	:	35-39	40-44	45-49	
No. of women ('000)	:	14.8	15.0	14.5	
Total births	:	916	280	145	

Assume that the proportion of female births is 46·2%.

   (b) Outline the uses of Makeham and Gompertz curves in life tables. 10

   (c) Describe stable and stationary populations. 10

   (d) Explain various mortality rates and standardized death rates. 10

7. (a) Write binary multiplication algorithm using register(s) and accumulator. 10

   (b) Discuss the following types of operating system : 10

   (i) Batch

   (ii) Multiprogramming

   (iii) Time-sharing

   (iv) Real-time

   (c) Given (X_i, Y_i) where i = 1, n. Write a flow chart to find a and b in fitting Y = a + bX. 10

   (d) Discuss error detecting and error correcting codes, and illustrate single error detecting code in detail. 10

8. (a) State the general procedure and steps for the construction of life tables. 10

   (b) From the data given below, calculate the gross reproduction rate and net reproduction rate: 10

Age group	No. of children born to 1000 women passing through the age group	Mortality rate (per 1000)
16-20	150	120
21-25	1500	180
26-30	2000	150
31-35	800	200
36-40	500	220
41-45	200	230
46-50	100	250

Sex ratio being males : females = 52 : 48.

(c) Illustrate mail merge application in detail describing the common features available in any word processing package. 10

(d) Discuss various features of graphics wizard 1n any spreadsheet package in· connection with statistical data processing. 10

STATISTICS-IV
2013

Time Allowed : Three Hours | *Maximum Marks: 200*

INSTRUCTIONS

Candidate should attempt FIVE questions in all including Question Nos 1 and 5 which are compulsory and attempt remaining THREE questions by choosing at least ONE each from Sections-A and B. The number of marks carried by each question is indicated at the end of the question. Answers must be written in ENGLISH. Symbols and abbreviations are as usual. If any data is required to be assumed for answering a question, it may be suitably assumed, indicating this clearly.

Section A

1. Attempt all of the following $8 \times 5 = 40$

(a) Show that a Markov chain is irreducible if and only if each state can be reached from every other state. 8

(b) If $\{X_t, t \geq 0\}$ is a Furry-Yule process with parameter λ and initial condition $P(X_0 = r) = 1$, where r is some natural number, then for $s < t$, obtain the joint distribution of the random variables X_s and X_t. 8

(c) Define-

(i) basic feasible solution;

(ii) non -degenerate basic feasible solution.

Establish that the set of all feasible solutions to the LPP is a convex set. 8

(d) Illustrate the following methods of generating random numbers from a given distribution-(i) inverse transformation, (ii) composition, (iii) convolution and (iv) acceptance and rejection methods, indicating clearly where a particular method is more suitable. 8

(e) An airline company has drawn up a new flight schedule involving five flights. To assist in allocating five pilots to the flights, it has asked them to state their preference scores by giving each flight a number out of 10. The higher the number, the greater is the preference. Certain of these flights are unsuitable to some pilots owing to domestic reasons which are marked with 'x' :

↓Pilot	Flight No.				
	1	2	3	4	5
A	8	2	×	5	4
B	10	9	2	8	4
C	5	4	9	6	×
D	3	6	2	8	7
E	5	6	10	4	3

What should be the allocation of pilots to flights in order to meet as many preferences as possible?

2. (a) State and prove Chapman-Kolmogorov equation. 10

(b) Define simple random walk. Obtain the first passage times in such a random walk. 10

(c) In an M | M| 1 queueing system in a steady state, show that the interdeparture times are independently distributed exponentially random variables with mean $1/\lambda$, where λ is the parameter of the input (Poisson) process. 10

(d) Prove that if the sum of two independent renewal processes is a Poisson process, then both renewal processes must be Poisson processes. 10

3. (a) Sunshine Electronics Ltd. assembles 3 types of Printed Circuit Boards (PCBs) used in personal computers such as motherboards, graphic cards and memory cards. The company wants to determine how many each of these boards should be produced next month. The component parts are placed on the board by a computer-controlled insertion machine called Dyna Assembler. The assembled boards are connected to Test Rig to verif'y all ' functioning of the boards. All the three types of boards must be processed and tested. The time required for these two processes for each of the products is given below :

	Production Processing Time (in minutes)		
	Mother-board	**Graphic Card**	**Memory Card**
Dyna Assembler	5	3	4
Test Rig	600	720	560

To assemble these 3 products next month, 65 hours of Dyna Assembler time and 4800 hours of Test Rig time are available. It is not necessary to use all the available time but it should not exceed the available hours.

As per accounting department, the direct production cost of using Dyna Assembler is ₹ 360 per hour and for Test Rig is ₹ 12 per hour (no matter what product is being produced in these machines). The material cost and revenue of each of these products are given below :

	Revenue and Material Cost (in ₹/unit)		
	Mother-board	**Graphic Card**	**Memory Card**
Revenue	750	350	600
Material Cost	250	210	200

The company faces tremendous demand for its products and is confident that it can sell everything it produces at the prices that are given. However, at least 20 graphic cards be produced in the next planning period (next month). The marketing department wants to ensure that the company should produce at least one memory card for every 20 motherboards that are produced next month.

Determine production plan to decide how many motherboards, graphic cards and memory cards are to be produced optimally during next month. 10

(b) Examine whether TPP is a particular case of LPP. If so--

(i) formulate TPP as an LPP;

(ii) mention the reason(s) why simplex procedure is not used to find optimal solution of TPP.

Further write down the algorithm of (1) VAM and (2) MODI methods m solving TPP. 10

(c) Generate 10 random numbers from the following density function, assuming ρ and μ values : 10

$$f(\theta) = \frac{1}{2\pi}[1 + 2\rho\cos(\theta - \mu)]$$

$$|\rho| < \frac{1}{2}; \theta \in [0, 2\pi]$$

$$\mu \in [0, 2\pi]$$

[Note: Random sampling numbers table is given in Page No. 11.]

(d) Write down the following algorithms: 10

(i) Two-phase simplex method

(ii) Charnes' perturbation method

4\. (a) At time '0', a blood culture starts with one red cell. At the end of one minute, the red cell dies and is replaced by one of the combinations with probabilities as indicated-2 red cells with probability 1 f 4, 1 red cell and 1 white cell with probability 2/3, 2 white cells with probability 1/12. Each red cell lives for one minute and gives birth to offsprings in the same way as the parent cell. Each white cell lives for one minute and dies without reproducing. Assuming that individual cell behaves independently, what is the probability that the entire culture dies out eventually? 10

(b) Write notes on the following : 10

(i) Divergent birth process

(ii) General birth process

(c) Generate ten pseudorandom numbers between 0 and 1, using-

(i) mixed congruential generator;

(ii) multiplicative congruential generator;

(iii) composite generator;

(iv) combined linear congruential generator. 10

(d) A company is considering a selective inventory control usmg the following data :

Item No. Requirement	:	1	2	3	4	5	6
(in no. of units)	:	6000	61200	16800	3000	55800	22680
Unit Cost (in ₹)	:	4	0.05	2.10	6	0.20	0.50
Item No. Requirement	:	7	8	9	10	11	12
(in no. of units)	:	26640	14760	20520	90000	29940	24660
Unit Cost (in ₹)	:	0.65	0.40	0.40	0.10	0.30	0.50

Carry out A, B, C analysis. 10

Section B

5. Attempt all of the following : 8×5=40

   (a) Discuss the sources, uses and limitations of demographic data in India. 8

   (b) Define CBR, GFR and ASFR, and indicate why each is considered an improvement on the preceding measure of fertility. 8

   (c) Describe a method of fitting Makeham's graduation formula using most of the available data. 8

   (d) Write an algorithm to implement binary multiplication on a digital system. 8

   (e) Explain (i) multiplication and (ii) division of normalized floating-point numbers. 8

6. (a) Distinguish between projection and forecast. Discuss the component method of population projection. 10

   (b) Describe King's method for constructing an abridged life table. 10

   (c) Show that the age distribution of two stable populations would be identical if they are such that their mortalities at all ages differ by a constant at all ages. 10

   (d) Give a short account of the mam findings of the Population Census of India, 2011. 10

7. (a) Draw a flow chart to fmd correlation coefficient and hence draw flow chart of the main program to find partial and multiple correlation coefficients of 3 variables. 10

   (b) Illustrate the following : 10

      (i) Batch processing

      (ii) Real-time processing

      (iii) Sequential processing

      (iv) Indexed sequential processing

      (v) Random files processing

   (c) Explain the following functions of any operating system

      (i) Processor

      (ii) Memory

      (iii) Device

      (iv) File managements

   (d) Illustrate the following conversion procedures :

      (i) Decimal to binary numbers

      (ii) Binary to octal numbers

      (iii) Octal to hexadecimal numbers

      (iv) Hexadecimal to binary numbers

      (v) Binary to decimal numbers

8. (a) For the following fertility data of a country, calculate GRR and NRR: 10

Age (in years)	Age-specific Fertility Rate	Female Life Table Stationary Population
15-19	0.0696	4180
20-24	0.2346	4123
25-29	0.1897	4063
30-34	0.1143	4001
35-39	0.0611	3934
40-44	0.0285	3860
45-49	0.0101	3763

The sex ratio at birth for the country may be assumed to be 105 males to 100 females.

(b) What do you understand by estimation of demographic measures from incomplete data? Explain how stable population concept ts used m estimating birth and death rates of a population. 10

(c) Explain the steps to solve an LPP problem using solver of MS-Excel and illustrate with suitable example. 10

(d) Explain the steps to solve ANOVA oneway classification using MS-Excel. 10

STATISTICS-IV
2012

Time Allowed : Three Hours

Maximum Marks: 200

INSTRUCTIONS

Candidate should attempt FIVE questions in all including Question Nos 1 and 5 which are compulsory and attempt remaining THREE questions by choosing at least ONE each from Sections-A and B. The number of marks carried by each question is indicated at the end of the question. Answers must be written in ENGLISH. Symbols and abbreviations are as usual. If any data is required to be assumed for answering a question, it may be suitably assumed, indicating this clearly.

Section A

1. (a) For an aperiodic, positive pers istent state j, s how that $\lim_{n\to\infty} p_{ij}^{(n)} = 1/\mu_j$, where μ_j denotes the mean recurrence time of state j. 8

   (b) For a Poisson process $\{X(t), t \geq 0\}$, show that the conditional distribution of X(s) given X(t), $0 < s < t$ is binomial. 8

   (c) Describe the pure birth process. Derive an expression for $P_{0n}(0, t) = P\{X(t) = n\{X(0) = 0\}$ for the Yule - Furry process. 8

   (d) Define (i) lead time {ii) buffer stock in an inventory problem. How do you determine the buffer stock in an EOQ situation ? 8

   (e) Explain the 'Gap test' and the 'Poker test' for testing randomness of observations from uniform distribution. 8

2. (a) Let $\{\xi_n, n \geq 1\}$ be a sequence of i.i.d.r.v.'s with $P\{\xi_k = 1) p$ and $P\{\xi_k = 0) = q, p + q = 1$.

   Define $Y_n = n - \sum_{i=1}^{n} \xi_i, n = 1, 2, ...$

   Show that $|X_n, n \geq 1|$ is a Markov chain. Obtain its one-step transition probability matrix.

   10

   (b) The t.p.m. of a M.C. with S = {1, 2, 3} is given below:

$$P = \begin{bmatrix} 2/3 & 0 & 1/3 \\ 1/4 & 3/4 & 0 \\ 0 & 1/2 & 1/2 \end{bmatrix}$$

Obtain the invariant distribution of the chain. 10

(c) Derive the difference-ditrcrcntial equations for the M I M I c I ∞ queueing system and obtain its solution in steady state conditions. 10

(d) Define G .W. branching process. Let $\{X_n\}$ denote a G.W. branching process with E $(X_1) = m$ and $Var(X_1) = \sigma^2$. Derive E (X_n) and $Var(X_n)$. 10

3. (a) Derive a set of suflicient conditions to declare a given basic feasible solution to be a n optimal solution to a L.P.P. 10

(b) Explain the problem of duality in L.P.P. Prove that if the primal has an optimal solution, then there exists an optimal solution to the dual. 10

(c) Derive the difference-differential equations for the finite capacity M I M I 1 : FIFO I N I ∞ queue and obtain the queue length distribution in steady state conditions. Derive an expression for the mean queue length. 10

(d) Derive the formula for the optimal order quantity for a single period deterministic inventory model assuming that the demand and replenishment both occur at a uniform rate. 10

4. (a) In the classical ruin problem, show that when the adversary is infinitely rich, the probability of gambler's ruin x_k is given by

$$x_k = \begin{cases} \left(\dfrac{q}{p}\right)^k & \text{if } p > q \\ 1 & \text{if } p \le q \end{cases}$$ 10

(b) Describe the M I M I c I ∞ queueing system. Show that it is a particular case of birth and death process. 10

(c) Solve the following L.P.P. by Big-M method :

Maximize $Z = -x_1 + 3x_2$

subject to $x_1 + 2x_2 \ge 2$

$3x_1 + x_2 \le 3$

$x_1 \le 4$

$x_1 . x_2 \ge 0$

(d) Expla in 'individual replacement policy' and 'group replacement policy'. Wh en do you prefer a group replacement policy to an individual replacement policy? 10

Section-B

5. (a) Discuss Chiang's method of constructing an abridged life table. 8

(b) "Model life table is used to estimate basic demographic measures from incomplete data." Discuss. 8

(c) Enumerate the factors influencing internal migration. Explain how internal migration affects the population composition of the sending and the receiving areas. 8

(d) Explain the following : 8

(i) Address Bus

(ii) Control Bus

(iii) Data Bus

(e) Describe memory systems for microcomputers. 8

6. (a) Show that age structure of stable population does not depend on the initial age distribution of the population. 10

(b) Discuss the properties of logistic curve. 10

(c) Calculate the crude and standardised death rates for the local population from the followi ng data a nd compare them with crude death rate of the standard population. 10

Age-group	Standard population	Deaths	Local population	Deaths
0-10	600	18	400	16
10-20	1000	5	1500	6
20-60	3000	24	2400	24
60-100	400	20	700	

(d) Explain Myer's index and discuss it s uses in detecting digit pre feren ce. 10

7. (a) Describe the main sources of dem og r aphic data in India a nd s uggest meas ures to improve th e quality of th e data. 10

(b) Describe two operating systems for personal computers. 10

(c) Explain the following : 10

(i) Bit density

(ii) Bit handling

(iii) Bit mapping

(iv) Bit rate

(d) Describe the hierarchical approach of database system . 10

8. (a) Describe the matrix method of population projection. 10

(b) Describe m brief the various stages and operation al sct-up of 2001 Census of India. 10

(c) Explain the following : 10

(i) Debugging

(ii) Bar coding

(iii) Indexed sequential file

(d) Describe a flow chart to find out the highest marks obtained in an examination and the roll number of the student obtaining the highest marks. 10

STATISTICS-IV
2011

Time Allowed : Three Hours | *Maximum Marks: 200*

INSTRUCTIONS

Candidate should attempt FIVE questions in all including Question Nos 1 and 5 which are compulsory and attempt remaining THREE questions by choosing at least ONE each from Sections-A and B. The number of marks carried by each question is indicated at the end of the question. Answers must be written in ENGLISH. Symbols and abbreviations are as usual. If any data is required to be assumed for answering a question, it may be suitably assumed, indicating this clearly.

Section A

1. Attempt any **FIVE** parts :-

   (a) Define persistent, transient and ergodic states. Show that if i <~> j and if state i is persistent, then state j is also persistent. 8

   (b) For the linear growth process with the usual notations and X(0) = m, show that

   $E[X(t)] = m \exp[\lambda - \mu) t]$. 8

   (c) Prove that every basic feasible solution to a linear programming problem (L.P.P.) corresponds to an extreme point of the convex set of constraints of the L.P.P. and conversely. 8

   (d) Explain duality in linear programming. Write down the dual of the following linear programming problem:

   Minimize $Z = 8x_1 - 5x_2 + 3x_3$

   subject to $3x_1 + 5x_2 \geq 12$

   $4x_1 - 5x_3 \leq 20$

   $5x_1 + 9x_2 - 2x_3 = 25$

   $x1, x2, x3 \geq 0$.

   (e) Describe a two period inventory problem when the demand is probabilistic. How do you solve it? 8

   (f) Describe the linear congruential method and the rejection technique of generating pseudo random numbers. 8

2. (a) Let $\{\xi_n, n \geq 1\}$ be a sequence of i.i.d.r.v.'s with $P\{\xi_k = j) = i/15, i = 1, 2, ... 5$.

Define $X_n = (\xi_k = i) = i/15, i = 1, 2, ..., 5$.

Show that $|X_n, n \geq 1|$ is a Markov chain. Obtain its one-step transition probability matrix. 10

(b) Consider a random walk with reflecting barriers on the state space $S = \{1, 2, ..., N\}$ and the transition probability matrix given by

$$P = \begin{bmatrix} q & p & 0 & 0 & \\ q & 0 & p & 0 & . \\ & & & & \\ & & & & \\ & & & q & p \end{bmatrix}$$

Classify the states of the chain and obtain its invariant distribution. 10

(c) Show that for a Poisson process $|X(t), t \geq 0\}$ the correlation coefficient between X(t) and X(t + s) is $\left\{\frac{t}{t+s}\right\}^{\frac{1}{2}}$. 10

(d) Describe Gaton-Watson branching process. For a Galton-Watson branching process $[X_n, n = 0, 1, 2, ...]$ with $E(X_1) = m$ show that $E[X_{n+r}] X_n = \_X_n m^r$, for r, n = 0, 1, 2, ... 10

3. (a) Given a basic feasible solution to a L.P.P. explain how you will derive a new improved basic feasible solution. 10

(b) State and prove the fundamental theorem of duality. 10

(c) Stating the assumption, derive the (s, S) inventory policy and show that it is optimal. 10

(d) Describe a method of simulating the $M|M|1|\infty$ queuenting sytem and a method of estimating the mean queue length and mean waiting time in the queue based on the simulated data. 10

4. (a) For a persistent non-null state j with period d, show that $\lim_{n\to\infty} p_{ij}^{(n)} = d/\mu_j$. 10

(i) What is the average number of customers in the fitting room ?

(ii) How much time should a customer expect to spend in the fitting room?

(iii) What percentage if the time is the tailor idle? 10

(b) If $X_n = \max\{Y_1, Y_2, ..., Y_n)$, where Y_j denotes the number on the face turning up in the ith toss of a die faces 1, 2, ..., 6. Show that $\{X_n\}$ is a Markov chain. Obtain its transition matrix. 10

(c) A large number of special light bulbs are used in a precision assembly shop all of which must be kept in working order. If a bulb fails in service it costs Rs. 20 to replace it. If we replace all the bulbs in the same operation, we can do it only for Rs. 7 a bulb. The probability distributio of lives are as follows:

Failure week:	1	2	3	4	5	6
Probability:	0.09	0.16	0.24	0.36	0.12	0.03

Calculate the week of group replacement so that the average cost is minimum. 10

(d) Describe the ABC inventory classification system. 10

Section-B

5. Attempt any FIVE parts :-

(a) Describe the structure of a complete life table. Explain how the different columns of a life table may be computed on the basis of observed agespecific mortality rates. 8

(b) Deline CBR, GFR and ASFR, and indicate why each is considered an improvement on the preceding measure of fertility. 8

(c) Derive Makeham's formula, starting from suitable assumptions. 8

(d) What do you mean by intrinsic growth rate? Derive an expression for intrinsic growth rate from Lotka 's renewal equation. 8

(e) (i) Find the binary equivalent of $(23)_{10}$.

(ii) Find the hexadecimal equivalent of $(41819)_{10}$.

(iii) Find the decimal equivalent of the hexadecimal number $(0.4c)_{16}$. 8

(f) Describe different types of databases. 8

6. (a) Discuss the relative importance of logistic and component methods of population projections. 10

(b) Describe the different methods of computing the infant mortality rate. 10

(c) The following table relates to the all India female population (1951), the number of female live births classified according to the age of mothers and the survival rate for females. Calculate the GRR and NRR.

Age	Female Population (100)	Total number of female live births (100)	Survival rate (per 100,000)
15–19	157670	4632	58065
20–24	147624	14443	55870
25–29	124200	14058	52981
30–34	105865	8329	48963
40–44	77887	2158	39154
45–49	61161	689	34198

(d) Explain the following:

(i) Age pyramid

(ii) Standardization of vital rates

(iii) Migration models. 10

7. (a) Discuss migration analysis based on place of birth data. What are the drawbacks of this method ? 10

   (b) What is age heaping ? How can you detect its presence in census age data ? Explain Wip-ple"s index. 10

   (c) What is the purpose of memory in a computer ? What are the main characteristics of a memory cell ? 10

   (d) Explain the following :

   (i) Data entry database

   (ii Data manipulation language

   (iii) On-line real time processing. 10

8. (a) What criteria are used in selecting a computer network topology ? 10

   (b) Outline the uses of SQL (Structured Query Language) for the d.a ta administration. 10

   (c) Describe the nature and properties of stable and stationary populations. 10

   (d) Define a Gompertz curve and explain a method of fitting the curve to a given set of population figures.

   10

STATISTICS-IV
2010

Time Allowed : Three Hours | *Maximum Marks: 200*

INSTRUCTIONS

Candidate should attempt FIVE questions in all including Question Nos 1 and 5 which are compulsory and attempt remaining THREE questions by choosing at least ONE each from Sections-A and B. The number of marks carried by each question is indicated at the end of the question. Answers must be written in ENGLISH. Symbols and abbreviations are as usual. If any data is required to be assumed for answering a question, it may be suitably assumed, indicating this clearly.

Section A

1. Attempt any **FIVE** parts :-

   (a) Give a brief critical account of Poisson process. 8

   (b) Let φ designate the set of all feasible solution to the linear program in standard form. Then prove that every extreme point of φ has at least n-m zero components and is a basic feasible solution. 8

   (c) Obtain differential-difference equations for a birth-death process. 8

   (d) Describe Vogel's method for solving a transportation problem. 8

   (e) Explain how the theory of replacement is used in:

   (i) replacement of items whose maintenance cost varies with time,

   (ii) replacement of items that fail completely. 8

   (f) Explain the terms :

   (i) Simulation of queues

   (ii) Average inventory level

   (iii) Group replacement. 8

2. (a) Show that in a simple Random walk with two reflecting barriers at 'o' and 'a', the stationary distribution π_j. is given by :

$$\pi_j = \frac{1-p/q}{1-(p/q)^{n+1}}(p/q)^j, j = 0, 1, ..., a$$

where $\pi_j = \lim_{n\to\infty} p_{ij}^{(n)}$: and $p_{ij}^{(n)}$ has the usual interpretation that it represents the probability that the particle occupies the state j at time n having started in the state i; what will be the value of π_j. when the Random walk is homogeneous (i..e., p = q) ?. 10

(b) Investigate the M |M| 1 queueing model by the Markov chain technique. 10

(c) Let $\{X_t\}$ be· a stochastic process of independent increments. If $P(X_{t_0} = \alpha) = 1$ for some epoch t_0 and some constants a, then show that $\{X_t\}$ is a Markov process. 10

(d) Let X denote the size of nth generation, n = 0, 1, 2, ... , and $X_0 = 1$. Then the r.v. $y_n = \sum_{i=0}^{n} X_i$ denotes the total number of progeny. Then, show that the p.g.f. $R_n(s)$ of Y satisfy the recurrence relation :

$R_n(s) = sP(R_{n-1}(s))$,

where P(s) being the p.g.f. of the offspring distribution. 10

3. (a) If either the primal or the dual problem has a finite optimum solution, then show that the other problem has a finite optimum solution. 10

(b) Define a transportation problem. Obtain the necessary and sufficient condition for the existence of a feasible solution to a transportation problem. 10

(c) For a given homogeneous M |M} K queuemg system, if the steady state probabilities exist, then prove that the traffic intensity of the system is less than unity. 10

(d) Solve the following LP problem by two-phase Simplex method :

Minimize:

$Z = 80x_1 + 60x_2$

subject to :

$0.20x_1 + 0.32x_2 \le 0.25$

$x_1 + x_2 = I$

with x_1 and x_2 non-negative. 10

4. (a) The men's department of a large store employs one tailor for customer fittings. The number of customers requiring fittings appears to follow a Poisson distribution with mean arrival rate 24 per hour. Customers are fitted on a first-come, firstserved basis, and they are always willing to wait for the tailor's service, because alterations are free.

The time it takes to fit a customer appears to be exponentially distributed, with a mean of 2 min.

(i) What is the average number of customers in the fitting room ?

(ii) How much time should a customer expect to spend in the fitting room?

(iii) What percentage if the time is the tailor idle? 10

(b) If $X_n = \max\{Y_1, Y_2, ..., Y_n\}$, where Y_j denotes the number on the face turning up in the ith toss of a die faces 1, 2, ..., 6. Show that $\{X_n\}$ is a Markov chain. Obtain its transition matrix. 10

(c) A large number of special light bulbs are used in a precision assembly shop all of which must be kept in working order. If a bulb fails in service it costs Rs. 20 to replace it. If we replace all the bulbs in the same operation, we can do it only for Rs. 7 a bulb. The probability distributio of lives are as follows:

Failure week:	1	2	3	4	5	6
Probability:	0.09	0.16	0.24	0.36	0.12	0.03

Calculate the week of group replacement so that the average cost is minimum. 10

(d) Describe the ABC inventory classification system. 10

Section-B

5. Attempt any FIVE parts :-

(a) Describe the structure of a complete life table. Explain how the different columns of a life table may be computed on the basis of observed agespecific mortality rates. 8

(b) Deline CBR, GFR and ASFR, and indicate why each is considered an improvement on the preceding measure of fertility. 8

(c) Derive Makeham's formula, starting from suitable assumptions. 8

(d) What do you mean by intrinsic growth rate? Derive an expression for intrinsic growth rate from Lotka 's renewal equation. 8

(e) (i) Find the binary equivalent of $(23)_{10}$.

(ii) Find the hexadecimal equivalent of $(41819)_{10}$.

(iii) Find the decimal equivalent of the hexadecimal number $(0.4c)_{16}$. 8

(f) Describe different types of databases. 8

6. (a) Discuss the relative importance of logistic and component methods of population projections. 10

(b) Describe the different methods of computing the infant mortality rate. 10

(c) The following table relates to the all India female population (1951), the number of female live births classified according to the age of mothers and the survival rate for females. Calculate the GRR and NRR.

Age	Female Population (100)	Total number of female live births (100)	Survival rate (per 100,000)
15–19	157670	4632	58065
20–24	147624	14443	55870
25–29	124200	14058	52981
30–34	105865	8329	48963
40–44	77887	2158	39154
45–49	61161	689	34198

(d) Explain the following:

(i) Age pyramid

(ii) Standardization of vital rates

(iii) Migration models. 10

7. (a) Discuss migration analysis based on place of birth data. What are the drawbacks of this method ? 10

(b) What is age heaping ? How can you detect its presence in census age data ? Explain Wipple"s index. 10

(c) What is the purpose of memory in a computer ? What are the main characteristics of a memory cell ? 10

(d) Explain the following :

(i) Data entry database

(ii Data manipulation language

(iii) On-line real time processing. 10

8. (a) What criteria are used in selecting a computer network topology ? 10

(b) Outline the uses of SQL (Structured Query Language) for the d.a ta administration. 10

(c) Describe the nature and properties of stable and stationary populations. 10

(d) Define a Gompertz curve and explain a method of fitting the curve to a given set of population figures. 10

STATISTICS-IV
2009

Time Allowed : Three Hours | *Maximum Marks: 200*

INSTRUCTIONS

Candidate should attempt FIVE questions in all including Question Nos 1 and 5 which are compulsory and attempt remaining THREE questions by choosing at least ONE each from Sections-A and B. The number of marks carried by each question is indicated at the end of the question. Answers must be written in ENGLISH. Symbols and abbreviations are as usual. If any data is required to be assumed for answering a question, it may be suitably assumed, indicating this clearly.

Section A

1. Attemet any **FIVE** parts:

   (a) Show that in an irreducible Markov chain, all the states are of same type. 8

   (b) The inter-arrival time of customers in M|M| I queuing system follows negative exponential distribution with parameter the arrival rate of the system. Prove this. 8

   (c) Find the differential equation of pure death process. 8

   (d) Explain the terms:

   (i) Convex set

   (ii) Optimum basic feasible solution

   (iii) Basic feasible solution

   (iv) Degeneracy. 8

   (e) Describe the basic EOQ inventory model. 8

   (e) Explain the geometric interpretation of the Simplex procedure. 8

2. (a) Show that a Markov vhain remains Markov if the time is reversed. 10

   (b) Define:

   (i) Random walk with absorbing barriers

   (ii) Random walk with reflecting barriers

(iii) Random walk with elastic barriers

(iv) Correlated random walk. 10

(c) A barber opens up for business at $t = 0$. Customers arrive at random in a Poisson fashion; that is, the pdf of interarrival time is $f(t) = \lambda e^{-\lambda t}$. Each haircut takes X seconds (where 'X' is a random variable).

Find the probability that the second arriving customer will not have to wait and also find 'W', the average value of his waiting time for the following two cases:

(i) $X = \text{constant} = c$

(ii) X is exponentially distributed with pdf: $g(x) = \mu \exp(-\mu x)$. 10

(d) Consider the discrete-state, discrete-time Markov Chain whose transition probability matrix is given by

$$P = \begin{bmatrix} \frac{1}{2} & \frac{1}{2} \\ \frac{3}{4} & \frac{1}{4} \end{bmatrix}$$

Find:

(i) The stationary state probability vector π,

(ii) $[I - zP]^{-1}$ and

(iii) P^n 10

3. (a) If the objective function of a linear programming problem posses a finite maximum, show that at least one optimal solution is a basic feasible solution.

(b) Describe the economic interpretation of the primaldual problems. 10

(c) If there exists a stationary distribution, show that it is necessarily unique. 10

(d) Using duality theory, solve the following L.P. problem:

Minimize $Z = 2x_1 + 2x_2$

$$x_1 + 4x_2 \geq 1$$

$$2x_1 + x_2 \geq 1$$

$$x_1, x_2 \geq 0.$$

4. (a) Let $\{N_1(t), t \geq 0\}$ and $\{N_2(t), t \geq 0\}$ be two independent homogencous Poisson processes with means $\lambda_1 t$ and $\lambda_2 t$ respectively. Define the process $\{N(t), t \geq 0\}$, where $N(t) = N_1(t) - N_2(t)$.

Find $P[N(t) = n]$ for any integer n. 10

(b) Let $\{X_n, n = 0, 1, 2, ...\}$ denote a branching process such that $X_{n+1} = \sum_{i=1}^{n} Z_i$,

where Z_{is} are idd with distribution $\{p_k\}$. Define $E(Z_1) = m$ and $Var(Z_1) = \sigma^2$.

Then show that:

(i) $E(X_n) = m^n$

(ii) $Var(x_n) = \sigma^2 m^{n-1} \frac{(m^n - 1)}{m - 1}$, if $m \neq 1$

$= n\sigma^2$, if $m = 1$.

(c) Describe two methods for generating random variables for given continuous probability distribution.

(d) Introduce the concept of individual and group replacement policies. Derive the optimal group replacement policy under the usual setup. 10

Section B

5. Attempt any FIVE parts:

(a) State briefly how you can use the abridged life table to prepare a complete life table. 8

(b) Explain 'push-pull-obstacle' theory of migration. 8

(c) Show that in a stationary population, the birth rate is the reciprocal of the expectation of life at birth. 8

(d) Show that the age distribution of two stable populations would be identical if they are such that their mortality at all ages differs by a constant factor. 8

(e) Explain the following:

(i) Data hierachy

(ii) Data inteegrity

(iii) Data logging. 8

(f) Draw a flowchart to arrange 'n' numbers in the ascending order. 8

6. (a) Describe the various methods for obtaining intercensal and post-censal estimates of population total. 10

(b) What are the different measures of mortality? Discuss the merits and demerits of each, 10

(c) Give a short account of the main findings of the population census of India, 2001. 10

(d) Complete the following life table:

Age (years)	I_x	d_x	q_x	L_x	T_x	e^0_x
65	4412	–	–	–	–	–
66	3724	–	–	–	–	–
67	3201	642	–	–	26567	–

7. (a) Describe the indirect measures fo net internal migration. 10

(b) Distinguish between sequential files and direct files. 10

(c) What do you understant by a Spreadsheet Package? Describe the features of a popular Spreadsheet Software Package. 10

(d) Explain the following:

(i) Binary and octal number systems

(ii) Database administrator

(iii) Database language

(iv) Data logging. 10

8. (a) Derive the logistic model of population growith. Find the final size of the total population with this model. 10

(b) Derive the characterictic equation of stable population stating the underlying assumptions. 10

(c) Explain the following:

(i) Client-server architecture

(ii) Multiprogramming

(iii) Development of Personal Computer. 10

(d) Explain classification of Algorithms with examples. 10